PEARSON   ALWAYS LEARNING

Human Impact on the Environment

Custom Edition for University of Guelph

Taken from:
Environment: The Science Behind the Stories, Second Canadian Edition
by Jay Withgott, Scott Brennan and Marmara Murck

Pearson Learning Solutions, 501 Boylston Street, Suite 900, Boston, MA 02116
A Pearson Education Company
www.pearsoned.com

Printed in Canada.

2 3 4 5 6 7 8 9 10 XXXX 17 16 15 14 13

000200010271676717

CG/CB

PEARSON   ISBN 10: 1-256-82398-8
                ISBN 13: 978-1-256-82398-8

Brief Contents

About the Authors xvii

PART ONE
FOUNDATIONS OF ENVIRONMENTAL GEOGRAPHY 1

1   An Introduction to Environmental Geography 2
2   Environmental Systems and Ecosystem Ecology 30
3   Evolution, Biodiversity, and Population Ecology 61
4   Species Interactions and Community Ecology 72
5   Soil Resources 105
6   Agriculture, Food, and Biotechnology 137
7   Conservation of Species and Habitats 172
8   Forests and Forest Management 212
9   Freshwater Systems and Water Resources 242
10   Marine and Coastal Systems and Fisheries 276
11   Atmospheric Science and Air Pollution 308
12   Fossil Fuels: Energy Use and Impacts 337
13   Energy Alternatives 371
14   Managing Our Waste 413
15   Environmental Ethics and Economics: Values and Choices 445
16   Space, Time & Life 479

Contents

About the Authors xvii

PART ONE
FOUNDATIONS OF ENVIRONMENTAL GEOGRAPHY 1

1 AN INTRODUCTION TO ENVIRONMENTAL GEOGRAPHY 2

CENTRAL CASE
EARTH FROM SPACE: THE POWER OF AN IMAGE 3

Our Island, Earth 4

Our environment is more than just our surroundings 4

Environment 5

Geography explores interactions between humans and the physical and biological world 5

Natural resources are vital to our survival 6

Human population growth has shaped our resource use 7

Resource consumption exerts social and environmental impacts 8

Environmental knowledge can help us avoid mistakes made in the past 10

The Nature of Environmental Geography 10

Geography is an interdisciplinary pursuit 10

People differ in their perception of environmental problems 11

Environmental science is not the same as environmentalism 11

The nature of science 12

Science 12

THE SCIENCE BEHIND THE STORY: The Lesson of Rapa Nui 13

Social and Natural scientists test ideas by critically examining evidence 14

The scientific method is a key element of science 14

There are different ways to test hypotheses 16

The scientific process does not stop with the scientific method 17

Science may go through "paradigm shifts" 19

Sustainability and the Future of Our World 19

Population and consumption lie at the root of many environmental impacts 19

We face many environmental challenges 19

Solutions to environmental problems must be global and sustainable 20

THE SCIENCE BEHIND THE STORY: Mission to Planet Earth: Monitoring Environmental Change 21

Our energy choices will influence our future immensely 22

Fortunately, potential solutions abound 22

Are things getting better, or worse? 23

Sustainability involves meeting environmental, social, and economic goals 23

CANADIAN ENVIRONMENTAL PERSPECTIVES: David Suzuki 24

Conclusion 25

Reviewing Objectives **25**, Testing Your Comprehension **26**, Thinking It Through **27**, Interpreting Graphs and Data **27**, Chapter Endnotes **28**

2 ENVIRONMENTAL SYSTEMS AND ECOSYSTEM ECOLOGY   30

CENTRAL CASE
THE PLIGHT OF THE ST. LAWRENCE BELUGAS   31

Earth's Environmental Systems   33

Systems are networks of relationships   33

Feedbacks are common in environmental systems   33

Homeostasis is a state of balance   34

A whole may be more than the sum of its parts   35

Complex systems have multiple subsystems   35

Environmental systems may be perceived in various ways   36

Ecosystems   37

Ecosystems are systems of interacting biotic and abiotic components   37

Energy is converted to biomass   38

Nutrient availability limits productivity   39

Ecosystems are integrated spatially   40

Landscape ecologists study geographic patterns   41

Remote sensing and GIS are important tools   42

Models help scientists understand complex systems   43

Ecosystems provide vital services   43

Biogeochemical Cycles   44

Nutrients and other materials move in biogeochemical cycles   44

The hydrologic cycle influences all other cycles   46

Our impacts on the hydrologic cycle are extensive   46

The carbon cycle circulates a vital organic nutrient   47

We are shifting carbon from the geosphere to the atmosphere   48

The nitrogen cycle involves specialized bacteria   49

We have greatly influenced the nitrogen cycle   49

THE SCIENCE BEHIND THE STORY: The Gulf of Mexico's "Dead Zone"   52

The phosphorus cycle involves mainly geosphere and ocean   54

We affect the phosphorus cycle   54

Conclusion   55

CANADIAN ENVIRONMENTAL PERSPECTIVES: Robert Bateman   56

Reviewing Objectives **56**, Testing Your Comprehension **57**, Thinking It Through **58**, Interpreting Graphs and Data **59**, Chapter Endnotes **60**

3 EVOLUTION, BIODIVERSITY, AND POPULATION ECOLOGY   61

Populations may grow, shrink, or remain stable   62

Unregulated populations increase by exponential growth   62

Limiting factors restrain population growth   63

Carrying capacities can change   64

Reproductive strategies vary from species to species   64

Changes in populations influence the composition of communities   65

THE SCIENCE BEHIND THE STORY: Climate Change, Disease, and the Amphibians of Monteverde   66

Conclusion   67

CANADIAN ENVIRONMENTAL PERSPECTIVES: Maydianne Andrade   68

Reviewing Objectives **69**, Testing Your Comprehension **70**, Thinking It Through **70**, Interpreting Graphs and Data **70**, Chapter Endnotes **71**

4   SPECIES INTERACTIONS AND COMMUNITY ECOLOGY   72

CENTRAL CASE
BLACK AND WHITE AND SPREAD ALL OVER:
ZEBRA MUSSELS INVADE THE
GREAT LAKES   73

Species Interactions   74

Competition can occur when resources are limited   75

Several types of interactions are exploitative   76

Predators kill and consume prey   76

Parasites exploit living hosts   77

Herbivores exploit plants   78

Mutualists help one another   79

Some interactions have no effect on some participants   79

Ecological Communities   80

Energy passes among trophic levels   80

Energy, biomass, and numbers decrease at higher trophic levels   80

Food webs show feeding relationships and energy flow   82

Some organisms play especially important roles in communities   82

Communities respond to disturbance in different ways   84

Succession follows severe disturbance   84

THE SCIENCE BEHIND THE STORY: Otters, Urchins, Kelp, and a Whale of a Chain Reaction   86

Invasive species pose new threats to community stability   87

Some altered communities can be restored to their former condition   89

Earth's Biomes   90

Climate influences the locations of biomes   91

We can divide the world into roughly 10 terrestrial biomes   92

Altitude creates patterns analogous to latitude   98

Aquatic and coastal systems also show biome-like patterns   98

CANADIAN ENVIRONMENTAL PERSPECTIVES: Zoe Lucas   100

Conclusion   100

Reviewing Objectives **101**, Testing Your Comprehension **102**, Thinking It Through **102**, Interpreting Graphs and Data **103**, Chapter Endnotes **103**

5   SOIL RESOURCES   105

CENTRAL CASE
MER BLEUE: A BOG OF INTERNATIONAL
SIGNIFICANCE   106

Soil as a System   107

Soil is a complex, dynamic mixture   107

Soil formation is slow and complex   108

A soil profile consists of layers known as horizons   110

Soils vary in colour, texture, structure, and pH   111

Biogeochemical Cycling in Soils   113

Soils support plant growth through ion exchange   113

Soil is a crucial part of the nitrogen cycle   114

Soil is an important terrestrial reservoir for carbon   114

Soil Degradation: A Global Concern   116

Regional differences affect soil productivity   117

Erosion can degrade ecosystems and agriculture   119

Soil erodes by several mechanisms   119

Soil erosion is widespread   121

Desertification reduces productivity of arid lands   121

The Dust Bowl was a monumental event in North America   123

The Soil Conservation Council emerged from the experience of drought   123

Protecting Soils   124

Erosion-control practices protect and restore plant cover   124

Irrigation can cause long-term soil problems   127

THE SCIENCE BEHIND THE STORY: Dark Earth: A New (Old) Way to Sequester Carbon   128

Other chemicals also contribute to soil contamination   129

Grazing practices can contribute to soil degradation   130

CANADIAN ENVIRONMENTAL PERSPECTIVES: Myrna Simpson   131

Conclusion   132

Reviewing Objectives **132**, Testing Your Comprehension **133**, Thinking It Through **134**, Interpreting Graphs and Data **134**, Chapter Endnotes **136**

6   AGRICULTURE, FOOD, AND BIOTECHNOLGY   137

CENTRAL CASE
GM MAIZE AND ROUNDUP-READY CANOLA   138

The Race to Feed the World   140

Agriculture first appeared around 10 000 years ago   140

Industrialized agriculture is more recent   141

We are producing more food per person   142

We face undernourishment, overnutrition, and malnutrition   143

Impacts of the Green Revolution   144

The Green Revolution led to dramatic increases in agricultural productivity   144

The Green Revolution has had both positive and negative impacts   144

Pests and Pollinators   147

Thousands of chemical pesticides have been developed   147

Pests evolve resistance to pesticides   147

Biological control pits one organism against another   148

Biocontrol agents themselves may become pests   149

IPM combines biocontrol and chemical methods   150

We depend on insects to pollinate crops   150

Conservation of pollinators is vital   151

THE SCIENCE BEHIND THE STORY: The Alfalfa and the Leafcutter   152

Genetically Modified Food   152

Genetic modification of organisms depends on recombinant DNA   152

Genetic engineering is like, and unlike, traditional breeding   153

Biotechnology is transforming the products around us   155

What are the impacts of GM crops?   155

Debate over GM foods involves more than science   156

Preserving Crop Diversity   157

Crop diversity provides insurance against failure   157

Seed banks are living museums for seeds   158

Raising Animals for Food   159

Consumption of animal products is growing   159

High consumption has led to feedlot agriculture   159

Our food choices are also energy choices   160

We also raise fish on "farms"   161

Aquaculture has benefits and drawbacks   162

Sustainable Agriculture   162

As population and consumption increase, soils are being degraded   163

Organic agriculture is on the increase   164

THE SCIENCE BEHIND THE STORY: Organic Farming Put to the Test   165

Locally supported agriculture is growing   165

Organic agriculture can even succeed in cities   166

CANADIAN ENVIRONMENTAL PERSPECTIVES: Alisa Smith and James MacKinnon   167

Conclusion   167

Reviewing Objectives **168**, Testing Your Comprehension **169**, Thinking It Through **169**, Interpreting Graphs and Data **170**, Chapter Endnotes **170**

7   CONSERVATION OF SPECIES AND HABITATS   172

CENTRAL CASE
SAVING THE POLAR BEAR: WHAT WILL IT TAKE?   173

Our Planet of Life   175

Biodiversity encompasses several levels   176

Some groups hold more species than others   178

Measuring biodiversity is not easy   179

Biodiversity is unevenly distributed on the planet   180

Biodiversity Loss and Species Extinction   182

Extinction and extirpation occur naturally   182

Some species are more vulnerable to extinction than others   183

Humans may have started a sixth mass extinction   184

There are several major causes of biodiversity loss   186

THE SCIENCE BEHIND THE STORY: Amphibian Diversity and Decline   190

Benefits of Biodiversity   190

Biodiversity provides ecosystem services   191

Biodiversity helps maintain ecosystem integrity   192

Biodiversity enhances food security   192

Biodiversity provides drugs and medicines   192

Biodiversity provides additional economic benefits   194

People value and seek out connections with nature   195

Approaches to Conservation   196

Conservation biology addresses habitat degradation and species loss   196

Island biogeography can help address habitat fragmentation   197

Captive breeding and cloning are single-species approaches   199

Some species act as "umbrellas" to protect communities   201

Conservation efforts are both international and national   201

Hot spots highlight areas of high biodiversity   202

Community-based conservation is increasingly popular   203

Innovative economic strategies are being employed   203

Parks and Reserves   204

Why do we create parks and reserves?   204

Parks and reserves are increasing internationally   205

Conclusion   206

CANADIAN ENVIRONMENTAL PERSPECTIVES: Biruté Mary Galdikas   207

Reviewing Objectives **208**, Testing Your Comprehension **209**, Thinking It Through **209**, Interpreting Graphs and Data **210**, Chapter Endnotes **210**

8   FORESTS AND FOREST MANAGEMENT   212

CENTRAL CASE
BATTLING OVER THE LAST BIG TREES AT CLAYOQUOT SOUND   213

The Forest and the Trees   215

Trees have several basic requirements   215

There are three major groups of forest biomes   217

Forests grade into open wooded lands   219

Canada is a steward for much of the world's forest   219

Canada's forests are varied   220

Forests are ecologically valuable   221

Trees provide ecosystem services of value to people   222

Harvesting Forest Products   222

Forest products are economically valued   222

Timber is harvested by several methods   222

Plantation forestry has grown in North America   224

Land Conversion and Deforestation   225

The growth of Canada and the U.S. were fuelled by land clearing and logging   226

THE SCIENCE BEHIND THE STORY: Changing Climate and the Spruce Budworm on Vancouver Island   228

Agriculture is the major cause of conversion of forests and grasslands   229

Livestock graze one-fourth of Earth's land surface   229

Bad practices and other pressures have led to deforestation   230

Deforestation is proceeding rapidly in many developing nations   230

Forest Management Principles   231

Public forests in Canada are managed for many purposes   231

THE SCIENCE BEHIND THE STORY: Surveying Earth's Forests   232

Today many managers practise ecosystem-based management   234

Adaptive management evolves and improves   234

Fire is a natural phenomenon in forests   235

Fire policy has stirred controversy   235

Sustainable forestry is gaining ground   236

CANADIAN ENVIRONMENTAL PERSPECTIVES: Tzeporah Berman   237

Conclusion   238

Reviewing Objectives **238**, Testing Your Comprehension **239**, Thinking It Through **239**, Inerpreting Graphs and Data **240**, Chapter Endnotes **240**

9   FRESHWATER SYSTEMS AND WATER RESOURCES   242

CENTRAL CASE
TURNING THE TAP: THE PROSPECT OF CANADIAN BULK WATER EXPORTS   243

Freshwater Systems   245

Rivers and streams wind through landscapes   245

Wetlands include marshes, swamps, and bogs   246

Lakes and ponds are ecologically diverse systems   246

Groundwater plays key roles in the hydrologic cycle   248

Water is unequally distributed across Earth's surface   249

Climate change will cause water problems and shortages   250

How We Use Water   251

Water supplies our households, agriculture, and industry   251

We have erected thousands of dams   251

China's Three Gorges Dam is the world's largest   252

Some dams are now being removed   253

Dikes and levees are meant to control floods   254

We divert—and deplete—surface water to suit our needs   255

Inefficient irrigation wastes water   256

Wetlands have been drained for a variety of reasons   258

We are depleting groundwater   258

Our thirst for bottled water seems unquenchable   259

Will we see a future of water wars?   260

Solutions to Depletion of Fresh water   260

    Solutions can address supply or demand   260

    Desalination "makes" more water   261

    Agricultural demand can be reduced   261

    We can lessen residential and industrial water use in many ways   261

    Economic approaches to water conservation are being debated   262

Freshwater Pollution and Its Control   262

    Water pollution takes many forms   262

    Water pollution comes from point and non-point sources   264

    Scientists use several indicators of water quality   264

    Groundwater pollution is a serious problem   264

    There are many sources of groundwater pollution, including some nature sources   265

    Legislative and regulatory efforts have helped reduce pollution   266

        THE SCIENCE BEHIND THE STORY: Arsenic in the Waters of Bangladesh   267

    We treat our drinking water   268

    It is better to prevent pollution than to mitigate the impacts after it occurs   268

Waste water and Its Treatment   268

    Municipal wastewater treatment involves several steps   268

        THE SCIENCE BEHIND THE STORY: When Water Turns Deadly: The Walkerton Tragedy   270

        CANADIAN ENVIRONMENTAL PERSPECTIVES: David Schindler   271

    Artificial wetlands can aid treatment   272

Conclusion   272

Reviewing Objectives **272**, Testing Your Comprehension **273**, Thinking It Through **273**, Interpreting Graphs and Data **274**, Chapter Endnotes **274**

10 MARINE AND COASTAL SYSTEMS AND FISHERIES   276

CENTRAL CASE
LESSONS LEARNED: THE COLLAPSE
OF THE COD FISHERIES   277

The Ocean   279

    Ocean covers most of Earth's surface   279

    The ocean contains more than water   279

    Ocean water is vertically structured   280

    Ocean water flows vertically and horizontally, influencing climate   281

        THE SCIENCE BEHIND THE STORY: Tip Jets and NADW off the Coast of Greenland   282

    La Niña and El Niño demonstrate the atmosphere–ocean connection   283

    Seafloor topography can be rugged and complex   284

Marine and Coastal Ecosystems   285

    Open-ocean ecosystems vary in their biological diversity   285

    Shallow-water systems are highly productive   286

    Intertidal zones undergo constant change   288

    Coastal ecosystems protect shorelines   289

    Freshwater meets saltwater in estuaries   290

Human Use and Impact   290

    The ocean provides transportation routes   290

    We extract energy and minerals   291

    Marine pollution threatens resources and marine life   291

    Oil pollution comes from many sources   292

    Pollutants can contaminate seafood   293

Emptying the Ocean   293

    We have long overfished   294

    Fishing has become industrialized   295

    Some fishing practices kill nontarget animals and damage ecosystems   296

    Several factors mask declines   297

We are "fishing down the food chain"   298

Aquaculture has benefits and drawbacks   298

Consumer choice can influence marine harvest practices   299

Marine biodiversity loss erodes ecosystem services   300

Marine Conservation   301

Fisheries management has been based on maxium sustainable yield   301

We can protect areas in the ocean   301

Reserves can work for both fish and fishers   302

How should reserves be designed?   302

CANADIAN ENVIRONMENTAL PERSPECTIVES: Farley Mowat   303

Conclusion   304

Reviewing Objectives **304**, Testing Your Comprehension **305**, Thinking It Through **306**, Interpreting Graphs and Data **306**, Chapter Endnotes **307**

11 ATMOSPHERIC SCIENCE AND AIR POLLUTION   308

CENTRAL CASE
THE RAIN AND THE BIG NICKEL   309

The Atmosphere and Weather   311

The atmosphere is layered   311

Atmospheric properties include temperature, pressure, and humidity   312

Solar energy heats the atmosphere, helps create seasons, and causes air to circulate   313

The atmosphere drives weather and climate   313

Air masses interact to produce weather   314

Large-scale circulation systems produce global climate patterns   315

Outdoor Air Pollution   317

Natural sources can pollute   317

We create various types of outdoor air pollution   319

CEPA identifies harmful airborne substances   319

Government agencies share in dealing with air pollution   321

Monitoring shows that many forms of air pollution have decreased   322

Smog is the most common widespread air quality problem   323

Photochemical smog is produced by a complex series of reactions   326

Air quality is a rural issue, too   327

Industrializing nations are suffering increasing air pollution   328

Synthetic chemicals deplete stratospheric ozone   328

There are still many questions to be resolved about ozone depletion   328

The Montreal Protocol addressed ozone depletion   330

Acidic deposition is another transboundary pollution problem   331

THE SCIENCE BEHIND THE STORY: Identifying CFCs as the Main Cause of Ozone Depletion   332

Acid deposition has not been reduced as much as scientists had hoped   334

12 FOSSIL FUELS: ENERGY USE AND IMPACTS   337

CENTRAL CASE
ON, OFF, ON AGAIN? THE MACKENZIE VALLEY NATURAL GAS PIPELINE   338

Sources of Energy   340

We use a variety of energy sources   340

Fossil fuels are indeed fuels created from "fossils"   342

Fossil fuel reserves are unevenly distributed   342

Developed nations consume more energy than developing nations   343

It takes energy to make energy   344

Coal, Natural Gas, and Oil   344

Coal is the world's most abundant fossil fuel   344

Coal use has a long history   344

Coal is mined from the surface and from below ground   345

Coal varies in its qualities   345

Natural gas is the fastest-growing fossil fuel in use today   346

Natural gas is formed in two ways   346

Natural gas has only recently been widely used   347

Natural gas extraction becomes more challenging with time   347

Offshore drilling produces much of our gas and oil   347

Oil is the world's most-used fuel   348

Heat and pressure underground form petroleum   349

Petroleum geologists infer the location and size of deposits   349

THE SCIENCE BEHIND THE STORY: Clean Coal for Electricity Generation   350

We drill to extract oil   351

Petroleum products have many uses   352

We may have already depleted half our oil reserves   352

"Unconventional" Fossil Fuels   354

Canada owns massive deposits of tar sands   354

Oil shale is abundant in the American West   355

THE SCIENCE BEHIND THE STORY: How Crude Oil Is Refined   356

Methane hydrate is another form of natural gas   356

Alternative fossil fuels have significant environmental impacts   357

Environmental impacts of fossil fuel use   358

Fossil fuel emissions cause pollution and drive climate change   358

Some emissions from fossil fuel burning can be "captured"   359

Coal mining affects the environment   360

Oil and gas extraction also alter the environment   361

Political, Social, and Economic Aspects   361

Oil supply and prices affect the economies of nations   362

Residents may or may not benefit from fossil fuel resources   362

We need to conserve energy and find renewable resources   364

Personal choice and increased efficiency are two routes to conservation   364

CANADIAN ENVIRONMENTAL PERSPECTIVES: Mary Griffiths   365

Conclusion   366

Reviewing Objectives 366, Testing Your Comprehension 368, Thinking It Through 368, Interpreting Graphs and Data 369, Chapter Endnotes 369

13 ENERGY ALTERNATIVES   371

CENTRAL CASE
HARNESSING TIDAL ENERGY AT THE BAY OF FUNDY   372

Alternatives to Fossil Fuels   373

Hydro, nuclear, and biomass are "conventional" alternatives   374

Hydroelectric Power   374

Modern hydropower uses two approaches   374

Hydropower generates relatively little air pollution   376

Hydropower has many negative impacts, too   377

Hydropower may not expand much more   377

Nuclear Power   378

Fission releases nuclear energy   378

Enriched uranium is used as fuel in nuclear reactors 379

Fission takes place in nuclear power plants 379

Nuclear power generates little air pollution 380

Nuclear power poses small risk of large accidents 381

Radioactive waste disposal remains problematic 383

Multiple dilemmas have slowed nuclear power's growth 385

Fusion remains a dream 385

Traditional Biomass Energy 386

Biomass energy means different things to different users 386

Traditional biomass sources are widely used in the developing world 386

Traditional biomass energy has environmental pros and cons 387

"New" Renewable Energy Sources 388

"New" renewable contributions are small but growing quickly 388

The transition won't happen overnight 389

Biofuels and Biopower 389

Biomass can be processed to make vehicle fuels 389

Electricity can be generated from biomass 391

Biofuels have environmental and economic benefits 392

Biofuels also have drawbacks 392

THE SCIENCE BEHIND THE STORY: Energy from Landfill Gas at Beare Road 393

Solar Energy 394

Passive solar heating is simple and effective 394

Active solar energy can heat air and water in buildings 394

PV cells generate electricity directly 395

Solar panels offers many benefits 396

Location and cost can be drawbacks 397

Wind Energy 397

Modern wind turbines convert kinetic energy to electrical energy 398

Wind power is the fastest-growing energy sector 398

Wind power has many benefits 399

Wind power has some downsides—but not many 400

Geothermal Energy 400

We can harness geothermal energy for heating and electricity 402

Use of geothermal power is growing 402

Geothermal power has benefits and limitations 402

Ocean Energy 402

THE SCIENCE BEHIND THE STORY: Water and Earth Energy for Heating and Cooling in Toronto and Ottawa 403

We can harness energy from tides, waves, and currents 404

The ocean stores thermal energy 405

Hydrogen Fuel and Power Storage 405

Hydrogen may be produced from water or from other matter 405

Fuel cells can be used to produce electricity 406

CANADIAN ENVIRONMENTAL PERSPECTIVES: David Keith 407

Hydrogen and fuel cells have many benefits 407

Conclusion 408

Reviewing Objectives 408, Testing Your Comprehension 409, Thinking It Through 410, Interpreting Graphs and Data 411, Chapter Endnotes 411

14 MANAGING OUR WASTE   413

CENTRAL CASE
THE BEARE ROAD LANDFILL: MAKING GOOD USE OF OLD GARBAGE   414

Approaches to Waste Management   416

We have several aims in managing waste   416

Municipal solid waste   417

Patterns in the municipal solid waste stream vary from place to place   417

Waste generation is rising in all nations   418

Open dumping of the past has given way to improved disposal methods   419

Waste disposal is regulated by three levels of government   419

Sanitary landfills are engineered to minimize leakage of contaminants   420

Landfills can be transformed after closure   421

Landfills have drawbacks   421

Incinerating trash reduces pressure on landfills   422

Many incinerators burn waste to create energy   423

Landfills can produce gas for energy   423

THE SCIENCE BEHIND THE STORY: Digging Garbage: The Archaeology of Solid Waste   424

Reducing waste is a better option   425

Reuse is one main strategy for waste reduction   425

Composting recovers organic waste   426

Recycling consists of three steps   426

Recycling has grown rapidly and can expand further   427

Financial incentives can help address waste   428

Edmonton showcases reduction and recycling   428

Industrial Solid Waste   429

Regulation and economics each influence industrial waste generation   429

Industrial ecology seeks to make industry more sustainable   429

Businesses are adopting industrial ecology   430

Waste exchanges are an offshoot of industrial ecology   430

Hazardous Waste   431

Hazardous wastes have diverse sources   431

Organic compounds and heavy metals can be hazardous   432

"E-waste" is a new and growing problem   432

Several steps precede the disposal of hazardous waste   435

There are three disposal methods for hazardous waste   436

Radioactive waste is especially hazardous   437

Contaminated sites are being cleaned up, slowly   437

Conclusion   438

CANADIAN ENVIRONMENTAL PERSPECTIVES: Brennain Lloyd   439

Reviewing Objectives **440**, Testing Your Comprehension **440**, Thinking It Through **441**, Interpreting Graphs and Data **441**, Chapter Endnotes **443**

15 ENVIRONMENTAL ETHICS AND ECONOMICS: VALUES AND CHOICES   445

CENTRAL CASE
MINING DENENDEH   446

Culture, World View, and the Environment   448

Culture, world views, and values influence our understanding of the environment   448

THE SCIENCE BEHIND THE STORY: The Mirrar Clan Confronts the Jabiluka Uranium Mine   449

Many factors shape our world views and perception of the environment   450

There are many ways to understand the environment   451

Environmental Ethics   451

Environmental ethics pertains to humans and the environment   452

We extend ethical consideration to non-human entities   453

Environmental ethics has ancient roots   454

The Industrial Revolution inspired environmental philosophers   455

Conservation and preservation arose at the start of the twentieth century   455

The land ethic and deep ecology enlarged ethical boundaries   456

Ecofeminists see parallels between the oppression of nature and of women   457

Environmental justice seeks equitable access to resources and protection from environmental degradation   458

Economics: Approaches and Environmental Implications   460

Economics studies the allocation of scarce resources   460

Several types of economics exist today   461

Environment and economy are intricately linked   461

Classical economics promoted the free market   463

Neoclassical economics considers price, supply, and demand   464

Cost-benefit analysis is a useful tool   464

Aspects of neoclassical economics have profound implications for the environment   465

Is the growth paradigm good for us?   467

Economists disagree on whether economic growth is sustainable   467

We can measure economic progress differently   468

We can give ecosystem goods and services monetary values   469

Corporations are responding to sustainability concerns   472

CANADIAN ENVIRONMENTAL PERSPECTIVES: Matthew Coon Come   473

Conclusion   474

Reviewing Objectives **474**, Testing Your Comprehension **475**, Thinking It Through **475**, Interpreting Graphs and Data **476**, Chapter Endnotes **477**

16 HUMANS AS A FORCE IN EVOLUTION AND EXTINCTION   481

Humans as an Evolutionary Force   482

Animal and plant domestication   482

Questions of the origin and spread of agriculture   486

Humans as a Force of Extinction   489

Prehistoric extinctions   490

Historic extinctions   493

Key Words and Terms **496**, References and Further Reading **497**

About the Authors

Jay H. Withgott is a science and environmental writer with a background in scientific research and teaching. He holds degrees from Yale University, the University of Arkansas, and the University of Arizona. As a researcher, he has published scientific papers on topics in ecology, evolution, animal behaviour, and conservation biology in journals including *Proceedings of the National Academy of Sciences, Proceedings of the Royal Society of London B, Evolution*, and *Animal Behavior*. He has taught university-level laboratory courses in ecology, ornithology, vertebrate diversity, anatomy, and general biology. Jay has authored articles for a variety of journals and magazines including *Science, New Scientist, BioScience, Smithsonian, Current Biology, Conservation in Practice*, and *Natural History*. He combines his scientific expertise with his past experience as a reporter and editor for daily newspapers to make science accessible and engaging for general audiences. Jay lives with his wife, biologist Susan Masta, in Portland, Oregon.

Barbara Murck has taught environmental and Earth science at the University of Toronto Mississauga for more than 20 years. Her academic background is in geology, with degrees from Princeton University and the University of Toronto. Barb has worked on a wide variety of environmental management projects in the developing world, from Africa to Asia, mainly as an expert on training and curriculum development. She has published numerous books on topics ranging from physical geology to environmental science to sustainability. She was honoured with the University of Toronto President's Teaching Award in 2010. She lives with her family, including the world's best cat and dog, in a 110-year-old house in Southern Ontario. When not at work, she is likely to be found hiking the Bruce Trail. She greatly appreciates having had the opportunity to influence the lives and learning of thousands of students over the years.

Scott Brennan has taught environmental science, ecology, resource policy, and journalism at Western Washington University and at Walla Walla Community College. He has also worked as a journalist, photographer, and consultant.

About the cover . . .

"We've never stopped taking things from nature. Even the act of taking from the earth is natural since we are not outside of nature. What is different today is the scale. Current society is searching for a way to come to terms with that taking from the earth. Recycling is one way we can put a stop to a certain amount of damage to the earth. This material comes from and collects around urban centres in large recycling yards. These yards are like secondary mines."

"The 'Urban Mines' photographs are a testament to Burtynsky's ability to balance the form and content of his images. He avoids emphasizing content to the point where his photographs might become *reportage*, but includes enough information so that they are more than mere exercises in formalism."

extracts from the book: *Manufactured Landscapes* essay: *Seeing the Big Picture* by Lori Pauli—National Gallery of Canada.

This is Combers Beach in Pacific Rim National Park Reserve, British Columbia.

FOUNDATIONS OF ENVIRONMENTAL GEOGRAPHY

An Introduction to Environmental Geography

Earth is like an island.

Upon successfully completing this chapter, you will be able to

- Define the term *environment*
- Describe natural resources and explain their importance to human life
- Characterize the interdisciplinary nature of geography

- Understand the scientific method and how science operates
- Diagnose and illustrate some of the pressures on the global environment
- Articulate the concepts of sustainability and sustainable development

CENTRAL CASE:
EARTH FROM SPACE: THE POWER OF AN IMAGE

"The two-word definition of sustainability is 'one
planet.'"

—MATHIS WACKERNAGEL, ECOLOGICAL ECONOMIST AND
CO-DEVELOPER OF THE ECOLOGICAL FOOTPRINT CONCEPT

"We're not the first to discover this, but we'd like to
confirm, from the crew of *Apollo 17*, that the world
is round."

—EUGENE CERNAN, *APOLLO 17* COMMANDER

Consider the following: Prior to November 9, 1967,
no one had *ever seen* a photograph of the whole planet
Earth, because no such thing existed.

Those of us who were alive back in 1967 were not
completely clueless. We knew that Earth is a planet, surrounded by space. We knew that Earth is round (although
visual confirmation of this fact still made a considerable
impact on *Apollo 17* astronauts a few years later). Yet a
simple photograph of Earth—floating in space, blue and
shining and covered by clouds, vegetation, and a whole
lot of water—managed to take everyone by surprise and
changed both society and history in the process.

Actually, the very first photographs of the whole
Earth, taken in 1967, were not the ones that eventually
caught the imagination of the general public. The 1967
photographs were taken by automated camera from
the unmanned *Apollo 4* spacecraft, the first spacecraft
to get far enough away from Earth to photograph the
entire planet. Only part of the planet was in sunlight,
so the photographs show only a "crescent" Earth (see
photo). Not long after, on December 24, 1968, *Apollo 8*
astronauts took the first hand-held photographs
showing Earth rising over the horizon of the Moon (the
closing photo of this book). The crew did a live radio
broadcast that day, during which astronaut James Lovell
commented, "The Earth from here is a grand oasis in
the big vastness of space."[1]

It was not until 1972 that the *Apollo 17* mission put astronauts in a position to photograph the entire *illuminated* planet Earth. The result was the famous Blue Marble[2] image, a version of which opens this chapter. The photograph was beautiful, its impact stunning, even unsettling. The original image was oriented with Antarctica at the top of the globe and an "upside-down" Africa in the middle. The unfamiliar perspective caused consternation among those who had never stopped to consider that the convention of orienting maps with north at the top is completely arbitrary.

The Blue Marble photograph is widely credited with kick-starting the modern environmental movement. Just five years elapsed between the first whole-Earth photographs in 1967 and the last ones to be recorded by human hands. (Since 1972, no manned space flight has been far enough away for the planet to be photographed in its entirety by astronauts.) In that five-year period was the summer of love, and war—the Vietnam War, the Six Days War, the Cold War. The Beatles sang on the first live international satellite television production. Canada celebrated the hundredth year of Confederation. Neil Armstrong became the first person to walk on the Moon. Civil rights activist Martin Luther King, Jr., died; so did J. Robert Oppenheimer, the "father of the atomic bomb." The first hand-held calculator was sold (for almost $400).

Society changed dramatically during those five years, and it was a period of dawning awareness and public involvement in environmental issues. The first major oil spill happened in 1967, when the *Torrey Canyon* ran aground near England with 120 000 tonnes of crude oil on board. The first hints of trouble began to surface (literally) from hazardous chemicals stored underground at Love Canal, New York. Within a few years the site would be infamous, leading to the first declaration of an environmental state of emergency in the United States and making a grassroots hero of local activist Lois Gibbs. Books on environmental topics began to appear on bestseller lists, including *Limits to Growth*,[3] *The Population Bomb*,[4] *Small Is Beautiful*,[5] and their predecessor, *Silent Spring*.[6] The 1970s opened with the signing of the first federal environmental legislation, the United States' *Environmental Protection Act* (1970). The first Earth Day was held (1970). Greenpeace was founded (1971). The *United Nations Environment Programme* was established (1972).

British astronomer Sir Frederick Hoyle is reputed to have said, in 1948, "Once a photograph of the Earth, taken from outside, is available—once the sheer isolation of the Earth becomes known—a new idea as powerful as any in history will be let loose." To what extent were these and subsequent milestones in environmental history descended from the first glimpses of our planet from space, with all of its fragility and limitations? We will never know with certainty, but the Blue Marble is considered to be one of the most influential photographs in history—possibly the most widely distributed image of all time—and it remains an iconic symbol of the modern environmental movement.

Our Island, Earth

Viewed from space, our home planet appears suspended against a vast inky-black backdrop. Although few of us will ever witness that sight directly, photographs taken from space convey a sense that Earth is small, isolated, and fragile. From an astronaut's perspective it is apparent that Earth and its natural systems are not unlimited. As our population, our technological powers, and our consumption of resources increase, so does our ability to alter our planet and damage the very systems that keep us alive.

Our environment is more than just our surroundings

A photograph of Earth reveals a great deal, but it does not adequately convey the complexity of our environment. Our **environment** is more than water, land, and air; it is the sum total of our surroundings. It includes all of Earth's **biotic** components, or living things, as well as the **abiotic** components, or nonliving things, with which we interact. Our environment has abiotic constituents—the continents, oceans, clouds, rivers, and icecaps that you can see in the photo of Earth from space. It also has biotic constituents—the animals, plants, forests, soils, and people that occupy the landscape. In a more inclusive sense, it also encompasses the built environment—the structures, urban centres, and living spaces humans have created. In its *most* inclusive sense, our environment includes the complex webs of scientific, ethical, political, economic, and social relationships and institutions that shape our daily lives.

Environment

People commonly use the term *environment* in a narrower sense—of a nonhuman or "natural" world apart from human society. This connotation is unfortunate, because it masks the important fact that humans exist within the environment and are a part of the interactions that characterize it. As one of many species, we share with others a fundamental dependence on a healthy, functioning planet. The limitations of language make it all too easy to speak of "people and nature," or "society and the environment," as though they were separate and did not interact. However, the fundamental insight of environmental science is that we are part of the natural world, and our interactions with its other parts matter a great deal.

Why is it important that we give careful consideration to the meaning of the term *environment*? Back in 1970, when the federal government passed Canada's first environmental legislation, the environmental awareness of most North Americans was limited. If they thought about it at all, most people would have equated *environment* with *wilderness*, although this oversimplification was changing as public consciousness of environmental issues grew. Wilderness preservation is still an important concern, but our understanding of the environment, our impacts on it, and its role in our health and daily lives has broadened dramatically.

Today our definition of *environment* must be sufficiently comprehensive to include its legal, social,

economic, and scientific aspects. Consequently, the mandate of **Environment Canada** is equally comprehensive:[7] to preserve and enhance the quality of Canada's natural environment, conserve our renewable resources, and protect our water resources. International relations, politics, ethics, business management, economics, social equity, engineering, law enforcement—all of these now play a role in managing and protecting the environment.

To accomplish this, our environmental leaders and policymakers need to know what they are talking about. As a community, we must constantly improve and refine our basic scientific understanding of water, air, land and soils, wildlife, weather and climate, and the dynamic interactions among all the components of which ecosystems are composed. That is where *environmental science*—the central focus of this book—comes in.

Geography explores interactions between humans and the physical and biological world

Appreciating how we interact with our environment is crucial for a well-informed view of our place in the world and for a mature awareness that we are one species among many on a planet full of life. Understanding our relationship with the environment is vital because we are altering the natural systems we need, in ways we do not yet fully comprehend.

We depend utterly on our environment for air, water, food, shelter, and everything else essential for living. However, our actions modify our environment, whether we intend them to or not. Many of these actions have enriched our lives, bringing us longer life spans, better health, and greater material wealth, mobility, and leisure time; however, many of them have damaged the natural systems that sustain us. Such impacts as air and water pollution, soil erosion, and species extinction compromise the well-being of living organisms, pose risks to human life, and threaten our ability to build a society that will survive and thrive in the long term. The natural environment was functioning long before the human species appeared, and we would be wise to do our best to maintain its integrity and keep its key elements in place.

Environmental geography is a study of the interrelationships between human and biophysical systems of a variety of spatial and temporal scales. We need to understand our interactions with—and our role in—the environment. Such knowledge is the essential first step toward devising solutions to our most pressing environmental problems. Many Geographers are taking this step, trying to apply their knowledge to develop solutions to the many environmental challenges we face. Part 1 of this book provides an introduction to the abiotic and biotic components of our environment, and to the basic concepts and principles of science as applied to the study of the environment.

It can be daunting to reflect on the magnitude of environmental dilemmas that confront us today. We will examine these challenges and issues in Part 2, starting with a look at the human population itself and how it has grown and changed over time.

Fortunately, with these problems also come countless opportunities for devising creative solutions. Right now, global conditions are changing more quickly than ever. Right now, through social and natural sciences, we as a civilization are gaining knowledge more rapidly than ever. And right now, the window of opportunity for acting to solve problems is still open. With such bountiful challenges and opportunities, this particular moment in history is an exciting time to be studying geography. This book will show you how to apply your knowledge of environmental geography to begin an exploration of solutions for our current challenges.

Natural resources are vital to our survival

Islands are finite, and their inhabitants must cope with limitations in the material resources. On our island, Earth, human beings, like all living things, ultimately face environmental constraints. Specifically, there are limits to many of our **natural resources**, the various substances and energy sources we need to survive. We can view the renewability of natural resources as a continuum from the most to the least renewable (**FIGURE 1.1**).

Natural resources that are replenishable over short periods are **renewable natural resources**. Some renewable resources, such as sunlight, wind, and wave energy, are perpetually renewed and essentially inexhaustible. Others renew themselves more slowly, and they may become nonrenewable if we use them at a rate that exceeds the rate at which they are renewed or replenished. Populations of animals and plants that we harvest from the wild may be renewable if we do not overharvest them but may vanish if we do.

Renewable resources such as groundwater and soil can be harvested according to principles similar to those that govern living resources. However, the rate of regeneration of such resources is limited by the rates of physical processes, such as the infiltration of groundwater to replenish an aquifer, or the physical and chemical weathering of rock to produce soil. Because these rates can be quite slow—it can take up to 10 000 years for soil formation to occur in cold climates like those of northern Canada, for example—it may take a very long time for these resources, once damaged or depleted, to be replenished.

Resource management is strategic decision making and planning aimed at balancing the use of a resource with its protection and preservation. The basic premise of renewable resource management—for both living and nonliving resources—is to balance the *rate of withdrawal* from the stock with the *rate of renewal* or *regeneration*. The **stock** is the harvestable portion of the resource. If the stock is being harvested or withdrawn at a faster rate than it can be replenished—faster than trees can be seeded and grow to maturity or faster than fish can be born and grow to a harvestable age or faster than precipitation can infiltrate to replenish the groundwater—then the stock will eventually be depleted. Renewable resources are sometimes called *stock-and-flow resources*, highlighting the importance of this balance in their management.

FIGURE 1.1
Natural resources lie along a continuum from perpetually renewable to nonrenewable. Perpetually renewable or inexhaustible resources, such as sunlight, will always be there for us. Nonrenewable resources, such as oil and coal, exist in limited amounts that cannot be renewed on a humanly accessible time scale and could one day be gone. Other resources, such as timber, groundwater, soils, and food crops, can be renewed if we are careful not to deplete them or damage them.

Renewable natural resources

- Sunlight
- Wind energy
- Wave energy
- Geothermal energy

- Agricultural crops
- Fresh water
- Forest products
- Soils

Nonrenewable natural resources

- Crude oil
- Natural gas
- Coal
- Copper, aluminum, and other metals

In contrast, **nonrenewable natural resources**, like fossil fuels and mineral deposits, are in finite supply and are depletable, because they are formed *much* more slowly than we use them; it can take 100 million years for natural geological processes to form an ore deposit or a petroleum deposit. Once we use them up, they are no longer available because they will not be replenished on a humanly accessible time scale. Simply by withdrawing from the stock we are depleting the resource. These resources lie at the other end of the continuum in FIGURE 1.1.

Our civilization depends on numerous minerals: Iron is mined and processed to make steel. Copper is used in pipes, electrical wires, and a variety of other applications. Aluminum is extracted via bauxite ore and used in packaging and other end products. Lead is used in batteries, to shield medical patients from radiation, and in many other ways. Zinc, tungsten, phosphate, uranium, gold, silver—the list goes on and on. Although we rely on these resources, we do not manage their extraction in the way we manage renewable natural resources. Like fossil fuels, minerals are nonrenewable resources that are *mined* rather than *harvested*. Therefore, the mining industry benefits by extracting as much as it can as fast as it can and then, once extraction becomes too inefficient to be profitable, moving on to new sites. From a consumer's perspective, the management of nonrenewable mineral resources demands conservation, reuse, and recycling.

Still other resources are *truly* nonrenewable and nonreplenishable: once an atom has been split to release its nuclear energy, it will never return to its original state; once a species has become extinct, it will never return to life.

We need to manage the resources we take from the natural world carefully and effectively, because many of them are limited or may become so. Resource managers are guided in their decision making by available research in the natural sciences, but their decisions are also influenced by political, economic, and social factors. A key question in managing resources is whether to focus narrowly on the resource of interest or to look more broadly at the environmental system of which the resource is a part. Taking a broader view can often help avoid damaging the system and can thereby help sustain the availability of the resource in the long term.

Preserving natural resources is an important consideration for the future, but it also speaks to the past and to our shared history as Canadians. Our economy, our identity, and even our national symbols have always been closely linked to the abundant physical resources of our environment. In recent years, however, the consumption of natural resources has increased greatly—in Canada and throughout the world—driven by rising affluence and the growth of the largest global human population in history.

Human population growth has shaped our resource use

For nearly all of human history, only a few million people populated Earth at any one time. Although past populations cannot be calculated precisely, FIGURE 1.2 gives some idea of how recently and suddenly our population has grown, surpassing 7 billion people in 2011.[8]

Four significant periods of societal change appear to have triggered remarkable increases in population size, concomitant with greatly increased environmental impacts. The first happened as many as 2.5 million years ago during the *paleolithic* (or *Old Stone Age*) *period*, when early humans gained control of fire and began to shape and use stones as tools with which to modify their environment.

The second was the transition from a nomadic, hunter-gatherer lifestyle to a settled, agricultural way of life. This change began to occur around 10 000 to 12 000 years ago, and it is formally known as the *neolithic period* or *Agricultural Revolution*.

The third major societal change, known as the *Industrial Revolution*, began in the mid-1700s and entailed a shift from rural life, animal-powered agriculture, and manufacturing by craftspeople, to an urban society powered by fossil fuels. Life improved in many ways as a result of the Industrial Revolution, but it also marked the beginning of industrial-scale pollution and many other environmental and social problems that had not previously been experienced. Air quality declined dramatically as a result of the new reliance on coal. Water quality declined, and so did the urban landscape, as a result of the gathering of people into densely populated city centres. Workplace health and safety, too, underwent a dramatic decline as factories were hastily erected and expanded. In many respects, the modern environmental movement had its roots in the efforts taken by concerned citizens during the Industrial Revolution to ensure a cleaner, safer environment for working and living.

Today we are in the midst of a fourth transition, which some have labelled the modern *Medical–Technological Revolution*. Advances in medicine and sanitation, the explosion of communication technologies, and the shift to modern agricultural practices collectively known as the Green Revolution have allowed more people to live longer, healthier lives. However, as in the Industrial Revolution, we are facing new environmental challenges as a result of the technological advancements. For example, new approaches to food production could bring an end to hunger but have the potential for environmental and health impacts that are beyond our current understanding.

Each major societal transition introduced technological advancements that made life easier and resources

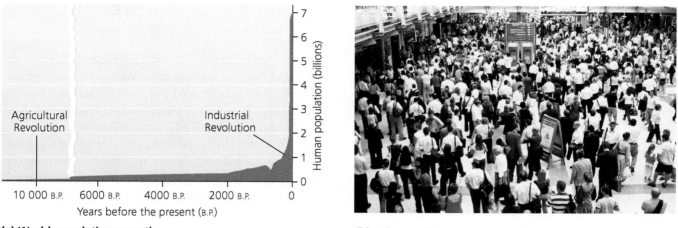

(a) World population growth

(b) Urban society

FIGURE 1.2   For almost all of human history, the world's population was low and relatively stable. It increased significantly as a result of the Agricultural Revolution and then as a result of the Industrial Revolution **(a)**. Our skyrocketing population has given rise to congested urban areas, such as this city **(b)**.

more available, effectively increasing the carrying capacity of the environment for humans and allowing the human population to increase dramatically. The modern Medical–Technological Revolution is still ongoing, and the ultimate impacts on population and the environment are as yet unknown. Much future human well-being will depend on the urban environment and the creation of sustainable, liveable cities for growing human populations around the world.

Resource consumption exerts social and environmental impacts

Population growth affects resource use and availability, and it is unquestionably at the root of many environmental problems. However, patterns and habits of resource consumption are also to blame. The Industrial Revolution enhanced the material affluence of many of the world's people, raising standards of living by raising consumption. It led to an increase in population, but the new technologies (e.g., coal-fired steam engines) and increased levels of consumption also increased pressures on the environment. We can expect that the same will be true of the Medical–Technological Revolution.

One approach to this relationship represents our total impact (I) on the environment as the product of population (P), affluence (A), and technology (T), as follows:

$$I = P \times A \times T$$

This "IPAT" model shows that impact is a function not only of population but also of affluence (which stands in for "level of consumption") and technology. An increase in the *number of people* (P) has impacts on the global

environment, but we must also concern ourselves with the impacts of *increased consumption* of natural resources and manufactured goods by the world's people (A), and the impacts of *new technologies* (T) on the environment, sometimes in ways that we can just barely imagine.

Carrying capacity and the "tragedy of the commons"   When we think about Earth's limited resources and the capacity of the planet to support a growing human population, it is useful to consider the idea of carrying capacity. **Carrying capacity** is a measure of the ability of a system to support life. Environmental scientists quantify carrying capacity in terms of the number of individuals of a particular species that can be sustained by the biological productivity of a given area of land. When the carrying capacity of the land (or water) system is exceeded—that is, when there are simply too many individuals for the system to support—one of two things will typically happen: either the population of that species will decline or collapse, or the system itself will be altered, damaged, or depleted.

Ecologist Garrett Hardin of the University of California, Santa Barbara, illustrated this process while disputing the economic theory that the unregulated exercise of individual self-interest serves the public good. According to Hardin's best-known essay, "The Tragedy of the Commons," published in the journal *Science* in 1968,[9] resources that are open to unregulated exploitation inevitably become overused and, as a result, are damaged or depleted.

Hardin based his argument on the scenario of a public pasture, or "commons" that is open to unregulated grazing. He argued that each person who puts animals to graze on the commons will be motivated by selfish interests to increase the number of his or her animals in the pasture. Because no single person owns the pasture, no one has the incentive to limit the number of grazing animals or to expend money or effort to care for the pasture. This is known as the **tragedy of the commons**: each individual withdraws whatever benefits are available from the common property as quickly as possible, until the resource becomes overused and depleted. Ultimately, the carrying capacity of the pasture will be exceeded, and its food production capacity will collapse.

In some situations, private ownership may address this problem. In China, for example, private land ownership—illegal for many decades, under Communism—has recently become possible in some rural areas. These limited experiments with private ownership have shown that landowners tend to be better environmental stewards than are short-term tenants, primarily because they are willing to make long-term investments in land management. In other cases, people who share a common resource may voluntarily organize and cooperate in enforcing its responsible use. In other cases the dilemma may require government regulation of the use of resources held in common by the public, from forests to air to freshwater. Each approach has its own strengths and weaknesses.

Calculating our ecological footprint   As global affluence has increased, human society has consumed more and more of the planet's limited resources. We can quantify resource consumption by using the concept of the "ecological footprint," developed in the 1990s

weighing the issues

THE TRAGEDY OF THE COMMONS

Imagine you make your living by fishing. You are free to boat anywhere and set out as many traps as you like, and fish have been abundant. Limits and regulations are rarely enforced. However, the fishing grounds are getting crowded. Catches begin to decline, leaving you and all the others with catches too meagre to support your families. Some call for dividing the waters and selling access to individuals plot by plot. Others urge the fishers to team up, set quotas among themselves, and prevent newcomers from entering the market. Still others implore the government to get involved and pass laws regulating the size of the catch.

What do you think is the best way to combat this tragedy of the commons and save the fishery?

by environmental scientists Mathis Wackernagel and William Rees, working together at the University of British Columbia. The **ecological footprint** is a tool that can be used to express the environmental impact of an individual or a population. It is calculated in terms of the area of land and water required to provide the raw materials that person or population consumes, and to absorb or recycle the wastes produced. The footprint calculation gives the total surface area "used" by a given person or population, including direct and indirect impacts. The ecological footprint is essentially the *inverse* of carrying capacity—it is a measure of the land (and water) required to sustain an individual, rather than the number of individuals that can be sustained by an area of land (or water). The capacity of a terrestrial or aquatic system to be biologically productive and to absorb waste, especially carbon dioxide, is called **biocapacity**. When a population exceeds or overshoots the carrying capacity or biocapacity of a system, the system will be at risk of permanent damage.

Researchers calculate that our species is now using 39% more resources than are available on a sustainable basis from all the land on the planet. That is, we are exceeding the biocapacity of the planet, and depleting renewable resources 39% faster than they are being replenished. This is like drawing the principal out of a bank account, rather than living off the interest. Furthermore, people from wealthy nations have much larger ecological footprints than do people from poorer nations. The ecological footprint of an average Canadian is approximately 7.6 hectares—roughly two to four city blocks.[10] Yet, if we could divide up all the productive, habitable land of this planet equally among the 7 billion people who are now alive, each person would receive less than one city block. If all of the world's people consumed resources at the rate of North Americans, we would need the equivalent of at least two additional planet Earths to meet our resource needs.

Footprint calculations vary dramatically—you will probably even find some variations among the footprint calculation exercises in this book. This is because the calculation depends heavily on how certain components are defined. For example, different approaches to the ecological footprint calculation use different methodologies to account for the surface area of the oceans (which clearly does not have the same significance as land area does for humans, as "living space" or even "biologically productive space"). Sometimes these differences can become political; for example, various energy sources—fossil fuels, nuclear energy, hydroelectric power—have very different environmental impacts. How should the impacts of different energy sources be accounted for in footprint calculations? When is one impact "more negative" than another? The Global Footprint Network[11] is an international nongovernmental organization that is working toward standardizing ecological footprint calculations worldwide. This should make the calculations more robust and their application to questions of environmental impact and sustainability more effective.

Environmental Knowledge can help us avoid mistakes made in the past

There is historical evidence that civilizations can crumble when pressures from population and consumption overwhelm resource availability (see "The Science Behind the Story: The Lesson of Rapa Nui"). Many great civilizations have fallen after depleting resources or damaging their environment. The Greek and Roman empires show evidence of this, as do the civilizations of the Maya, the Anasazi, and other New World peoples. Plato wrote of the deforestation and environmental degradation accompanying ancient Greek cities, and today further evidence is accumulating from research by archeologists, historians, and paleoecologists, who study past societies and landscapes. The arid deserts of today's Near Eastern and Middle Eastern countries were far more lushly vegetated when the great ancient civilizations thrived there.

Researchers have now learned enough about ancient civilizations and their demise that scientist and author Jared Diamond—in his 2005 book, *Collapse*—could hypothesize why civilizations succeed and persist, or fail and collapse.[12] Diamond identified five critical factors that determine the survival of civilizations: climate change, hostile neighbours, trade partners, environmental problems, and, finally, the society's response to environmental problems. It is interesting to note that only one of these factors—the response to environmental problems—is wholly controllable, and it is this factor that has been the crucial determinant of survival. Success and persistence, it turns out, depend largely on how societies interact with their environments.

Today we are confronted with news and predictions of environmental catastrophes on a regular basis, but it can be difficult to assess the reliability of such reports. It is even harder to evaluate the causes and effects of environmental change. Perhaps most difficult is to devise solutions to environmental problems. Studying environmental geography will outfit you with the tools to evaluate information on environmental change and think critically and creatively about possible actions to take in response.

The Nature of Environmental Geography

Geography is an interdisciplinary pursuit

Studying and addressing environmental problems is a complex endeavour that requires expertise from many disciplines, including ecology, geology, chemistry, biology, economics, political science, demography, ethics, and many others. Geography is thus an **interdisciplinary field**—one that employs concepts and techniques from numerous disciplines and brings research results from these disciplines together into a broad synthesis. Traditional disciplines are valuable because their scholars delve deeply into topics, uncovering new knowledge and developing expertise in particular areas. Interdisciplinary fields are valuable because their practitioners take specialized knowledge from different disciplines, consolidate it, synthesize it, and apply it in a broad context to serve the multifaceted interests of society.

Geography is especially broad because it encompasses not only the social sciences (disciplines that study human interactions and institutions) but also the natural sciences (disciplines that study the natural world). The natural sciences provide us with the means to gain accurate information about our environment and to interpret it reasonably. Addressing environmental problems, however, also involves weighing values and understanding human behaviour, and this requires the social sciences. Most environmental science programs focus predominantly on the natural sciences as they pertain to environmental issues. In contrast, programs heavily incorporating the social sciences often prefer the use of the term *environmental studies* to describe their academic umbrella. Environmental geography incorporates both approaches.

Just as an interdisciplinary approach to studying issues can help us better understand them, an integrated approach to addressing problems can produce effective and lasting solutions. For example, consider how the Canadian mining industry is approaching the problem of *acid drainage*, which can occur wherever sulphur is present at a mine site. Sulphur is a very common constituent of coal and metal ores, both of which are important to the Canadian economy. If sulphur-bearing waste rock at a mine site interacts with rain or surface water, sulphuric acid is formed; if it is not contained, the acid can enter local streams, where it is devastating to affected ecosystems. To solve a problem involving acid drainage, a mining company would need to consult a biologist or an ecologist regarding the impacts of the acid on local plants and animals. A hydrologist would be helpful, to understand the flow of water at the site. A mining engineer could help decide how best to contain and isolate the waste rock piles. The company would want to consult with a chemist about the nature and behaviour of the acidic solution and how it interacts with rocks and soils. A resource manager, of course, would also be helpful, to act as a liaison between the scientists and the mine management team. Canadian mining companies routinely make use of teams like this in their efforts to control acid drainage.

People differ in their perception of environmental problems

Environmental knowledge arose in the latter half of the twentieth century, as people sought to better understand environmental problems and their origins. However, the perception of what constitutes an environmental problem may vary from one person or group of people to another, or from one context or situation to another. A person's age, gender, class, race, nationality, employment, and educational background can all affect whether he or she considers a given environmental change to be a "problem."

For instance, people today are more likely to view the spraying of the pesticide DDT as a problem than people did in the 1950s, because today more is known about the health risks from pesticides (FIGURE 1.3). However, a person living today in a malaria-infested village in Africa or India may still welcome the use of DDT if it kills mosquitoes that transmit malaria, because malaria is viewed as a more immediate health threat. Thus, an African and a North American who have each knowledgeably assessed the pros and cons may, because of differences in their circumstances, differ in their judgment of the severity of DDT as an environmental problem.

People also vary in their awareness of problems. For example, in many cultures women are responsible for collecting water and fuelwood. As a result, they are often the first to perceive environmental degradation affecting these resources. In most societies, information about environmental health risks tends to reach wealthy people more readily than poor people. Thus, who you are, where you live, what you do, your income, your gender, and your socioeconomic status can have a huge effect on how you perceive your environment, how you react to change, and what impact those changes may have on how you live your life.

FIGURE 1.3
How a person or society defines an environmental problem can vary with time and circumstance. In 1945, health hazards from the pesticide DDT were not yet known, so children were doused with the chemical to treat head lice. Today, knowing of its toxicity to people and wildlife, developed nations have banned DDT. However, in some countries where malaria is a threat, DDT is still used as an effective means of eradicating mosquitoes, which transmit the disease.

Environmental science is not the same as environmentalism

Although many environmental scientists are interested in solving problems, it is incorrect to confuse environmental science with environmentalism or environmental activism. They are *not* the same. *Environmental science* is the pursuit of knowledge about the workings of the environment and our interactions with it. **Environmentalism** is a social movement dedicated to protecting the natural world—and, by extension, humans—from undesirable changes brought about by human choices (FIGURE 1.4). Although environmental scientists study many of the same issues environmentalists care about, as scientists they attempt to maintain an objective approach in their work. Remaining as free as possible from personal or ideological bias—and open to whatever conclusions the data demand—is a hallmark of the effective scientist.

In each chapter of this book you will find *Canadian Environmental Perspectives*, offering brief profiles of Canadian environmental scientists as well as individuals in non-scientific professions who contribute to the understanding, protection, management, and sustainable use of the natural environment. These people play a

FIGURE 1.4
Environmental scientists play roles very different from those of the environmental activists shown here. Some scientists do become activists to promote what they feel are workable solutions to environmental problems. However, those who do so generally try to keep their advocacy separate from their scientific work. This photograph shows Greenpeace activists protesting on Parliament Hill in Ottawa. Greenpeace is an international organization of environmental activists that was founded in Vancouver in 1971.

wide range of roles, from policy maker to activist, artist, journalist, hunter, or animal rescuer. Many of them are scientists *and* writers, or scientists *and* filmmakers or gardeners or politicians or musicians—and, yes, many of them are also environmentalists. All these people have made a difference, one way or another. All of them rely on and contribute to our knowledge, as well as to our intuitive appreciation of the natural environment. Environmental science is *distinct* from philosophy, law, commerce, religion, politics, art, and activism, but is it necessarily *exclusive* of these human undertakings? You will have to judge this for yourself, but you can count on this book to help you make a more informed judgment of what you read, hear, and experience in your encounters with the natural environment.

The *Canadian Environmental Perspective* presented in this chapter highlights David Suzuki—scientist, activist, and environmentalist. Admired by many, but controversial for his activist stance on environmental issues, Suzuki exemplifies what a multifaceted undertaking it can be to work on behalf of the environment in today's world.

The Nature of Science

Science is a systematic process for learning about the world and testing our understanding of it. The term *science* is also commonly used to refer to the accumulated

body of knowledge that arises from this dynamic process of observation, testing, and discovery.

Science

The word *science* originates from the Latin word *scientia*, meaning "knowledge," and the Latin verb *scire*, meaning "to know." The latter probably originally meant "to separate or distinguish one thing from another," pointing to the role of classification in science over the ages.

Knowledge gained from science can be applied to societal problems. Among the most important applications of science are its use in developing new technologies, and its use in informing policy and management decisions (**FIGURE 1.5**). These pragmatic applications in themselves are not science, but they must be informed by science in order to be effective. Many scientists are motivated simply by a desire to know how the world works, and others are motivated by the potential for developing useful applications and solutions to problems.

Geography is a dynamic yet systematic means of studying the world, and it is also the body of knowledge

roots
SCIENCE

The word **science** originates from the Latin word *scientia*, meaning "knowledge," and the Latin verb *scire*, meaning "to know." The latter probably originally meant "to separate or distinguish one thing from another," pointing to the role of classification in science over the ages.

FIGURE 1.5
Scientific knowledge can be applied in policy and management decisions and in technology. Prescribed burning, shown here, is a management practice to restore healthy forests and is informed by scientific research into forest ecology.

The Lesson of Rapa Nui

These immense moai (statues) are on Easter Island.

Rapa Nui (Easter Island) is one of the most remote islands on the globe. When European explorers reached the island in 1722, they found a barren landscape populated by fewer than 2000 people, living a marginal existence in caves. The desolate island featured gigantic statues of carved stone, evidence that a sophisticated civilization had once lived there. How could people without wheels or ropes, on an island without trees, have moved statues 10 m high, weighing 80 metric tons? The answer lies in the fact that the island did not always lack trees, and its people were not always without rope.

Scientists have determined that the island was once lushly forested, supporting a prosperous society of 6000 to 30 000 people. This once-flourishing civilization exceeded the carrying capacity of the island by overusing resources and cutting down trees, destroying itself in a downward spiral of starvation and conflict. Today, Rapa Nui stands as a demonstration of what can happen when a population consumes too much of the limited resources that support it.

To solve the mystery of the island's past, scientists have used various methods. British scientist John Flenley excavated sediments from the bottoms of the island's volcanic crater lakes, examining ancient grains of pollen to reconstruct changes in vegetation over time. Flenley and other researchers found that when Polynesian people first arrived (between 300 C.E. and 900 C.E.), the island was covered with a species of palm tree related to the tall, thick-trunked Chilean wine palm.

The palms would have provided fuelwood, building material for houses and canoes, fruit, and fibre—and, presumably, logs to move the stone statues. Scientists have tested hypotheses about how the islanders moved their monoliths, recreating the feat by using great quantities of rope, with tree trunks as rollers or sleds. The only likely source of rope on the island is the fibrous inner bark of the *hauhau* tree, a species that today is near extinction.

At least 21 other species of plants (including trees) that were once common on the island are now completely gone. Around 750 C.E., tree populations began to decline, and ferns and grasses became more common. By 950 C.E., the trees were largely gone. Around 1400 C.E., pollen levels plummeted, indicating a dearth of vegetation. The same sequence occurred two centuries later at two other sites, more remote from village areas. Evidence now supports the hypothesis that people gradually denuded the island.

With the trees gone, soil would have eroded away—confirmed by sediment that accumulated in Rapa Nui's lakes. Faster runoff of rainwater would have meant less freshwater available for drinking. Erosion would have degraded agricultural lands, lowering crop yields. Reduced agricultural production would have led to starvation and population decline.

Analyses by ornithologist David Steadman show that at least 6 species of land birds and 25 species of seabirds nested on Rapa Nui and were eaten by islanders. Today, no native land birds and only one type of seabird are left. Early islanders also feasted on porpoises, fish, sharks, turtles, octopi, and shellfish. Analyses of islanders' diets in the later years indicate that little seafood was consumed. With the trees gone, islanders could not build the great double-canoes their ancestors used for fishing. Europeans who visited in the eighteenth century observed only a few old small canoes and flimsy rafts made of reeds.

As resources declined, the islanders' main domesticated food animal, the chicken, became more valuable. Archeologists found that later islanders kept chickens in stone fortresses designed to prevent theft. The once prosperous and peaceful civilization fell into clan warfare, revealed by

The haunting statues of Rapa Nui (Easter Island) were erected by a sophisticated civilization that collapsed after depleting its resource base and devastating its island environment.

unearthed weapons made of hard volcanic rock and skeletons with head wounds.

Canadian economists Scott Taylor and James Brander took a different approach to investigating what happened at Rapa Nui.[13] They developed a computer model of the interplay between renewable resources and population. The model is based on standard ecological *predator–prey models*, with people in the role of predator, and resources as their prey. This scenario generates "feast-and-famine" cycles of rising and falling population and resource stocks. The researchers speculate that such cycles may account for the decline and eventual collapse of other civilizations as a result of rapid population growth and consequent resource degradation.

Is the story of Rapa Nui as unique and isolated as the island itself, or does it hold lessons for our world today? Earth may be vastly larger and richer in resources than was Rapa Nui, but the human population is also much larger. The islanders must have seen that they were depleting their resources, but they could not stop. Perhaps we can learn from them, and act wisely to conserve the resources on our island, Earth.

accumulated from this process. Like science in general, environmental geography informs its practical applications and often is motivated by them.

Why does science matter? The late American astronomer Carl Sagan wrote the following in his 1995 treatise *The Demon-Haunted World: Science as a Candle in the Dark*:

> *We've arranged a global civilization in which the most crucial elements—transportation, communications, and all other industries; agriculture, medicine, education, entertainment, protecting the environment; and even the key democratic institution of voting—profoundly depend on science and technology.*[14]

Sagan and many others have argued that science is essential if we hope to develop solutions to the problems—environmental and otherwise—that we face today. We might go a step further and suggest that the *democratization* of science—making the science of our world accessible and understandable to as many people as possible—is also essential if we are to make informed decisions about the management of this planet.

Social & Natural scientists test ideas by critically examining evidence

How can we tell whether warnings of impending environmental catastrophes—or any other claims, for that matter—are based on scientific thinking? Scientists examine ideas about how the world works by designing tests to determine whether these ideas are supported by evidence. If a particular statement or explanation is testable and resists repeated attempts to disprove it, scientists are likely to accept it as a useful explanation. Scientific inquiry is thus an incremental approach to the truth.

The scientific method is a key element of science

Scientists generally follow a process called the **scientific method**. A technique for testing ideas with observations, it involves several assumptions and a series of interrelated steps. There is nothing mysterious about the scientific method; it is merely a formalized version of the procedure any of us might naturally take, using common sense, to answer a question.

The scientific method is a theme with variations, however, and scientists pursue their work in many different ways. Because science is an active, creative, imaginative process, an innovative scientist may find good reason to stray from the traditional scientific method when a particular situation demands it. Scientists from different fields approach their work differently because they deal with dissimilar types of information. A natural scientist, such as a chemist, will conduct research quite differently from a social scientist, such as a sociologist. Because geography includes both natural and social sciences, in our discussion here we use the term *science* in its broad sense, to include both. Despite their many differences, scientists of all persuasions broadly agree on the fundamental elements of scientific inquiry.

The scientific method relies on the following assumptions:

■ The universe functions in accordance with fixed natural laws that do not change from time to time or from place to place.

■ All events arise from some cause and, in turn, lead to other events.

■ We can use our senses and reasoning abilities to detect and describe natural laws that underlie the cause-and-effect relationships we observe in nature.

As practised by individual researchers or research teams, the scientific method (**FIGURE 1.6**) typically consists of the steps outlined below.

Make observations Advances in science typically begin with the observation of a phenomenon that the scientist wants to explain. Observations set the scientific method in motion and function throughout the process.

Ask questions Scientists are naturally curious about the world and love to ask questions. Why are certain plants or animals less common today than they once were? Are storms becoming more severe, or flooding more frequent? Why? What causes excessive growth of algae in local ponds? Do the impacts of pesticides on fish or frogs mean that people could be affected in the same ways? All of these are questions environmental scientists have asked and attempted to answer.

Develop a hypothesis Scientists attempt to answer their questions by devising explanations that can be tested. A **hypothesis** is an educated guess that explains a phenomenon or answers a scientific question. For example, a scientist investigating the question of why algae are growing excessively in local ponds might observe chemical fertilizers being applied on farm fields nearby. The scientist might then state a hypothesis as follows: "Agricultural fertilizers running into ponds cause the algae in the ponds to increase." Sometimes this

Scientific method

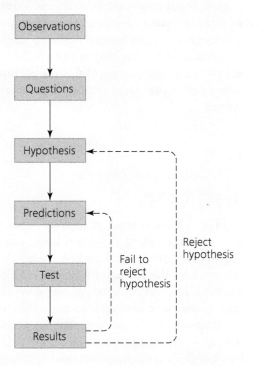

FIGURE 1.6
The scientific method is the observation-based hypothesis-testing approach that scientists use to learn how the world works. This diagram is a simplified generalization that, although useful for instructive purposes, cannot convey the true dynamic and creative nature of science. Moreover, researchers from different disciplines may pursue their work in ways that legitimately vary from this model.

takes the form of a *null hypothesis*, a statement that the scientist is expecting no relationship between variables, such as between fertilizer and algal growth in a pond.

Make predictions   The scientist next uses the hypothesis to generate **predictions**, which are specific statements that can be directly and unequivocally tested. In our algae example, a prediction might be: "If agricultural fertilizers are added to a pond, the quantity of algae in the pond will increase." A null hypothesis can also lead to predictions; for example, the scientist might predict that adding agricultural fertilizer to a pond will cause no change in the amount of algae growing in the pond.

Test the predictions   Predictions are tested one at a time by gathering evidence that could potentially refute the prediction and thus disprove the hypothesis. The strongest form of evidence comes from experimentation. An **experiment** is an activity designed to test the validity of a hypothesis. It involves manipulating **variables**, conditions that can

change. For example, a scientist could test the hypothesis linking algal growth to fertilizer by selecting two identical ponds and adding fertilizer to one while leaving the other in its natural state. In this example, fertilizer input is an *independent variable*, a variable the scientist manipulates, whereas the quantity of algae that results is the *dependent variable*, one that depends on the fertilizer input. If the two ponds are identical except for a single independent variable (fertilizer input), then any differences that arise between the ponds can be attributed to that variable. Such an experiment is known as a *controlled experiment* because the scientist controls for the effects of all variables except the one being tested—the dependent variable. In our example, the pond left unfertilized serves as a **control**, an unmanipulated point of comparison for the manipulated or treated pond. Whenever possible, it is best to reproduce an experiment; that is, to stage multiple tests of the same comparison of control and treatment. Our scientist could perform a *replicated experiment* on, say, 10 pairs of ponds, adding fertilizer to one of the ponds in each pair.

Experiments can establish *causal relationships*, showing that changes in an independent variable cause changes in a dependent variable. However, experiments are not the only means of testing a hypothesis. Sometimes a hypothesis can be convincingly addressed through *correlation*—that is, searching for relationships and patterns among variables.

Suppose our scientist surveys 50 ponds, 20 of which are fed by fertilizer runoff from nearby farm fields and 30 of which are not. Let us also say he or she finds seven times as much algal growth in the fertilized ponds as in the unfertilized ponds. The scientist would conclude that algal growth is correlated with fertilizer input—that is, that one tends to increase along with the other.

Although this type of evidence is weaker than the causal demonstration that controlled experiments can provide, sometimes it is the best approach, or the only feasible one. For example, in studying the effects of global climate change, we could hardly run an experiment that involved adding carbon dioxide to 10 treatment planets and comparing the result to 10 control planets.

Analyze and interpret results   Scientists record **data**, or information, from their studies. They particularly value *quantitative* data, information expressed numerically, because numbers provide precision and are easy to compare. The scientist running the fertilization experiment, for instance, might quantify the area of water surface covered by algae in each pond, or measure the dry weight of algae in a certain volume of water taken from each pond. Even with the precision that numbers provide, however, a scientist's results may not be clearcut. Experimental data may differ from control data only slightly, or different replicates may yield different results. The scientist must therefore analyze the data by using statistical tests. With these mathematical methods, scientists can determine objectively and precisely the strength and reliability of patterns they find. If the results are unreliable or cannot be replicated, it may be necessary to attempt a different kind of test.

Some research, especially in the social sciences, involves information that is *qualitative*, or not expressible in terms of numbers. Research involving historical texts, personal interviews, surveys, detailed examination of case studies, or descriptive observations of behaviour can include qualitative data on which statistical analyses may not be possible. Such studies are still scientific in the broad sense, because their data can be interpreted systematically by using other accepted methods of analysis.

If experiments disprove a hypothesis, the scientist will reject the hypothesis and may develop a new one to replace it. If experiments fail to disprove the hypothesis, this outcome lends support to the hypothesis but does not *prove* it is correct. The scientist may choose to generate new predictions to test the hypothesis in a different way and further assess its likelihood of being true. Thus, the scientific method loops back on itself, often giving rise to repeated rounds of hypothesis revision, prediction, and testing (see FIGURE 1.6).

If repeated tests fail to disprove a particular hypothesis, and evidence in its favour is accumulating, the researcher may eventually conclude that the idea is well supported. Ideally, a scientist would want to test all possible explanations for the question of interest. For instance, our scientist might propose an additional hypothesis that algae increase in fertilized ponds because numbers of fish or invertebrate animals that eat algae decrease. It is possible, of course, that both hypotheses could be correct and that each may explain some portion of the initial observation that local ponds were experiencing algal blooms.

There are different ways to test hypotheses

An experiment in which the researcher actively chooses and manipulates the independent variable is known as a *manipulative experiment* (FIGURE 1.7A). A manipulative experiment provides the strongest type of evidence a scientist can obtain. In practice, however, some modes of scientific inquiry are more amenable to manipulative experimentation than others. Physics and chemistry tend to involve manipulative experiments, but many other fields deal with entities less easily manipulated than are physical forces and chemical reagents. This is true of *historical sciences*, such as cosmology, which deals with the history of the universe, and paleontology, which explores the history of past life. It is difficult to experimentally manipulate a star thousands of light years away, or the tooth from a

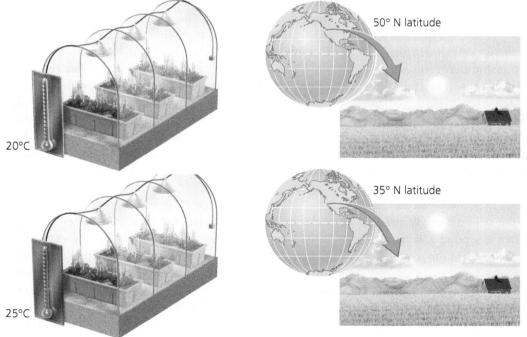

FIGURE 1.7
A researcher wanting to test how temperature affects the growth of a crop might run a manipulative experiment in which the crop is grown in two identical greenhouses: one kept at 20°C and the other kept at 25°C **(a)**. Alternatively, the researcher might run a natural experiment in which he or she compares the growth of the crop in two fields at different latitudes: a cool northerly location and a warm southerly one **(b)**. Because it would be difficult to hold all variables besides temperature constant, the researcher might want to collect data on a number of northern and southern fields and correlate temperature and crop growth using statistical methods.

50° N latitude

35° N latitude

20°C

25°C

(a) Manipulative experiment

(b) Natural experiment, or correlational study

mastodon that lived 15 000 years ago. Moreover, many of the most interesting questions in these fields centre on the causes and consequences of particular historical events, rather than the behaviour of general constants.

Disciplines that do not quite fit the "physics model" of science sometimes rely on *natural experiments* rather than manipulative ones (**FIGURE 1.7B**). For instance, an evolutionary biologist might want to test whether animal species isolated on oceanic islands tend to evolve large body sizes over time. The biologist cannot run a manipulative experiment by placing animals on islands and continents and waiting long enough for evolution to do its work. However, this is exactly what nature has already done. The biologist might test the idea by comparing pairs of closely related species, in which one of each pair lives on an island and the other on a continental mainland, or one is a modern species and the other an ancient, fossilized relative. The experiment has in essence been conducted naturally, and it is up to the scientist to interpret the results.

In many disciplines, both manipulative and natural experimentation are used. For example, an ecologist wanting to measure the importance of a certain insect in pollinating the flowers of a given crop plant might fit some flowers with a device to keep the insects out while leaving other flowers accessible, and later measure the fruit output of each group. Other questions that involve large spatial scales or long time scales may instead require natural experiments.

The social sciences generally involve less experimentation than the natural sciences, depending more on careful observation and statistical interpretation of patterns in data. For example, a geographer, studying how people in different places react and/or adapt to natural hazards or resource scarcity, might conduct a survey and analyze responses to the questions, looking for similarities and differences among respondents. Such analyses may be either quantitative or qualitative, depending on the nature of the data and the researchers' particular questions and approaches.

Descriptive observational studies and natural experiments can show correlation between variables, but they cannot demonstrate that one variable *causes* change in another, as manipulative experiments can. Not all variables are controlled for in a natural experiment, so a single result could give rise to several interpretations. However, correlative studies, when done well, can make for very convincing science, and they preserve the real-world complexity that manipulative experiments often sacrifice. Moreover, sometimes correlation is all we have. Because large-scale manipulations are difficult, some of the most important questions in environmental science tend to be addressed with correlative data.

The large scale and complexity of many questions in environmental science also mean that few studies, manipulative or correlative, come up with neat and absolute results. As such, scientists are not always able to give policymakers and society definitive answers to questions. Even when science is able to provide answers, deciding upon the optimal social response to a problem can still be very difficult.

The scientific process does not stop with the scientific method

Individual researchers or teams of researchers follow the scientific method as they investigate questions that interest them. However, scientific work takes place within the context of a community of peers, and to have any impact, a researcher's work must be published and made accessible to this community. Thus, the scientific method is embedded within a larger process that takes place at the level of the scientific community as a whole (**FIGURE 1.8**).

Peer review   When a researcher's work is done and the results have been analyzed, he or she writes up the findings and submits them to a journal for publication. Several other scientists specializing in the topic of the paper examine the manuscript, provide comments and criticism (generally anonymously), and judge whether the work merits publication. This procedure, known as **peer review**, is an essential part of the scientific process. Peer review is a valuable guard against faulty science contaminating the literature on which all scientists rely. However, because scientists are human and may have their own personal biases and agendas, politics can sometimes creep into the review process. Fortunately, just as the vast majority of individual scientists strive to remain accurate and objective in conducting their research, the scientific community does its best to ensure fair review of all work.

Conference presentations   Scientists frequently present their work at professional conferences, where they interact with colleagues and receive comments informally on their research. Feedback from colleagues can help improve the quality of a scientist's work before it is submitted for publication.

Grants and funding   Research scientists spend large portions of their time writing grant applications requesting money to fund their research from private foundations or government agencies, such as the Natural Sciences and Engineering Research Council or the Social Sciences and Humanities Research Council.

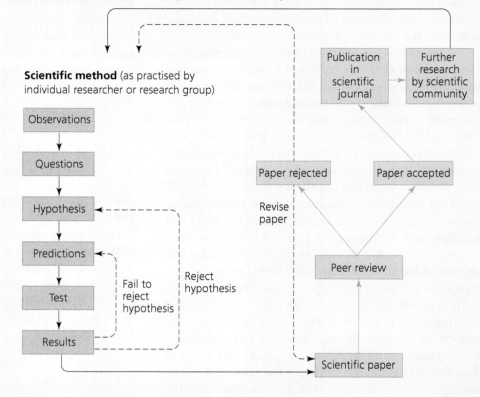

FIGURE 1.8
The scientific method (inner box) followed by individual researchers or research teams exists within the context of the overall process of science at the level of the scientific community (outer box). This process includes peer review and publication of research, acquisition of funding, and the development of theory through the cumulative work of many researchers.

Grant applications undergo peer review just as scientific papers do, and competition for funding is often intense. Scientists' reliance on funding sources can also lead to potential conflicts of interest. A scientist who obtains data showing his or her funding source in an unfavourable light may be reluctant to publish the results for fear of losing funding—or, worse yet, may be tempted to doctor the results. This situation can arise, for instance, when an industry funds research to test its products for safety or environmental impact. Most scientists do not

weighing the issues

FOLLOW THE MONEY

Let us say that you are a research scientist and are interested in studying the impacts of chemicals released by pulp-and-paper mills on nearby freshwater lakes. Obtaining research funding has been difficult; then a representative from a large pulp-and-paper company contacts you. The company also is interested in the impacts of its chemical effluents on nearby water bodies, and it would like to fund your research project. What are the pros and cons of this offer?

succumb to these pressures, but some funding sources have been known to influence scientists toward certain results. This is why as a student or an informed citizen, when critically assessing a scientific study, you should always try to find out where the researchers obtained funding.

Repeatability   Sound science is based on doubt rather than certainty and on repeatability rather than one-time occurrences. Even when a hypothesis appears to explain observed phenomena, scientists are inherently wary of accepting it. The careful scientist will test a hypothesis repeatedly in various ways before submitting the findings for publication. Following publication, other scientists usually will attempt to reproduce the results in their own experiments and analyses.

Theories   If a hypothesis survives repeated testing by numerous research teams and continues to predict experimental outcomes and observations accurately, it may potentially be incorporated into a theory. A **theory** is a widely accepted, well-tested explanation of one or more cause-and-effect relationships, which has been extensively validated by extensive research. Whereas a hypothesis is a simple explanatory statement that may be refuted by a single experiment, a theory consolidates many related hypotheses that have been tested and supported by a large body of experimental and observational data.

Note that scientific use of the word *theory* differs from popular usage of the word. In everyday language, when we say something is "just a theory," we are suggesting it is a speculative idea without much substance. Scientists, however, mean just the opposite when they use the term; to them, a theory is a conceptual framework that effectively explains a phenomenon and has undergone extensive and rigorous testing, such that confidence in it is extremely strong. For example, Darwin's *theory of evolution by natural selection* has been supported and elaborated upon by many thousands of studies over 150 years of intensive research. Such research has shown repeatedly and in great detail how plants and animals change over generations, or evolve, to express characteristics that best promote survival and reproduction. Because of its strong support and explanatory power, the evolutionary theory is the central unifying principle of modern biology.

Science may go through "paradigm shifts"

Results obtained by the scientific method may sometimes later be reinterpreted to show that earlier interpretations were incorrect. Science goes through periodic revolutions, or dramatic upheavals in thought, in which one scientific *paradigm*, or dominant view, is abandoned for another. For example, before the sixteenth century, scientists believed that Earth was at the centre of the universe. They made accurate measurements of the movement of the planets, then applied elaborate corrections that seemed to be needed in order to explain their measurements from a geocentric (Earth-centred) viewpoint. Nicolaus Copernicus eventually disproved the geocentric model of the solar system by demonstrating that placing the Sun at the centre of the solar system explained the planetary data and observations much better. A similar paradigm shift occurred in the 1960s, when geologists accepted the theory of plate tectonics because evidence for the movement of continents and the action of tectonic plates had accumulated and had become overwhelmingly convincing.

Understanding how science works is vital to assessing how scientific ideas and interpretations change through time, with new information. This process is especially relevant in environmental science, a young field that is changing rapidly as we gather vast amounts of new information, as human impacts on the planet multiply, and as lessons from the consequences of our actions become apparent. Because so much remains unstudied and undone, and because so many issues we cannot foresee are likely to arise in the future, environmental science will remain an exciting frontier for you to explore as a student and as an informed citizen throughout your life.

Sustainability and the Future of Our World

Population and consumption lie at the root of many environmental impacts

We modify our environment in diverse ways, but the steep and sudden rise in human population has amplified nearly all our impacts. Our numbers have nearly quadrupled in the past 100 years, reaching 7 billion in 2012. We add about 80 million people to the planet each year—more than 200 000 per day. Today, the rate of population growth is slowing, but our absolute numbers continue to increase and shape our interactions with one another and with our environment.

Our consumption of resources has risen even faster than our population growth. The rise in affluence has been a positive development for humanity, and our conversion of the planet's natural capital has made life more pleasant for us so far. However, like rising population, rising per capita consumption amplifies the demands we make on our environment.

Moreover, affluence and consumption have not grown equally for all the world's citizens. Today, the 20 wealthiest nations boast 40 times the income of the 20 poorest nations—twice the gap that existed four decades ago. The ecological footprint of the average citizen of a developed nation, such as Canada or the United States, is considerably larger than that of the average resident of a developing country (FIGURE 1.9).

We face many environmental challenges

The dramatic growth in human population and consumption is due in part to our successful efforts to expand and intensify the production of food. Since the origins of agriculture and the Industrial Revolution, new technologies have enabled us to grow increasingly more food per unit of land. These advances in agriculture must be counted as one of humanity's great achievements, but they have come at some cost. We have converted nearly half the planet's land surface for agriculture; our extensive use of chemical fertilizers and pesticides

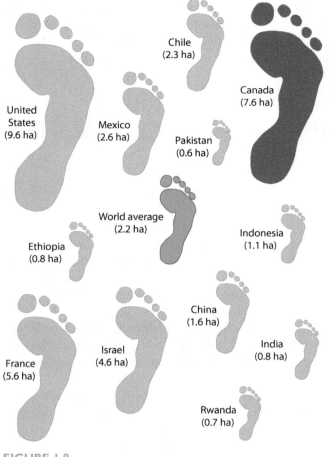

FIGURE 1.9
The citizens of some nations have larger ecological footprints than others. Shown here are ecological footprints for average citizens of several developed and developing nations, as of 2003.
Source: Data from Global Footprint Network, 2006.

FIGURE 1.10
Indoor and outdoor air pollution contribute to millions of premature deaths each year. Environmental scientists and policymakers are working to reduce these problems in a variety of ways.

negatively affects organisms and alters natural systems; and erosion, climate change, and poorly managed irrigation are destroying 5 million to 7 million hectares of productive cropland each year.

Meanwhile, pollution from our farms, industries, households, and individual actions dirties our land, water, and air (**FIGURE 1.10**). Outdoor air pollution, indoor air pollution, and water pollution contribute to the deaths of millions of people each year. Environmental toxicologists are chronicling the impacts on people and wildlife of the many synthetic chemicals and other pollutants we emit into the environment.

Perhaps our most pressing pollution challenge may be to address the looming spectre of global climate change. Scientists have firmly concluded that human activity is altering the composition of the atmosphere and that these changes are affecting Earth's climate. Since the start of the Industrial Revolution, atmospheric carbon dioxide concentrations have risen to a level not present in hundreds of thousands—likely millions—of years.

This increase has resulted from our reliance on burning fossil fuels to power our civilization. Carbon dioxide and several other gases absorb heat and warm Earth's surface. The anthropogenic enhancement of this process is likely responsible for glacial melting, sea-level rise, impacts on wildlife and crops, and increased episodes of destructive weather. Atmospheric carbon dioxide also contributes to the acidification of ocean water.

The combined impact of human actions, such as climate change, overharvesting, pollution, the introduction of non-native species, and particularly habitat alteration, has driven many aquatic and terrestrial species out of large parts of their ranges and toward the brink of extinction. Today Earth's *biological diversity*, or **biodiversity**, the cumulative number and diversity of living things, is declining dramatically. Many biologists say we are already in a mass extinction event comparable to only five others documented in all of Earth's history. Biologist Edward O. Wilson has warned that the loss of biodiversity is our most serious and threatening environmental dilemma, because it is not the kind of problem that responsible human action can remedy. The extinction of species is irreversible; once a species has become extinct, it is lost forever.

Solutions to environmental problems must be global and sustainable

The nature of virtually all these environmental issues is being changed by the set of ongoing phenomena commonly dubbed *globalization*. Our increased global interconnectedness in trade, politics, and the movement of people and

THE SCIENCE BEHIND THE STORY

Mission to Planet Earth: Monitoring Environmental Change

Ellesmere Island National Park Reserve is the most northerly park on Earth.

Science begins with observation. One of the most significant legacies of the space program is the ability to observe Earth from afar. The development of this ability changed our perspective on this planet permanently, leading to a new sense of respect, care, and concern for the environment that continues to grow as a social priority.

Since the last hand-held photograph of the whole planet was taken in 1972 by Apollo 17 astronauts, scientists and technologists have dramatically improved their ability to capture and interpret a wide variety of images of this planet. Hand-held photography continues to provide an important part of the data returned by manned space missions (you can see many of these photographs archived at NASA's website, www.nasa.gov). Today, satellites and the sophisticated instrumentation they carry provide us with the opportunity to observe, study, monitor change, and gather an unprecedented amount of information about the planet, through technologies and processes that are collectively referred to as *remote sensing*.

By the early 1980s, NASA scientists and administrators had faced the reality that they were unlikely to obtain the necessary funding to return to the Moon any time in the near future. Instead, they began to turn their attention to another nearby planetary object: Earth. They called the new scientific approach *Earth system science*

and defined as its goal "to obtain a scientific understanding of the entire Earth system on a global scale by describing how its component parts and their interactions have evolved, how they function, and how they may be expected to continue to evolve on all timescales."[15] The observation and interpretation of environmental change was fundamental to this new scientific approach, right from the beginning.

To achieve the goals of Earth system science, scientists began to use technologies that had been developed for other purposes—space exploration, communications, even warfare—to observe Earth and its component parts over time, and they called the new endeavour *Mission to Planet Earth*. The scientific results of this mission have been and continue to be spectacular. Satellites and remote detection and measuring technologies have provided a massive amount of information about the environment, how it changes over time, and how human activity affects it—information with a depth and

breadth that would have been unimaginable back when those first whole-planet photographs were taken. The photo of Ellesmere Island National Park Reserve (top left), acquired in August 2003 by the Advanced Spaceborne Thermal Emission and Reflection Radiometer (ASTER) aboard NASA's *Terra* satellite, shows a tidewater glacier in Greely Fjord, situated in the southwestern corner of the Reserve. Icebergs floating in the fjord are chunks that have broken off the glacier. The corrugated surface on the glacier near its terminus (or end) is a network of crevasses. The strong linear features running through the glacier are flow lines. The dark blue features are melt ponds; they are darker than the ice and absorb more sunlight, thus melting more ice. A great deal of what environmental scientists now know about this planet as a coherent system, how its various parts interact, and how it is changing and evolving has been based on information derived from the Mission to Planet Earth.

This satellite image shows Lake Athabasca, the dark, irregular patch straddling the border between Alberta (west) and Saskatchewan (east), and numerous active summer forest fires (indicated by red dots). A large smoke plume stretches across Saskatchewan and into Manitoba, to the east. This image was acquired by the Moderate Resolution Imaging Spectroradiometer aboard the Terra satellite in July 2002.

other species poses many challenging problems, but it also sets the stage for novel and effective solutions.

The most comprehensive scientific assessment of the present condition of the world's ecological systems and their ability to continue supporting our civilization was completed in 2005, when more than 2000 of the world's leading environmental scientists from nearly 100 nations completed the *Millennium Ecosystem Assessment*. The four main findings of this exhaustive project are summarized in TABLE 1.1. The Assessment makes clear that our degradation of the world's environmental systems is having negative impacts on all of us but that with care and diligence we can still turn many of these trends around.

Our energy choices will influence our future immensely

Our reliance on fossil fuels to power our civilization has intensified virtually every negative impact we have on the environment, from habitat alteration to air pollution to climate change. Fossil fuels have also brought us the material affluence we enjoy. By taking advantage of the richly concentrated energy in coal, oil, and natural gas, we have been able to power the machinery of the Industrial Revolution, produce the chemicals that boosted agricultural yields, run the vehicles and transportation networks of our mobile society, and manufacture and distribute our countless consumer products. It is little exaggeration to say that the lives we live today are a result of the availability of fossil fuels.

However, in extracting fossil fuels, we are splurging on a one-time bonanza. Scientists calculate that we have depleted half the world's oil supplies and that we are in for a rude awakening very soon, once the supply begins to decline while the demand continues to rise. Coal and natural gas are also nonrenewable and available in limited supply, although we are likely farther from reaching the limits of those resources. The search is now on for alternative sources of energy that will allow us to maintain an acceptable standard of living while minimizing the environmental impacts of energy use. How we handle the imminent crisis of fossil fuel depletion and the search for replacements will largely determine the nature of our lives in the twenty-first century.

Fortunately, potential solutions abound

We cannot, of course, live without exerting *any* impact on Earth's systems. We face trade-offs with many environmental issues, and the challenge is to develop solutions that increase our quality of life while minimizing harm to the environment that supports us. Fortunately, many workable solutions are at hand, and we can achieve many more potential solutions with further effort.

In response to agricultural problems, scientists and others have developed and promoted soil conservation, high-efficiency irrigation, and organic agriculture. In addition, technological advances and new laws have greatly reduced the pollution emitted by industry and automobiles in wealthier countries. Canadian scientists have been at the forefront of many of these technological advances and have made fundamental contributions to global environmental management theories and to our current understanding of the human–environment relationship. Amid ample reasons for concern about the state of global biodiversity, advances in conservation biology are enabling scientists and policymakers in many cases to work together to protect habitat, slow extinction, and safeguard endangered species (FIGURE 1.11).

Recycling is helping to relieve our waste disposal problems, and alternative renewable energy sources are being developed to take the place of fossil fuels (FIGURE 1.12). These are but a few of the many solutions we will explore in the course of this book, and we will examine some of the new structures, programs, processes, and technologies that are emerging in support of these solutions.

Table 1.1   Main Findings of the Millennium Ecosystem Assessment
■ Over the past 50 years, humans have changed ecosystems more rapidly and extensively than in any comparable period of time in human history, largely to meet rapidly growing demands for food, freshwater, timber, fibre, and fuel. This has resulted in a substantial and largely irreversible loss in the diversity of life on Earth.
■ The changes made to ecosystems have contributed to substantial net gains in human well-being and economic development, but these gains have been achieved at growing costs. These costs include the degradation of ecosystems and the services they provide for us, and the exacerbation of poverty for some groups of people.
■ This degradation could grow significantly worse during the first half of this century.
■ The challenge of reversing the degradation of ecosystems while meeting increasing demands for their services can be partially overcome, but doing so will involve significantly changing many policies, institutions, and practises.

Source: Adapted from Millennium Ecosystem Assessment, *Synthesis Report, 2005.*

FIGURE 1.11
Human activities are pushing many organisms toward extinction. Efforts to save endangered species and reduce biodiversity loss include many approaches, but all require that adequate areas of appropriate habitat be preserved in the wild. The habitat of polar bears, for example, is increasingly threatened by global climate change.

FIGURE 1.12
Our dependence on fossil fuels has caused a wide array of environmental impacts. Although fossil fuels have powered our civilization since the Industrial Revolution, many renewable energy sources exist, such as solar energy, which can be collected with panels like these. Such alternative energy sources could be further developed for sustainable use now and in the future.

Are things getting better, or worse?

Despite the myriad challenges we face, some people maintain that the general conditions of human life and the environment are getting better, not worse.

Furthermore, some people maintain that we will find ways to make Earth's natural resources meet all our needs indefinitely and that human ingenuity will see us through any difficulty. Such views are sometimes characterized as *cornucopian*. (In Greek mythology, *cornucopia*—literally "horn of plenty"—is the name for a magical goat's horn that overflowed with limitless grain, fruit, and flowers.) In contrast, people who predict doom and disaster for the world because of our impact upon it have been called *Cassandras*, after the mythical princess of Troy with the gift of prophecy, whose dire predictions were not believed.

At least three questions are worth asking each time you are confronted with seemingly conflicting statements from Cassandras and cornucopians:

1. Do the impacts being debated pertain only to humans or also to other organisms and natural systems?
2. Are the debaters thinking in the short term or the long term?
3. Are they considering all costs and benefits relevant for the question at hand, or only some?

As you proceed through this book and encounter many contentious issues, consider how a person's perception of them may be influenced by these three factors.

Sustainability involves meeting environmental, social, and economic goals

The primary challenge in our increasingly populated world is how to live within our planet's means, such that Earth and its resources can sustain us, and the rest of Earth's biota, for the foreseeable future. This is the challenge of **sustainability**, a guiding principle of modern environmental science. Sustainability means leaving our children and grandchildren a world as rich and full as the world we live in now. It means not depleting Earth's natural capital, so that after we are gone our descendants will enjoy the use of resources, as we have. It means developing solutions that are able to work in the long term. Sustainability requires maintaining fully functioning ecological systems, because we cannot sustain human civilization without sustaining the natural systems that nourish it.

Environmental protection is often cast as being in opposition to the economic and social needs of human society, but environmental scientists have long recognized that our civilization cannot exist without a functional natural environment. In recent years, people of all persuasions have increasingly realized the connection between environmental quality and human quality of life. Moreover, we now recognize that often it is society's poorer people who suffer the most from environmental degradation. This realization has led advocates of environmental protection, economic development, and social justice to begin working together toward common goals. This cooperative approach has given rise to the modern drive for sustainable development.

CANADIAN ENVIRONMENTAL PERSPECTIVES

David Suzuki

David Suzuki is an environmentalist, but he was trained as a scientist.

- **Zoologist, geneticist**, and **professor** University of British Columbia, Sustainable Development Research Institute
- **Environmentalist** and **activist**
- **Writer** *The Sacred Balance: Rediscovering Our Place in Nature*
- **Radio and TV broadcast journalist** *Quirks & Quarks* and *The Nature of Things*

What remains to be said about a man who has been called "Canada's environmental conscience"? He has a long list of honorary degrees. He is a Companion of the Order of Canada, placed fifth in the Canadian Broadcasting Corporation's "Greatest Canadian" contest, and has received scores of major environmental and journalism awards. He was the subject of the acclaimed 2010 documentary *Force of Nature: The David Suzuki Movie*. We see him on TV often, exhorting us not to air condition our homes to the point at which penguins would be comfortable.

What we sometimes forget is that before he was a journalist, writer, activist, or TV broadcaster, David Suzuki was a scientist.[17] He completed a degree in biology in 1958, spent that summer working as a fish biologist for the Department of Lands and Forests in Ontario, and then went on to graduate school in zoology at the University of Chicago. By 1962 Suzuki had accepted an appointment in the Department of Genetics at the University of Alberta, moving a year later to a faculty position at the University of British Columbia.

When Suzuki started out as a young professor teaching genetics—a science he adored for its precision and the promise it held for society—he encountered questions at the intersection between science and ethics. Specifically, he learned how genetics had been used by the Nazis and others with an interest in institutionalizing racism.[18] Suzuki's own family had had property seized and been placed in internment camps by the Government of Canada during the Second World War. "Once a Jap, always a Jap," a Member of Parliament said at the time,[19] echoing the belief that treachery and untrustworthiness were genetically encoded into anyone of Japanese descent.

This history makes Suzuki a perfect starting point for a discussion about the difference between environmentalism and environmental science. They are different—but not entirely separate. Ideally, science informs and responds to political and social influences, without being overly influenced by them. David Suzuki has consciously given up "doing" science on an everyday basis, freeing himself to focus on the more political side of science. Today he is much better known for his activism and journalism than for his science. On the rapidly developing field of biotechnology, so close to his own scientific background, he comments:

There is absolutely no reason to suppose that biologists know enough to anticipate the ecological and health ramifications of a revolutionary technology such as genetic engineering. Governments must resist the economic pressures and show leadership and concern for the long-term health of people and nature. And scientists involved in this exciting area should learn from history and welcome free and open discussion about ecological, health, and social implications of their work.[20]

Science is a human endeavour; it can never be entirely free of political or social influence. We want our leaders to incorporate scientific understanding into their social decisions, but there is no foolproof way to ensure that science is not misused to serve political ends. By becoming aware of the complex relationships among science, society, and politics, we can work to ensure that an appropriate balance is maintained.

"We must reinvent a future free of blinders so that we can choose from real options."
—David Suzuki

Thinking About Environmental Perspectives

David Suzuki is no stranger to controversy. Throughout much of his career he has faced criticism for speaking out on environmental issues. Is it acceptable, in your view, for a scientist also to be an activist, or a spokesperson, for a cause? To what extent, if at all, does environmental activism compromise a person's ability to function as a scientist? If a scientist uncovers something in the course of doing research that may be of importance to the general public, is it appropriate for him or her to speak out about this discovery? Or does the act of speaking out compromise objectivity as a scientist?

Economists employ the term *development* to describe the use of natural resources for economic advancement (as opposed to simple subsistence, or survival). Construction of homes, schools, hospitals, power plants, factories, and transportation networks are all examples of development. **Sustainable development** is the use of renewable and nonrenewable resources in a manner that satisfies our current needs without compromising future availability of resources. The United Nations has defined sustainable development as development that " . . . meets the needs of the present without sacrificing the ability of future generations to meet their needs."[16] This definition is taken from the United Nations–sponsored *Brundtland Commission* (named after its chair, Norwegian prime minister Gro Harlem Brundtland), which published an influential 1987 report entitled *Our Common Future*.

Prior to the Brundtland Report, people aware of human impact on the environment might have thought *sustainable development* to be an oxymoron—a phrase that contradicts itself. Although development involves making purposeful changes intended to improve the quality of human life, environmental advocates have long pointed out that development often so degrades the natural environment that it threatens the very improvements for human life that were intended. Conversely, many people remain under the impression that protecting the environment is incompatible with serving people's economic needs.

Fortunately, sustainable development efforts by governments, businesses, industries, organizations, and individuals everywhere—from students on campus to international representatives at the United Nations—are beginning to alter these perceptions. These efforts are generating sustainable solutions that meet environmental, economic, and social goals simultaneously, satisfying the so-called "triple bottom line."

Sustainability and the triple bottom line demand that our current human population limit its environmental impact while also promoting economic well-being and social equity. These aims require us to make an ethical commitment to our fellow citizens and to future generations. They also require that we apply knowledge from the sciences to help us devise ways to limit our impact and maintain the functioning environmental systems on which all life depends.

"Will we develop in a sustainable way?" may well be the single most important question in the world today. Environmental geography holds one crucial key to addressing it: Because so much remains unstudied and undone, and because it is so central to our modern world, environmental geography will remain an exciting frontier for you to explore as a student and as an informed citizen throughout your life.

Conclusion

Finding effective ways of living peacefully, healthfully, and sustainably on our diverse and complex planet will require a thorough scientific understanding of both natural and social systems. Geography helps us understand our intricate relationship with the environment and informs our attempts to solve and prevent environmental problems.

Identifying a problem is the first step in devising a solution to it. Many of the trends detailed in this book may cause us worry, but others give us reason to hope. One often-heard criticism of environmental science courses and books is that they emphasize the negative. Recognizing the validity of this criticism, in this book we attempt to balance the discussion of environmental problems with a corresponding focus on potential solutions. Solving environmental problems can move us toward health, longevity, peace, and prosperity. Social and natural sciences in general, and environmental geography in particular, can aid us in our efforts to develop balanced and workable solutions to the many environmental dilemmas we face today and to create a better world for ourselves and our children.

REVIEWING OBJECTIVES

You should now be able to:

Define the term *environment*

- Our environment consists of everything around us, including living and nonliving things.
- Humans are a part of the environment and are not separate from it.

Describe natural resources and explain their importance to human life

- Resources from nature are essential to human life and civilization.
- Some resources are inexhaustible or perpetually renewable, others are nonrenewable, and still others

are renewable if we are careful not to exploit them at too fast a rate.

■ Hardin articulated the concept of carrying capacity, the number of individuals who can be sustained by a given area of productive land. Wackernagel and Rees pioneered the idea of the ecological footprint, a measure of the amount of productive land it would take to support an individual at a certain level of consumption.

Characterize the interdisciplinary nature of geography

■ Geography uses the approaches and insights of numerous disciplines from the natural sciences and the social sciences.

Understand the scientific method and how science operates

■ Science is a process of using observations to test ideas.

■ The scientific method consists of a series of steps, including making observations, formulating questions, stating a hypothesis, generating predictions, testing predictions, and analyzing the results obtained from the tests.

■ The scientific method has many variations, and there are many different ways to test questions scientifically.

■ Scientific research occurs within a larger process that includes peer review of work, journal publication, and interaction with colleagues.

Diagnose and illustrate some of the pressures on the global environment

■ The increasing human population and increasing per capita consumption exacerbate human impacts on the environment.

■ Human activities, such as industrial agriculture and the use of fossil fuels for energy, are having diverse environmental impacts, including resource depletion, air and water pollution, habitat destruction, and the diminishment of biodiversity.

Articulate the concepts of sustainability and sustainable development

■ Sustainability means living within the planet's means, such that Earth's resources can sustain us—and other species—for the foreseeable future.

■ Sustainable development means pursuing environmental, economic, and social goals in a coordinated way, and it is the most important pursuit in our society today.

TESTING YOUR COMPREHENSION

1. What do renewable resources and nonrenewable resources have in common? How are they different? Identify two renewable and two nonrenewable resources.

2. How did the Agricultural Revolution affect human population size and the environment? How did the Industrial Revolution affect human population size and the environment? Explain your answers.

3. What is the tragedy of the commons? Explain how the concept might apply to an unregulated industry that is a source of water pollution.

4. What is environmental geography?

5. What are the two meanings of the word *science*? Name three applications of science.

6. Describe the scientific method. What is the typical sequence of steps?

7. Explain the difference between a manipulative experiment and a natural experiment.

8. What needs to occur before a researcher's results are published? Why is this important?

9. Give examples of three major environmental problems in the world today, along with their causes.

10. How would you define the term "sustainable development"?

THINKING IT THROUGH

1. Many resources are renewable if we use them in moderation but can become nonrenewable if we overexploit them. Order the following resources on a continuum of renewability (see **FIGURE 1.1**), from most renewable to least renewable: soils, timber, freshwater, food crops, and biodiversity. What factors influenced your decision? For each of these resources, what might constitute overexploitation, and what might constitute sustainable use?

2. Why do you think the inhabitants of Rapa Nui did not or could not stop themselves from stripping their island of all its trees? Do you see similarities between the history of Rapa Nui and the modern history of our society? Why, or why not?

3. What environmental problem do *you* feel most acutely yourself? Do you think there are people in the world who do not view your issue as an environmental problem? Who might they be, and why might they take a different view?

4. If the human population were to stabilize tomorrow and never surpass 7 billion people, would that solve our environmental problems? Which types of problems might be alleviated, and which might continue to become worse?

5. Consider the historic expansion of agriculture and our ability to feed increasing numbers of people, as described in this chapter. Now ask yourself, "Are things getting better or worse?" Ask this question from four points of view: (1) the human perspective, (2) the perspective of other organisms, (3) a short-term perspective, and (4) a long-term perspective. Do your answers to this question change? If so, how?

6. You have become the head of a major funding agency that disburses funding to researchers pursuing work in environmental science. You must give your staff several priorities to determine what types of scientific research to fund. What environmental problems would you most like to see addressed with research? Describe the research you think would need to be completed so that workable solutions to these problems could be developed. Would more than science be needed to develop sustainable solutions? How might knowledge of environmental geography help?

7. If you were an environmental geographer, and were asked to provide an assessment of a complex environmental situation, what kinds of experts would you call upon? Think about the various specialists and team members who might be needed to contribute their expertise to the following situations: the construction of a new hydroelectric dam; the proposed draining of a wetland to build a new subdivision; a proposal to permit moose hunting in a national park; or the management of a large oil spill just offshore from a pristine beach.

INTERPRETING GRAPHS AND DATA

Environmental geographers study phenomena that range in size from individual molecules to the entire Earth and that occur over time periods lasting from fractions of a second to billions of years. To simultaneously and meaningfully represent data covering so many orders of magnitude, scientists have devised a variety of mathematical and graphical techniques, such as exponential notation and logarithmic scales. Below are two graphical representations *of the same data*, representing the growth of a hypothetical population from an initial size of 10 individuals at a rate of increase of approximately 2.3% per generation. The graph in part (a) uses a conventional linear scale for the population size; the graph in part (b) uses a logarithmic scale.

1. Using the graph in part (a), what would you say was the population size after 200 generations? (Twenty-five years is a pretty standard length of time to use for one generation.) After 400? After 600? After 800? How would you answer the same questions by using the graph in part (b)? What impression does the graph in part (a) give about population change for

the first 600 generations? What impression does the graph in part (b) give?

2. Compare these graphs to FIGURE 1.2A. What does the human population appear to be doing between 10 000 B.P. and 2000 B.P.?

3. The size of a population that is growing by a constant rate of increase will plot as a straight line on a loga-rithmically scaled graph like the one in part (b), but if the annual rate of increase changes, the line will curve. Do you think the data for the human population over the past 12 000 years would plot as a straight line on a logarithmically scaled graph? If not, when and why do you think the line would bend?

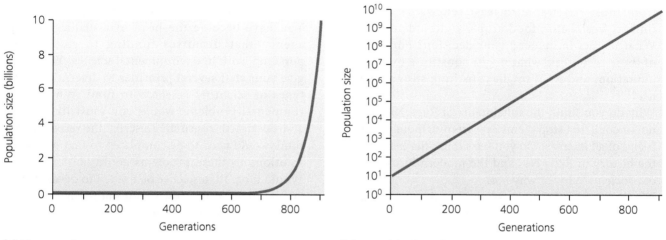

(a) Linear scale

(b) Logarithmic scale

Hypothetical population growth curves (a) and (b), assuming an initial size of 10 and a constant rate of increase of approximately 2.3% per generation.

CHAPTER ENDNOTES

1. NASA, The *Apollo 8* Christmas Eve Broadcast, http://nssdc.gsfc.nasa.gov/planetary/lunar/apollo8_xmas.html

2. Information about the Blue Marble and other photographs of Earth from space can be obtained from NASA's Earth Observatory website, http://earthobservatory.nasa.gov/Newsroom/BlueMarble/BlueMarble_history.html

3. Meadows, D., D. L. Meadows, J. Randers, and W. W. Behrens III (1972) *Limits to Growth*, New York, Universe Books.

4. Ehrlich, P. R. (1968) *The Population Bomb*, Sierra Club-Ballantine Books.

5. Schumacher, E. F. (1973) *Small Is Beautiful: Economics as If People Mattered*, New York, Harper & Row.

6. Carson, R. (1962) *Silent Spring*, Houghton Mifflin.

7. Environment Canada, www.ec.gc.ca

8. The United Nations officially marked the "Day of Seven Billion" on October 31, 2011.

9. Hardin, G. (1968). The Tragedy of the Commons, *Science*, Vol. 162, No. 3859, pp. 1243–1248.

10. Based on the assumption that an average city block is roughly 2–4 ha.

11. Global Footprint Network, www.footprintstandards.org

12. Diamond, J. (2005) *Collapse: How Societies Choose to Fail or Succeed*, Penguin Books.

13. Brander, J. A., M. S. Taylor (1998) The Simple Economics of Easter Island: A Ricardo-Malthus Model of Renewable Resource Use, *The American Economic Review*, Vol. 88, No. 1, pp. 119–138.

14. Sagan, C. (1995) *The Demon-Haunted World: Science as a Candle in the Dark*, Random House/Ballantine Books.

15. Earth System Science Committee (1986) *Earth System Science: A Program for Global Change*, NASA Advisory Council.

16. Brundtland, G. H. (1987) *Report of the World Commission on Environment and Development*: Our Common Future, Oxford University Press.

17. Based partly on information from the website of the David Suzuki Foundation, www.davidsuzuki.org/About_us/Dr_David_Suzuki/

18. Suzuki, David, Biotechnology: A Geneticist's Personal Perspective, www.davidsuzukifoundation.org/files/General/DTSbiotech.pdf

19. Ibid, p. 5.

20. Ibid, p. 23.

Environmental Systems and Ecosystem Ecology

2

The estuary of the St. Lawrence River, seen here in a satellite image, is intimately connected to its broader surroundings. The swirling, lighter-coloured water is evidence of a large algal bloom.

Upon completing this chapter, you will be able to

- Describe the fundamental properties of environmental systems and the importance of linkages among environmental systems and processes
- Define *ecosystem* and discuss how living and nonliving entities interact in ecosystems
- Outline the fundamentals of landscape ecology, GIS, and the use of modelling in environmental science

- Assess ecosystem services and their benefits to us
- Summarize the main features of the global water, carbon, nitrogen, and phosphorus cycles
- Explain how human activity is affecting biogeochemical cycles

Beluga whales in the St. Lawrence estuary are suffering from pollution-related health problems.

Hudson Bay

CANADA   *St. Lawrence Estuary*

CENTRAL CASE:
THE PLIGHT OF THE ST. LAWRENCE BELUGAS

"Nature does not show us any isolated 'building blocks,' but rather appears as a complicated web of relations between the various parts of the whole."
—FRITJOF CAPRA, THEORETICAL PHYSICIST

"The concept of a subtly interconnected world, of a whispering pond in and through which we are intimately linked to each other and to the universe ... is part of humanity's response to the challenges that we now face in common."
—ERVIN LASZLO, SYSTEMS THEORIST

This satellite image shows the St. Lawrence River and the estuary where it joins the Gulf of St. Lawrence and the Atlantic Ocean.

The St. Lawrence is one of the great river systems of Canada. From its origin in Lake Ontario (see map, above, and smaller satellite image) it flows approximately 1200 km to the Gulf of St. Lawrence, the world's largest estuary, where fresh water meets salt water. The cold Labrador Current brings an abundant food source of plankton and fish from the Atlantic Ocean into the estuary, supporting a small population of beluga whales. The playful, sociable beluga or white whale, *Delphinapterus leucas*, prefers cold salt-water estuaries as its habitat.

Health problems have plagued the St. Lawrence belugas for decades, causing their population to decrease to below 700—much less than the many thousands of belugas that occupied the estuary at the beginning of the twentieth century. The whales appear to be dying of cancer, at the rate of about 14 to 15 per year.

Daniel Martineau and a team of veterinarians from the Université de Montréal carried out autopsies on more than 100 dead whales from the St. Lawrence. They found that 27% of the adult and 17% of the young belugas had died of cancer, mainly gastrointestinal. "In dolphins and terrestrial animals, the figure is closer to 2%," says Dr. Martineau. In addition to cancers, the St. Lawrence belugas have very low reproductive rates and other health issues, including cysts and bacterial infections.

Toxicological studies show that the whales were exposed to organochloride pollutants, notably polycyclic aromatic hydrocarbons, or PAHs.[1] PAHs come primarily from the burning of fossil fuels and other combustion sources. They do not break down easily and have become one of the most widespread contaminants in aquatic and marine environments. Deposited from the air to the land surface, they are carried to waterways by runoff, accumulating in the bottom sediments of rivers and near shorelines. Belugas feed on organisms that live in these sediments. The concentration of contaminants increases in belugas and other animals that eat higher up the food chain. PAHs are also *lipophilic*, or "fat-loving" compounds, so they combine easily with fats and accumulate over time, or *bioaccumulate*, in the blubber of the belugas.

Where do the pollutants come from, and what does this have to do with the estuary and the health of the belugas? The answer may be found by looking at the Great Lakes and St. Lawrence River as a single, great, connected system, of which the beluga whales are a small but integral part. Any changes upstream in the system will be felt downstream. This includes the deposition of pollutants—some generated as far away as the Golden Horseshoe industrial zone in Ontario—that eventually make their way to the estuary and into the food chain of the beluga whales.

It is not clear to what extent the various health problems plaguing the belugas are directly attributable to exposure to PAH pollutants. Other organochloride compounds and toxic heavy metals from industrial, urban, and airborne sources are also concentrated in the waters of the estuary. Agricultural development along the St. Lawrence River has contributed pesticides into the system; some of these contaminants also find their way into the thousands of tonnes of fish harvested from St. Lawrence commercial fisheries each year.

Other factors may have additional indirect effects on the health of belugas and other organisms in the estuary. For example, excess organic matter and plant nutrients from fertilizer runoff and animal waste also have contributed to a sharp drop in oxygen concentration in the deepest waters of the estuary, where dissolved oxygen levels have declined by half since the 1930s. The lack of dissolved oxygen reflects a situation known as **hypoxia**, which is fairly common in estuarine and coastal waters around the world. It is caused by nutrient-rich runoff into the deep water of the estuary, where decomposition of the nutrients consumes the available oxygen. Nutrient over-enrichment can lead to algal overgrowths, called *blooms* (as seen in the satellite image of the St. Lawrence that opens this chapter), with subsequent decay of the organic matter and ecosystem degradation. The overall process of nutrient over-enrichment in a water body (either fresh or salt), leading to hypoxia, is called **eutrophication**; it can result from both natural and human (anthropogenic) influences. A probable natural contributor to hypoxia in the Gulf of the St. Lawrence is the influx of warm, oxygen-depleted water from the Gulf Stream, which displaces the cold, oxygen-rich water of the Labrador Current.

The most important thing to note is that all of these influences on the habitat and, ultimately, the health of the belugas come from sources that are external to the St. Lawrence Estuary but are intimately connected to it by a wide variety of environmental processes.

The St. Lawrence beluga population is classified as "threatened" by COSEWIC, the Committee on the Status of Endangered Wildlife in Canada. The health of the whales is an indicator of the overall health of the estuary, and a reminder of the interconnectedness of the Great Lakes–St. Lawrence ecosystem. Recognizing this interconnectedness, scientists are striving to understand the ecosystem as a whole and to develop strategies for protecting the estuary and the organisms that inhabit it.[2]

Earth's Environmental Systems

Our planet's environment consists of complex networks of interlinked systems. These systems include the webs of relationships among living species and the interactions of living species with the nonliving entities around them. Earth's systems also include **cycles** that shape the landscapes around us and guide the flow of key chemical elements and compounds that support life and regulate climate. We depend on these systems and cycles for our very survival.

Taking a "systems approach" to investigating problems such as the decline of the St. Lawrence belugas is helpful in environmental science, because so many issues are multifaceted and complex. Before we turn our attention to specific Earth systems and cycles, let's take a look at the general properties of systems.

Systems are networks of relationships

A **system** is a network of relationships among parts, elements, or components that interact with and influence one another through the exchange of energy, matter, or information. Systems receive inputs of energy, matter, or information, process these inputs, and produce outputs. Systems that receive inputs of both energy and matter and produce outputs of both are called **open systems**. Systems that receive inputs and produce outputs of energy, but not matter, are called **closed systems**. In a closed system, matter cycles among the various parts of the system but does not leave or enter the system. It is scientifically more straightforward to deal with closed systems, but in nature no system is truly, perfectly closed.

Energy inputs to Earth's environmental systems include solar radiation, as well as heat released by geothermal activity, organismal metabolism, and human activities such as fossil fuel combustion. Information inputs can come in the form of sensory cues from visual, olfactory (chemical), magnetic, or thermal signals. Inputs of matter occur when chemicals or physical material moves among systems, such as when seeds are dispersed long distances, migratory animals deposit waste far from where they consumed food, or plants convert carbon in the air to living tissue by photosynthesis.

As a system, for example, the Estuary of the St. Lawrence receives inputs of fresh water, sediments, nutrients, and pollutants from the St. Lawrence and other rivers, as well as salt water from the Atlantic Ocean. Large animals, such as the belugas, harvest some of the system's

output, and so do human fishers: matter and potential energy in the form of fish and plankton. This output subsequently becomes input to the human economic system and to the digestive systems of the people and whales that consume seafood from the St. Lawrence.

Feedbacks are common in environmental systems

Sometimes a system's output can serve as input to that same system, a circular process described as a **feedback loop**. Feedback loops are of two types, negative and positive.

In a **negative feedback loop**, output that results from a system moving in one direction acts as input that moves the system in the other direction. Input and output essentially neutralize one another's effects, stabilizing the system. A thermostat, for instance, stabilizes a room's temperature by turning the furnace on when the room gets cold and shutting it off when the room gets hot. Similarly, negative feedback regulates our body temperature. If we get too hot, our sweat glands pump out moisture that evaporates to cool us down, or we may move from sun to shade. If we get too cold, we shiver, creating heat, or we move into the sunlight or put on more clothing. Another example of negative feedback would be a predator–prey system in which the populations of predator and prey rise and fall in response to one another (**FIGURE 2.1A**). Most systems in nature involve negative feedback loops. Negative feedback loops enhance stability, and in the long run, only those systems that are stable will persist.

Positive feedback loops have the opposite effect. Rather than stabilizing a system, they drive it further toward one extreme or another. Erosion, the removal of soil by water or wind, is one example of positive feedback. Once vegetation has been cleared to expose soil, erosion may become progressively more severe if the forces of water or wind surpass the rate of vegetative regrowth. Another example is climatic warming leading to the melting of ice, which exposes underlying darker surfaces. Darker surfaces absorb more sunlight, causing further warming and leading to additional melting (**FIGURE 2.1B**). Positive feedbacks can alter a system substantially. Positive feedback loops are rare in nature, but they are common in natural systems that have been altered by human impact.

The inputs and outputs of complex natural systems usually occur simultaneously, keeping the system constantly active. Earth's climate system, for instance, does not ever stop. When processes within a system move in opposing directions at equivalent rates so that their effects

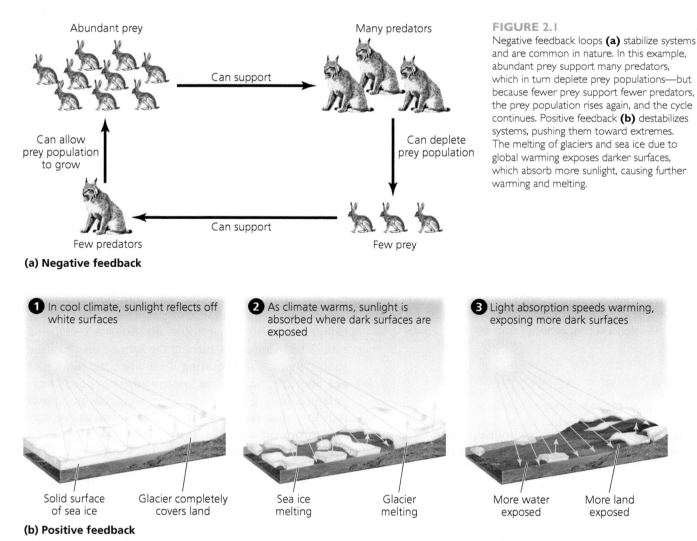

(a) Negative feedback

(b) Positive feedback

FIGURE 2.1
Negative feedback loops **(a)** stabilize systems and are common in nature. In this example, abundant prey support many predators, which in turn deplete prey populations—but because fewer prey support fewer predators, the prey population rises again, and the cycle continues. Positive feedback **(b)** destabilizes systems, pushing them toward extremes. The melting of glaciers and sea ice due to global warming exposes darker surfaces, which absorb more sunlight, causing further warming and melting.

balance out, the process is said to be in a state of **dynamic equilibrium**. The term *dynamic* is used to indicate that even though the system is in balance or at equilibrium, it is an ever-changing, ever-adjusting balance, not static or unchanging.

Homeostasis is a state of balance

Processes in dynamic equilibrium can contribute to **homeostasis**, the tendency of a system to maintain constant or stable internal conditions. *Resistance* is a property of homeostatic systems; it refers to the strength of the system's tendency to remain constant—that is, to resist disturbance. *Resilience*, another characteristic of homeostatic systems, is a measure of how readily the system will return to its original state once it has been disturbed.

To illustrate the concepts of resistance and resilience, let's say that someone gives you a sharp push. If you are resistant, you might sway a little bit, but you won't stumble or fall over. On the other hand, if you did stumble or fall but got right back up to a standing position with no trouble, then you were demonstrating the characteristic of resilience—after the disturbance you had the capacity to recover, and to return to your original standing position. In nature, we can think of the example of a forest that is being subjected to a pest invasion. A forest with the property of resistance would be little-altered by the pest invasion. A forest with the property of resilience, on the other hand, would be affected by the pest invasion—tree health would likely suffer, and some trees might die—but the forest would quickly recover its former healthy state.

Homeostatic systems are often said to be in a stable or **steady state**; however, the state itself may change over time, even while the system maintains its ability to stabilize conditions internally. For instance, organisms grow, mature, and change, yet at each stage of life the organism can be said to be in a stable state. Similarly, Earth has experienced changes in the composition of the atmosphere over geologic time; yet life has adapted, and Earth remains, by most definitions, a homeostatic system.

A whole may be more than the sum of its parts

It is difficult to understand systems fully by focusing on their individual components because systems can show **emergent properties**, characteristics not evident in the components alone. Stating that systems possess emergent properties is a lot like saying, "The whole is more than the sum of its parts." For example, if you were to reduce a tree to its component parts (leaves, branches, trunk, bark, roots, fruit, and so on), you would not be able to predict the whole tree's emergent properties, which include the role the tree plays as habitat for birds, insects, parasitic vines, and other organisms (**FIGURE 2.2**). You could analyze the tree's chloroplasts (photosynthetic cell organelles), diagram its branch structure, and evaluate its fruit's nutritional content, but you would still be unable to understand the tree as habitat, as part of a forest landscape, or as a reservoir for carbon storage.

Complex systems have multiple subsystems

Systems seldom have well-defined boundaries, so deciding where one system ends and another begins can be difficult. No matter how we attempt to isolate or define a system, we soon see that it has many connections to systems larger and smaller than itself. Systems may exchange energy, matter, and information with other systems, and they may contain or be contained within other systems— so where we draw boundaries may depend on the spatial or temporal scale we wish to consider.

Consider a desktop computer system. It is certainly a network of parts that interact and exchange energy and information, but what are its boundaries? Is the system just what arrives in a packing crate and sits on top of your desk? Or does it include the network you connect it to? What about the energy grid you plug it into, with its distant power plants and transmission lines? What about the Internet? Browsing the web, you are drawing in digitized text, light, and sound from around the world. And what about the smaller systems that together comprise the computer, such as the motherboard, the keyboard, and the mouse? All of these systems, large and

small, contribute and are linked to the complex system that is your desktop computer.

The Great Lakes, St. Lawrence River, and Atlantic Ocean are examples of environmental systems that interact with one another. On a map, the river appears as a branched network of water channels (**FIGURE 2.3**). But where are this system's boundaries? You might argue that the river consists primarily of water, originates in Ontario, and ends in the Atlantic Ocean. But what about the rivers that feed it, and the farms, cities, and forests that line its banks? Major rivers such as the Ottawa and

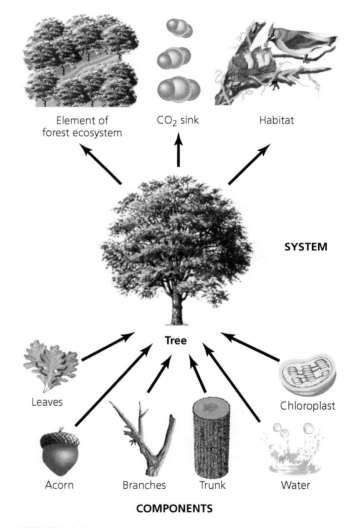

EMERGENT PROPERTIES

Element of forest ecosystem

CO_2 sink

Habitat

SYSTEM

Tree

Leaves

Chloroplast

Acorn

Branches

Trunk

Water

COMPONENTS

FIGURE 2.2
A system's emergent properties are not evident when we break the system down into its component parts. For example, a tree serves as wildlife habitat and plays roles in forest ecology and global climate regulation, but you would not know that from considering the tree only as a collection of leaves, branches, and chloroplasts. If we try to understand systems solely by breaking them into component parts, we will miss much of what makes them important.

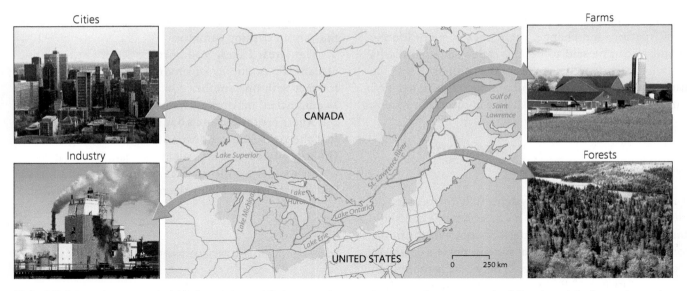

FIGURE 2.3 The watershed of the Great Lakes and St. Lawrence is a complex system that covers much of Ontario and Québec and extends into the northern United States. Runoff from the land into the river carries water, sediment, and pollutants from a variety of sources downstream to the Gulf of the St. Lawrence, where pollution has given rise to a hypoxic zone and other environmental problems. Farms, cities, and industry are all contributors; so are natural sources, such as forests and soils.

Saguenay rivers flow into the St. Lawrence. Hundreds of smaller tributaries drain vast expanses of farmland, woodland, fields, cities, towns, and industrial areas before their water joins the St. Lawrence. These waterways carry with them millions of tonnes of sediment, hundreds of species of plants and animals, and numerous pollutants. The St. Lawrence River system is also intimately interconnected with the entire Great Lakes system—together they constitute an integrated hydrological system.

For an environmental scientist interested in runoff and the flow of water, sediment, or pollutants, it would make sense to view the Great Lakes–St. Lawrence River watershed as one great system. One must consider the entire area of land a river drains to comprehend and solve problems of river pollution. In contrast, for a scientist interested in the estuary's hypoxic zone, it might make the best sense to view the river + the Gulf + the coastal waters of the Atlantic as the system of interest, because their interaction is central to the problem. For a scientist interested in the question of beluga whale contamination, another useful system might be the whale + the fish and plankton eaten by the whale + the bottom sediments and local water in which the contaminants have accumulated. In environmental science, one's delineation of a system can and should depend on the questions one is addressing and on the temporal and spatial scale of interest.

Environmental systems may be perceived in various ways

There are many ways to delineate natural systems, and your choice will depend on the particular issues in which you are interested. Categorizing environmental systems can help make Earth's dazzling complexity comprehensible to the human brain and accessible to problem solving.

Scientists divide Earth's components into broad structural systems (**FIGURE 2.4**). The **geosphere** is the rock and sediment beneath our feet, in the planet's uppermost layers. (This is sometimes called the *lithosphere*, but as you may recall from the chapter on matter, energy, and the physical environment, geologists have a very specific definition for the term *lithosphere*, which refers to the topmost portion of the mantle and the crust.) The **atmosphere** is composed of the air surrounding our planet. The **hydrosphere** encompasses all water—salt or fresh, liquid, ice, or vapour—in surface water bodies and glaciers, the near underground. (Water in the atmosphere technically does not belong to the hydrosphere, but the two systems are linked through the water cycle.) The subsystem that consists of the perennially frozen parts of the hydrosphere has its own name: the **cryosphere**. The **biosphere** consists of all the planet's living (and recently deceased and decaying) organisms.

FIGURE 2.4
Scientists divide the complex Earth system into smaller subsystems that interact with each other.

roots

BIOTIC AND ABIOTIC

The word **biotic** refers to anything having to do with life or living organisms. It derives from the Greek word *biotikos*, "pertaining to life," and originally from the Greek *bios*, "life." (The same root is in the term *biosphere*.) The word **abiotic** refers to the nonliving parts of the environment. Any time you see the prefix *a-* you can assume that it means "not." It probably came originally from Latin and Greek words that meant "not" or "away from," and it is related in both meaning and word origin to the prefix *an-*. Other examples of similar word pairs in environmental science include *photic–aphotic* and *aerobic–anaerobic*.

Today many scientists also are arguing for the inclusion of another subsystem, variously called the **anthroposphere** (or *anthrosphere* or *technosphere*). This encompasses the parts of the environment that are built or modified by humans for human use, including the built environment in which we live, work, and study. In many ways, environmental science is the study of the interactions of the anthroposphere with the other subsystems of Earth.

Although these categories are useful, it is important to remember that their boundaries overlap and the subsystems interact. Picture a robin plucking an earthworm from the ground after a rain. You are witnessing an organism (the robin, part of the biosphere) consuming another organism (the earthworm) by removing it from part of the geosphere (the soil) that the earthworm had been modifying. This is possible because rain (from the hydrosphere) recently wet the ground. The robin might then fly through the air (the atmosphere) to a tree (an organism), in the process respiring (combining oxygen from the atmosphere with glucose from the organism, and adding water to the hydrosphere and carbon dioxide and heat to the atmosphere). Finally, the bird might defecate, returning nutrients to the geosphere.

The study of such cyclical interactions among the **biotic**, or living, and the **abiotic**, or nonliving, components of the environment is a key part of ecology at the ecosystem level, as scientists become more inclined to approach Earth systems holistically.

Ecosystems

An **ecosystem** consists of all organisms and nonliving entities that occur and interact in a particular area at the same time. The ecosystem concept is related to the idea of a biological community (a group of interacting organisms of various types, living together in a specific habitat), which we will address in subsequent chapters. It is important to note that ecosystems encompass abiotic as well as biotic components. In ecosystems, energy flows and matter cycles among these components.

Ecosystems are systems of interacting biotic and abiotic components

The idea of ecosystems originated in the early twentieth century, championed by British ecologist Arthur Tansley, who saw that biological entities are tightly intertwined with chemical and physical entities. Tansley and others felt that there was so much interaction and feedback between organisms and their abiotic environments that it made most sense to view living and nonliving elements together. Since then, **ecosystem ecology** has come to refer to the study of energy and nutrient flows among living and nonliving components of systems.

Ecosystem ecologists began analyzing ecosystems as an engineer might analyze the operation of a machine. In this view, ecosystems are systems that receive inputs of energy, process and transform that energy while cycling matter internally, and produce a variety of outputs (such as heat, water flow, and animal waste products) that can move into other ecosystems. Energy and matter are passed among organisms through feeding relationships. Energy flows *through* ecosystems, in one direction; most arrives as radiation from the Sun, powers the system, and exits in the form of heat (**FIGURE 2.5A**). Matter, in contrast, is generally recycled *within* ecosystems (**FIGURE 2.5B**).

roots

ECOSYSTEM

The term **ecosystem** was first used in 1930 by British botanist Arthur Roy Clapham and was later expanded upon by Arthur Tansley and others. It was based on the term **ecology**, referring to the branch of science dealing with the relationship between living things and their environment, which was coined by German zoologist Ernst Haeckel in 1866. The *eco-* in both terms is derived from the Greek word *oikos*, meaning "house or dwelling place." Interestingly, the Greek *systema*, or "system," originally had the connotation of "an organized whole."

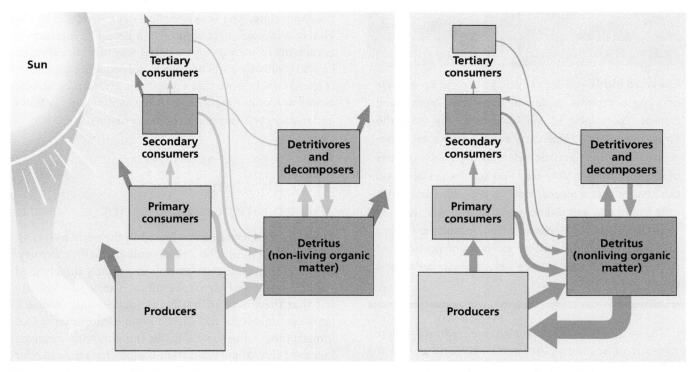

(a) Energy flowing through an ecosystem

(b) Matter (nutrients) cycling within an ecosystem

FIGURE 2.5   Energy enters, flows through, and exits an ecosystem. In **(a)**, light energy from the Sun (yellow arrow) drives photosynthesis in producers, which begins the transfer of chemical energy (green arrows) among organisms. Energy exits the system through respiration and other chemical conversions processes, in the form of heat (red arrows). In contrast, matter cycles within an ecosystem. In **(b)**, blue arrows show the movement of nutrients among organisms by way of their feeding relationships. In both diagrams, box sizes represent relative magnitudes of energy or matter content, and arrow widths represent relative magnitudes of energy or matter transfer. Such magnitudes may vary tremendously from one ecosystem to another. Some abiotic components (such as water, air, and inorganic soil content) of ecosystems are omitted from these schematic diagrams.

Matter is recycled because when organisms die and decay their nutrients remain in the system. In contrast, most energy that organisms take in is later lost through respiration, and the excess energy released as heat. The two flows are intimately related; the flow of energy through the ecosystem is what drives the constant recycling of matter.

Energy is converted to biomass

Energy flow in most ecosystems begins with radiation from the Sun. You have learned how autotrophs, such as green plants and phytoplankton, use photosynthesis to capture the Sun's energy and produce food. The result of this process is the production of **biomass**, organic material of which living organisms are formed.

The conversion of solar energy to the energy of chemical bonds in sugars by autotrophs is termed **gross primary production (GPP)**. Autotrophs use a portion of this production to power their own metabolism by respiration. The energy that remains after respiration, and that is used to generate biomass, is the **net primary production (NPP)**. Thus, net primary production equals gross primary production minus respiration (or NPP = GPP – respiration by autotrophs). Net primary production can

be measured by the organic matter stored by plants after they have metabolized enough for their own maintenance.

Another way to think of net primary production is that it represents the energy or biomass that is available for consumption by heterotrophs. Heterotrophs eat plants and use the energy they gain from plants for their own metabolism, growth, and reproduction (or they eat animals that have eaten plants and gain energy in that way). The total biomass that heterotrophs generate by consuming autotrophs is termed **secondary production**.

Ecosystems vary in the rate at which plants convert energy to biomass. The rate at which production occurs is termed **productivity**, and ecosystems whose plants convert solar energy to biomass rapidly are said to have high net primary productivity. (Note that because productivity is a *rate*, it is generally described in terms of an amount of production in a given area, *per unit of time*.)

Freshwater wetlands, tropical forests, coral reefs, and algal beds tend to have the highest net primary productivities, whereas deserts, tundra, and open ocean tend to have the lowest (**FIGURE 2.6A**). Variation in net primary productivity among ecosystems and biomes results in geographic patterns of variation across the globe (**FIGURE 2.6B**). In terrestrial ecosystems, net primary productiv-

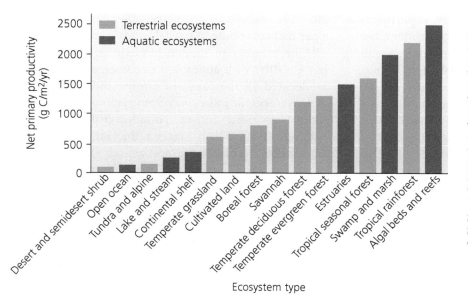

(a) Net primary productivity for major ecosystem types

FIGURE 2.6
(a) Freshwater wetlands, tropical forests, coral reefs, and algal beds show high net primary productivities on average. Deserts, tundra, and the open ocean are lower. **(b)** On land, net primary production varies geographically with temperature and precipitation. In the ocean, net primary production is highest around the margins of continents, where nutrients (of both natural and human origin) run off from land, and where deep, cold, nutrient-rich waters commonly well up to the surface. *Source: Data in (a) from Whittaker, R. H. (1975) Communities and Ecosystems, 2nd ed. New York, MacMillan. Map in (b) from satellite data presented by Field, C. B., et al. (1998) Primary production of the biosphere: Integrating terrestrial and oceanic components. Science 281: 237–240.*

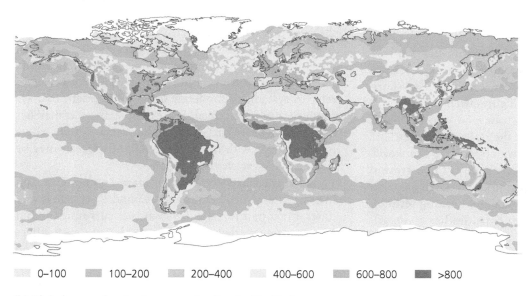

0–100   100–200   200–400   400–600   600–800   >800

(b) Global map of net primary production (g C/m²/yr)

ity tends to increase with temperature and precipitation. In aquatic ecosystems, net primary productivity tends to rise with light and the availability of nutrients.

Nutrient availability limits productivity

Nutrients are elements and compounds that organisms consume and require for survival. Organisms need several dozen naturally occurring chemical elements to survive. Elements and compounds required in relatively large amounts are called *macronutrients*; these include nitrogen, carbon, and phosphorus. Nutrients needed in small amounts are called *micronutrients*.

Nutrients stimulate production by autotrophs, and lack of nutrients can limit production. The availability of nitrogen or phosphorus frequently is a **limiting factor** for plant or algal growth. When these nutrients are added to a system, producers show the greatest response to whichever nutrient has been in shortest supply. Phosphorus tends to be limiting in freshwater systems, and nitrogen in marine systems. Thus marine hypoxic zones result primarily from excess nitrogen, whereas freshwater ponds and lakes tend to suffer eutrophication when they contain too much phosphorus.

Canadian ecologist David Schindler (profiled in "Canadian Environmental Perspectives" in the chapter on "Freshwater Systems and Water Resources") and colleagues demonstrated the effects of phosphorus on freshwater systems in the 1970s by experimentally manipulating entire lakes. In one experiment, the researchers divided a 16-ha lake in Ontario in half with a plastic barrier. To one half they added carbon, nitrate, and phosphate; to the other they added only carbon and nitrate. Soon after the experiment began, they saw a dramatic increase in algae in the half of the lake that received phosphate, whereas the other half hosted algal levels typical for lakes in the region (FIGURE 2.7). This difference held until shortly after they stopped fertilizing seven years later, when algae decreased to normal levels in the half that had previously received phosphate. Such experiments showed clearly that phosphorus addition can markedly increase primary productivity in lakes.

Similar experiments in coastal ocean waters show nitrogen to be the more important limiting factor for primary productivity. In experiments in the 1980s and 1990s, Swedish ecologist Edna Granéli took samples of ocean water from the Baltic Sea and added phosphate, nitrate, or nothing. Chlorophyll and phytoplankton increased greatly in the flasks with nitrate, whereas those with phosphate did not differ from the controls. Experiments in Long Island Sound by other researchers show similar results. For open ocean waters far from shore, research indicates that iron is a highly effective nutrient.

Because nutrients run off from land into the Baltic Sea, Long Island Sound, Gulf of the St. Lawrence, the Gulf of Mexico, and other coastal waters around the world, primary productivity in the oceans tends to be greatest in nearshore waters, and lowest in open ocean areas far from land (see FIGURE 2.6B). Satellite imaging technology that reveals phytoplankton densities has given scientists an improved view of productivity at regional and global scales, which has helped them track blooms of algae that contribute to coastal hypoxic zones.

The number of known hypoxic zones is increasing globally, with about 400 documented so far. Most are located off the coasts of Europe and eastern North America. Specific causes vary from place to place, but most result from rising nutrient pollution from farms, cities, and industry. In North America, the Gulf of Mexico and Chesapeake Bay may be the most severely affected. Decades of pollution and human impact have devastated fisheries and greatly altered the ecology of these water bodies.

Ecosystems are integrated spatially

Like all systems, we can conceptualize ecosystems at different scales. An ecosystem can be as small as an ephemeral puddle of water where brine shrimp and tadpoles feed on algae and detritus with mad abandon as the pool dries up. Or an ecosystem might be as large as a bay, lake, or forest. For some purposes, scientists even view the entire biosphere as a single all-encompassing ecosystem. The term is most often used, however, to refer to systems of moderate geographic extent that are somewhat self-contained. For example, the salt marshes that line the outer part of the St. Lawrence estuary where its waters mix with those of the Atlantic Ocean may be classified as ecosystems.

Adjacent ecosystems often share components and interact extensively. For instance, a pond ecosystem is very different from a forest ecosystem that surrounds it, but salamanders that develop in the pond live their adult lives under logs on the forest floor until returning to the pond to breed. Rainwater that nourishes forest plants may eventually make its way to the pond, carrying with it nutrients from the forest's leaf litter. Likewise, coastal dunes, the ocean, and a lagoon or salt marsh all may interact, as do forests and prairies where they converge. Areas where ecosystems meet often consist of transitional zones called **ecotones**, in which elements of each ecosystem mix.

FIGURE 2.7
A portion of this lake in Ontario was experimentally treated with the addition of phosphate. The treated portion experienced an immediate, dramatic, and prolonged algal bloom, visible in the opaque water in the topmost part of this photo.
Source: David W. Schindler.

weighing the issues
ECOSYSTEMS WHERE YOU LIVE

Think about the area where you live. How would you describe the ecosystems? How do these systems interact with one another? If one ecosystem were greatly disturbed (say, a wetland or forest replaced by a shopping mall), what impacts might that have on the system and others nearby?

Landscape ecologists study geographic patterns

Because components of different ecosystems may intermix, ecologists often find it useful to view these systems on a larger geographic scale that encompasses multiple ecosystems. For instance, if you are studying large mammals such as black bears, which move seasonally from mountains to valleys or between mountain ranges, you had better consider the overall landscape that includes all these areas. If you study fish such as salmon, which move between marine and freshwater ecosystems, you need to know how these systems interact.

In such a broad-scale approach, called **landscape ecology**, scientists study how landscape structure affects the abundance, distribution, and interaction of organisms. A landscape-level approach is also useful for scientists, citizens, planners, and policymakers in planning for sustainable regional development (see "The Science Behind the Story: Biodiversity Portrait of the St. Lawrence," available on myenvironmentplace).

For a landscape ecologist, a landscape is made up of a spatial array of *patches*, which may be ecosystems or areas of habitat for a particular organism. Patches are spread spatially over a landscape in a *mosaic*. This metaphor reflects how natural systems often are arrayed across landscapes in complex patterns, like an intricate work of art. Thus, a forest ecologist might refer to a mosaic of forested patches within an agricultural landscape, or a butterfly biologist might speak of a mosaic of grassland patches that acts as habitat for a particular species of butterfly.

One can view landscapes at different spatial scales. FIGURE 2.8 illustrates a landscape consisting of four ecosystem types, with ecotones along their borders indicated by thick red lines. At this scale, we perceive a mosaic consisting of four patches plus a river. However, the inset shows a magnified view of an ecotone. At this finer resolution, we see that the ecotone consists of patches of forest and grassland in a complex arrangement. The scale at which an ecologist focuses will depend on the particular questions or organisms he or she is studying.

Every organism has specific habitat needs, so when its habitat is distributed in patches across a landscape, individuals may need to expend energy and risk predation travelling from one to another. If the patches are distant enough, the organism's population may become divided into subpopulations, each occupying a different patch in the mosaic. Such a network of subpopulations, most of whose members stay within their respective patches but some

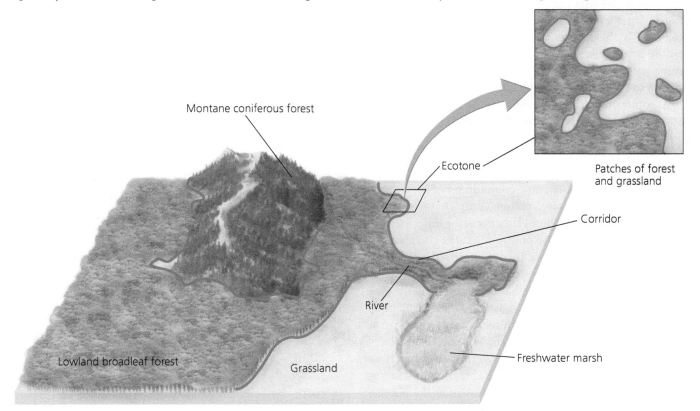

FIGURE 2.8 Landscape ecology deals with spatial patterns above the ecosystem level. This generalized diagram of a landscape shows a mosaic of patches of five ecosystem types (three terrestrial types, a marsh, and a river). Thick red lines indicate ecotones. A stretch of lowland broadleaf forest running along the river serves as a corridor connecting the large region of forest on the left to the smaller patch of forest alongside the marsh. The inset shows a magnified view of the forest–grassland ecotone and how it consists of patches on a smaller scale.

of whom move among patches or mate with members of other patches, is called a *metapopulation*. When patches are still more isolated from one another, individuals may not be able to travel between them at all. In such a case, smaller subpopulations may be at risk of extinction.

Because of this extinction risk, metapopulations and landscape ecology are of great interest to *conservation biologists*, who study the loss, protection, and restoration of species and their habitats. Of particular concern is the fragmentation of habitat into small and isolated patches—something that often results from human impact. Establishing corridors to link patches is one approach that conservation biologists pursue as they attempt to maintain biodiversity in the face of human impact. We will return to these issues when we consider conservation biology and habitat fragmentation in subsequent chapters.

Remote sensing and GIS are important tools

Remote sensing technologies—that is, technologies that collect information about a target object from a distance—are improving our ability to take a landscape perspective on complex ecosystems. Satellites orbiting Earth are sending us more and better data than ever before on what the surface of our planet looks like (the chapter-opening photo is an example). By helping us monitor our planet from above, satellite imagery has become a vital tool in modern environmental science. (See also "The Science Behind the Story: Mission to Planet Earth," in the introductory chapter.)

A common tool that makes use of remotely sensed data is the **geographic information system (GIS)**. A GIS consists of computer software that takes multiple types of spatially referenced data (for instance, on geology, hydrology, vegetation, animal species, and human development) and combines them on a common set of geographic coordinates. The idea is to create a complete picture of a landscape and to analyze how elements of the different data sets are arrayed spatially and how they may be correlated.

FIGURE 2.9 illustrates in a simplified way how different datasets of a GIS are combined, layer upon layer, to form a composite map. GIS has become a valuable tool for geographers, landscape ecologists, resource managers, and conservation biologists. GIS technology also brings insights that affect planning and land-use decisions.

Principles of landscape ecology, and tools such as GIS, are increasingly used in local and regional planning processes. Some conservation groups, such as the Nature Conservancy of Canada, a land trust, apply a landscape ecology approach in their land acquisition and management strategies. (A *land trust* is an organization, usually nonprofit, that acquires land for the purpose of protec-

tion and conservation. The Bruce Trail Conservancy, mentioned in "Canadian Environmental Perspectives," is another example of a land trust.)

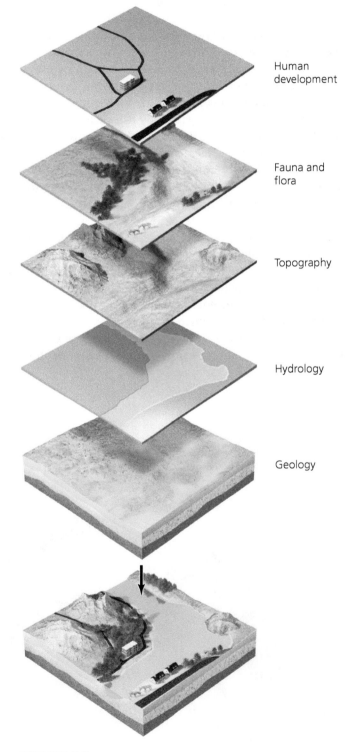

Human development

Fauna and flora

Topography

Hydrology

Geology

FIGURE 2.9
Geographic information systems (GIS) allow scientists to layer different types of data on natural landscape features and human land uses, from both remote sensing and ground-based observations, and to produce maps integrating this information. GIS can be used to explore correlations among these data sets.

Models help scientists understand complex systems

Another way in which ecologists and other environmental scientists seek to make sense of the complex systems they study is by working with models. In science, a **model** is a simplified representation of a complex natural process, designed to help us understand how the process occurs and to make predictions. Modelling is the practice of constructing and testing models that aim to explain and predict how natural systems function.

Models of complex natural systems such as ecosystems or the global climate system can be mathematically complicated. However, the general approach of modelling is easy to understand (FIGURE 2.10). Researchers gather data from nature on relationships that interest them and then form a hypothesis about what those relationships are. They construct a model that attempts to explain the relationships in a generalized way so that people can use the model to make predictions about how the system will behave. Modellers test their predictions by gathering new data from natural systems, and they use these new data to refine the model, making it increasingly accurate.

The process illustrated in FIGURE 2.10 resembles the scientific method in general, in that it moves from observation through hypothesis, prediction, and refinement of the hypothesis. This is because models are essentially, themselves, hypotheses about how systems function. Accordingly, the use of models is a key part of environmental research today. For example, University of Michigan researcher Donald Scavia and colleagues have modelled nitrogen and phosphorus transport by the Mississippi River along with hypoxia in the Gulf of Mexico. Using models, they were able to reconstruct what past conditions were like before monitoring for the dead zone had begun. They concluded that hypoxic events in the Gulf started in the mid-1970s. They were also able to forecast future trends. As a result of these forecasts, they advised that the government's recommendation to reduce nutrient loads by 30% would not be enough to prevent hypoxia, but rather that reductions of 40–45% would be needed.

Ecosystems provide vital services

When scientists try to understand how ecosystems function, it is not simply out of curiosity about the world. They also know that human society depends on healthy, functioning ecosystems. When Earth's ecosystems function normally and undisturbed, they provide goods and services that we could not survive without. We rely not just on natural resources (which can be thought of as goods from nature), but also on the ecosystem services that our planet's systems provide (TABLE 2.1).

Ecological processes form the soil that nourishes our crops, purify the water we drink and the air that we breathe, store and stabilize supplies of water that we use, pollinate the food plants we eat, and receive and break down (some of) the waste we dump and the pollution we emit. The negative feedback cycles that are typical of ecosystems regulate and stabilize the climate and help

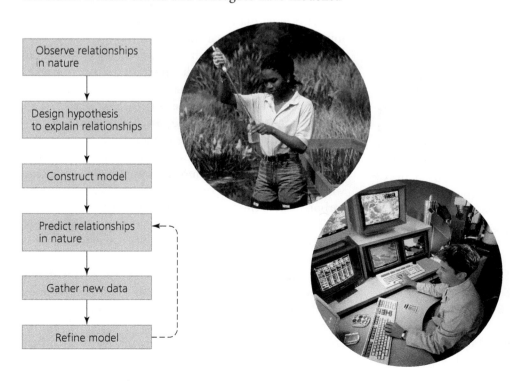

Observe relationships in nature

↓

Design hypothesis to explain relationships

↓

Construct model

↓

Predict relationships in nature

↓

Gather new data

↓

Refine model

FIGURE 2.10
Modellers observe relationships among variables in nature and then construct models to explain those relationships and make predictions. They test and refine the models by gathering new data from nature and seeing how well the models predict those data.

Table 2.1   Ecosystem Services

Ecosystems provide many services that benefit us. They:

- Regulate oxygen, carbon dioxide, stratospheric ozone, and other atmospheric gases
- Regulate temperature and precipitation with ocean currents, cloud formation, and so on
- Protect against storms, floods, and droughts, mainly with vegetation
- Store and regulate water supplies in watersheds and aquifers
- Prevent soil erosion
- Form soil by weathering rock and accumulating organic material
- Cycle carbon, nitrogen, phosphorus, sulphur, and other nutrients
- Filter waste, remove toxins, recover nutrients, and control pollution
- Pollinate plant crops and wild plants so they reproduce
- Control crop pests with predators and parasites
- Provide habitat for organisms to breed, feed, rest, migrate, and winter
- Produce fish, game, crops, nuts, and fruits that people eat
- Supply lumber, fuel, metals, fodder, and fibre
- Furnish medicines, pets, ornamental plants, and genes for resistance to pathogens and crop pests
- Provide recreation such as ecotourism, fishing, hiking, birding, hunting, and kayaking
- Provide aesthetic, artistic, educational, spiritual, and scientific amenities

to dampen the impacts of the disturbances we create in natural systems. On top of all these services that are vital for our very existence, ecosystems also provide services that enhance the quality of our lives, ranging from recreational opportunities to scenery for aesthetic enjoyment to inspiration and spiritual renewal. Ecosystem goods and ecosystem services (**FIGURE 2.11**) support our lives and society in profound and innumerable ways.

Biogeochemical Cycles

Materials move through the environment in complex and fascinating ways. Energy enters an ecosystem from the Sun, flows from one organism to another, and is dissipated to the atmosphere as heat, but physical matter is circulated through natural systems over and over again. The cycling of nutrients is one of the most important and fundamental of the ecosystem services that support life on this planet. Through the processes that take place within and among ecosystems, the chemical elements and compounds that we need—carbon, nitrogen, phosphorus, water, and many more—move through the environment in complex, global biogeochemical cycles.

Nutrients and other materials move in biogeochemical cycles

Nutrients move through ecosystems in **nutrient cycles** or **biogeochemical cycles**. They are called *biogeochemi-*

cal because the processes involved are biological, geological, and chemical (as well as physical). In these cycles, materials travel through the atmosphere, hydrosphere, and geosphere, and from one organism to another, in dynamic equilibrium. A carbon atom in your fingernail today might have resided in the muscle of a cow a year ago, in a blade of grass a month before that, in soil organic matter a year before that, and in a dinosaur's tooth 100 million years before that. After we die, the nutrients in our bodies will spread widely through the physical environment, eventually being incorporated by an untold number of organisms far into the future.

Nutrients and other materials (including toxins, as you will see in subsequent chapters) move from one *pool*, or **reservoir**, to another, remaining for varying amounts of time—the **residence time**—in each reservoir. The dinosaur, the soil, the grass, the cow, and you are each reservoirs for carbon atoms. The average residence time for an atom of carbon in your body is longer than the average residence time for an atom of carbon in a blade of grass, which has a short lifespan and will soon die, releasing its carbon back to the surrounding environment.

The movement of materials among reservoirs is termed a **flux** (**FIGURE 2.12**). Fluxes are rates, so they are stated in terms of mass or volume of material moving among reservoirs *per unit of time*. The flux of a material between reservoirs can change over time. Human activity has influenced the fluxes of certain materials. For example, we have increased the flux of nitrogen from the atmosphere to terrestrial reservoirs, and we have shifted the flux of carbon in the opposite direction.

FIGURE 2.11   Ecosystems provide countless valuable services that support both natural and human systems; some of these services are illustrated here.

Reservoirs that release more nutrients (or any other material of interest) than they accept are called **sources**; reservoirs that accept more nutrients than they release are called **sinks**. Carbon sinks are of particular importance today, as we struggle to lower the rate at which carbon is released into the atmosphere, potentially affected our global climate system.

The time it would take for all of the atoms (or particles) of a particular material to be flushed through a particular reservoir is called the **turnover time**. Turnover time is a function of the balance between fluxes *into* the reservoir (from a source) and fluxes *out of* the reservoir (to a sink). If we stop all new sources of material incoming into the reservoir, then the turnover time is the amount of time it would take for the material to be completely flushed through and out of the system.

Turnover time also depends on processes that influence the residence time of the material, including any processes that might hold or bind the material within the reservoir or cause it to be flushed through more quickly.

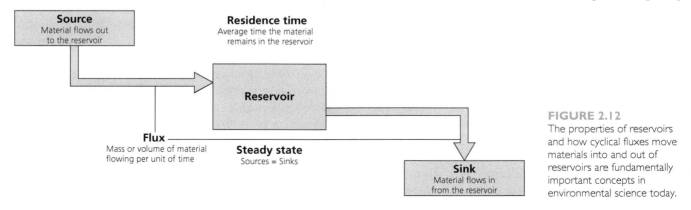

FIGURE 2.12
The properties of reservoirs and how cyclical fluxes move materials into and out of reservoirs are fundamentally important concepts in environmental science today.

For example, let us say that we are interested in mercury in the water of a particular lake. The turnover time for mercury in the lake will depend on how quickly fresh water runs into the lake, and how quickly the mercury-laden water leaves the lake. It will also depend on other sources of mercury inputs, such as mercury deposited onto the lake surface from the air, or taken up from mercury-bearing rocks in the lake bed. Now, what if some of the mercury in the water sinks to the bottom and binds chemically to bottom sediments? This would greatly increase both the residence time (how long the mercury stays in the lake) and the turnover time (how quickly the mercury will be flushed through the lake).

These are extremely important concepts in environmental science today. For example, we are concerned about the presence in the atmosphere of substances that damage the stratospheric ozone layer. Many of these substances have very long residence times in the atmosphere. Even if we stop producing them altogether—which we have almost accomplished as a result of the Montreal Protocol—the turnover time for these materials to be cleared out of the atmosphere by natural processes will be measured in decades. As we discuss various biogeochemical cycles, think about how human actions can influence fluxes and generate feedback loops in these cycles.

Let's start with a look at the most fundamental of the biogeochemical cycles: the water cycle.

The hydrologic cycle influences all other cycles

Water is so integral to life that we take it for granted. The essential medium for all manner of biochemical reactions, water plays key roles in nearly every environmental system, including each of the nutrient cycles we have just discussed. Water carries nutrients and sediments from the continents to the oceans via rivers, streams, and surface runoff, and it distributes sediments onward in ocean currents. Increasingly, water also distributes artificial pollutants.

The *water cycle*, or **hydrologic cycle** (FIGURE 2.13), summarizes how water—in liquid, gaseous, and solid forms—flows through our environment. A brief introduction to the hydrologic cycle will set the stage for our more in-depth discussion of freshwater and marine systems in subsequent chapters.

The oceans are the main reservoir in the hydrologic cycle, holding 97% of all water on Earth. The fresh water we depend on for our survival accounts for less than 3% of the total, and two-thirds of this small amount is tied up in glaciers, snowfields, and ice caps. Thus, considerably less than 1% of the planet's water is in a form that we can

readily use—groundwater, surface fresh water, and rain from atmospheric water vapour.

Water moves from oceans, lakes, ponds, rivers, and moist soil into the atmosphere by **evaporation**, the conversion of a liquid to gaseous form. Warm temperatures and strong winds speed rates of evaporation. A greater degree of exposure has the same effect; an area logged of its forest or converted to agriculture or residential use will lose water more readily than a comparable area that remains vegetated. Water also enters the atmosphere by **transpiration**, the release of water vapour by plants through their leaves. Transpiration and evaporation act as natural processes of distillation, effectively creating pure water by filtering out minerals carried in solution.

Water returns from the atmosphere to Earth's surface as **precipitation** when water vapour condenses and falls as rain or snow. Precipitation may be taken up by plants and used by animals, but much of it flows as **runoff** into streams, rivers, lakes, ponds, and oceans. Amounts of precipitation vary greatly from region to region globally, helping give rise to the variety of biomes.

Some precipitation and surface water soaks down through soil and rock to recharge underground reservoirs called *aquifers*. Aquifers are porous bodies of rock and soil that hold **groundwater**, water found underground beneath layers of soil. Aquifers may hold groundwater for long periods of time, so the water may be quite ancient. In some cases groundwater can take hundreds or even thousands of years to recharge fully after being depleted. Where groundwater intersects the surface, the exposed water becomes surface runoff or evaporates into the atmosphere.

Our impacts on the hydrologic cycle are extensive

Human activity affects every aspect of the water cycle. By damming rivers to create reservoirs, we increase evaporation and, in some cases, infiltration of surface water into aquifers. By altering Earth's surface and its vegetation, we increase surface runoff and erosion. By spreading water on agricultural fields, we can deplete rivers, lakes, and streams and can increase evaporation. By removing forests and other vegetation, we reduce transpiration and may lower water tables. By emitting into the atmosphere pollutants that dissolve in water droplets, we change the chemical nature of precipitation, in effect sabotaging the natural distillation process that evaporation and transpiration provide.

Perhaps most threatening to our future, we are overdrawing groundwater to the surface for drinking, irrigation, and industrial use and have thereby begun to deplete groundwater resources. Water shortages have already given rise to numerous conflicts worldwide, and many

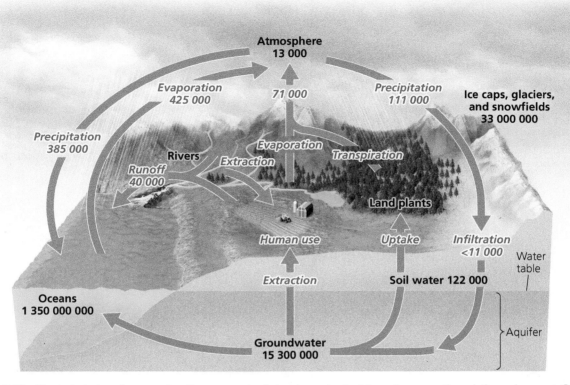

FIGURE 2.13   The hydrologic cycle summarizes the many routes that water molecules take as they move through the environment. Grey arrows represent fluxes. The hydrologic cycle is a system itself, but it also plays key roles in other biogeochemical cycles. Reservoir names are in black type, and the black numbers represent reservoir sizes expressed in units of cubic kilometres (km^3). Transfer processes (red) give rise to fluxes, expressed in km^3 per year.   *Source: Data from Schlesinger, W.H. (1997). Biogeochemistry: An Analysis of Global Change, 2nd ed. London, Academic Press.*

people think this situation will worsen (see the Central Case "Turning the Tap: The Prospect of Canadian Bulk Water Exports" in the chapter on "Freshwater Systems and Water Resources").

The carbon cycle circulates a vital organic nutrient

As the definitive component of organic molecules, **carbon (C)** is an ingredient in carbohydrates, fats, and proteins and in the bones, cartilage, and shells of all living things. From fossil fuels to DNA, from plastics to pharmaceuticals, carbon atoms are everywhere. The **carbon cycle** describes the routes that carbon atoms take through the environment (**FIGURE 2.14**).

Producers, including terrestrial and aquatic plants, algae, and cyanobacteria, pull carbon dioxide out of the atmosphere and out of surface water to use in photosynthesis. Photosynthesis breaks the bonds in carbon dioxide (CO_2) and water (H_2O) to produce oxygen (O_2) and carbohydrates (e.g., glucose, $C_6H_{12}O_6$). Autotrophs use some of the carbohydrates to fuel their own respiration, thereby releasing some of the carbon back into the atmo-

sphere and oceans as CO_2. When producers are eaten by primary consumers, which in turn are eaten by secondary consumers, more carbohydrates are broken down in respiration, producing carbon dioxide and water. The same process occurs when decomposers consume waste and dead organic matter. Respiration from all these organisms releases carbon back into the atmosphere and oceans.

All organisms use carbon for structural growth, so a portion of the carbon an organism takes in becomes incorporated into its tissues. The abundance of plants and the fact that they take in so much carbon dioxide for photosynthesis make plants a major reservoir for carbon. Because CO_2 is a greenhouse gas of primary concern, much research on global climate change is directed toward measuring the amount of CO_2 that plants tie up. Scientists are working toward understanding exactly how and to what extent this portion of the carbon cycle influences Earth's climate.

As organisms die, their remains may settle in sediments in ocean basins or in freshwater wetlands. As layers of sediment accumulate, older layers are buried more deeply, experiencing high pressure over long periods of time. These conditions can convert soft tissues into fossil fuels—coal, oil, and natural gas—and shells and skeletons into sedimentary rock, such as limestone.

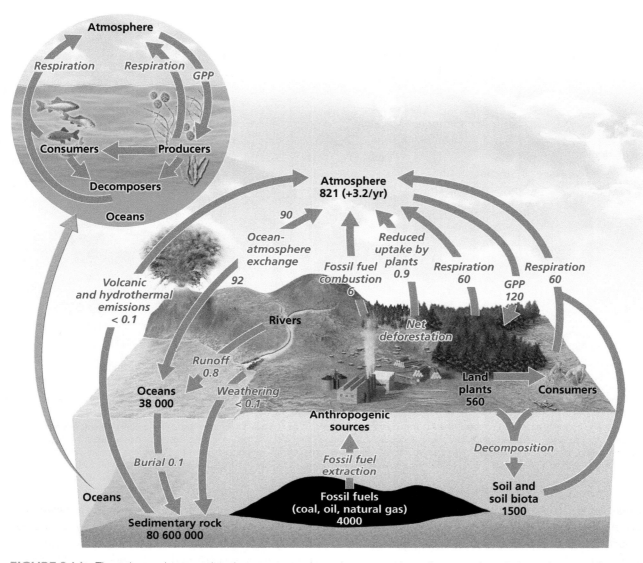

FIGURE 2.14   The carbon cycle summarizes the many routes that carbon atoms take as they move through the environment. Grey arrows represent fluxes among carbon reservoirs. Reservoir names are in black, and the black numbers represent reservoir sizes expressed in petagrams (units of 10^{15} g) of C. Transfer processes give rise to fluxes, in red, expressed in petagrams (billion metric tons) of C per year. Fluxes of carbon to the atmosphere from human sources (fossil fuels and deforestation) have increased in recent decades.   *Source: Data from Schlesinger, W.H. (1997) Biogeochemistry: An Analysis of Global Change, 2nd ed. London, Academic Press.*

Sedimentary rock comprises the largest single reservoir in the carbon cycle. Although any given carbon atom spends a relatively short time in the atmosphere, carbon trapped in sedimentary rock may reside there for hundreds of millions of years.

Carbon trapped in sediments and fossil fuel deposits may eventually be released into the oceans or atmosphere by geological processes such as tectonic uplift and volcanic eruptions. It also re-enters the atmosphere when we extract and burn fossil fuels.

The ocean is the second-largest reservoir in the carbon cycle. Ocean waters absorbs carbon compounds from the atmosphere, from terrestrial runoff, from undersea volcanoes, and from the waste and detritus of marine organisms. Some carbon atoms absorbed by the ocean—in the form of carbon dioxide, carbonate ions (CO_3^{2-}), and

bicarbonate ions (HCO_3^-)—combine with calcium ions (Ca^{2+}) to form calcium carbonate ($CaCO_3$), an essential ingredient in the skeletons and shells of microscopic marine organisms. As these organisms die, their calcium carbonate shells sink to the ocean floor and begin to form sedimentary rock. The rates at which ocean water absorbs and release carbon depend on many factors, including temperature and the number of marine organisms converting CO_2 into carbohydrates and carbonates.

We are shifting carbon from the geosphere to the atmosphere

By mining fossil fuel deposits, we are removing carbon from an underground reservoir with a residence time of millions of years. When we combust fossil fuels in our automobiles, homes, and industries, we release carbon dioxide and greatly increase the flux of carbon from the geosphere to the atmosphere. Since the mid-eighteenth century, fossil fuel combustion has added over 250 billion metric tonnes of carbon to the atmosphere. Meanwhile, the movement of CO_2 *from* the atmosphere *back* to the hydrosphere, geosphere, and biosphere has not kept pace.

In addition, cutting down forests and burning fields removes carbon from the vegetation reservoir and releases it to the air. If less vegetation is left on the surface, there are fewer plants to draw CO_2 back out of the atmosphere.

As a result, scientists estimate that today's atmospheric carbon dioxide reservoir is the largest that Earth has experienced in at least the past 800 000 years, and perhaps in the past 20 million years. The anthropogenic flux of carbon out of the fossil fuel reservoir and into the atmosphere is a driving force behind global climate change. Some of the excess CO_2 in the atmosphere is now being absorbed by ocean water. This is causing ocean water to become more acidic, leading to problems that threaten many marine organisms.

Our understanding of the carbon cycle is not yet complete. Scientists have long been baffled by the so-called "missing carbon sink." Of the carbon dioxide we emit by fossil fuel combustion and deforestation, scientists have measured how much goes into the atmosphere and oceans, but there remain roughly 1 billion to 2 billion metric tonnes per year unaccounted for. Many researchers think this is taken up by plants or soils of the northern temperate and boreal forests. But they'd like to know for sure—because if forests are acting as a major sink for carbon, it would be a good idea to keep it that way. If forests that today are sinks were to turn into sources and begin releasing the "missing" carbon, climate change could accelerate drastically.

The nitrogen cycle involves specialized bacteria

Nitrogen (N) makes up 78% of our atmosphere by mass, and is the sixth most abundant element on Earth. It is an essential ingredient in the proteins that build our bodies, and an essential nutrient for plant growth. Thus the **nitrogen cycle** (FIGURE 2.15) is of vital importance to all organisms. Despite its abundance in air, nitrogen gas (N_2) is chemically inert and cannot cycle out of the atmosphere and into living organisms without assistance from lightning, highly specialized bacteria, or human intervention. For this reason, nitrogen in elemental form is scarce in the geosphere and hydrosphere and in organisms. However, once nitrogen undergoes the right kind of chemical change, it becomes biologically active and available to the organisms that need it. Its scarcity makes biologically active nitrogen a limiting factor for plant growth.

To become biologically available, inert nitrogen gas (N_2) must be "fixed," or combined with hydrogen in nature to form ammonia (NH_3), whose water-soluble ions of ammonium (NH_4^+) can be taken up by plants. **Nitrogen fixation** in nature is accomplished in two ways: by the intense energy of lightning strikes, or by the action of specialized bacteria. One such group is aquatic cyanobacteria, either free-living or living inside corals; another group of specialized bacteria fixes nitrogen on land, in the top layer of soil. These bacteria live in a mutually beneficial relationship with many types of land plants, including clover, soybeans, and other legumes, providing them with nutrients by converting nitrogen to a usable form. Farmers have long nourished their soils by planting crops that host nitrogen-fixing bacteria among their roots (FIGURE 2.16).

Other types of specialized soil bacteria then perform a process known as **nitrification**, in which ammonium ions are first converted into nitrite ions (NO_2^-), and then into nitrate ions (NO_3^-). Plants can take up these ions, which can also become available after atmospheric deposition on soils or in water or after application of nitrate-based fertilizer.

Animals obtain the nitrogen they need by consuming plants or other animals, and decomposers obtain nitrogen from dead and decaying plant and animal matter and from animal urine and feces. Once the decomposers process the nitrogen-rich compounds they take in, they release ammonium ions, making these available to nitrifying bacteria to convert again to nitrates and nitrites. The final step in the nitrogen cycle occurs when denitrifying bacteria convert nitrates in soil or water back into gaseous nitrogen, via a multistep process. Denitrification thereby completes the cycle by releasing nitrogen back into the atmosphere as a gas.

Nitrogen fixation, nitrification, and denitrification are crucial processes in the nitrogen cycle, which are hosted by soils and facilitated by the resident soil bacteria. We will revisit these processes and the role of soil in the chapter on soil resources.

We have greatly influenced the nitrogen cycle

The impacts of excess nitrogen from agricultural fertilizers in the Great Lakes and St. Lawrence system have had a negative impact on both water quality and the health of marine organisms in downstream areas, as discussed in the

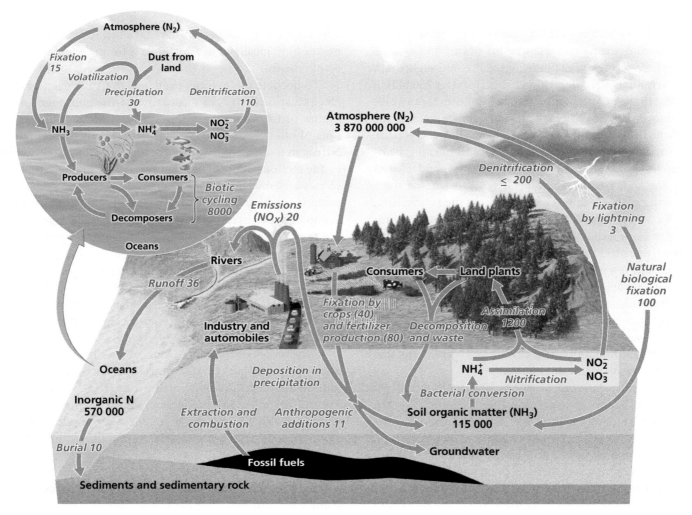

FIGURE 2.15 The nitrogen cycle summarizes the many routes that nitrogen atoms take as they move through the environment. Grey arrows represent fluxes among reservoirs for nitrogen. Reservoir names are in black, and the black numbers are reservoir sizes expressed in teragrams (units of 10^{12} g) of N. Transfer processes give rise to fluxes, in red, expressed in teragrams of N per year. *Source: Data from Schlesinger, W.H. (1997) Biogeochemistry: An Analysis of Global Change, 2nd ed. London, Academic Press.*

FIGURE 2.16
Specialized bacteria live in nodules on the roots of leguminous plants. Through nitrogen fixation, the bacteria convert nitrogen to a form that the plant can take up into its roots.

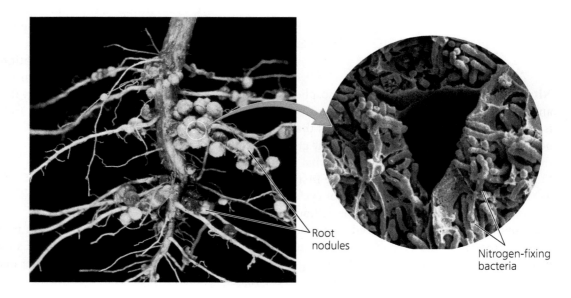

Central Case. Similar impacts in Mississippi River watershed have become painfully evident to shrimpers and scientists with an interest in the Gulf of Mexico (see "The Science Behind the Story: The Gulf of Mexico's "Dead Zone").

Fertilizer-laden runoff increases the nitrogen available to aquatic plants and algae, boosting their growth (FIGURE 2.17). Algal populations soon outstrip the availability of other required nutrients and begin to die and decompose. As in the St. Lawrence estuary and Gulf of Mexico, this large-scale decomposition can lead to hypoxia, robbing aquatic organisms of oxygen and leading to shellfish die-offs and other significant impacts on ecosystems.

Hypoxia and eutrophication are not the only problems resulting from human manipulation of the nitrogen cycle. Historically, rates of nitrogen fixation limited the flux of nitrogen out of the atmosphere, but this changed when two German chemists discovered how to fix nitrogen industrially. Fritz Haber worked in the German army's chemical weapons program during World War I. He found a way to combine nitrogen and hydrogen gases to synthesize ammonia, a key ingredient in modern explosives and agricultural fertilizers. Several years later, Carl Bosch built on Haber's work and devised methods to produce ammonia on an industrial scale.

The work of these two scientists enabled people to overcome the limits on productivity long imposed by nitrogen scarcity in nature. The widespread application of their findings has made modern agriculture possible, but it has also led to dramatic alteration of the nitrogen cycle. Today, using the Haber-Bosch process, our species is fixing more nitrogen artificially than is fixed naturally. We have effectively doubled the natural rate of nitrogen fixation on Earth. By fixing atmospheric nitrogen, we increase its flux out of the atmosphere and into other reservoirs.

Human activity also affects fluxes in other parts of the cycle. When we burn forests and fields, we force nitrogen out of soils and vegetation and into the atmosphere. When we burn fossil fuels, we increase the rate at which nitric oxide (NO) enters the atmosphere and reacts to form nitrogen dioxide (NO_2). This compound is a precursor to nitric acid (HNO_3), a key component of acid precipitation. We introduce nitrous oxide (N_2O) by allowing anaerobic bacteria to break down the tremendous volume of animal waste produced in agricultural feedlots. We have also accelerated the introduction of nitrogen-rich compounds into terrestrial and aquatic systems by destroying wetlands and by cultivating crops that host nitrogen-fixing bacteria in their roots.

Researchers report that human activities have had the following impacts on the global nitrogen cycle:

■ Doubled the rate at which fixed nitrogen enters terrestrial ecosystems (and the rate is still increasing).

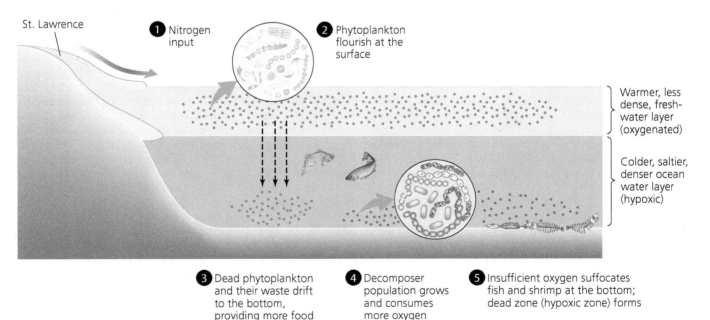

FIGURE 2.17 Excess nitrogen causes eutrophication in marine and freshwater systems such as the St. Lawrence Estuary. Coupled with stratification (layering) of the water, eutrophication can severely deplete dissolved oxygen. Surface water is warmer and fresher, and thus less dense; deeper water is colder and saltier, and thus denser. Nitrogen from river water (1) boosts the growth of phytoplankton in surface layers (2), which eventually die and are decomposed at the bottom by bacteria (3). Phytoplankton in surface water absorb light, preventing photosynthesis from occurring in deeper layers (thus inhibiting oxygen production in deeper waters). Stability of the surface layer also prevents deeper water from absorbing atmospheric oxygen to replace oxygen consumed by decomposers (4). Oxygen depletion in lower layers suffocates or drives away bottom-dwelling marine life (5), and gives rise to hypoxic zones.

THE SCIENCE BEHIND THE STORY

The Gulf of Mexico's "Dead Zone"

Fishers in the Gulf of Mexico have been dealt numerous challenging blows in recent years.

Fishers in Louisiana ply the rich waters of the Gulf of Mexico to send shrimp, fish, and shellfish to dinner tables around the world. But fishing in the Gulf has become difficult; catches of shrimp and other common species are half of what they were in the 1980s. The fisheries began declining years before oil gushed from the BP *Deepwater Horizon* drilling platform and fouled the region in 2010, and before Hurricanes Katrina and Rita pummelled the region in 2005 and left boats, docks, and marinas in ruins. Those disasters worsened a long decline that was already under way.

The reason for the decline? Billions of marine organisms have been suffocating in a hypoxic "dead zone," a region of water in the Gulf that is so depleted of oxygen that organisms are killed or driven away. Determining the causes of such dead zones involves understanding environmental systems and the complex behaviour they exhibit.

Aquatic animals obtain oxygen through their gills, and, like us, will asphyxiate if deprived of oxygen. Fully oxygenated water contains up to 10 parts per million (ppm) of oxygen. When concentrations drop below 2 ppm, creatures will leave, or die. The Gulf's hypoxic dead zone appears each spring and grows through the summer and fall, beginning in Louisiana waters offshore from the mouths of the Mississippi and Atchafalaya rivers. The zone reached

its largest size in 2002 when it covered 22 000 km^2—almost half the size of Nova Scotia.

What is starving these waters of oxygen? Scientists studying the dead zone are pointing a finger at human activities hundreds of kilometres away.

Rain and runoff carry excess nitrogen and phosphorus from fertilized agricultural fields and into streams and rivers, eventually flushing these nutrients down the Mississippi and Atchafalaya rivers, which drain into the Gulf. Once the excess nutrients reach the Gulf, they trigger blooms of plankton in the surface waters. As the masses of plankton begin to die and drift toward the bottom, they nourish bacteria, which also become overabundant. Bacteria need oxygen, and as they decompose the masses of dead plankton, they deplete dissolved oxygen from the bottom waters. Urban runoff, industrial discharges, fossil fuel emissions, and municipal sewage outflow add additional nitrogen and phosphorus pollution to the rivers as they head toward the Gulf.

In 1985, Dr. Nancy Rabalais and other researchers from the Louisiana Universities Marine Consortium (LUMCON) began tracking oxygen levels at dozens of sites in the Gulf and nearshore locations. Sensors lowered into the water were used to measure oxygen levels, sending continuous readings back to a shipboard computer. Further data come from fixed, submerged oxygen meters that continuously measure dissolved oxygen and store the data. They collected hundreds of water samples and measured nitrogen, salt, bacteria, and phytoplankton. They monitored more than 70 sites in the Gulf, and donned scuba gear to observe the condition of shrimp, fish, and other sea life.

The long-term data collection allowed the researchers to build a "map" of the dead zone, tracking its location and its consequences. In 1991, Rabalais made that map public, earning immediate headlines. That year, her group mapped the size of the dead zone at more than 10 000 km^2. Bottom-dwelling shrimp were stretching out of their burrows, straining for oxygen.

Many fish had fled. The bottom waters, infused with sulphur from bacterial decomposition, smelled of rotten eggs.

The group's years of monitoring enabled them to predict the dead zone's emergence. As rivers rose each spring, and as fertilizers were applied on midwestern farms, oxygen would start to disappear in the northern Gulf. The hypoxia would last through the summer or fall, until seasonal storms mixed oxygen into hypoxic areas. The monitoring also linked the dead zone's size to the volume of river flow and its nutrient load. The 1993 flooding of the Mississippi created a zone much larger than the year before, whereas a drought in 2000 brought low river flows, low nutrient loads, and a small dead zone (see figure). In 2005, the dead zone was predicted to be large, but Hurricanes Katrina and Rita stirred oxygenated surface water into the depths, decreasing the dead zone that year.

In response to these findings, U.S. government regulators proposed that farmers in Midwestern states be required to cut down on fertilizer use. Farmers' advocates protested that farmers were being singled out while urban pollution sources are ignored. Meanwhile, scientists have documented coastal dead zones in 400 other areas throughout the world, from Chesapeake Bay to the St. Lawrence Estuary to the Black Sea.

Midwestern farming advocates and some scientists, such as Derek Winstanley, chief of the Illinois State Water Survey, challenged the link to farm practices. They argued that the Mississippi naturally carries high loads of nitrogen from the rich prairie soil, and that Rabalais' team had not ruled out upwelling in the Gulf as a source of nutrients. But sediment analyses showed that Mississippi River mud contained many fewer nitrates early in the twentieth century. In 2000, a federal assessment team of dozens of scientists laid the blame for the dead zone on nutrient runoff from fertilizers and other sources.

Then in 2004, U.S. Environmental Protection Agency water quality scientist Howard Marshall suggested that the best way to alleviate the dead zone would be

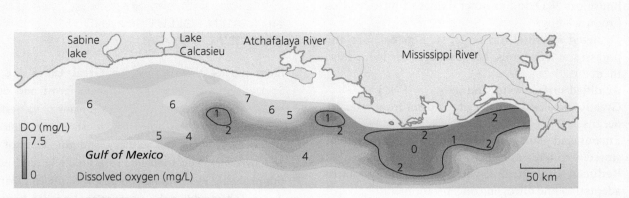

(a) Dissolved oxygen at bottom, July 2009

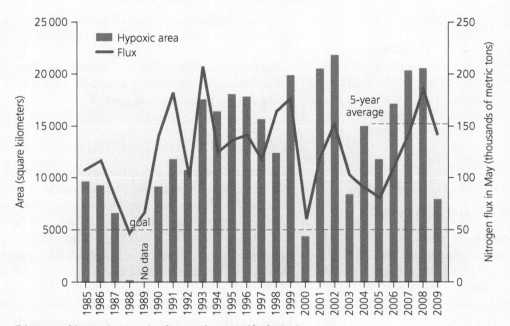

(b) Area of hypoxic zone in the northern Gulf of Mexico

The map in **(a)** shows dissolved oxygen concentrations in bottom waters of the Gulf of Mexico off the Louisiana coast from the July 2009 survey. Areas in red indicate the lowest oxygen levels. Regions considered hypoxic (< 2 mg/L) are encircled with a black line. The size of the Gulf's hypoxic zone varies **(b)** as a result of several factors. Floods increase its size by bringing additional runoff (as in 1993), whereas tropical storms decrease its size by mixing oxygen-rich water into the dead zone (as in 2003). Between 2005 and 2009, the hypoxic zone averaged 15 670 km² in size.   *Source: Data from Nancy Rabalais, LUMCON.*

to reduce phosphorus pollution from industry and sewage treatment. His reasoning: Phytoplankton need both nitrogen and phosphorus, but there is now so much nitrogen in the Gulf that phosphorus has become the principal limiting factor on phytoplankton growth.

Research has supported this contention, and most scientists now agree that nitrogen and phosphorus should be managed jointly. Large-scale restoration of wetlands along the river and at the river's delta would best effectively filtre pollutants before they reach the Gulf. The research is

guiding a plan to reduce farm runoff, clean up the Mississippi, restore wetlands, and ultimately, hopefully, shrink the Gulf's dead zone. It has also led to a better understanding of hypoxic zones around the world.

- Increased atmospheric concentrations of the greenhouse gas N_2O and of other oxides of nitrogen that produce smog.
- Depleted essential nutrients, such as calcium and potassium, from soils, because fertilizer helps flush them out.
- Acidified surface water and soils.
- Greatly increased transfer of nitrogen from rivers to oceans.
- Encouraged plant growth, causing more carbon to be stored within terrestrial ecosystems.
- Reduced biological diversity, especially plants adapted to low nitrogen concentrations.
- Changed the composition and function of estuaries and coastal ecosystems.
- Harmed many coastal marine fisheries.

Many of the impacts associated with excess nitrogen, including eutrophication, also occur when phosphorus—another plant nutrient that boosts the growth of phytoplankton—is present in excess in aquatic systems. Let's look briefly at the phosphorus cycle, the third major biogeochemical cycle.

The phosphorus cycle involves mainly geosphere and ocean

The element **phosphorus (P)** is a key component of cell membranes and of several molecules vital for life, including DNA, RNA, ATP, and ADP. Although phosphorus is indispensable for life, the amount of phosphorus in organisms is dwarfed by the vast amounts in rocks, soil, sediments, and the oceans. Unlike the carbon and nitrogen cycles, the **phosphorus cycle** (FIGURE 2.18) has no appreciable atmospheric component, aside from tiny amounts of windblown dust and sea spray.

The vast majority of Earth's phosphorus is contained in rocks and mobilized only by weathering, which releases phosphate ions (PO_4^{3-}) into water. Phosphates dissolved in lakes or in the oceans precipitate into solid form, settle to the bottom, and re-enter the geosphere's phosphorus reservoir in the form of sediment. Because most phosphorus is bound up in rock, environmental concentrations of phosphorus available to organisms tend to be very low. This relative rarity explains why phosphorus is frequently a limiting factor for plant growth, and why an artificial influx of phosphorus can produce immediate and dramatic effects.

Plants can take up phosphorus through their roots only when phosphate is dissolved in water. Primary consumers acquire phosphorus from water and plants, and pass it on to secondary consumers. Consumers release phosphorus

through the excretion of waste. Decomposers break down phosphorus-rich organisms and their wastes and, in so doing, return phosphorus to the soil.

We affect the phosphorus cycle

Humans influence the phosphorus cycle in several ways. We mine rocks containing phosphorus to extract this nutrient for the inorganic fertilizers we use on crops and lawns. Our wastewater discharge also tends to be rich in phosphates. Phosphates that run off into waterways can boost algal growth and cause eutrophication, leading to murkier waters and altering the structure and function of aquatic ecosystems. Phosphates are also present in detergents, so one way each of us can reduce phosphorus input into the environment is to purchase phosphate-free detergents.

In the 1970s Lake Erie began to exhibit signs of hypoxia (see "Central Case: The Death and Rebirth of Lake Erie," in the chapter on freshwater systems and water resources). As in the Gulf of Mexico and St. Lawrence examples that we have touched on, the problem was traced to human inputs of phosphate from fertilizers, detergents, and municipal sewage. The sources were land based, but runoff carried the phosphate-bearing materials into the lake from surrounding farms and towns in Canada and the United States.

The International Joint Commission (IJC), set up under the International Boundary Waters Treaty of 1909, adopted the Great Lakes Water Quality Agreement (GLWQA) in 1972 to address the problems of eutrophication and phosphate runoff into Lake Erie. The broader goal of the agreement was to promote an integrated, cooperative, scientific, and ecosystem-based approach to the management of the international waters of the Great

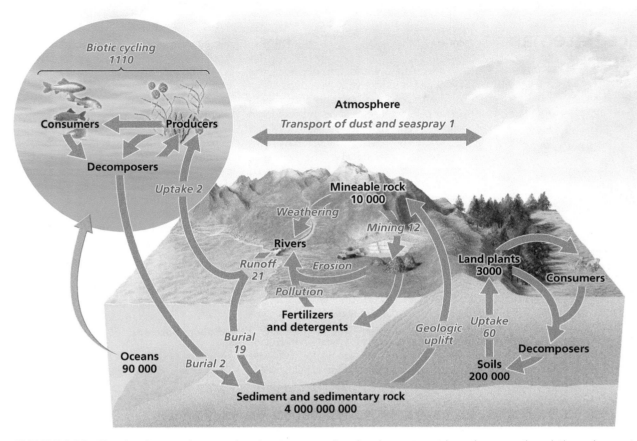

FIGURE 2.18 The phosphorus cycle summarizes the many routes that phosphorus atoms take as they move through the environment. Grey arrows represent fluxes among reservoirs for phosphorus. Reservoir names are in black, and the black numbers represent reservoir sizes expressed in teragrams (units of 10^{12} g) of P. Transfer processes give rise to fluxes, in red, expressed in teragrams of P per year. *Source: Data from Schlesinger, W.H. (1997). Biogeochemistry: An Analysis of Global Change, 2nd ed. London, Academic Press.*

Lakes. Initially, IJC activities under the GLWQA focused on reducing phosphate from detergents and municipal sewage, as these were the best understood pollutants from a scientific perspective.

Since then, the agreement has grown in both strength and scope, and now deals with all threats to water quality in the Great Lakes system from chemical, physical, and biological factors, as well as from other causes such as habitat destruction. Phosphate runoff into the lakes has been controlled to a degree, and Lake Erie has recovered from its most severely oxygen-depleted state. However, runoff of phosphates and many other pollutants into the Great Lakes continues to be problematic, and all of the lakes still face periodic episodes of oxygen depletion.

Conclusion

Thinking in terms of systems is important in understanding Earth's dynamics, so that we may learn how to avoid disrupting its processes. Addressing problems such as those in the St. Lawrence Estuary and the Gulf of Mexico requires us to study the environment from a systems perspective and to integrate scientific findings with the policy and decision-making processes.

Earth hosts many interacting systems. The way we perceive them and define them depends on the questions we want to investigate. Life interacts with its nonliving environment in ecosystems, systems through which energy flows and matter is recycled. Understanding the biogeochemical cycles that describe the movement of nutrients within and among ecosystems is crucial, because human activities are causing significant changes in the ways those cycles function.

Unperturbed ecosystems use renewable solar energy, recycle nutrients, and are stabilized by negative feedback loops. The environmental systems we see on Earth today are those that have survived the test of time. Our industrialized civilization is young in comparison. Might we not take a few lessons about sustainability from a careful look at the natural systems of our planet?

CANADIAN ENVIRONMENTAL PERSPECTIVES

Robert Bateman

Robert Bateman is one of Canada's leading artists, and a lifelong naturalist.

- Award-winning and internationally recognized **artist**
- **Naturalist** and **environmentalist**
- **Teacher**

It is hard to think of a painter with broader popular appeal than Robert Bateman. His works are so realistic, so close to the natural subjects he portrays, that we can almost smell the hot breath of the bear or the feel the dry, choking dust stirred by the buffalo's hooves.

Bateman started life as both an artist and a naturalist when, as a young boy in Toronto, he undertook a project to draw all of the birds in the neighbouring ravine. He describes his life since then as having been "immersed in nature."[3] Although he claims to have always been an artist at heart, there was a time when Bateman thought he could not make a living as an artist, so he chose to become a teacher. But he kept painting, travelling, and observ-

ing the natural world, and eventually his work began to receive wider notice.

Although he experimented with other painting styles, such as impressionism and even cubism, Bateman has settled into a meticulously realistic style that pays homage to each tiny detail of the ecological communities he portrays. He was inspired in this by American painter Andrew Wyeth, another great realist interpreter of the natural world.

Having spent his life devoted to the detailed interpretation and representation of the natural world, Bateman is a committed environmentalist. He actually destroyed one of his works—a painting of orca whales—to protest the possibility that oil tankers would be allowed into the pristine Douglas Channel of British Columbia. Bateman also was instrumental in the establishment of the 890-km Bruce Trail, the oldest and longest continuous public hiking path in Canada, which runs from Niagara to Tobermory along the Niagara Escarpment in Ontario.[4] He has expressed a wish that students could spend at least half of their time in the wilderness, stating that "In outdoor education you not only learn about nature, you learn about yourself, your limits and your relationship with others."[5]

In 2005 Bateman volunteered to be a test subject for Toxic Nation, an initiative of Environmental Defence, a Canadian environmental organization. For this study, children and adults—celebrities like Bateman,

as well as ordinary citizens—were tested for 88 toxic chemicals. All subjects were found to contain at least some of the toxins. The tests on Bateman detected 32 carcinogens, 19 hormone disruptors, 16 respiratory toxicants, and 42 reproductive/developmental toxicants.[6] (You will learn more about these various categories of toxins in subsequent chapters.) Bateman viewed his participation in this study as a way to convince decision makers to take action on behalf of the natural environment and the health of humans.

"I can't conceive of anything being more varied and rich and handsome than the planet Earth. And its crowning beauty is the natural world. I want to soak it up, to understand it as well as I can, and to absorb it."
—**Robert Bateman**

Thinking About Environmental Perspectives

Robert Bateman spends a lot of time observing and studying the natural world. It is extremely important to him to portray the plant and animal communities in his paintings with as much scientific accuracy as possible. However, he has been known to say that "art wins" if he ever comes up against a conflict between science and art. Do you think this compromises the value of his works from a naturalist's perspective? Or does it add power to his environmental message?

REVIEWING OBJECTIVES

You should now be able to:

Describe the fundamental properties of environmental systems and the importance of linkages among environmental systems and processes

- Systems are networks of interacting components that generally involve feedback loops, show dynamic equilibrium, and result in emergent properties.
- Earth's natural systems are complex, so environmental scientists often take a holistic approach to studying environmental systems.

- Because environmental systems interact and overlap, how we delineate and define systems depends on the questions we are interested in investigating.

Define *ecosystem* and evaluate how living and nonliving entities interact in ecosystem-level ecology

- Ecosystems consist of all organisms and nonliving entities that occur and interact in a particular area at the same time.
- Energy flows in one direction through ecosystems, whereas matter is recycled.

- Energy is converted to biomass, and ecosystems vary in their productivity.
- Input of nutrients can boost productivity, but an excess of nutrients can alter ecosystems in ways that cause severe ecological and economic consequences.

Outline the fundamentals of landscape ecology, GIS, and the use of modelling in environmental science

- Landscape ecology studies how landscape structure influences organisms.
- Landscapes consist of patches spatially arrayed in a mosaic. Organisms dependent on certain types of patches may occur in metapopulations.
- Remote sensing technology and GIS are assisting the use of landscape ecology in conservation and regional planning.
- Models help ecologists and other environmental scientists make sense of the complex systems they study.

Assess ecosystem services and their benefits to us

- Ecosystems provide "goods" we know as natural resources.
- Ecosystem processes naturally provide a wide variety of services that we depend on for everyday living.

Summarize the main features of the global water, carbon, nitrogen, and phosphorus cycles

- Water moves throughout the global environment as a result of processes in the hydrologic cycle.

- The carbon flux between organisms and the atmosphere occurs via photosynthesis and respiration. Most carbon is contained in sedimentary rock, but substantial amounts also occur in the oceans and in soil.
- Nitrogen is a vital nutrient for plant growth. Most nitrogen is in the atmosphere and must be "fixed" by specialized bacteria or lightning before plants can use it.
- Phosphorus is most abundant in sedimentary rock, with substantial amounts in soil and the oceans. Phosphorus, a key nutrient for plant growth, has no appreciable atmospheric pool.

Explain how human activity is affecting global biogeochemical cycles

- Humans are causing substantial impacts to Earth's biogeochemical cycles.
- These impacts include shifting carbon from long-term fossil fuel reservoirs into the atmosphere, shifting nitrogen from the atmosphere to the surface by industrial fixation, and depleting groundwater supplies, among many others.

TESTING YOUR COMPREHENSION

1. Which type of feedback loop is most common in nature, and which more commonly results from human action? How might the emergence of a positive feedback loop affect a system in homeostasis?
2. Describe how hypoxic conditions can develop in coastal marine ecosystems such as the Gulf of the St. Lawrence.
3. What is an ecosystem?
4. Describe the typical movement of energy through an ecosystem. Describe the typical movement of matter through an ecosystem.
5. What is the difference between net primary productivity and gross primary productivity?
6. Why are patches in a landscape mosaic important to scientists with an interest in conservation?

7. What role does each of the following play in the carbon cycle?
   - Cars
   - Photosynthesis
   - The oceans
   - Earth's crust
8. Contrast the function performed by nitrogen-fixing bacteria with that performed by denitrifying bacteria.
9. How has human activity altered the carbon cycle? The phosphorus cycle? The nitrogen cycle? To what environmental problems have these changes given rise?
10. What is the difference between evaporation and transpiration? Give examples of how the hydrologic cycle interacts with the carbon, phosphorus, and nitrogen cycles.

THINKING IT THROUGH

1. Once vegetation is cleared from a riverbank, water begins to erode the bank away. This erosion may dislodge more vegetation. Would you expect this to result in a feedback process? If so, which type—negative or positive? Explain your answer. How might we halt or reverse this process?

2. Consider the ecosystem(s) that surround(s) your campus. How do some of the principles from our discussion on ecosystems apply to the ecosystem(s) around your campus?

3. For an ecologist interested in sustaining populations of each organism below, why would it be helpful to take a landscape ecology perspective? Explain your answer in each case.
   - A forest-breeding warbler that suffers poor nesting success in small, fragmented forest patches
   - A bighorn sheep that must move seasonally between mountains and lowlands
   - A toad that lives in upland areas but travels cross-country to breed in localized pools each spring

4. A simple change in the flux rate between just two reservoirs in a single nutrient cycle can potentially have major consequences for ecosystems and, indeed, for the globe. Explain how this can be, using one example from the carbon cycle and one example from the nitrogen cycle.

5. One goal of this book is to encourage you to approach problems from a scientist's perspective; another goal, of this chapter in particular, is to introduce a systems perspective to the way we approach environmental problems. Please apply these perspectives to the following task:

You are a scientist with Environment Canada. You know that the beluga whale population in the St. Lawrence Estuary is stable but very low and that it is considered to be threatened. It has been proposed that a cause of the decline of the beluga population may be the influx of chemical pollutants into the river and estuary from adjacent farmlands, cities, suburbs, and industrial areas (see table, below). Your task is to design a scientific program of monitoring, observation, and/or experimentation that will help you determine whether contaminants are the main contributor to the poor status of the beluga population. Your answer should include a brief overview of how you see the problem and a description of your approach to solving the problem (that is, your proposed scientific program of monitoring, experimentation, and/or observation).

Theories explaining why the beluga population of the St. Lawrence Estuary shows no apparent signs of recovery

Anthropogenic
- Habitat degradation and changes
- Diseases (microorganisms from wastewater, agricultural and coastal runoff)
- Maritime traffic (noise disturbance, collisions with ships)
- Contaminants (carcinogenic, immunotoxic, neurotoxic, endocrine disruptors)

Ecosystemic
- Changes in prey abundance, diversity, and quality
- Competition with other marine mammals or with fisheries for prey
- New diseases or exotic diseases
- Decline in the area's carrying capacity

Genetic
- Inbreeding, low genetic diversity
- Immune incompetence
- Genetic predisposition to infectious and non-infectious diseases
- High frequency of deleterious genes caused by the absence of predators to eliminate weak, sick, or old individuals

Emigration
- Individuals emigrating outside the Estuary and Gulf of St. Lawrence and not contributing to growth of the population

Source: Table from Measures, Lena, Jean-François Gosselin, and Michel Lebeuf, Maurice Lamontagne Institute Fisheries and Oceans Canada, (2009) Beluga Whale Population of the Estuary, 2nd ed. www.planstlaurent.qc.ca/sl_obs/sesl/publications/fiches_indicateurs/Beluga2009_e_final.pdf

6. Imagine that you are a fisher in the St. Lawrence estuary and that your income is decreasing because nutrient pollution is causing algal blooms that affect your catch. One day your MP comes to town, and you have a one-minute audience with her. What steps would you urge her to take in Ottawa, to try to help alleviate the nutrient pollution in the St. Lawrence and help maintain the quality of the fishery?

Now imagine that you are a farmer in rural Québec who has learned that the government is insisting that you use 30% less fertilizer on your crops each year. In good growing years you could do without that fertilizer, and you'd be glad not to have to pay for it. But in bad growing years, you need the fertilizer to ensure a harvest so that you can continue making a living. You must apply the fertilizer each spring before you know whether it will be a good or bad year. What would you tell your MP when she comes to town?

INTERPRETING GRAPHS AND DATA

The use of PCBs has been closely regulated in Canada since 1970. In contrast, PBDEs have only recently been regulated in a few jurisdictions in North America. Environment Canada is still working with industry to regulate the production and release of PBDEs in Canada. The graph documents trends in the concentrations of two major pollutant groups (PCB, or polychlorinated biphenyls, and PBDE, or polybrominated diphenyl ethers) in the fatty tissues of beluga whales from the St. Lawrence. (The unit "ng/g lw" refers to "nanograms per gram of lipid weight," which is a unit of measure for the concentration of a material in fat.) The pie chart shows the causes of death of beluga whales in the St. Lawrence from 1983 to 2002, based on studies of 148 whale carcasses.

1. Are the data shown on the graph consistent with the regulatory histories of these two groups of pollut-

ants? Why (or why not)? Are there other factors that should be considered in interpreting the graph?
2. Are there any causes of death shown on the pie chart that you think might be directly attributable to the whales' exposure to toxic pollutants? Are there any that might be indirectly related to exposure to toxins? Are there any causes of death illustrated here that definitely do not seem to be related to exposure to toxins? (Note that the term *neoplasia* refers to the abnormal and uncontrolled growth of cells, resulting in the formation of tumours.)

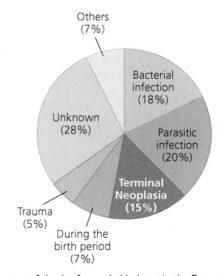

Principal causes of death of stranded belugas in the Estuary and Gulf of St. Lawrence from 1983 to 2002
Source: *Pie chart based on studies of 148 whale carcasses; from Measures, Lena, Jean-François Gosselin, and Michel Lebeuf, Maurice Lamontagne Institute Fisheries and Oceans Canada (2009)* Beluga Whale Population of the Estuary, *2nd ed.* www.planstlaurent.qc.ca/sl_obs/sesl/publications/fiches_indicateurs/Beluga2009_e_final.pdf

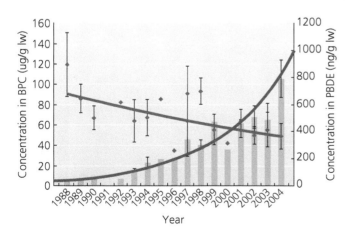

Trends over time of PCB (diamonds) and PBDE (bars) accumulations in the fatty tissue of male belugas between 1988 and 2004
Source: *Graph from Measures, Lena, Jean-François Gosselin, and Michel Lebeuf, Maurice Lamontagne Institute Fisheries and Oceans Canada (2009)* Beluga Whale Population of the Estuary, *2nd ed.* www.planstlaurent.qc.ca/sl_obs/sesl/publications/fiches_indicateurs/Beluga2009_e_final.pdf

CHAPTER ENDNOTES

1. Environment Canada Enviro-Zine, *Great Lakes–St. Lawrence Basin: A Freshwater Giant*, www.ec.gc.ca/EnviroZine/english/issues/61/feature2_e.cfm

2. This piece is based on information from:
   IUCN Red List of Endangered Species (2007) www.iucnredlist.org/search/details.php/6335/summ;
   Université de Montréal Faculté de Médecine Vétérinaire, www.medvet.umontreal.ca/pathologie_microbiologie/beluga/anglais/default_ang.asp;
   Minister of the Environment, Canada (1999) *The Contribution of Agriculture to the Deterioration of the St. Lawrence River*, www.slv2000.qc.ec.gc.ca/communiques/phase3/enjeu_agricoles_a.pdf;

   Environment Canada Enviro-Zine, *Great Lakes–St. Lawrence Basin: A Freshwater Giant*, www.ec.gc.ca/EnviroZine/english/issues/61/feature2_e.cfm; and Environment Canada St. Lawrence Centre, www.qc.ec.gc.ca/csl/inf/inf069_e.html

3. Robert Bateman on Outdoor Education, www.batemanideas.com/outdooreducation.html

4. The Bruce Trail Conservancy, "What Is the Bruce Trail?" http://brucetrail.org/pages/what-is-the-bruce-trail, accessed May 20, 2011.

5. Robert Bateman on Education, www.batemanideas.com/education.html.

6. Environmental Defence, Toxic Nation Reports, Robert Bateman, www.toxicnation.ca/toxicnation-studies/pollution-in-adults/Robert

MyEnvironmentPlace

Go to **www.myenvironmentplace.ca** where you will find quizzes, animations, your Pearson eText, and more.

3

Evolution, Biodiversity, and Population Ecology

The Monteverde cloud forest in Costa Rica is a hotspot of biodiversity.

Upon successfully completing this chapter, you will be able to

- Explain the process of natural selection and cite evidence for this process
- Describe the ways in which evolution results in biodiversity and what the fossil record has taught us about evolution
- Discuss reasons for species extinction and mass extinction events

- Summarize the levels of ecological organization
- Outline the characteristics of populations that help predict population growth
- Define *logistic growth*, *carrying capacity*, *limiting factors*, and other fundamental concepts of population ecology

Populations may grow, shrink, or remain stable

Population growth, or decline, is determined by four factors:

1. Births within the population, or **natality**
2. Deaths within the population, or **mortality**
3. **Immigration**, the arrival of individuals from outside the population
4. **Emigration**, the departure of individuals from the population

Births and immigration add individuals to a population, whereas deaths and emigration remove individuals. If we are not interested in the effects of migration, we can measure the **natural rate of population growth** by subtracting the crude death rate from the crude birth rate:

Crude birth rate – Crude death rate = Natural rate of population growth

The natural rate of population growth reflects the degree to which a population is growing or shrinking as a result of its own internal factors.

To obtain an overall **population growth rate**, the total rate of change in a population's size per unit of time, we must also take into account the effects of migration. Thus, we include terms for immigration and emigration (each expressed per 1000 individuals per year) in the formula for the population growth:

(Crude birth rate – Crude death rate) + (Immigration rate – emigration rate) = Population growth rate

The resulting number tells us the net change in a population's size per 1000 individuals per year. For example, a population with a crude birth rate of 18 per 1000/yr, a crude death rate of 10 per 1000/yr, an immigration rate of 5 per 1000/yr, and an emigration rate of 7 per 1000/yr would have a population growth rate of 6 per 1000/yr:

$$(18/1000 - 10/1000) + (5/1000 - 7/1000) = 6/1000$$

Thus, a population of 1000 in one year will reach 1006 in the next. If the population is 1 000 000, it will reach 1 006 000 the next year. Such population increases are often expressed as percentages, which we can calculate using the following formula:

Population growth rate × 100%

Thus, a growth rate of 6/1000 would be expressed as:

$$6/1000 \times 100\% = 0.6\%$$

By measuring population growth in terms of percentages, scientists can compare increases and decreases in species that have far different population sizes. They can also project changes that will occur in the population over longer periods.

Unregulated populations increase by exponential growth

When a population, or anything else, increases by a fixed percentage each year, it is said to undergo *geometric growth*, or **exponential growth**. A savings account is a familiar frame of reference for describing exponential growth. If at the time of your birth your parents had invested $1000 in a savings account earning 5% interest compounded each year, with no additional investments you would have $1629 by age 10, and $2653 by age 20, but you would have over $30 000 when you turn 70. If you could wait just 10 years more, that figure would rise to nearly $50 000. Only $629 was added during your first decade, but approximately $19 000 was added during the decade between ages 70 and 80. The reason is that a fixed percentage of a small number produces a small increase, but that same percentage of a large number produces a large increase. Thus, as populations (or savings accounts) become larger, each incremental increase likewise gets larger. Such acceleration is a fundamental characteristic of exponential growth.

In contrast, if your parents added a fixed amount to your savings account every year, your savings would still grow, but by *arithmetic growth*, or **linear growth**. If both accounts (linear growth, with interest at a fixed *amount* per year, and exponential growth, with interest at a fixed *percentage* per year) were allowed to proceed unchecked, the account with the exponential growth would necessarily outstrip the linear-growth account. This will be the case even if the balance in the linear-growth account is higher for the first few years.

We can visualize changes in population size using population growth curves. The J-shaped curve in FIGURE 3.1 shows an example of an exponential population increase. Populations of organisms can increase exponentially until they meet constraints. Each organism reproduces by a certain amount, and as populations get larger, more individuals reproduce by that amount. If there were no external limits on growth, ecologists theoretically would expect exponential growth to occur.

Exponential growth usually occurs in nature when a population is small, competition is minimal, and environmental conditions are ideal for the organism in question. Most often, these conditions occur when organisms are introduced to a new environment. Mould growing on a

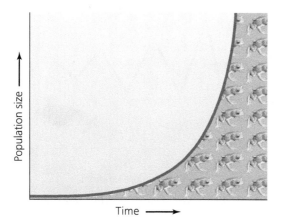

FIGURE 3.1
No species can maintain exponential growth indefinitely, but some may grow exponentially for a time when colonizing an unoccupied environment or exploiting an unused resource.

piece of bread or fruit, and bacteria colonizing a recently dead animal are cases in point. But species of any size may show exponential growth under the right conditions. We sometimes see this in urban areas where animals such as squirrels, raccoons, Canada geese, coyotes, and even moose can become nuisances when their populations expand quickly as a result of easy access to food supplies.

Limiting factors restrain population growth

Exponential growth rarely lasts long. If even a single species in Earth's history had increased exponentially for very many generations, it would have blanketed the planet's surface, and nothing else could have survived. Instead, every population eventually is constrained by **limiting factors**—physical, chemical, and biological characteristics of the environment that restrain population growth. The combination of these factors exerts environmental resistance on the population. Environmental resistance ultimately determines the **carrying capacity**, the maximum population size of a species that a given environment can sustain.

Ecologists use the S-shaped (or *sigmoidal*) curve in **FIGURE 3.2** to show how an initial exponential increase is slowed and finally brought to a standstill by limiting factors. Called a **logistic growth curve**, it rises sharply at first but then begins to level off as the effects of limiting factors become stronger. Eventually the force of these factors stabilizes the population size at its carrying capacity.

The logistic curve is a simplified model; real populations can behave quite differently. Some may cycle indefi-

nitely above and below the carrying capacity. Some may show cycles that become less extreme and approach the carrying capacity. Others may overshoot the carrying capacity and then crash, fated either for extinction or recovery (**FIGURE 3.3**).

Many factors contribute to environmental resistance and influence carrying capacity and population growth and decline. Space limits the number of individuals a given environment can support; if there is no physical room for additional individuals, they are unlikely to survive. Other limiting factors for animals in the terrestrial environment include the availability of food, water, mates, shelter, and suitable breeding sites; temperature extremes; prevalence of disease; and abundance of predators. Plants are often limited by amounts of sunlight and moisture, and the availability of nutrients from the soil, as well as disease and attack by plant-eating animals. In aquatic systems, limiting factors include salinity, sunlight, temperature, dissolved oxygen, and water chemistry. To determine limiting factors, ecologists often conduct experiments in which they increase or decrease a hypothesized limiting factor to observe its effects on population size.

The influence of limiting factors can vary with changing conditions. In particular, the density of a population can increase or decrease the impact of certain factors on that population. Recall that high population density can help organisms find mates, but also increases competition and the risk of predation and disease. Such

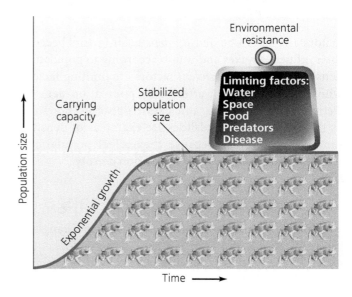

FIGURE 3.2
The logistic growth curve shows how population size may increase rapidly at first, then grow more slowly, and finally stabilize at a carrying capacity. Carrying capacity is determined both by the biotic potential of the organism and by various external limiting factors, collectively termed *environmental resistance*.

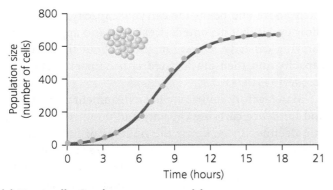

(a) Yeast cells, *Saccharomyces cerevisiae*

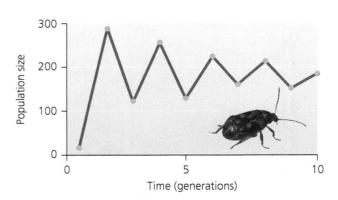

(c) Stored-product beetle, *Callosobruchus maculatus*

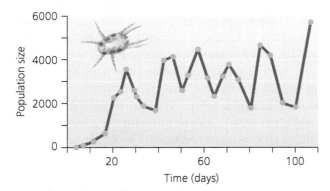

(b) Mite, *Eotetranychus sexmaculatus*

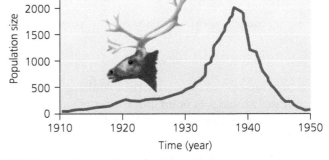

(d) St. Paul reindeer, *Rangifer tarandus*

FIGURE 3.3   Population growth in nature often departs from the stereotypical logistic growth curve, and it can do so in several fundamental ways. Yeast cells from a lab experiment show logistic growth **(a)** that closely matches the theoretical model. Some organisms, like the mite **(b)**, show cycles in which population fluctuates indefinitely above and below the carrying capacity. Population oscillations can also dampen, lessening in intensity and eventually stabilizing at carrying capacity **(c)**, as in a lab experiment with the stored-product beetle. Populations that rise too fast and deplete resources may crash just as suddenly **(d)**, like the population of reindeer introduced to the Bering Sea island of St. Paul.   *Source: Data from Pearl, R. (1927) The growth of populations.* Quarterly Review of Biology 2: 532–548, (a); Huffaker, C. B. (1958) Experimental studies on predation: Dispersion factors and predator-prey oscillations, Hilgardia 27: 343–383, (b); Utida, S. (1967) Damped oscillation of population density at equilibrium, Researches on Population Ecology 9: 1–9, (c); Scheffer, V.C. (1951) Rise and fall of a reindeer herd, Scientific Monthly 73: 356–362, (d).

factors are said to be *density-dependent* factors because their influence waxes and wanes according to population density. *Density-independent* factors are limiting factors whose influence is not affected by population density. Temperature extremes and catastrophic events such as floods, fires, and landslides are examples of density-independent factors because they affect populations without being influenced by population density.

Carrying capacities can change

Because environments are complex and ever-changing, carrying capacity can vary. If a fire destroys a forest, for example, the carrying capacities for most forest species will decline, whereas those for species that benefit from fire will increase. If limiting factors change as a result of environmental change, the carrying capacity for a species may increase (or decrease).

Our own species has proved capable of intentionally altering our environment so as to reduce environmen-

tal resistance and raise our carrying capacity. When our ancestors began to build shelters and use fire for heating and cooking, they reduced the environmental resistance of areas with cold climates and were able to expand into new territory. People have managed so far to increase the planet's carrying capacity for our species, but we have done so by appropriating immense proportions of the planet's resources. In the process, we have reduced the carrying capacities for countless other organisms and have called into question our own long-term survival.

Reproductive strategies vary from species to species

Limiting factors from an organism's environment provide only half the story of population regulation. The other half comes from the attributes of the organism itself. For example, organisms differ in their **biotic potential**, or maximum capacity to produce offspring under ideal

CARRYING CAPACITY AND HUMAN POPULATION GROWTH

The global human population has risen from fewer than 1 billion 200 years ago to 7 billion today, and we have far exceeded our historic carrying capacity. In fact, some demographers argue that Earth's true carrying capacity for the human species is only about 10 million (the estimated human population at the time when the human species had expanded to cover most of the globe). What factors increased Earth's carrying capacity for people? Are there limiting factors for the human population? What might they be? Do you think we can keep raising Earth's carrying capacity in the future? Are there any factors that might cause Earth's carrying capacity for the human species to decrease?

environmental conditions. A fish with a short gestation period that lays thousands of eggs at a time has high biotic potential, whereas a whale with a long gestation period that gives birth to a single calf at a time has low biotic potential. The interaction between an organism's biotic potential and the environmental resistance to its population growth helps determine the fate of its population.

Giraffes, elephants, humans, and other large animals with low biotic potential produce a relatively small number of offspring and take a long time to gestate and raise each of their young. Species that take this approach to reproduction compensate by devoting large amounts of energy and resources to caring for and protecting the relatively few offspring they produce during their lifetimes. Such species are said to be **K-selected** (or are called *K-strategists*). K-selected species are so named because their populations tend to stabilize over time at or near their carrying capacity, and K is a commonly used abbreviation for carrying capacity. Because their populations stay close to carrying capacity, natural selection in these species favours individuals that invest in producing offspring of high quality that can be good competitors.

In contrast, species that are **r-selected** focus on quantity, not quality. Species considered to be r-selected (or are called *r-strategists*) have high biotic potential and devote their energy and resources to producing as many offspring as possible in a relatively short time. Their offspring do not require parental care after birth, and r-strategists commonly leave the survival of their offspring to chance. The abbreviation r denotes the rate at which a population increases in the absence of limiting factors. Population sizes of r-selected species fluctuate

greatly, so they are often below carrying capacity. This is why natural selection in these species favours traits that lead to rapid population growth. Many fish, plants, frogs, insects, and others are r-selected. The golden toad is one example. Each adult female laid 200 to 400 eggs, and its tadpoles spent five weeks unsupervised in the breeding pools metamorphosing into adults.

TABLE 3.1 summarizes stereotypical traits of r-selected and K-selected species. However, it is important to note that these are two extremes on a continuum and that most species fall somewhere between these endpoints. Moreover, some organisms show combinations of traits that do not clearly correspond to a place on the continuum. A redwood tree (*Sequoia sempervirens*), for instance, is large and long-lived, yet it produces many small seeds and offers no parental care.

Changes in populations influence the composition of communities

In the late 1980s, the golden toad and the harlequin frog were the most diligently studied species that had been affected by changing environmental conditions in the Costa Rican cloud forest. However, once scientists began looking at populations of other species at Monteverde, they began to notice more troubling changes. By the early 1990s, not only had golden toads, harlequin frogs, and other organisms been pushed from their cloud-forest habitat into apparent extinction, but also many species from lower, drier habitats also had begun to appear at Monteverde. These immigrants included species tolerant of drier conditions, such as blue-crowned motmots (*Momotus momota*) and brown jays (*Cyanocorax morio*).

Table 3.1 Typical Characteristics of r-Selected and K-selected Species

r-selected species	K-selected species
Small size	Large size
Fast development	Slow development
Short-lived	Long-lived
Reproduction early in life	Reproduction later in life
Many, small offspring	Few, large offspring
Fast population growth rate	Slow population growth rate
No parental care	Parental care
Weak competitive ability	Strong competitive ability
Variable population size, often well below carrying capacity	Constant population size, close to carrying capacity
Variable and unpredictable mortality	More constant and predictable mortality

THE SCIENCE BEHIND THE STORY

Climate Change, Disease, and the Amphibians of Monteverde

Dr. J. Alan Pounds (left) with Dr. Luis Coloma, looking for harlequin frogs

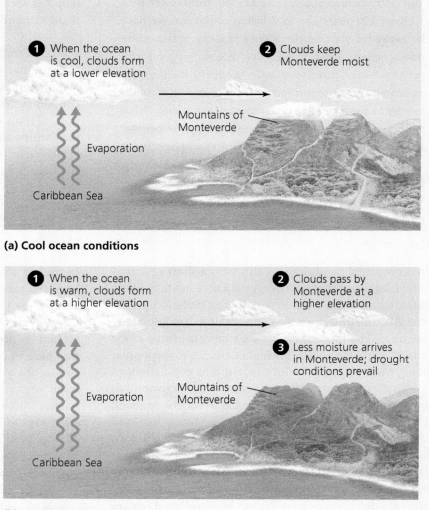

1 When the ocean is cool, clouds form at a lower elevation

2 Clouds keep Monteverde moist

Mountains of Monteverde

Evaporation

Caribbean Sea

(a) Cool ocean conditions

1 When the ocean is warm, clouds form at a higher elevation

2 Clouds pass by Monteverde at a higher elevation

3 Less moisture arrives in Monteverde; drought conditions prevail

Evaporation

Mountains of Monteverde

Caribbean Sea

(b) Warm ocean conditions

Monteverde's cloud forest gets its name and life-giving moisture from clouds that sweep inland from the oceans. When ocean temperatures are cool **(a)**, the clouds keep Monteverde moist. Warmer ocean conditions **(b)** resulting from global climate change cause clouds to form at higher elevations and pass over the mountains, drying the cloud forest.

Soon after the golden toad's disappearance, scientists began to investigate the potential role of global climate change in driving cloud-forest species toward extinction. The period from July 1986 to June 1987 was the driest on record at Monteverde, with unusually high temperatures and record-low stream flows. These conditions caused the golden toad's breeding pools to dry up in the spring of 1987, likely killing nearly all of the eggs and tadpoles in the pools.

By reviewing weather data, scientists found that the number of dry days and dry periods each winter in the Monteverde region had increased between 1973 and 1998. Because amphibians breathe and absorb moisture through their skin, they are susceptible to dry conditions. Based on these facts, herpetologists J. Alan Pounds and Martha Crump in 1994 hypothesized that hot, dry conditions were to blame for high adult mortality and breeding problems among golden toads and other amphibians.

Pounds and others reviewed the scientific literature on atmospheric and ocean science to analyze the impacts on Monteverde's local climate of warming patterns in the ocean regions around Costa Rica. Warmer oceans, the researchers

By the year 2000, 15 dry-forest species had moved into the cloud forest and begun to breed. Meanwhile, population sizes of several cloud-forest bird species had declined. After 1987, 20 of 50 frog species vanished from one part of Monteverde, and ecologists later reported more disappearances, including those of two lizards native to the cloud forest. Scientists hypothesized that the warming, drying trends that researchers were documenting were causing population fluctuations and unleashing changes in the composition of the community (see "The Science Behind the Story: Climate Change, Disease, and the Amphibians of Monteverde").

found, caused clouds to pass over at higher elevations, where they were no longer in contact with the trees. Once the cloud forest's moisture supply was pushed upward, out of reach of the mountaintops, the forest began to dry out (see first figure).

In a 1999 paper in the journal *Nature*, Pounds and two colleagues reported that climate modification was causing local changes at the species, population, and community levels. They argued that higher clouds and decreasing moisture in the forest could explain the disappearance of the golden toad and harlequin frog and also the concurrent population crashes and subsequent disappearance of 20 other species of frogs and toads from the Monteverde region. As the forests dried out, drought-tolerant species of birds and reptiles shifted upslope, and moisture-dependent species were stranded at the mountaintops by a rising tide of aridity.

Pounds and his colleagues expanded the story further in *Nature* in 2006. Although clouds had risen higher in the sky, the extra moisture evaporating from warming oceans was increasing cloud cover overall, blocking sunlight during the day and trapping heat at night. As a result, at Monteverde and other tropical locations, daytime and nighttime temperatures were becoming more similar. Such conditions are optimal for chytrid fungi, pathogens that can lethally infect amphibians. In recent years the chytrid fungus *Batrachochytrium dendrobatidis* is thought to have contributed to the likely extinction of 67 of the world's 113 species of harlequin frogs. At Monteverde and elsewhere, Pounds' team argued, climate change is promoting disease epidemics that are driving extinct many of the world's amphibians.

Other researchers agree that chytrid fungus is a major threat but dispute

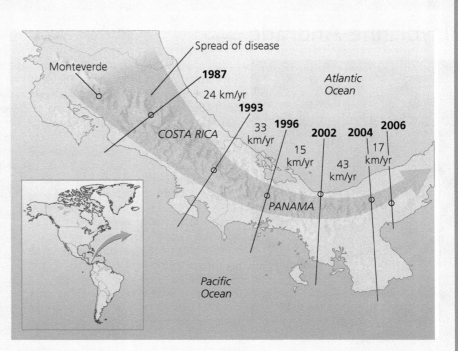

Dr. Karen Lips' research team used known dates of decline (years in figure) in harlequin frog populations at sites in Costa Rica and Panama to infer the spread of a wave of infection (arrow) by chytrid fungus across the region. By their analysis, chytrid reached Monteverde before 1987 and was well into Panama by 2000.
Source: Adapted from Lips, K.R., et al. (2008) Riding the wave: Reconciling the roles of disease and climate change in amphibian declines. PLoS Biology 6: 441–454.

a connection to climate change. In 2008, one team led by biologist Karen Lips of Southern Illinois University at Carbondale mapped amphibian declines and inferred the rapid spread of non-native and invasive chytrid fungus in waves across Central America and South America in recent years (see second figure). The analysis by Lips and her team suggested that the dramatic amphibian die-offs at Monteverde and elsewhere are directly due to the arrival of this devastating pathogen and do not necessarily involve climate change.

Additional research has since shown that harlequin frog extinctions were correlated with rising tropical air temperatures; however this does not confirm climate as a direct causal factor. Climate change is a fundamental influence on biological systems. It is likely a factor in amphibian declines, but as yet the evidence for a causal link is not solid. Clearly more research into the effects of both disease and climate change is needed. Biologists today are racing to find the answers, hoping to save many of the world's amphibian species from extinction.

Conclusion

Changes in populations and communities have been taking place naturally as long as life has existed. Studies of both living and long-extinct organisms have helped illuminate fundamental concepts of evolution and population ecology that are integral to environmental science. The evolutionary processes of natural selection, speciation, and extinction have been the driving forces behind the development of Earth's biodiversity.

Today human development, resource extraction, and population pressure are speeding the rate of

CANADIAN ENVIRONMENTAL PERSPECTIVES

Maydianne Andrade

Professor Maydianne Andrade studies how sex and cannibalism come together to ensure reproductive success for the redback spider.

- **Professor** of ecology and evolutionary biology at the University of Toronto at Scarborough
- **Entomologist, arachnologist,** and "Spider Woman"
- One of *Popular Science*'s **"Brilliant 10"** Scientists for 2005

Maydianne Andrade is interested in sex, but not just any kind of sex. She studies how sexual selection, social behaviour, and ecological conditions interact to affect the evolution of mating systems in the redback spider, *Latrodectus hasselti.*[1]

Andrade is an assistant professor in the Department of Ecology and Evolutionary Biology at the University of Toronto's Scarborough campus. She completed her B.Sc. at Simon Fraser University, her M.Sc. at the University of Toronto, and her Ph.D. at Cornell University. The animals she studies—the redback spider and its close relative, the black widow spider—are unusual because the males of the species make an extreme investment, actually, a "terminal investment," in seeking success in the mating process. This means pretty much what it sounds like: the male sacrifices himself to ensure his success in mating. He actually does this by offering himself to the female as "dinner." Yes, female redback spiders are cannibals.

This may seem counterintuitive; how can it be a beneficial adaptation for a male spider to sacrifice himself to achieve success in mating? Doesn't this mean that he gives up all possibility of any future mating opportunities?

Andrade has discovered some interesting features of the species. For one thing, the physiology of the male redback spider is such that he can transfer sperm to the female even as he is being consumed. Furthermore, the self-sacrifice gives such an enormous advantage to the male redback spider—which would likely mate only once anyway, even in the absence of cannibalism—that it is worth his while to give up future mating opportunities for success just this one time.

As Andrade points out,

This extreme form of male mating investment provides a unique opportunity to test sexual selection and life history theory because males are under strong selection to succeed in their single mating opportunity, but are constrained by ecology and physically dominant females. We have a good understanding of factors affecting the strength and natural selection on redback males, and can manipulate cues indicating the strength of selection in the field and laboratory.[2]

Andrade's current work, which has ramifications for the study not only of spiders but also of natural selection and evolutionary theory, is focused on furthering our understanding of the effects of factors such as diet on the ratio of males to females and how male competition and female choice affect the mating process.

*"When we talk about 'thinking outside the box,' that's what thinking like a scientist is all about."***—Maydianne Andrade**

Thinking About Environmental Perspectives

How do researchers like Maydianne Andrade advance our *general* understanding of evolutionary theory through the study of *specific* unusual or extreme mating habits in individual organisms, such as those of the redback spiders? Visit Andrade's website and read some of her research papers to find out more about this (www.scar.utoronto.ca/~mandrade).

---

environmental change, altering the types of change, and threatening specific organisms and biodiversity as a whole. The ways we modify our environment cannot be understood in a scientific vacuum, however. Understanding how ecological processes work at the population level is crucial to protecting biodiversity threatened by the mass extinction event that many biologists maintain is already under way. The factors that threaten biodiversity have complex social, economic, and political roots, and environmental scientists appre-

ciate that we must understand these aspects if we are to develop solutions.

Fortunately, there are things people can do to forestall population declines of species threatened with extinction. Millions of people around the world are already taking action to safeguard the biodiversity and ecological and evolutionary processes that make Earth such a unique place. We will look at many of these efforts in future chapters.

REVIEWING OBJECTIVES

You should now be able to:

Explain the process of natural selection and cite evidence for this process

- Because organisms produce excess young, individuals vary in their traits, and many traits are inherited, some individuals will prove better at surviving and reproducing. Their genes will be passed on and become more prominent in future generations.
- Mutations and recombination provide the genetic variation for natural selection.
- We have produced our pets, farm animals, and crop plants through artificial selection.

Describe the ways in which evolution results in biodiversity and what the fossil record has taught us about evolution

- Natural selection can act as a diversifying force as organisms adapt to their environments in myriad ways.
- Speciation (by geographic isolation and other means) produces new species.
- The branching patterns of phylogenetic trees reflect the historical pattern by which lineages of organisms have diverged.
- By preserving some of the long history of life on this planet, the fossil record has shown us that early organisms have evolved into later ones and that the number of species alive at any given time has generally increased through time.

Discuss reasons for species extinction and mass extinction events

- Extinction may occur when species that are highly specialized or that have small populations encounter rapid environmental change.
- Earth's life has experienced five known episodes of mass extinction, which were due to asteroid impact and possibly volcanism and other factors.

- Today, human impact may be initiating a sixth great extinction.

Summarize the levels of ecological organization

- Life is organized hierarchically, starting with the atoms, molecules, and cells that make up individual organisms.
- Ecologists study phenomena on the organismal, population, community, and ecosystem levels—and, increasingly, on the biosphere level.
- Habitat, niche, and specialization are important ecological concepts.

Outline the characteristics of populations that help predict population growth

- Populations are characterized by population size, population density, population distribution, sex ratio, age structure, and birth and death rates.
- Immigration and emigration, as well as birth and death rates, determine how a population will grow or decline.

Define *logistic growth*, *carrying capacity*, *limiting factors*, and other fundamental concepts of population ecology

- Populations unrestrained by limiting factors will undergo exponential growth until they meet environmental resistance.
- Logistic growth describes the effects of density dependence; exponential growth slows as population size increases, and population size levels off at a carrying capacity.
- K-selection and r-selection describe theoretical extremes in how organisms can allocate growth and reproduction.

TESTING YOUR COMPREHENSION

1. Explain the premises and logic that support the concept of natural selection.
2. How does allopatric speciation occur?
3. Name two examples of evidence for natural selection.
4. Name three organisms that have gone extinct, and give a probable reason for each extinction.
5. What is the difference between a species and a population? Between a population and a community?
6. Contrast the concepts of habitat and niche.
7. List and describe each of the five major population characteristics discussed in this chapter. Explain how each shapes population dynamics.
8. Could any species undergo exponential growth forever? Explain your answer.
9. Describe how limiting factors relate to carrying capacity.
10. Explain the difference between K-selected species and r-selected species. Can you think of examples of each that were not mentioned in the chapter?

THINKING IT THROUGH

1. In what ways has artificial selection changed people's quality of life? Give examples. Can you imagine a way in which artificial selection could be used to improve our quality of life further? Can you imagine a way it could be used to lessen our environmental impact?
2. What types of species are most vulnerable to extinction, and what kinds of factors threaten them? Can you think of any species in your region that are threatened with extinction today? What reasons lie behind their endangerment?
3. Do you think the human species can continue raising its global carrying capacity? How so, or why not? Do you think we *should* try to keep raising our carrying capacity? Why or why not?
4. Describe the evidence suggesting that changes in temperature and precipitation led to the extinction of the golden toad and to population crashes for other amphibians at Monteverde. Why do scientists think that disease also played a role? What do you think could be done to help make such declines less likely in the future?
5. If you were given the task of counting all of the species alive on Earth, how would you go about it? If you were asked to measure the biodiversity of one area and contrast it with that of another area, what indicators of biodiversity would you measure? (We will return to this question in the chapter on conservation of species and habitats.)
6. Let us say that you are a population ecologist studying animals in a national park. The government is asking for advice on how to focus its limited conservation funds. How would you rate the following three species, from most vulnerable (and thus most in need of attention) to least vulnerable? Give reasons for your choices.
   - A bird with an even sex ratio that is a habitat generalist
   - A salamander that is endemic to the park and lives only in high-elevation forest
   - A fish that specializes on a few types of invertebrate prey and has a large population size

INTERPRETING GRAPHS AND DATA

Amphibians are sensitive biological indicators of climate change because their reproduction and survival are so closely tied to water. One way in which drier conditions may affect amphibians is by reducing the depth of the pools of water in which their eggs develop. Shallower pools offer less protection from UV-B (ultraviolet) radiation, which some scientists maintain may kill embryos directly or make them more susceptible to disease.

Herpetologist Joseph Kiesecker and colleagues conducted a field study of the relationships among water depth, UV-B radiation, and survivorship of western toad *(Bufo boreas)* embryos in the Pacific Northwest. In manipulative experiments, the researchers placed toad embryos in mesh enclosures at three different depths of water. The researchers placed protective filters that blocked all UV-B radiation over some of these embryos, while leaving other embryos unprotected without the filters. Some of the study's results are presented in the accompanying graph.

1. If the UV-B radiation at the surface has an intensity of 0.27 watts/m^2, approximately what is its intensity at depths of 10 cm, 50 cm, and 100 cm?

2. Approximately how much did survival rates at the 10-cm depth differ between the protected and unprotected treatments? Why do you think survival rates differed significantly at the 10-cm depth but not at the other depths?

3. What do you think would be the effect of drier-than-average years on the western toad population if the average depth of pools available for toad spawning dropped? How do the data above address your hypothesis? Do they support cause-and-effect relationships among water depth, UV-B exposure, disease, and toad mortality?

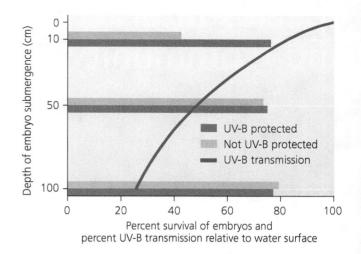

Embryo survivorship in western toads *(Bufo boreas)* at different water depths and UV-B light intensities. Red bars indicate embryos protected under a filter that blocked UV-B light; orange bars indicate unprotected embryos. The blue line indicates the amount of UV-B light reaching different depths in the water column, expressed as a percentage of the UV-B radiation at the water surface.
Source: Data from Kiesecker, J.M., et al. (2001) Complex causes of amphibian population declines. Nature *410: 681–684.*

CHAPTER ENDNOTES

1. Andrade Lab Research, Department of Ecology and Evolutionary Biology, University of Toronto Scarborough, www.scar.utoronto.ca/~mandrade

2. Andrade Lab Research, Department of Ecology and Evolutionary Biology, University of Toronto Scarborough, www.scar.utoronto.ca/~mandrade

MyEnvironmentPlace

Go to **www.myenvironmentplace.ca** where you will find quizzes, animations, your Pearson eText, and more.

Species Interactions and Community Ecology

This marsh–wetland community is one of the few remaining along the shores of Lake Ontario.

Upon successfully completing this chapter, you will be able to

- Compare and contrast the major types of species interactions
- Characterize feeding relationships and energy flow, using them to construct trophic pyramids and food webs
- Distinguish characteristics of a keystone species
- Describe how communities respond to disturbances

- Perceive and predict the potential impacts of invasive species on communities
- Explain the goals and methods of ecological restoration
- Describe and illustrate the terrestrial biomes of the world

This is a typical aggregation of zebra mussels, like those that have invaded the Great Lakes.

CANADA

UNITED STATES

Great Lakes

CENTRAL CASE:
BLACK AND WHITE AND SPREAD ALL OVER: ZEBRA MUSSELS INVADE THE GREAT LAKES

"The zebra mussel is helping us understand what makes a good invader."
—ANTHONY RICCIARDI, MCGILL UNIVERSITY

"The zebra mussel has altered aquatic ecosystems beyond recognition."
—MICHAEL BARDWAJ, *CANADIAN GEOGRAPHIC*[1]

As if the Great Lakes had not been through enough, the last thing they needed was the zebra mussel. The pollution-fouled waters of Lake Erie and the other Great Lakes had become gradually cleaner in the years following the establishment of the International Joint Commission and the signing of the Great Lakes Water Quality Agreement between Canada and the United States in 1972. As these international efforts brought industrial discharges under control, people once again began to use the lakes for recreation, and populations of fish rebounded.

Then the zebra mussel arrived. Black-and-white-striped shellfish the size of a dime (see photo), zebra mussels (*Dreissena polymorpha*) attach to hard surfaces and feed on algae by filtering water through their gills. This mollusc is native to the Caspian Sea, Black Sea, and Azov Sea in western Asia and eastern Europe. It made its North American debut in 1988 when it was discovered in Canadian waters at Lake St. Clair, which connects Lake Erie with Lake Huron. Evidently ships arriving from Europe had discharged ballast water containing the mussels or their larvae into the Great Lakes.

Within two years of their discovery in Lake St. Clair, zebra mussels had reached all five of the Great Lakes. The next year, they entered New York's Hudson River to the east and the Illinois River at Chicago to the west.

From the Illinois River and its canals, they soon reached the Mississippi River, giving them access to a vast watershed covering 40% of the United States. By 2012, zebra mussel colonies and sightings had been confirmed in Ontario, Québec, and 40 U.S. states.

How could a mussel spread so quickly? The zebra mussel's larval stage is well adapted for long-distance dispersal. Its tiny larvae drift freely for several weeks, travelling as far as the currents take them. Adults that attach themselves to boats and ships may be transported from one place to another, even to isolated lakes and ponds well away from major rivers. They can survive out of the water for several days and are known to have been transported overland to many locations. In North America the mussels encountered none of the predators, competitors, and parasites that had evolved to limit their population growth in the Old World.

Why the fuss? Zebra mussels are best known for clogging up water intake pipes at factories, power plants, municipal water supplies, and wastewater treatment facilities. At one power plant, workers counted 700 000 mussels per square metre of pipe surface. Great densities of these organisms can damage boat engines, degrade docks, foul fishing gear, and sink buoys that ships use for navigation. Through such impacts, it is estimated that zebra mussels cost hundreds of millions of dollars each year. Over the first 10 years of the zebra mussel invasion, the total cost to Great Lakes economies is estimated to have reached $5 billion, with ongoing annual costs of $20 000 to $350 000 per industrial facility. These figures include only costs to industry, not to individuals or cottagers, who also suffer costs such as clogged water pipes, ruined motorboats, and fouled beaches.[2]

Zebra mussels also have severe impacts on the ecological systems they invade. They eat **phytoplankton**, microscopic algae that drift in open water. Because each mussel filters a litre or more of water every day, they consume so much phytoplankton that they can deplete populations. Phytoplankton is the foundation of the Great Lakes food web, so its depletion is bad news for **zooplankton**, the tiny aquatic animals that eat phytoplankton—and for the fish that eat both. Water bodies with zebra mussels have fewer zooplankton and open-water fish than water bodies without them, researchers are finding.

However, zebra mussels also provide benefits to some bottom-feeding invertebrates and fish. By filtering algae and organic matter from open water and depositing nutrients in their feces, they shift the community's nutrient balance to the bottom and benefit the species that feed there. Once they have cleared the water, sunlight penetrates deeper, spurring the growth of large-leafed underwater plants and algae. Such changes have ripple effects throughout the community that scientists are only beginning to understand.

In the past several years, scientists have noticed a surprising twist: One invader is being displaced by another. The quagga mussel (*Dreissena buensis*), a close relative of the zebra mussel, is spreading through the Great Lakes, replacing the zebra mussel in many locations. What consequences this may have for ecological communities, scientists are only beginning to understand.

Species Interactions

By interacting with many species in a variety of ways, zebra mussels have set in motion an array of changes in the ecological communities they have invaded. Interactions among species are the threads in the fabric of communities, holding them together and determining their nature. Ecologists have organized species interactions into several fundamental categories. Most prominent are competition, predation, parasitism, herbivory, and mutualism. TABLE 4.1 summarizes the positive (+) and negative (−) impacts of each type of interaction for each participant. An interaction with no impact is shown by a "0" in the table.

Table 4.1 Effects of Species Interactions on Their Participants

Type of interaction	Effect on Species 1	Effect on Species 2
Mutualism	+	+
Commensalism	+	0
Predation, parasitism, herbivory	+	−
Amensalism	−	0
Competition	−	−

"+" denotes a positive effect; "−" denotes a negative effect; "0" denotes no effect.

Competition can occur when resources are limited

When multiple organisms seek the same limited resource, their relationship is said to be one of **competition**. Competing organisms do not usually fight with one another directly and physically. Competition is commonly more subtle and indirect, involving the consequences of one organism's ability to match or outdo others in procuring resources. The resources for which organisms compete can include just about anything an organism might need to survive, including food, water, space, shelter, mates, sunlight, and more. Competitive interactions can take place among members of the same species (*intraspecific competition*) or among members of two or more different species (*interspecific competition*).

We have already discussed intraspecific competition, without naming it as such. Recall that density dependence limits the growth of a population; individuals of the same species compete with one another for limited resources, such that competition is more acute when there are more individuals per unit area (denser populations). Thus, intraspecific competition is really a population-level phenomenon.

In contrast, interspecific competition can have substantial effects on the composition of communities. If one species is a very effective competitor, it may exclude another species from resource use entirely. This outcome, called **competitive exclusion**, occurred in Lake St. Clair and western Lake Erie as the zebra mussel outcompeted a native mussel species.

Alternatively, if neither competing species fully excludes the other, the species may live side by side at a certain ratio of population sizes. This result, called *species coexistence*, may produce a stable point of equilibrium, in which the population size of each remains fairly constant through time.

Coexisting species that use the same resources tend to adjust to their competitors to minimize competition with them. Individuals can do this by changing their behaviour so as to use only a portion of the total array of resources they are capable of using. In such cases, individuals are not fulfilling their entire *niche*, or ecological role. The full niche of a species is called its **fundamental niche** (**FIGURE 4.1A**). An individual that plays only part of its role because of competition or other species interactions is said to be displaying a **realized niche** (**FIGURE 4.1B**), the portion of its fundamental niche that is actually filled, or realized.

Species make similar adjustments over evolutionary time. They adapt to competition by evolving to use slightly different resources or to use their shared resources in different ways. If two bird species eat the same type of seeds, one might come to specialize on larger seeds and the other to specialize on smaller seeds. Or one bird might become more active in the morning and the other more active in the evening, thus avoiding direct interference. This process is called **resource partitioning**, because the species divide, or partition, the resource they use in common by specializing in different ways (**FIGURE 4.2**).

Resource partitioning can lead to *character displacement*, which occurs when competing species evolve physical characteristics that reflect their reliance on the portion of the resource they use. By becoming more different from one another, two species reduce their competition. Through natural selection, birds that specialize on larger seeds may evolve larger bills that enable them to make best use of the resource, whereas birds specializing on smaller seeds may evolve smaller bills. This is precisely

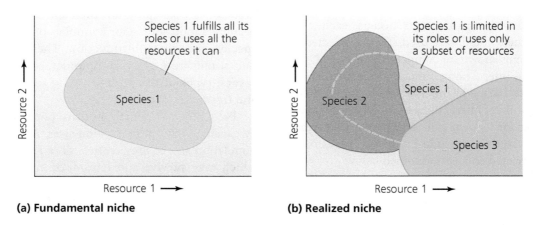

(a) Fundamental niche

Species 1 fulfills all its roles or uses all the resources it can

Species 1

Resource 2

Resource 1 →

(b) Realized niche

Species 1 is limited in its roles or uses only a subset of resources

Species 2

Species 1

Species 3

Resource 2

Resource 1 →

FIGURE 4.1 An organism facing competition may be forced to play a lesser ecological role or use fewer resources than it would in the absence of its competitor. With no competitors, an organism can exploit its full fundamental niche **(a)**. But when competitors restrict what an organism can do or what resources it can use, the organism is limited to a realized niche **(b)**, which covers only a subset of its fundamental niche. In considering niches, ecologists have traditionally focused on competition, but they now recognize that other species interactions are also influential.

FIGURE 4.2
When species compete, they tend to partition resources, each specializing on a slightly different resource or way of attaining a shared resource. A number of types of birds—including the woodpeckers, creeper, and nuthatch shown here—feed on insects from tree trunks, but they use different portions of the trunk, seeking different foods in different ways.

what extensive research has revealed about the finches from the Galápagos Islands that were first described by Charles Darwin.

Several types of interactions are exploitative

In competitive interactions, each participant has a negative effect on other participants, because each takes resources the others could have used. This is reflected in the two minus signs shown for competition in TABLE 4.1. In other types of interactions, some participants benefit while others are harmed (the +/– interactions in the table). We can think of interactions in which one member exploits another for its own gain as exploitative interactions. Such interactions include predation, parasitism, herbivory, and related concepts, outlined below.

Predators kill and consume prey

Every living thing needs to procure food and, for most animals, that means eating other living organisms. **Predation** is the process by which individuals of one

FIGURE 4.3
Predator–prey interactions have ecological and evolutionary consequences for both prey and predator. Here, a fire-bellied snake (*Liophis epinephalus*) devours a frog in the Monteverde cloud forest.

species—the **predator**—hunt, capture, kill, and consume individuals of another species, the **prey** (FIGURE 4.3). Along with competition, predation has traditionally been viewed as one of the primary organizing forces in community ecology. Interactions between predators and prey structure the food webs that we will examine shortly, and they influence community composition by helping determine the relative abundance of predators and prey.

Zebra mussel predation on phytoplankton has reduced phytoplankton populations by up to 90%, according to many studies in the Great Lakes and Hudson River. Zebra mussels also consume the smaller types of zooplankton. This predation, combined with the competition mentioned above, has caused zooplankton population sizes and biomass to decline by up to 70% in Lake Erie and the Hudson River since zebra mussels arrived. Meanwhile, the mussels do not readily digest some cyanobacteria, so concentrations of these cyanobacteria rise in lakes with zebra mussels. Most predators are also prey, however, and zebra mussels have become a food source for a number of North American species since their introduction. These include diving ducks, muskrats, crayfish, flounder, sturgeon, eels, and several types of fish with grinding teeth, such as carp and freshwater drum.

Predation can sometimes drive population dynamics by causing cycles in population sizes. An increase in the population size of prey creates more food for predators, which may survive and reproduce more effectively as a result. As the predator population rises, additional predation drives down the population of prey. Fewer prey in turn causes some predators to starve, so that the predator population declines. This allows the prey population to begin rising again, starting the cycle anew. Most natural systems involve so many factors that such cycles

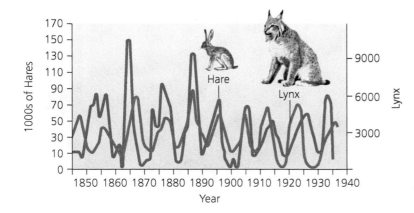

FIGURE 4.4
Predator–prey systems sometimes show paired cycles, in which increases and decreases in one organism apparently drive increases and decreases in the other. Although such cycles are predicted by theory and are seen in lab experiments, they are very difficult to document conclusively in natural systems.
Source: Data from Maclulich, D.A. (1937) Fluctuation in the numbers of varying hare (Lepus americanus). Univ. Toronto Stud. Biol. Ser. No. 43. Toronto, University of Toronto Press.

do not last long, but in some cases we see extended cycles (**FIGURE 4.4**).

Predation also has evolutionary ramifications. Individual predators that are more adept at capturing prey will likely live longer, healthier lives and be better able to provide for their offspring than will less adept individuals. Thus, natural selection on individuals within a predator species leads to the evolution of adaptations that make them better hunters. Prey are faced with an even stronger selective pressure—the risk of immediate death. For this reason, predation pressure has caused organisms to evolve an elaborate array of defences against being eaten (**FIGURE 4.5**).

Parasites exploit living hosts

Organisms can exploit other organisms without killing them. **Parasitism** is a relationship in which one organism, the **parasite**, depends on another, the **host**, for nourish-ment or some other benefit while simultaneously doing the host harm. Unlike predation, parasitism usually does not result in an organism's immediate death, although it sometimes contributes to the host's eventual death.

Many parasites live in close contact with their hosts. These parasites include disease pathogens, such as the protists that cause malaria and dysentery, as well as animals, such as tapeworms, that live in the digestive tracts of their hosts. Other parasites live on the exterior of their hosts, such as the ticks that attach themselves to their hosts' skin, and the sea lamprey (*Petromyzon marinus*), another invader of the Great Lakes (**FIGURE 4.6A**). Sea lampreys are tube-shaped vertebrates that grasp the bodies of fish by using a suction-cup mouth and a rasping tongue, sucking blood from the fish for days or weeks. Sea lampreys invaded the Great Lakes from the Atlantic Ocean after people dug canals to connect the lakes for shipping, and the lampreys soon devastated economically important fisheries of chub, lake herring, whitefish, and lake trout. Since the 1950s, Great Lakes

(a) Cryptic coloration **(b) Warning coloration** **(c) Mimicry**

FIGURE 4.5 Natural selection to avoid predation has resulted in many fabulous adaptations. Some prey hide from predators by *crypsis*, or camouflage, such as this gecko on tree bark **(a)**. Other prey are brightly coloured to warn predators that they are toxic or distasteful, such as this monarch butterfly **(b)**. Still others fool predators with mimicry. Some, like walking sticks imitating twigs, mimic for crypsis. Others mimic toxic, distasteful, or dangerous organisms, like this caterpillar **(c)**; when it is disturbed, the caterpillar swells and curves its tail end and shows eyespots, to look like a snake's head.

(a) Sea lamprey

(b) *Fungus Cordyceps* infecting an insect

FIGURE 4.6   Parasites harm their host organism. With its suction-like mouth and rasping tongue, the sea lamprey (*Petromyzon marinus*) **(a)** attaches itself to fish and sucks the fish's blood for days or weeks, sometimes killing the fish. In **(b)**, an ant (*Pachycondlyla*) is infected by a fungus (*Cordyceps*) that will eventually kill it. In the meantime, fruiting bodies of the fungus are sprouting from the ant. The fungus will soon alter the ant's behaviour, causing it to climb to the highest branches of a nearby plant, so its spores will attain the broadest possible distribution.

fisheries managers have reduced lamprey populations by applying chemicals that selectively kill lamprey larvae.

Other types of parasites are free-living and come into contact with their hosts only infrequently. For example, the cuckoos of Eurasia and the cowbirds of the Americas parasitize other birds by laying eggs in their nests and letting the host bird raise the parasite's young.

Some parasites cause little harm, but others may kill their hosts. Many insects parasitize other insects, often killing them in the process, and are called *parasitoids*. Various species of parasitoid wasps lay eggs on caterpillars. When the eggs hatch, the wasp larvae burrow into the caterpillar's tissues and slowly consume them. The wasp larvae metamorphose into adults and fly from the body of the dying caterpillar.

Just as predators and prey evolve in response to one another, so do parasites and hosts, in a process termed *coevolution*. Hosts and parasites can become locked in a duel of escalating adaptations, a situation sometimes referred to as an "evolutionary arms race." Like rival nations racing to stay ahead of one another in military technology, host and parasite may repeatedly evolve new responses to the other's latest advance. In the long run, though, it may not be in a parasite's best interests to become too harmful to its host. Instead, a parasite might leave more offspring in the next generation—and thus be favoured by natural selection—if it allows its host to live a longer time, or even to thrive.

Herbivores exploit plants

One of the most common types of exploitation is **herbivory**, which occurs when animals feed on the tissues of plants. Insects that feed on plants are the most widespread type of herbivore; just about every plant in the world is attacked by some type of insect (**FIGURE 4.7**). In most cases, herbivory does not kill a plant outright, but may affect its growth and reproduction.

FIGURE 4.7
Herbivory is a common way to make a living. The world holds many thousands, perhaps millions, of species of plant-eating insects, such as this larva (caterpillar) of the death's head hawk moth (*Acherontia atropos*) from western Europe.

Like animal prey, plants have evolved a wide array of defences against the animals that feed on them. Many plants produce chemicals that are toxic or distasteful to herbivores. Others arm themselves with thorns, spines, or irritating hairs. In response, herbivores may evolve ways to overcome these defences, and the plant and the animal may embark on an evolutionary arms race.

Some plants go a step further and recruit certain animals as allies to assist in their defence. Many such plants encourage ants to take up residence by providing thorns or swelled stems for the ants to nest in or nectar-bearing structures for the ants to feed from. These ants protect the plant in return by attacking other insects that land or crawl on it. Other plants respond to herbivory by releasing volatile chemicals when they are bitten or pierced. The airborne chemicals attract predatory insects that may attack the herbivore. Such cooperative strategies as trading defence for food are examples of our next type of species interaction, mutualism.

Mutualists help one another

Mutualism is a relationship in which two or more species benefit from interaction with one another. Generally each partner provides some resource or service that the other needs.

Many mutualistic relationships—like many parasitic relationships—occur between organisms that live in close physical contact. (Indeed, biologists hypothesize that many mutualistic associations evolved from parasitic ones.) Such physically close association is called **symbiosis**. Thousands of terrestrial plant species depend on mutualisms with fungi; plant roots and some fungi together form symbiotic associations called mycorrhizae. In these symbioses, the plant provides energy and protection to the fungus, while the fungus assists the plant in absorbing nutrients from the soil, detoxifies some harmful substances, and provides protection from some pathogens. In the ocean, coral polyps, the tiny animals that build coral reefs, share beneficial arrangements with algae known as zooxanthellae. The coral provide housing and nutrients for the algae in exchange for a steady supply of food—up to 90% of their nutritional requirements.

You, too, are part of a symbiotic association. Your digestive tract is filled with microbes that help you digest food—microbes for which you are providing a place to live. Indeed, we may owe our very existence to symbiotic mutualisms. It is now widely accepted that the eukaryotic cell originated after certain prokaryotic cells engulfed other prokaryotic cells and established mutualistic symbioses. Scientists have inferred that some of the engulfed cells eventually evolved into cell organelles.

Not all mutualists live in close proximity. One of the most important mutualisms in environmental science involves free-living organisms that may encounter each other only once in their lifetimes. This is *pollination* (**FIGURE 4.8**), an interaction of key significance to agriculture and our food supply. Bees, birds, bats, and other creatures transfer pollen (male sex cells) from one flower to the ova (female cells) of another, fertilizing the female egg, which subsequently grows into a fruit. The pollinating animals visit flowers for their nectar, a reward the plant uses to entice them. The pollinators receive food, and the plants are pollinated and reproduce. Various types of bees alone pollinate 73% of our crops, one expert has estimated—from soybeans to potatoes to tomatoes to beans to cabbage to oranges.

Some interactions have no effect on some participants

Two other types of species interaction get far less attention. **Amensalism** is a relationship in which one organism is harmed and the other is unaffected. In **commensalism**, one

FIGURE 4.8
In mutualism, organisms of different species benefit one another. An important mutualistic interaction for environmental science is pollination. This hummingbird visits flowers to gather nectar and in the process transfers pollen between flowers, helping the plant reproduce. Pollination is of key importance to agriculture, ensuring the reproduction of many crop plants.

species benefits and the other is unaffected. Amensalism has been difficult to pin down, because it is hard to prove that the organism doing the harm is not in fact besting a competitor for a resource. For instance, some plants release poisonous chemicals that harm nearby plants (a phenomenon called *allelopathy*), and some experts have suggested that this is an example of amensalism. However, allelopathy can also be viewed as one plant investing in chemicals to outcompete others for space.

One association commonly cited as an example of commensalism occurs when the conditions created by one plant happen to make it easier for another plant to establish and grow. For instance, palo verde trees in the Sonoran Desert create shade and leaf litter that allow the soil beneath them to hold moisture longer, creating an area that is cooler and moister than the surrounding sun-baked ground. Young plants find it easier to germinate and grow in these conditions, so seedling cacti and other desert plants generally grow up directly beneath "nurse" trees, such as palo verde. This phenomenon, called *facilitation*, influences the structure and composition of communities and how they change through time.

Ecological Communities

We have defined a *community* as a group of populations of organisms that live in the same place at the same time. The members of a community interact with one another in the ways described above, and the direct interactions among species often have indirect effects that ripple outward to affect other community members. The strength of interactions also varies, and together species' interactions determine the species composition, structure, and function of communities. *Community ecologists* are interested in which species coexist, how they relate to one another, how communities change through time, and why these patterns exist.

Energy passes among trophic levels

The interactions among members of a community are many and varied, but some of the most important involve who eats whom. The energy that drives such interactions in most systems comes ultimately from the sun via photosynthesis. As organisms feed on one another, this energy moves through the community, from one rank in the feeding hierarchy, or **trophic level**, to another (**FIGURE 4.9**).

Producers   **Producers**, or **autotrophs** ("self-feeders"), compose the first trophic level. Terrestrial green plants, cyanobacteria, and algae capture solar energy and use photosynthesis to produce sugars. The chemosynthetic bacteria of hot springs and deep-sea hydrothermal vents use geothermal energy in a similar way to produce food.

Consumers   Organisms that derive their food energy from other organisms, **heterotrophs**, are called **consumers**. Consumers that eat producers are known as *primary consumers*; they compose the second trophic level. Grazing animals, such as deer and grasshoppers, are primary consumers. The third trophic level consists of *secondary consumers*, which prey on primary consumers. Wolves that prey on deer are considered secondary consumers, as are rodents and birds that prey on grasshoppers. Predators that feed at even higher trophic levels are known as *tertiary consumers*. Examples of tertiary consumers include hawks and owls that eat rodents that have eaten grasshoppers. Note that most primary consumers are **herbivores** because they consume plants, whereas secondary and tertiary consumers are **carnivores** because they eat animals. Animals that eat both plant and animal food are referred to as **omnivores**.

Detritivores and decomposers   Some organisms consume nonliving organic matter. **Detritivores**, such as millipedes and soil insects, scavenge the waste products or the dead bodies of other community members. **Decomposers**, such as fungi and bacteria, break down leaf litter and other nonliving matter further into simpler constituents that can then be taken up and used by plants. These organisms play an essential role as the community's recyclers, making nutrients from organic matter available for reuse by living members of the community.

In Great Lakes communities, phytoplankton are the main producers, floating freely and photosynthesizing with sunlight that penetrates the upper layer of the water. Zooplankton are primary consumers, feeding on the phytoplankton. Phytoplankton-eating fish are primary consumers, and zooplankton-eating fish are secondary consumers. At higher trophic levels are tertiary consumers, such as larger fish and birds that feed on plankton-eating fish. Zebra mussels, by eating both phytoplankton and zooplankton, function on multiple trophic levels. When any of these organisms dies and sinks to the bottom, detritivores scavenge its tissues and microbial decomposers recycle its nutrients.

Energy, biomass, and numbers decrease at higher trophic levels

At each trophic level, most of the energy that organisms use is lost through respiration. Only a small amount of

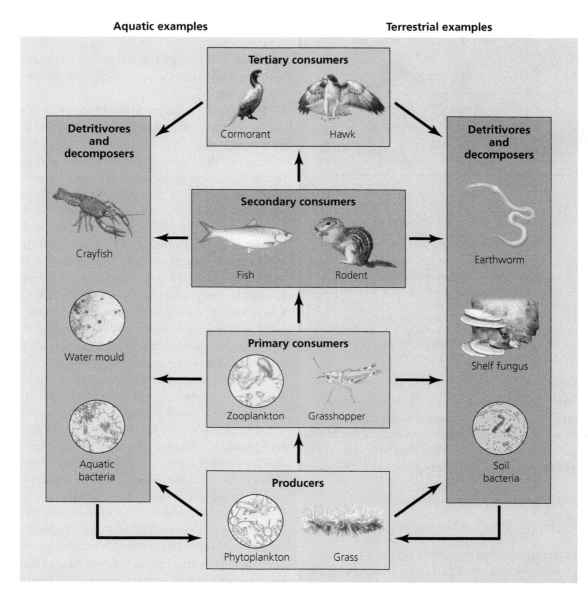

FIGURE 4.9 Ecologists organize species hierarchically by their feeding rank, or trophic level. The diagram shows aquatic (left) and terrestrial (right) examples at each level. Arrows indicate the direction of energy flow. Producers produce food by photosynthesis, primary consumers (herbivores) feed on producers, secondary consumers eat primary consumers, and tertiary consumers eat secondary consumers. Communities can have more or fewer trophic levels than in this example. Detritivores and decomposers feed on nonliving organic matter and the remains of dead organisms from all trophic levels, and they "close the loop" by returning nutrients to the soil or the water column for use by producers.

the energy is transferred to the next trophic level through predation, herbivory, or parasitism. The first trophic level (producers) contains a large amount of energy, but the second (primary consumers) contains less energy—only that amount gained from consuming producers. The third trophic level (secondary consumers) contains still less energy, and higher trophic levels (tertiary consumers) contain the least. A general rule of thumb is that each trophic level contains just 10% of the energy of the trophic level below it, although the actual proportion can vary greatly.

This pattern, which can be visualized as a **trophic pyramid**, generally also holds for the numbers of

organisms at each trophic level (**FIGURE 4.10**). Typically, fewer organisms exist at higher trophic levels than at lower trophic levels. A grasshopper eats many plants in its lifetime, a rodent eats many grasshoppers, and a hawk eats many rodents. Thus, for every hawk in a community there must be many rodents, still more grasshoppers, and an immense number of plants. Because the difference in numbers of organisms among trophic levels tends to be large, the same pyramid-like relationship also often holds true for biomass. Even though rodents are larger than grasshoppers, and hawks larger than rodents, the sheer number of prey relative to the predators means that prey biomass will likely be greater overall. Unlike the pyramid

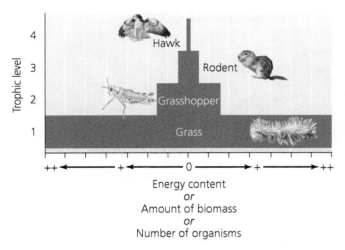

FIGURE 4.10
A trophic pyramid illustrates a rough rule of thumb for the way ecological communities are structured. Organisms at lower trophic levels generally exist in far greater numbers, with greater energy content and greater biomass, than organisms at higher trophic levels. When one organism consumes another, most energy gets used up in respiration rather than in building new tissue. The example shown here is generalized; the actual shape of any given pyramid may be different.

of energy, however, the pyramids of numbers and biomass can occasionally be inverted. For example, the number of trees is much smaller than the number of insects feeding on them, and in the ocean, a small biomass of producers often supports a higher biomass of zooplankton.

Food webs show feeding relationships and energy flow

As energy is transferred from species on one trophic level to species on other trophic levels, it is said to pass up a **food chain**. Plant, grasshopper, rodent, and hawk make up a food chain (as in **FIGURE 4.10**), a linear series of feeding relationships. Thinking in terms of food chains is conceptually useful, but in reality ecological systems are far more complex than simple linear chains. A more

roots
TROPHIC

Trophic means "pertaining to nutrition or food." In the context of ecosystems, it also carries a connotation of "energy" (because in ecosystems, food is energy and energy is food). It comes from the Greek root *trophe*, meaning "nourishment." If you consider terms like **autotroph** ("self-feeder"), **heterotroph** ("other-feeder"), and **trophic level** (a position in a food chain), you can easily find the root meaning of *trophe*.

accurate representation of the feeding relationships in a community is a **food web**, a visual map of feeding relationships and energy flow, showing the many paths by which energy passes among organisms as they consume one another.

FIGURE 4.11 shows a food web from a temperate deciduous forest of eastern North America. Like virtually all diagrams of ecological systems, it is greatly simplified, leaving out the vast majority of species and interactions that occur. Note, however, that even within this simplified diagram, we can pick out a number of different food chains involving different sets of species.

A Great Lakes food web would involve the phytoplankton and cyanobacteria that photosynthesize near the water's surface, the zooplankton that eat them, the fish that eat all these, the larger fish that eat the smaller fish, and the lampreys that parasitize the fish. It would include a number of native mussels and clams and, since 1988, the zebra and quagga mussels that are crowding them out. It would include diving ducks that used to feed on native bivalves and now are preying on mussels.

This food web would also show that an array of bottom-dwelling invertebrates feed from the refuse of the exotic mussels. These waste products promote bacterial growth and disease pathogens that harm native bivalves, but they also provide nutrients that nourish crayfish and many smaller *benthic* (bottom-dwelling) invertebrate animals. Finally, the food web would include underwater plants and macroscopic algae, whose growth is promoted by the non-native mussels. The mussels clarify the water by filtering out phytoplankton, and sunlight penetrates deeper into the water column, spurring photosynthesis and plant growth. Thus, zebra and quagga mussels alter this food web essentially by shifting productivity from the open-water regions to the benthic and *littoral* (nearshore) regions. In so doing, the mussels affect fish indirectly, helping benthic and littoral fishes and making life harder for open-water fishes (see "The Science Behind the Story: Assessing the Ecological Impacts of Zebra Mussels," available on myenvironmentplace).

Some organisms play especially important roles in communities

"Some animals are more equal than others," George Orwell wrote in his 1945 book *Animal Farm*. Although Orwell was making wry sociopolitical commentary, his remark hints at a truth in ecology. In communities, ecologists have found, some species exert greater influence than do others. A species that has a particularly strong or far-reaching impact is often called a **keystone species**. A keystone is the wedge-shaped stone at the top of an arch

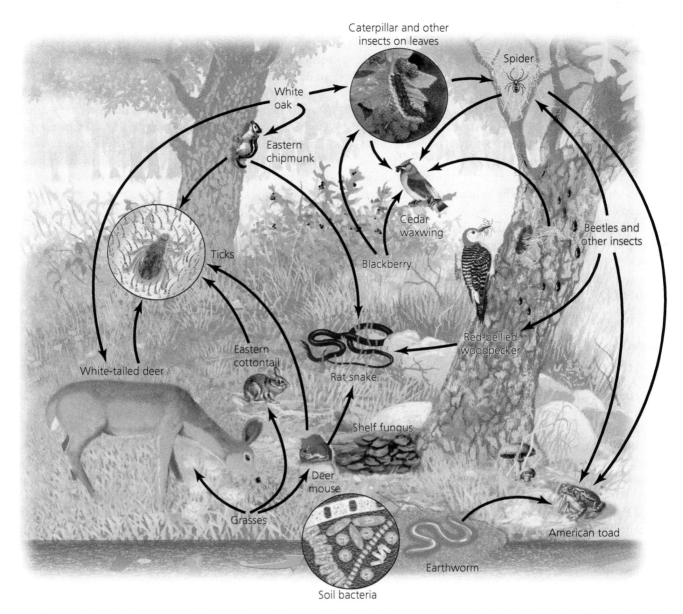

FIGURE 4.11   Food webs are conceptual representations of feeding relationships in a community. This food web pertains to eastern North America's temperate deciduous forest and includes organisms on several trophic levels. In a food web diagram, arrows are drawn from one organism to another to indicate the direction of energy flow as a result of predation, parasitism, or herbivory. For example, an arrow leads from the grass to the cottontail rabbit to indicate that cottontails consume grasses. The arrow from the cottontail to the tick indicates that parasitic ticks derive nourishment from cottontails. Communities include so many species and are complex enough, however, that most food web diagrams are bound to be gross simplifications.

that is vital for holding the structure together; remove the keystone, and the arch will collapse. In an ecological community, removal of a keystone species will have substantial ripple effects and will alter a large portion of the food web.

Some keystone species have been removed from their natural communities with unintended consequences, in what are essentially uncontrolled large-scale experiments. A well-known example is the elimination of wolves (intentionally, for the most part) from many parts of North America. Wolves are voracious predators; when

they are eliminated from an area, the populations of large herbivores, such as elk and moose, can grow out of control. This can have far-reaching impacts on vegetation and, consequently, on all other animals in the area.

Ecologists also have verified the keystone species concept by careful observation and controlled experiments. For example, classic work by marine biologist Robert Paine established that the predatory starfish *Pisaster ochraceus* has great influence on the community composition of intertidal organisms on the Pacific coast of North America. When *Pisaster* is present in this community, species diversity is high, with several types of barnacles, mussels, and algae. When *Pisaster* is removed, the mussels it preys on become numerous and displace other species, suppressing species diversity. More recent work off the Atlantic coast published in 2007 suggests that the reduction of shark populations by commercial fishing has allowed populations of certain skates and rays to increase, which has depressed numbers of bay scallops and other bivalves they eat.

To understand the significance of one or two large species in an ecosystem, and the delicacy of the balance, we can consider the case of moose and wolves in the boreal forest of Cape Breton Highlands National Park. Moose were rare by 1900 and had completely disappeared from the area by 1924, because of excessive hunting and habitat destruction. Parks Canada reintroduced moose to the park during 1947 and 1948, by importing and releasing 18 animals from Elk Island National Park. The reintroduction was highly successful, and moose are currently plentiful in the park, possibly too plentiful.[3] In the absence of the moose's natural predator, the wolf, which disappeared from the area as early as the mid-1800s, there are few natural controls on the moose population within the park. Moose are selective eaters; their preferred winter food is the balsam fir. By browsing heavily on certain types of food but not others, they can alter the forest landscape, leading to significant changes in the ecosystem. The success of the reintroduced moose population in Cape Breton Highlands National Park may be leading to changes in the composition of the boreal forest there. In addition to dramatic impacts on vegetation, moose may have contributed to the decline of native caribou in some areas, by preventing regeneration of the mature forests, limiting the caribou's food, and opening the landscape to predators.

Animals at high trophic levels, such as wolves, starfish, and sea otters, are most often seen as keystone species. Other species attain keystone status as "ecosystem engineers" by physically modifying the environment shared by community members. Beavers build dams and turn streams into ponds, flooding vast expanses of dry land and turning it to swamp. Prairie dogs dig burrows that aerate the soil and serve as homes for other animals. Bees are absolutely crucial, for example, even for human food security, because they are pollinators, moving pollen from male to female plants to facilitate the plants' sexual reproduction, as well as ensuring plant genetic diversity.

Less conspicuous organisms and those toward the bottoms of food chains can potentially be viewed as keystone species, too. Remove the fungi that decompose dead matter or the insects that control plant growth or the phytoplankton that are the base of the marine food chain and a community may change very rapidly indeed. Because there are usually more species at lower trophic

levels, however, it is less likely that any one of them alone might have wide influence; if one species is removed, other species that remain may be able to perform many of its functions.

Identifying keystone species is no simple task, and there is no cut-and-dried definition of the term to help us. Community dynamics are complex, species interactions differ in their strength, and the strength of species interactions can vary through time and space. "The Science Behind the Story: Otters, Urchins, Kelp, and a Whale of a Chain Reaction" gives an idea of the surprises that are sometimes in store for ecologists studying these interactions.

Communities respond to disturbance in different ways

The removal of a keystone species is just one of many types of disturbance that can modify the composition, structure, or function of an ecological community. Over time, any given community may experience natural disturbances ranging from gradual phenomena, such as climate change, to sudden events, such as hurricanes, floods, or avalanches.

Communities are dynamic systems and may respond to disturbance in several ways. A community that resists change and remains stable despite disturbance is said to show **resistance** to the disturbance. Alternatively, a community may show **resilience**, meaning that it changes in response to disturbance but later returns to its original state. Or a community may be modified by disturbance permanently and may never return to its original state.

Succession follows severe disturbance

If a disturbance is severe enough to eliminate all or most of the species in a community, the affected site will undergo a somewhat predictable series of changes that ecologists call **succession**. In the traditional view of this process, ecologists described two types of succession.

Primary succession follows a disturbance so severe that no vegetation or soil life remains from the community that occupied the site. Primary succession starts with a clean slate; the biotic community is built essentially from scratch. In contrast, **secondary succession** begins when a disturbance dramatically alters an existing community but does not destroy all living things or all organic matter in the soil. In secondary succession, vestiges of the previous community remain; the surviving organisms have a head start over other organisms and these building blocks help shape the process of reconstruction.

FIGURE 4.12
As this glacier retreats, small pioneer plants (foreground) begin the process of primary succession.

At terrestrial sites, primary succession takes place after a bare expanse of rock, sand, or sediment becomes newly exposed to the atmosphere. This can occur when glaciers retreat, lakes dry up, or volcanic lava flows spread across the landscape (**FIGURE 4.12**). Species that arrive first and colonize the new substrate are referred to as **pioneer species**. Pioneer species are well adapted for colonization, having such traits as spores or seeds that can travel long distances.

The pioneers best suited to colonizing bare rock are the mutualistic aggregates of fungi and algae known as **lichens**. Lichens succeed because their algal component provides food and energy via photosynthesis while the fungal component takes a firm hold on rock and captures the moisture that both organisms need to survive. As lichens grow, they secrete acids that break down the rock surface. The resulting waste material forms the beginnings of soil, and once soil begins to form, small plants, insects, and worms find the rocky outcrops more hospitable. As new organisms arrive, they provide more nutrients and habitat for future arrivals. As time passes, larger plants establish themselves, the amount of vegetation increases, and species diversity rises.

Secondary succession on land begins when a fire, a hurricane, logging, or farming removes much of the biotic community. Consider a farmed field in eastern North America that has been abandoned (**FIGURE 4.13**). In the first few years after farming ends, the site will be colonized by pioneer species of grasses, herbs, and forbs that were already in the vicinity and that disperse effectively. As time passes, shrubs and fast-growing trees, such as aspens, rise from the field. Pine trees subsequently rise above the aspens and shrubs, forming a pine-dominated forest. This pine forest develops an understory of hardwood trees, because pine seedlings do not grow well under mature pines, whereas some hardwood seedlings do. Eventually the hardwoods outgrow the pines, creating a hardwood forest (see **FIGURE 4.13**).

Processes of succession occur in many diverse ecological systems, from ponds to rocky intertidal areas to the carcasses of animals. A lake or pond that originates as nothing but water on a lifeless substrate begins to undergo succession as it is colonized by algae, microbes, plants, and zooplankton. As these organisms grow, reproduce, and die, the water body slowly fills with organic matter. The lake or pond acquires further organic matter and sediments from the water it receives from rivers, streams, and surface runoff. Eventually, the water body fills in, becoming a bog or even a terrestrial ecosystem.

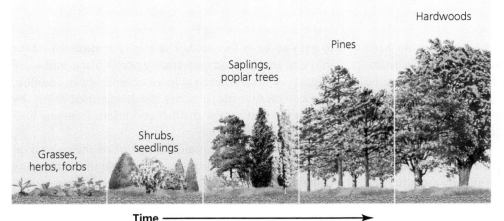

Hardwoods

Pines

Saplings, poplar trees

Shrubs, seedlings

Grasses, herbs, forbs

Time ⟶

FIGURE 4.13
Secondary succession occurs after a disturbance, such as fire, landslides, or farming, removes most of the vegetation from an area. Shown here is a typical series of changes in a plant community of eastern North America following the abandonment of a farmed field.

THE SCIENCE BEHIND THE STORY

Otters, Urchins, Kelp, and a Whale of a Chain Reaction

Dr. James Estes, University of California at Santa Cruz, works at sea in Alaska.

Sea otters (*Enhydra lutris*) live in coastal waters of the Pacific Ocean. These mammals float on their backs amid the waves, feasting on sea urchins (*Strongylocentrotus spp.*) that they pry from the ocean bottom. Once abundant, sea otters were hunted nearly to extinction for their fur. Protection by international treaty in 1911 allowed their numbers to grow. Otters returned to high densities in some regions but failed to return in others.

Biologists noted that regions with abundant otters hosted dense "forests" of kelp, a brown alga (seaweed) that anchors to the seafloor, growing up to 60 m high toward the sunlit surface. Kelp forests provide complex physical structures in which diverse communities of fish and invertebrates find shelter and food. In regions without sea otters, scientists found kelp forests absent. In the absence of otters, urchins become so numerous that they eat every last bit of kelp, creating empty seafloors called "urchin barrens" that are relatively devoid of life.

Ecologists determined that otters were largely responsible for the presence of the kelp forests, simply by keeping urchin numbers in check through predation. This research—mostly by James Estes of the University of California at Santa Cruz and his colleagues—established sea otters as a prime example of a keystone species. Jane Watson investigated 60 randomly selected sites in the shallow rocky communities off the northwest coast of Vancouver Island. Sea otters were present in 40 sites and absent from 20. In the locations where sea otters were absent, urchins occupied 84% of the sea bottom. In contrast, areas with sea otters hosted large populations of kelp, and urchins occupied only 1.8% of the bottom.

But the story did not end there. In the 1990s, otter populations dropped precipitously near Alaska and the Aleutians. No one knew why. Estes and his co-workers placed radio tags on Aleutian otters and studied them at sea. Their first hypothesis was that fertility rates had dropped, but radio-tracking observations showed that females were raising pups without problem. Their second hypothesis was that the otters were simply moving to other locations. But the radio tracking showed no unusual dispersals.

They were left with only one viable hypothesis: increased mortality. Then one day in 1991, Estes's team witnessed something never seen before. They watched as a sea otter was killed and eaten by an orca, or killer whale (*Orcinus orca*). These striking black-and-white predators grow up to 10 m long, hunt in groups, and usually attack larger prey. A sea otter to them is a mere snack. Yet over the following years, Estes's team saw more cases of orca predation on otters. Could killer whales be killing off the otters?

The researchers compared a bay where otters were vulnerable to orcas with a lagoon where they were protected. Otter numbers in the lagoon remained stable over four years, whereas those in the bay dropped by 76%. Radio tracking showed no movement between these locations. Using data on otter birth rates, death rates, and population age structure, they estimated that to account for the otter decline, 6788 orca attacks per year would have had to occur in their study area. This *expected* rate of observed attacks matched their *actual* number of observed attacks. These lines of evidence led the researchers to propose that predation by orcas was eliminating otters.

As otters declined in the Aleutians, urchins increased, and kelp density fell dramatically (see figure). These changes supported the idea that otters were a keystone species, but now it seemed that one keystone species was being controlled by another.

Why had the orcas suddenly started eating otters? A possible answer came in 2003, after Alan Springer, James Estes, and others determined that sea otters were only the latest in a series of population crashes in the northern Pacific. Harbour seals had declined by more than 90%; fur seals had fallen by 60%; sea lions had crashed by 80%. Preceding these declines were collapses of the great grey, blue, and humpback whale populations.

Most orcas specialize in eating great whales, which they kill in groups, like a wolf pack taking down an elk. But industrial

---

In this traditional view of succession that we have described, the transitions between stages of succession eventually lead to a **climax community**, which remains in place, with little modification, until some disturbance restarts succession. Early ecologists felt that each region had its own characteristic climax community, determined by the region's climate.

Today, ecologists recognize that succession is far more variable and less predictable than originally thought. The trajectory of succession can vary greatly according to chance factors, such as which particular species happen to gain an early foothold. The stages of succession blur into one another and vary from place to place, and some stages may sometimes be skipped completely. In addition, climax communities are not predetermined solely by climate but may vary with other conditions from one time or place to another.

Once a climax community is disturbed and succession is set in motion, there is no guarantee that the community will ever return to that climax state. Many communities disturbed by human impact have not returned to their former conditions. This is the case with vast areas of the

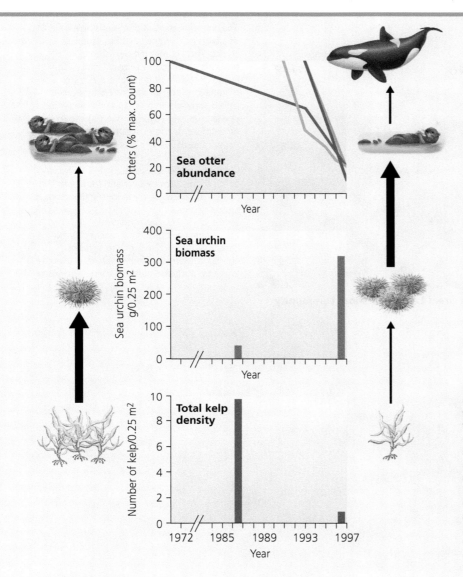

whaling by ships from Japan, Russia, and other nations caused populations of great whales to plummet by 99% between 1965 and 1973 in the northern Pacific. When hunting decimated the great whales, the orcas turned to smaller, less-favoured seals and sea lions. When their predation had depleted those populations, they turned to smaller prey still—sea otters.

Not all scientists are convinced by this bold hypothesis, and the debate has been vigorous. In the meantime, Estes and his colleagues continue to learn more. In 2005, Shauna Reisewitz, Estes, and Charles Simenstad reported that when kelp forests vanish, so do rock greenling, the community's most abundant fish species. The few greenling left also change their diet. Thus, the whale-orca-otter-urchin-kelp system also influences fish and their prey. The ongoing discoveries highlight the intriguing complexity of the species interactions that affect ecological communities.

Before the 1990s (left side of figure), otters kept urchin numbers in check, allowing kelp forests to grow. By the end of the 1990s (right side of figure), orcas (killer whales), deprived of their usual food sources, were eating otters. This set off a chain reaction across several trophic levels: Otters decreased, sea urchins increased, and kelp decreased. The lines in the top graph indicate trends in otter populations from four different Aleutian islands. The width of the arrows indicates the strength of interaction. *Source: Estes, J., et al. (1998) Killer whale predation on sea otters linking oceanic and nearshore ecosystems. Science 282: 473–476.*

Middle East that once were fertile enough to support productive farming but now are deserts.

Invasive species pose new threats to community stability

Traditional concepts of communities and successions involve sets of organisms understood to be native to an area. But what if a new organism arrives from elsewhere? And what if this non-native (also called *alien* or **exotic**)

organism spreads widely and becomes dominant? Such **invasive species** can alter a community substantially and are one of the central ecological forces in today's world.

Most often, invasive species are non-native species that people have introduced, intentionally or by accident, from elsewhere in the world. Any non-native organism introduced into an ecosystem will require adjustments, but species become invasive **pests** when the negative impacts outweigh the benefits, especially when the limiting factors that might regulate their population

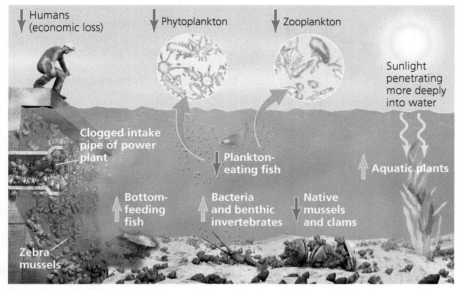

(a) Impacts of zebra mussels on members of a Great Lakes nearshore community

FIGURE 4.14
The zebra mussel is a prime example of a biological invader that has modified an ecological community. By filtering phytoplankton and small zooplankton from open water, it generates a number of impacts on other species, both negative (red downward arrows) and positive (green upward arrows) **(a)**. This map **(b)** shows the range of zebra and quagga mussels in North America as of 2011. In less than three decades the zebra mussel has spread to Ontario, Québec, and 30 U.S. states, mainly by boats but in some cases by overland transport. The quagga mussel is rapidly following the zebra mussel's spread.
Source for (b): U.S. Geological Survey. Map showing 2011 distribution of zebra mussel sightings, Benson, A.J. 2011. Zebra mussel sightings distribution. Retrieved from http://nas.er.usgs.gov/ tak/group/mollusks/zebramusseldistribution.aspx

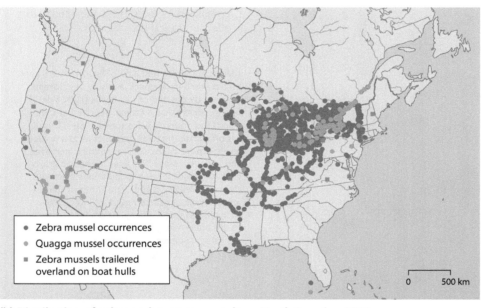

- Zebra mussel occurrences
- Quagga mussel occurrences
- Zebra mussels trailered overland on boat hulls

0   500 km

(b) Distribution of zebra and quagga mussels on North America, 2011

growth are absent. Thus, the main characteristics of *problematic* invasive species include the ability to spread rapidly, and unimpeded, in the new environment, and the ability to have a negative impact on native species and ecosystems into which it has been introduced.

Plants and animals brought to one area from another may leave their predators, parasites, and competitors behind, freeing them from natural constraints on their population growth (FIGURE 4.14). If there happen to be few organisms in the new environment that can act as predators, parasites, or competitors, the introduced species may do very well. As it proliferates, it may exert diverse influences on its fellow community members. An example is the chestnut blight, an Asian fungus that killed nearly

every mature American chestnut (*Castanea dentata*), the dominant tree species of many forests of eastern North America, in the quarter-century preceding 1930. Asian trees had evolved defences against the fungus over long millennia of coevolution, but the American chestnut had not.

In other cases, a species may be considered a pest even in regions where it is native. An example is the Asian long-horned beetle (*Anoplophora glabripennis*), a voracious wood-eating insect that is native to China but is also a pest, with few natural predators. The Asian long-horned beetle feeds on many different species of temperate hardwood trees, including maple, birch, horse chestnut, poplar, willow, elm, ash, and black locust. The beetle, introduced to North America from China via packaging materials, has the potential to cause widespread destruction. To date, the only approach to controlling the spread of the beetle is to cut down and burn any infested trees.[4]

So far we have considered examples of the impacts of a non-native insect, a fungus, and a mollusc, but virtually any type of organism can become an invasive pest, given circumstances that facilitate its spread. Introduced grasses and shrubs, such as the Scotch broom (*Cytisus scoparius*), have had dramatic impacts on the Garry oak (*Quercus garryana*)–based ecosystem of southeastern Vancouver Island and the Gulf Islands, a disappearing ecosystem that supports many rare plant species.[5] Fish introduced into streams purposely for sport or accidentally via shipping compete with and exclude native fish.

A particularly troublesome example of a native invasive species is the sea lamprey (*Petromyzon marinus*), an eel-like fish that is native to the Atlantic Ocean and was probably introduced to the Great Lakes as early as the 1830s by oceangoing vessels. The sea lamprey is a pretty unpleasant creature to begin with, as it lives by attaching itself to the flanks of other fish and feeding parasitically on their blood. But lampreys have had tremendous success as they have spread—mainly via shipping channels and canals—into the Great Lakes, devastating some local fish populations.

Hundreds of native island-dwelling animals and plants worldwide have been driven extinct by the goats, pigs, and rats intentionally or accidentally introduced by human colonists. The cane toad (*Bufo marinus*), introduced to Australia to control insects in sugar cane fields (which it never did very successfully), is poisonous to just about anything that tries to eat it and has been extremely damaging to a wide variety of indigenous animal populations.

The impact of invasive species on native species and ecological communities is severe and it is growing year by year with the increasing mobility of humans and the globalization of our society. Global trade helped spread zebra mussels, which were unintentionally transported in the ballast water of cargo ships. To maintain stability at sea, ships take water into their hulls as they begin their voyage and discharge that water at their destination. Decades of unregulated exchange of ballast water have ferried hundreds of species across the oceans.

In North America, zebra mussels—and the media attention they generated—helped put invasive species on the map as a major environmental and economic problem. Scientific research into introduced species has proliferated, and many ecologists view invasive species as the second-greatest threat to species and natural systems, behind only habitat destruction.

Funding has now become more widely available for the control and eradication of invasive species, and control mechanisms are widely researched and shared across juris-

weighing the issues
ARE INVASIVE SPECIES ALL BAD?

Some ethicists have questioned the notion that all invasive species should automatically be considered bad. If we introduce a non-native species to a community and it greatly modifies the community, is it always a bad thing? What if it drives another species extinct? What if the invasive species arrived on its own, rather than through human intervention? What ethical standard would you apply to determine whether an invasive species should be battled or accepted?

dictional boundaries. Managers at all levels of government have been trying a variety of techniques to control the spread of zebra and quagga mussels—removing them manually, applying toxic chemicals, drying them out, depriving them of oxygen, introducing predators and diseases, and stressing them with heat, sound, electricity, carbon dioxide, and ultraviolet light. However, most of these are localized and short-term fixes that are not capable of making a dent in the huge populations at large in the environment. In case after case, managers are finding that controlling and eradicating invasive species is so difficult and expensive that preventive measures (such as ballast water regulations) represent a much better investment.

Some altered communities can be restored to their former condition

Invasive species are adding to the tremendous transformations that humans have already forced on natural landscapes through habitat alteration, deforestation, hunting of keystone species, pollution, and other impacts. With so much of Earth's landscape altered by human impact, it is impossible to find areas that are truly pristine. This realization has given rise to the conservation effort known as **ecological restoration**. The practice of ecological restoration is informed by the science of **restoration ecology**. Restoration ecologists research the historical conditions of ecological communities as they existed before our industrialized civilization altered them. They then try to devise ways to restore some of these areas to an earlier condition, often to a natural "presettlement" condition.

For example, activities underway at Chatterton Hill Park in Saanich, British Columbia, are aimed at the ecological restoration of Garry oak–associated ecosystems (**FIGURE 4.15**). As mentioned above, these delicate,

FIGURE 4.15
Garry oak ecosystems in south Vancouver Island and the Gulf Islands of British Columbia, like the one shown here, are being invaded by aggressive exotic species. Some have been targeted for ecological restoration.

complex ecosystems, which occur almost exclusively in south Vancouver Island and the Gulf Islands, are being invaded by aggressive exotic species that suppress the growth of native plants. Ecological restoration activities at Chatterton Hill, which began in 2002, include active restoration, removal of invasive plants, natural feature inventories (soil, vegetation, and animals), monitoring, and educational activities. In 2006, local restoration ecologists reevaluated the site, comparing it with a similar nearby site where no restoration activities had taken place; they concluded that biodiversity at the restoration site was increasing. At the comparison site, the tree layer was similar, but the understory vegetation was still dominated by grasses and the invasive exotic, Scotch broom.[6]

weighing the issues

RESTORING "NATURAL" COMMUNITIES

Practitioners of ecological restoration in North America aim to restore communities to their natural state. But what is meant by "natural"? Is it the state of the community before industrialization? Before Europeans came to the New World? Before any people laid eyes on the community? Let us say Aborigines altered a forest community 8000 years ago by burning the underbrush to improve hunting, and continued doing so until Europeans arrived 400 years ago and cut down the forest for farming. Should restorationists try to recreate the forest of Aboriginal time, or the forest that existed even before the Aboriginal peoples arrived? What are some advantages and disadvantages of each approach?

Perhaps the world's largest restoration project is the ongoing effort to restore parts of the Florida Everglades. The Everglades, a unique 7500 km^2 ecosystem of interconnected marshes and seasonally flooded grasslands, has been drying out for decades because the water that feeds it has been heavily managed for flood control and overdrawn for irrigation and development. The water management system inadvertently caused extensive degradation of the environment, resulting in the loss of more than half of the Everglades and the elimination of whole classes of ecosystems. Populations of wading birds have dropped by 90–95%, and economically important fisheries have suffered greatly. Extensive engineering of river channels also led to a loss of aesthetic appeal, problems with stagnancy and pollution of water in the channels, and a host of other problems. The 30-year, $7.8 billion restoration project intends to restore water by undoing damming and diversions of 1600 km of canals, 1150 km of levees, and 200 water control structures.

Ecosystem restoration is almost always expensive and only sometimes, or partially, successful. Regardless, the more our population grows and development spreads, the more ecological restoration will become a vital conservation strategy for the future.

Earth's Biomes

Across the world, each portion of each continent has different sets of species, leading to endless variety in community composition. However, communities in far-flung places often share strong similarities in their structure and function. This allows us to classify communities into broad types. A **biome** is a major regional complex of similar communities—a large ecological unit recognized primarily by its dominant plant type and vegetation structure. The world contains a number of biomes, each covering large geographic areas (**FIGURE 4.16**).

A term that is often used interchangeably with biome, but probably should not be, is ecoregion. An **ecoregion** is defined by the World Wildlife Fund as a large area of land or water that contains a geographically distinct assemblage of natural communities that share a large majority of their species and ecological dynamics, share similar environmental conditions, and interact ecologically in ways that are critical for their long-term persistence.[7] A particular ecoregion—such as the short grasslands of the Canadian Prairies of southern Alberta and Saskatchewan, for example—is thus a representative of a biome (the "temperate grasslands" biome) that is broader in scope and occurs in numerous localities around the world.

The difference between an ecoregion and a biome might be easiest to grasp for a highly distinctive environment, such as a desert. The desert biome has certain climatic and

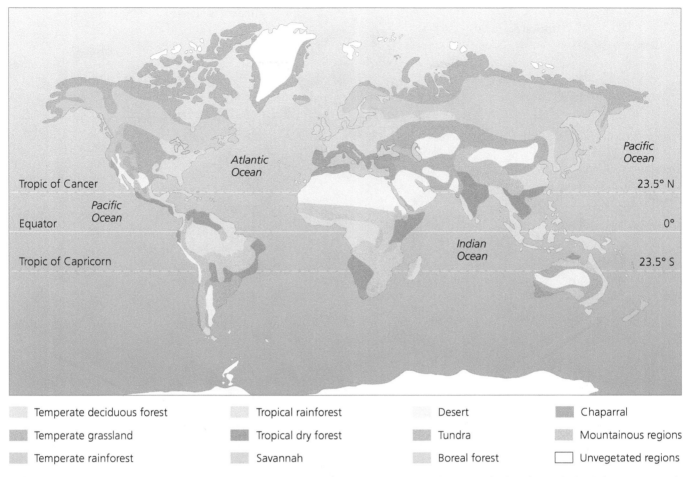

Temperate deciduous forest	Tropical rainforest	Desert	Chaparral
Temperate grassland	Tropical dry forest	Tundra	Mountainous regions
Temperate rainforest	Savannah	Boreal forest	Unvegetated regions

FIGURE 4.16   Biomes are distributed around the world according to temperature, precipitation, atmospheric and oceanic circulation patterns, and other factors.

ecological characteristics in common (see below), notably the lack of precipitation. There are many representatives of the desert biome around the world, including the Mojave Desert, the Gobi Desert, and the Sahara Desert, among many others. Each of these individual desert environments

roots

BIOME

The word **biome** comes from the Greek root *bios*, "life." The word is thought to have been first used in 1916 by American botanist and ecologist Frederic Clements, who defined it, at the time, as "the biotic community, regarded as an organic unit comprising all the species of plants and animals at home in a particular habitat." It is interesting that Clements considered a biome to consist solely of the *biotic community* and did not include abiotic components in his definition. Today, ecologists are still divided about whether biomes include abiotic factors or are simply influenced by them.

constitutes or is part of an eco-region, with its own particular characteristics and flora and fauna, but it is still consistent with the broad characteristics that define the desert biome.

Climate influences the locations of biomes

Which biome covers any particular portion of the planet depends on a variety of abiotic factors, including temperature, precipitation, atmospheric circulation, and soil characteristics. Among these factors, temperature and precipitation exert the greatest influence (**FIGURE 4.17**), because, as you will recall from our discussion about productivity, these two factors have the dominant effect on net primary productivity of terrestrial ecosystems. Because biome type is largely a function of climate, and because average monthly temperature and precipitation are among the best indicators of an area's climate, scientists often use climate diagrams, or **climatographs**, to depict such information.

Global climate patterns cause biomes to occur in large patches in different parts of the world. For instance,

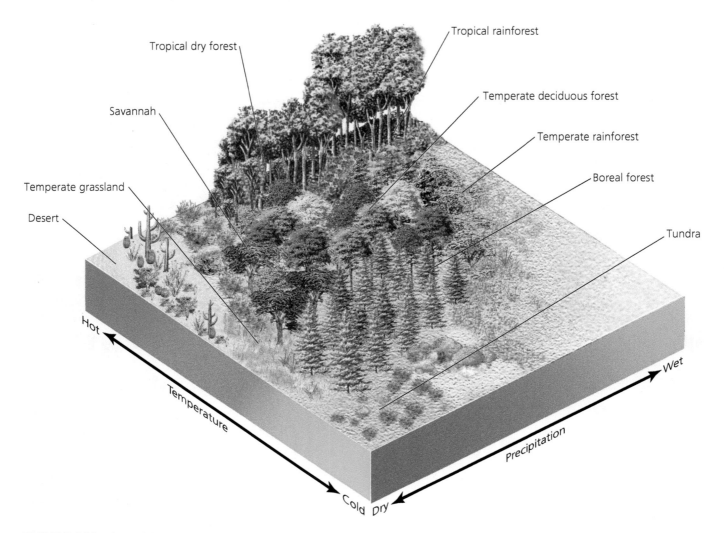

FIGURE 4.17   As precipitation increases, vegetation generally becomes taller and more luxuriant. As temperature increases, types of plant communities change. Together, temperature and precipitation are the main factors determining which biome occurs in a given area. For instance, deserts occur in dry regions, tropical rainforests occur in warm, wet regions, and tundra occurs in the cold, dry regions.

temperate deciduous forest occurs in eastern North America, north–central Europe, and eastern China. Note how patches representing the same biome tend to occur at similar latitudes. This is due to the north–south gradient in temperature and to atmospheric circulation patterns.

We can divide the world into roughly 10 terrestrial biomes

Each biome encompasses a variety of communities that share similarities. For example, the eastern United States and the southernmost part of eastern Canada support part of the temperate deciduous forest biome. From New Hampshire to the Great Lakes to eastern Texas, precipitation and temperature are similar enough that most of the region's natural plant cover consists of broadleafed trees that lose their leaves in winter. Within this region, however, exist many different types of temperate

deciduous forest, such as oak–hickory, beech–maple, and pine–oak forests, each sufficiently different to be designated a separate community.

Let us look briefly at the characteristics that define the world's 10 major terrestrial biomes.

Tundra   The **tundra** (**FIGURE 4.18**) is a dry biome—nearly as dry as a desert—but located at very high latitudes along the northern edges of Russia, Canada, and Scandinavia. Extremely cold winters with little daylight and moderately cool summers with lengthy days characterize this landscape of lichens and low, scrubby vegetation without trees. The great seasonal variation in temperature and day length results from this biome's high-latitude location, angled toward the sun in the summer and away from the sun in the winter.

Because of the cold climate, underground soil remains more or less permanently frozen and is called *permafrost*. During the long, cold winters, the surface soils freeze

(a) Typical location: Cumberland Sound, Baffin Island, Nunavut

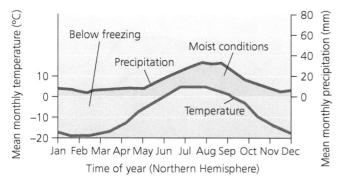

(b) Tundra

FIGURE 4.18
Tundra is a cold, dry biome found near the poles and atop high mountains at lower latitudes **(a)**. Scientists use climate diagrams **(b)** to illustrate an area's average monthly precipitation and temperature.[8] Typically in these diagrams, the x-axis marks months of the year (beginning in January for regions in the Northern Hemisphere and in July for regions in the Southern Hemisphere). Paired y-axes denote average monthly temperature and average monthly precipitation. The twin curves plotted on a climate diagram indicate trends in precipitation (blue) and in temperature (red) from month to month.

as well; then, when the weather warms, they melt and produce seasonal accumulations of surface water that make ideal habitat for mosquitoes and other biting insects. The swarms of insects benefit bird species that migrate long distances to breed during the brief but productive summer. Caribou also migrate to the tundra to breed, and then leave for the winter. Only a few large animals, such as polar bears (*Ursus maritimus*) and musk oxen (*Ovibos moschatus*), can survive year-round in this extreme climate. Tundra also occurs as **alpine tundra** at the tops of high mountains in temperate and tropical regions.

Because of the extreme climate in Canada's North, Alaska, Russia, and Scandinavia, much of the tundra biome remains intact and relatively unaltered by direct human occupation and interference. For example, the World Wildlife Fund reports the tundra ecoregions of North America to be 95–98% intact. However, much of

the tundra is unprotected by national or provincial or territorial legislation, rendering it potentially susceptible to alteration through human activities. Furthermore, the indirect effects of human modification of the global environment, especially the climate, are increasingly evident in the tundra. One problem that is of external origin is atmospheric fallout, which results in the deposition of heavy metals, and pesticide pollution.[9] In many areas of the tundra, seasonal ice connects the many islands with the mainland; with climatic warming and the associated melting of sea ice, these habitats and the animals that depend on them will be in increasing peril.

Boreal forest   The northern coniferous forest, or **boreal forest**, also called **taiga** (**FIGURE 4.19**), stretches in a broad band across much of Canada, Alaska, Russia, and Scandinavia. In Canada the boreal forest encompasses nearly 6 million km². A few species of **coniferous** or evergreen trees, which create seed cones, have needle-like leaves, and remain green year-round, dominate large stretches of the boreal forest, interspersed with bogs and

(a) Typical location: Jasper National Park, Alberta

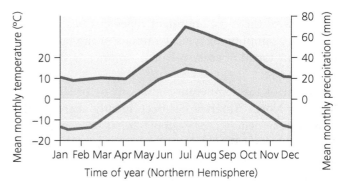

(b) Boreal forest

FIGURE 4.19
Boreal forest is defined by long, cold winters, relatively cool summers, and moderate precipitation.

lakes. The black spruce (*Picea mariana*) is a common evergreen species.

The boreal forest's uniformity over huge areas reflects the climate common to this latitudinal band of the globe: These forests develop in cooler, drier regions than do temperate forests, and they experience long, cold winters and short, cool summers. Soils are typically nutrient poor and somewhat acidic. As a result of the strong seasonal variation in day length, temperature, and precipitation, many organisms compress a year's worth of feeding, breeding, and rearing of young into a few warm, wet months. Year-round residents of boreal forest include mammals, such as moose (*Alces alces*), wolves (*Canis lupus*), bears, lynx (*Felis lynx*), and many burrowing rodents. This biome also hosts many insect-eating birds that migrate from the tropics to breed during the brief, intensely productive summer season.

The boreal forest, one-third of which resides in Canada, is one of the largest continuous forest ecosystems. It hosts more wetland area than any other ecosystem on Earth, providing invaluable habitat for many species. The enormous global importance of the boreal forest highlights Canada's role as a steward for much of the world's forested area. We will revisit this role in the chapter on forests and forest management.

Temperate deciduous forest   The **temperate deciduous forest** (FIGURE 4.20) that dominates the landscape around the central and southern Great Lakes is characterized by broad-leafed trees that are **deciduous**, meaning that they lose their leaves each fall and remain dormant during winter, when hard freezes would endanger leaves. These mid-latitude forests occur in much of Europe and eastern China as well as in eastern North America—all areas in which precipitation is spread relatively evenly throughout the year. Although soils of the temperate deciduous forest are relatively fertile, the biome generally consists of far fewer tree species than are found in tropical rainforests. Oaks, beeches, and maples are a few of the most abundant types of trees in these forests. A sampling of typical animals of the temperate deciduous forest of eastern North America is shown in FIGURE 4.11.

Much of the temperate deciduous or broad-leafed forest in North America has been greatly altered since European settlement; for example, it has been estimated that only about 5% of New England–Acadian mixed broad-leafed forest in Canada remains intact, with about 50% of the habitat in this region described as "heavily altered" by human activity.[10] However, forest cover has been making a comeback in the New England–Acadia region in recent decades, thanks to changing land use and conservation efforts.

(a) Typical location: Kejimkujik National Park, Nova Scotia

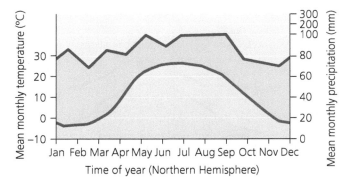

(b) Temperate deciduous forest

FIGURE 4.20
Temperate deciduous forests experience relatively stable seasonal precipitation but more variation in seasonal temperatures. When the precipitation curve falls well above the temperature curve, as shown here, the region experiences relatively moist conditions, as indicated by the green shading.

Temperate grassland   Moving westward from the Great Lakes, we find **temperate grasslands** (FIGURE 4.21). This is because temperature differences between winter and summer become more extreme, and rainfall diminishes. The limited amount of precipitation in the Prairies and the Great Plains region can support grasses more easily than trees. Also known as *steppes* or *prairies*, temperate grasslands were once widespread throughout parts of North and South America and much of central Asia.

Today people have converted most of the world's grasslands for agriculture, greatly reducing the abundance of native plants and animals. Both the tallgrass prairies that characterize the midwestern United States and the shortgrass prairies of southern Alberta and Saskatchewan are described by the World Wildlife Fund as having been "virtually converted," mainly for wheat production and grazing, with only small undisturbed patches remaining (less than 2% remaining "intact" in Canada). However,

(a) Typical location: Moose Jaw, Saskatchewan

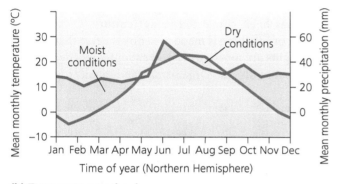

(b) Temperate grassland

FIGURE 4.21
Temperate grasslands experience temperature variations throughout the year and too little precipitation for many trees to grow. This climatograph indicates both "moist" (green) and "dry" (yellow) climate conditions. When the temperature curve is above the precipitation curve, as is the case in May and mid-June through September, the climate conditions are "dry."

restoration ecology efforts in this biome have seen some success, with efforts to reestablish populations of native species, such as the black-footed ferret (*Mustela nigripes*) and bison (*Bison bison*), well underway.[11] Other characteristic vertebrate animals of the North American grasslands include prairie dogs, pronghorn antelope (*Antilocapra americana*), and ground-nesting birds, such as meadowlarks.

Temperate rainforest   Moving still further west in North America, the topography becomes more varied, and biome types are intermixed. The coastal Pacific region, with heavy coastal mountain rainfall, features **temperate rainforest** (**FIGURE 4.22**), a forest type known for its potential to produce large volumes of commercially important forest products, such as lumber and paper. Coniferous trees such as cedars, spruces, hemlocks, and Douglas fir (*Pseudotsuga menziesii*) grow very tall in the temperate rainforest, so the forest interior is shaded

and damp. In the Queen Charlotte Islands, for example, moisture-loving animals, such as the bright yellow banana slug (*Ariolimax columbianus*) are common, and old-growth conifer stands host the endangered spotted owl (*Strix occidentalis*). The soils of temperate rainforests are usually quite fertile but are susceptible to landslides and erosion if forests are cleared.

Temperate rainforests have been the focus of controversy in Pacific coastal regions, where overharvesting has driven some species toward extinction. Clear-cut logging and road building into forested areas remain the greatest threats to temperate rainforest habitat in these areas (see "Central Case: Battling Over the Last Big Trees at Clayoquot Sound," in the chapter on forests and forest management).

Tropical rainforest   In tropical regions we see the same pattern found in temperate regions: Areas of high rainfall grow rainforests, areas of intermediate rainfall host dry or deciduous forests, and areas of lower rainfall become dominated by grasses. However, tropical biomes differ from their temperate counterparts in other ways

(a) Typical location: Queen Charlotte Islands and Vancouver, BC.

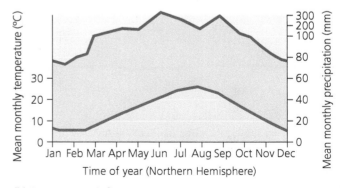

(b) Temperate rainforest

FIGURE 4.22
Temperate rainforests receive a great deal of precipitation and feature moist, mossy interiors.

because they are closer to the equator and therefore warmer on average year-round. For one thing, they hold far greater biodiversity.

The **tropical rainforest** biome (FIGURE 4.23) is found in Central America, South America, Southeast Asia, West Africa, and other tropical regions, and is characterized by year-round rain and uniformly warm temperatures. Tropical rainforests have dark, damp interiors, lush vegetation, and highly diverse biotic communities, with greater numbers of species of insects, birds, amphibians, and various other animals than any other biome. These forests are not dominated by single species of trees, as are forests closer to the poles, but instead consist of very high numbers of tree species intermixed, each at a low density. Any given tree may be draped with vines, enveloped by strangler figs, and loaded with *epiphytes* (orchids and other plants that grow in trees), such that trees occasionally collapse under the weight of all the life they support. Despite this profusion of life, tropical rainforests have very poor, acidic soils that are low in organic matter. Nearly all nutrients present in this biome are contained in the trees, vines, and other

plants—not in the soil. An unfortunate consequence is that once tropical rainforests are cleared, the nutrient-poor soil can support agriculture for only a short time. As a result, farmed areas are abandoned quickly, and the soil and forest vegetation recover very slowly.

Tropical dry forest   Tropical areas that are warm year-round but where rainfall is lower overall and highly seasonal give rise to **tropical dry forest**, or tropical deciduous forest (FIGURE 4.24), a biome widespread in India, Africa, South America, and northern Australia. Wet and dry seasons each span about half a year in tropical dry forest. Rains during the wet season can be extremely heavy and, coupled with erosion-prone soils, can lead to severe soil loss when forest clearing occurs over large areas. Across the globe, much tropical dry forest has been converted to agriculture. Clearing for farming or ranching is made easier by the fact that vegetation heights are much lower and canopies less dense than in tropical rainforest. Organisms that inhabit tropical dry

(a) Typical location: Bogor, Java, Indonesia

(a) Typical location: Darwin, Australia

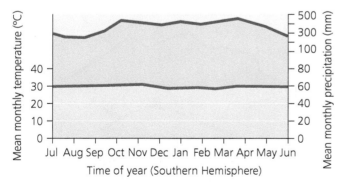

(b) Tropical rainforest

FIGURE 4.23
Tropical rainforests, famed for their biodiversity, grow under constant, warm temperatures and a great deal of rain.

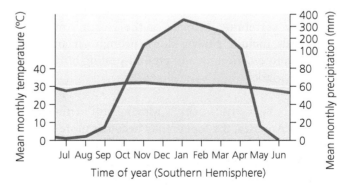

(b) Tropical dry forest

FIGURE 4.24
Tropical dry forests experience significant seasonal variations in precipitation and relatively stable warm temperatures.

forests have adapted to seasonal fluctuations in precipitation and temperature. For instance, plants are deciduous and often leaf out and grow profusely with the rains, then drop their leaves during the driest times of year.

Savannah   Drier tropical regions give rise to **savannah** (**FIGURE 4.25**), tropical grassland interspersed with clusters of acacias or other trees. The savannah biome is found today across stretches of Africa (the ancestral home of our species), South America, Australia, India, and other dry tropical regions. Precipitation in savannahs usually arrives during distinct rainy seasons and concentrates grazing animals near widely spaced water holes. Common herbivores on the African savannah include zebras, gazelles, and giraffes, and the predators of these grazers include lions, hyenas, and other highly mobile carnivores.

Desert   Where rainfall is very sparse, **desert** (**FIGURE 4.26**) forms. This is the driest biome on Earth; most deserts receive well under 25 cm of precipitation per year, much of it during isolated storms months or years

apart. Depending on rainfall, deserts vary greatly in the amount of vegetation they support. Some, like the Sahara and Namib deserts of Africa, are mostly bare sand dunes; others, like the Sonoran Desert of Arizona and northwest Mexico, are quite heavily vegetated. Deserts are not always hot; the high desert of the western United States is one example. Because deserts have low humidity and relatively little vegetation to insulate them from temperature extremes, sunlight readily heats them in the daytime, but daytime heat is quickly lost at night. As a result, temperatures vary widely from day to night and across seasons of the year. Desert soils can often be quite saline and are sometimes known as lithosols, or stone soils, for their high mineral and low organic-matter content.

Desert animals and plants have evolved many adaptations to deal with the harsh climatic conditions. Most reptiles and mammals, such as rattlesnakes and kangaroo mice, are active in the cool of night, and many Australian desert birds are nomadic, wandering long distances to find areas of recent rainfall and plant growth. Many desert plants have thick leathery leaves to reduce water

(a) Typical location: Harare, Zimbabwe

(a) Typical location: Cairo, Egypt

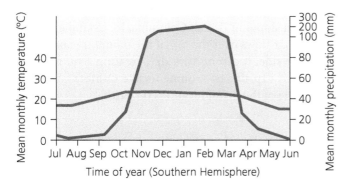

(b) Savannah

FIGURE 4.25
Savannahs are grasslands with clusters of trees. They experience slight seasonal variation in temperature but significant variation in rainfall.

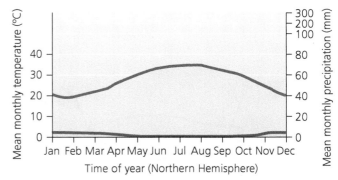

(b) Desert

FIGURE 4.26
Deserts are dry year-round, but they are not always hot. Precipitation can arrive in intense, widely spaced storm events, and temperatures can vary dramatically within a 24-hour period.

loss, or green trunks so that the plant can photosynthesize without leaves, which would lose water. The spines of cacti and many other desert plants guard those plants from being eaten by herbivores desperate for the precious water they hold. These are examples of convergent evolution of plants and animals, adapting separately to the dry conditions that are characteristic of the desert biome.

Mediterranean   In contrast to the boreal forest's broad, continuous distribution, *chaparral* or **Mediterranean** woodland (**FIGURE 4.27**) is limited to fairly small patches widely flung around the globe. Scrub woodland consists mostly of evergreen shrubs and is densely thicketed. This biome is also highly seasonal, with mild, wet winters and warm, dry summers. This type of climate is induced by oceanic influences; in addition to ringing the Mediterranean Sea, chaparral occurs along the coasts of California, Chile, and southern Australia. In Europe it is called *maquis*; in Chile, *matorral*; and in Australia, *mallee*. Mediterranean-type communities experience frequent fires, and their plant species are adapted to resist fire or even to depend on it for germination of their seeds.

(a) Typical location: Baja Peninsula, California, United States

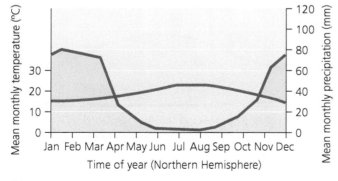

(b) Mediterranean or Chaparral

FIGURE 4.27
This is a highly seasonal biome dominated by shrubs, influenced by marine weather, and dependent on fire.

Altitude creates patterns analogous to latitude

As any hiker or skier knows, climbing in elevation causes a much more rapid change in climate than moving the same distance toward the poles. Vegetative communities change along mountain slopes in correspondence with this small-scale climate variation (**FIGURE 4.28**). These changes with altitude define the *alpine* biome. *Altitudinal zonation*, as it is referred to, is independent of latitude—the variation of temperature, precipitation, and ecological communities with altitude can occur anywhere from the equator to the Rockies. A hiker ascending one of southern Arizona's higher mountains, for example, would begin in the Sonoran Desert or desert grassland and proceed through oak woodland, pine forest, and finally spruce–fir forest—the equivalent of passing through several biomes, without any change in latitude. A hiker scaling one of the great peaks of the Andes in Ecuador, near the equator, could begin in tropical rainforest and end amid glaciers in alpine tundra.

Characteristics that are typical of the alpine biome on a high-mountain peak, compared with lowlands or foothills that surround it, include lower temperatures, lower atmospheric pressures (and less oxygen), higher exposure to ultraviolet radiation, and higher precipitation. The foothills of the Canadian Rockies, for example, are characterized by meadows, grasslands, and riparian (riverside) woodlands, which grade upward through boreal forests and into alpine tundra and glaciers on the mountain peaks; precipitation on the peaks can be as much as twice that of the foothill areas. The zonation of ecological communities on mountain slopes is also influenced by secondary climatic effects related to topographic relief, such as rainshadow effects and exposure to or shelter from the prevailing winds and sunlight.[12] For example, when moisture-laden air ascends a steep mountain, it releases precipitation as it cools; this explains the wet temperate rainforest on the ocean side of the mountain slopes in British Columbia, for example. By the time the air flows over the top of the mountain and down the other side, it can be very dry, creating a *rainshadow desert*; this explains environments like California's Death Valley, one of the driest locations on earth.

Aquatic and coastal systems also show biome-like patterns

In our discussion of biomes, we have focused exclusively on terrestrial systems, because the biome concept, as traditionally developed and applied, has been limited to terrestrial systems. Areas equivalent to biomes also exist in the oceans, but their geographic shapes would look very

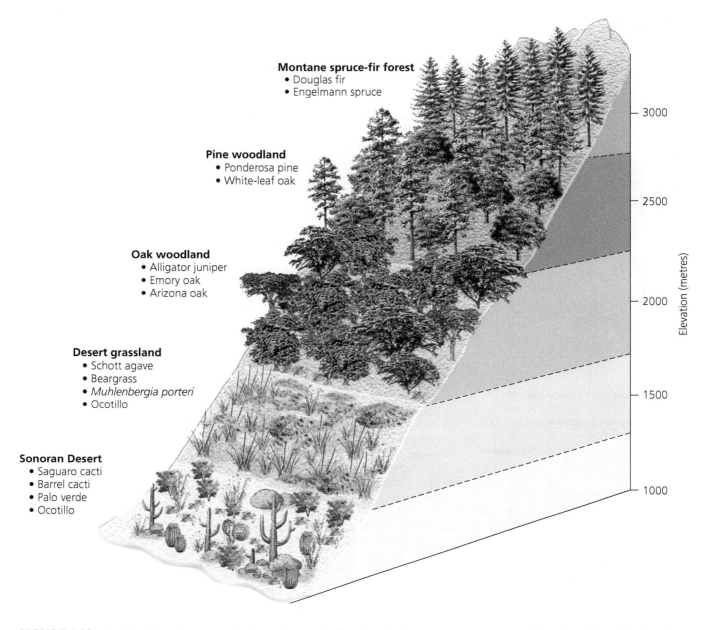

Montane spruce-fir forest
- Douglas fir
- Engelmann spruce

Pine woodland
- Ponderosa pine
- White-leaf oak

Oak woodland
- Alligator juniper
- Emory oak
- Arizona oak

Desert grassland
- Schott agave
- Beargrass
- *Muhlenbergia porteri*
- Ocotillo

Sonoran Desert
- Saguaro cacti
- Barrel cacti
- Palo verde
- Ocotillo

Elevation (metres)

3000

2500

2000

1500

1000

FIGURE 4.28   As altitude increases, vegetation changes in ways similar to how it changes as one moves toward the poles, taking a hiker through the local equivalent of several biomes.

different from those of terrestrial biomes if plotted on a world map, because the forces that determine the productivity of aquatic systems have very different geographical patterns than those which dominate the productivity of terrestrial systems. We can consider the thin strips along the world's coastlines to represent one aquatic system, the continental shelves another, and the open ocean, deep sea, coral reefs, and kelp forests as still other distinct sets of communities. There are also many coastal systems that straddle the line between terrestrial and aquatic, such as salt marshes, rocky intertidal communities, mangrove forests, and estuaries. And, of course, there are freshwater systems, such as those of the Great Lakes.

Unlike terrestrial biomes, aquatic systems are shaped not by air temperature and precipitation but by such factors as water temperature, salinity, dissolved nutrients, wave action, currents, depth, and type of substrate (e.g., sandy, muddy, or rocky bottom). Light levels can play a role, too. Surface-water tends to be saltier (because of the evaporation of fresh water from the surface), with higher light levels and warmer temperatures, in comparison with deep-water environments. Coastal waters tend to be both warmer and fresher (because of the influx of fresh water from rivers), but may be more turbid (because of sediment load) compared to open-ocean environments. Marine communities are also more clearly delineated by

CANADIAN ENVIRONMENTAL PERSPECTIVES

Zoe Lucas

Zoe Lucas works with the wild horses of Sable Island.

- ■ **Independent researcher** on the biology and ecology of wild horses
- ■ **Advocate** for Sable Island and its unique ecology
- ■ **Photographer** and **documenter** of life (and death) on Sable Island

As a student at the Nova Scotia School of Art and Design in Halifax, Zoe Lucas had not even considered environmental science as an option. Then Lucas had the opportunity to visit Sable Island, a 41 km patch of sand located about 300 km southeast of Halifax. Sable is known for its remote, windswept landscapes and bands of wild horses, as well as grey seals, harbour seals, and several types of rare and endangered migratory birds. It also boasts a long marine history involv-ing frequent shipwrecks. After a couple of days on Sable Island, Lucas was captivated and became driven to find her way back there. Completing her master of fine arts degree, Lucas eventually started teaching and opened her own studio, but her desire to return to Sable remained strong. She describes it as a combination of esthetics ("Sable is an extremely beautiful place; it's like living in a watercolour painting") and being highly activated by being outdoors.

Lucas eventually made it back to Sable Island as a volunteer cook with a university research group. Still driven largely by the esthetics of the place, she found that the longer she spent on the island, the more curious she became about its nature (in both senses of the word). Eventually she began to participate in scientific research and environmental monitoring projects. She has now authored or contributed to numerous reports and scientific studies on the island's horses, vegetation, and seals, and collaborates with researchers at various universities.

Lucas carries out a complete search of the island's shoreline once every four to five weeks, looking for oiled birds, stranded cetaceans, and marine litter. Between beach surveys she records field data on the feral horses, including their range, repro-ductive activities, and band structure. She also works on short-term projects, such as collecting invertebrate or plant specimens requested by researchers.

Lucas says that, in addition to the benefits of working in such a unique and beautiful place, the work of environmental monitoring appeals to her because there are endless questions. "Hardly a day passes without learning something new—some-times just a snippet of a detail, sometimes a big aha! Being able to do this work in such a wonderful and occasionally challenging environment is very compelling."

The island is administered by the Canadian Coast Guard, and landing there without permission (except in the case of an emergency) is against the law. Scientific research on the island is carried out with logistical support provided by the Sable Island Station, originally set up by the Meteorological Service of Canada (a branch of Environment Canada) as a meteorological station but now also used as a base for year-round environmental stewardship. There has been some discus-sion about initiating ecotourism trips to the island, but this would require significant care and planning to ensure preservation of the island's fragile ecosystems.

"I can't imagine anyone not wanting to live and work here."—**Zoe Lucas, about Sable Island**

Thinking About Environmental Perspectives

Sable Island is a remote wilderness. Great care has been taken to preserve the fragile ecosystems and unique wild populations that live there. However, few people will ever visit Sable Island. What do you think about this? What is the value of wilderness? Do you think more people should be able to visit, even if their presence would be disruptive and potentially damaging to the natural environment?

---

their animal life than by their plant life. We will examine freshwater, marine, and coastal systems in greater detail in subsequent chapters.

Conclusion

The natural world is so complex that we can visualize it in many ways and at various scales. Dividing the world's com-munities into major types, or biomes, is informative at the broadest geographic scales. Understanding how communi-ties function at more local scales requires understanding how species interact with one another. Species interactions, such as predation, parasitism, competition, and mutualism, give rise to effects that are both weak and strong, direct and indirect. Feeding relationships can be represented by the concepts of trophic levels and food webs, and particularly influential species are sometimes called keystone species. Increasingly, humans are altering communities, in part by introducing non-native species that may turn invasive. But increasingly, through ecological restoration, we are also attempting to undo the changes we have caused.

REVIEWING OBJECTIVES

You should now be able to:

Compare and contrast the major types of species interactions

- Competition results when individuals or species vie for limited resources. It can occur within or among species and can result in coexistence or exclusion. It also can lead to realized niches, resource partitioning, and character displacement.
- In predation, one species kills and consumes another. It is the basis of food webs and can influence population dynamics and community composition.
- In parasitism, one species derives benefit by harming (but usually not killing) another.
- Herbivory is an exploitative interaction whereby an animal feeds on a plant.
- In mutualism, species benefit from one another. Some mutualists are symbiotic, whereas other mutualists are free-living.

Characterize feeding relationships and energy flow, using them to construct trophic pyramids and food webs

- Energy is transferred in food chains among trophic levels.
- Lower trophic levels generally contain more energy, biomass, and numbers of individuals than higher trophic levels.
- Food webs illustrate feeding relationships and energy flow among species in a community.

Distinguish characteristics of a keystone species

- Keystone species have impacts on communities that are far out of proportion to their abundance.
- Top predators are frequently considered keystone species, but other organisms may be thought of as keystones for other reasons.

Describe how communities respond to disturbances

- Succession is a stereotypical pattern of change within a community through time.
- Primary succession begins with an area devoid of life. Secondary succession begins with an area that has been severely disturbed.

Perceive and predict the potential impacts of invasive species on communities

- Invasive species, such as the zebra mussel, have altered the composition, structure, and function of communities.
- Humans are the cause of most modern species invasions, but we can also respond to invasions with prevention and control measures.

Explain the goals and methods of ecological restoration

- Ecological restoration aims to restore communities to a more "natural" state, variously defined as before human or industrial interference.
- Restoration efforts in the field are informed by the growing science of restoration ecology.

Describe and illustrate the terrestrial biomes of the world

- Biomes represent major classes of communities spanning large geographic areas.
- The distribution of biomes is determined by temperature, precipitation, and other factors.
- The biome concept by tradition refers to terrestrial systems. Aquatic systems can be classified in similar ways, determined by different factors.

TESTING YOUR COMPREHENSION

1. How does competition lead to a realized niche? How does it promote resource partitioning?
2. Contrast the several types of exploitation. How do predation, parasitism, and herbivory differ?
3. Give examples of symbiotic and nonsymbiotic mutualisms. Describe at least one way in which mutualisms affect your daily life.
4. Explain how trophic levels, food chains, and food webs are related.
5. Name several ways in which a species could be considered a keystone species.
6. Explain and contrast primary and secondary terrestrial succession.

7. Name five changes to Great Lakes communities that have occurred since the invasion of the zebra mussel.
8. What is restoration ecology?
9. What factors most strongly influence the type of biome that forms in a particular place on land? What factors determine the type of aquatic system that may form in a given location?
10. Draw climate diagrams for a boreal forest, a temperate rainforest, and a desert. Label all parts of the diagrams, and describe all the types of information an ecologist could glean from such diagrams.

THINKING IT THROUGH

1. Imagine that you spot two species of birds feeding side by side, eating seeds from the same plant, and that you begin to wonder whether competition is at work. Describe how you might design scientific research to address this question. What observations would you try to make at the outset? Would you try to manipulate the system to test your hypothesis that the two birds are competing? If so, how?
2. Spend some time outside on your campus or in your yard or in the nearest park or natural area. Find at least 10 species of organisms, and observe them long enough to watch them feed or to make an educated guess about what they feed on. Now, using FIGURE 4.11 as a model, draw a simple food web involving all the organisms you observed.
3. Can you think of one organism not mentioned in this chapter as a keystone species that you believe may be a keystone species? For what reasons do you suspect this? How could you experimentally test whether an organism is a keystone species?
4. Why do scientists consider invasive species to be a problem? What makes a species "invasive," and what ecological effects can invasive species have?
5. From year to year, biomes are stable entities, and our map of world biomes appears to be a permanent record of patterns across the planet. But are the locations and identities of biomes permanent, or could they change over time? Provide reasons for your answers.

6. Can you devise possible responses to the zebra mussel invasion? What strategies would you consider if you were put in charge of the effort to control this species' spread and reduce its impacts? Name some advantages of each of your ideas, and identify some obstacles it might face in being implemented.
7. Consider this real-life example of invasive-species management and restoration ecology, and then answer the questions that follow, in your new role as an environmental land manager: The Garry oak meadows on Trinity Western University's Crow's Nest Ecological Research Area are experiencing encroachment by the Douglas fir (*Pseudotsuga menziesii*), which threatens the health and survival of the meadow. Traditionally, Aborigines maintained the Garry oak meadows with frequent burnings. However, with European settlement and the resulting control and suppression of fires, Douglas firs have been increasingly successful at invading the meadows. Some Garry oak restoration projects have undertaken to remove Douglas firs physically and/or using controlled fires. However, when the Douglas firs are removed, the resulting disturbance of the soil apparently facilitates the establishment of other invasive species.[13]
   (a) How would you design a comprehensive scientific study to determine the best ways of removing Douglas firs without enhancing conditions for encroachment by other invasive species?

(b) Removing Douglas firs from the Garry oak meadows would not return the meadows to their "natural," pristine, or pre-human state; instead, it would represent a return to an earlier phase of human (Aboriginal) ecosystem management. Is this the best approach? Do you think the Douglas firs should be allowed to advance naturally, without interference by fire or other removal techniques? Or is it worthwhile to preserve the meadows—which are disappearing rapidly, and host a variety of unusual and threatened species—by returning to an earlier land management approach?

(c) Can you think of some general guidelines that might be used to make ecosystem management decisions in other cases of this type?

INTERPRETING GRAPHS AND DATA

The grey wolf (*Canis lupus*) is a keystone species in Yellowstone National Park's ecosystem. Wolf packs hunt elk, gorge themselves on the kill, and leave the carcass as carrion for scavenger species, such as ravens, magpies, eagles, coyotes, and bears. As the global climate has warmed, winters in Yellowstone have become shorter over the past 55 years. Fewer elk weaken and die in milder weather, and so less carrion is available to scavengers during warmer, shorter winters. Biologists Christopher Wilmers and Wayne Getz studied the links among climate change, wolves, elk, and scavenger populations in Yellowstone. They used empirical field data on wolf predation rates and elk carrion availability recorded over 55 years to develop a model that estimated carrion availability with and without wolves for each winter month. Some of their findings are presented in the graph.

1. How much less carrion is available in April than in November when wolves are present? When wolves are not present?

2. Wolves were hunted nearly to extinction in the 1930s and were reintroduced to Yellowstone only in 1995. How, would you suspect, has their reintroduction affected scavenger populations since then? Why?

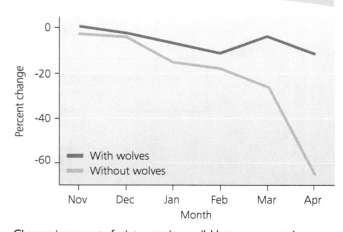

Changes in amount of winter carrion available to scavengers in Yellowstone National Park, with and without wolves, according to the model. Differences in March and April are statistically significant.
Source: Data from Wilmers, C.C. and W.M. Getz (2005) Gray wolves as climate-change buffers in Yellowstone. PLoS Biology 3(4): e92.

3. Predict what effect continued shorter, warmer winters would have on scavenger populations. Why? Are the predicted effects of wolf reintroduction and of climate change compounded, or do they tend to cancel one another out?

CHAPTER ENDNOTES

1. "'Musseling' in on an Ecosystem: Tracing the Natural History of the Zebra Mussel in Lake Erie," *Canadian Geographic*, September 2003.

2. Environment Canada Backgrounder: Lake Ontario Invasion Begins, (1999) www.on.ec.gc.ca/press/goby-invasion.html

3. Parks Canada Fact Sheet, (2007) "Moose a-plenty," Cape Breton Highlands National Park of Canada, www.pc.gc.ca/canada/pn-tfn/itm2/2007/2007-04-30_e.asp

4. Danoff-Burg, James, ed., *Introduced Species Summary Project*, Columbia University, Centre for Environmental Research and Conservation, and other sources.

5. Haber, Erich, *Guide to Monitoring Exotic and Invasive Plants*, Environment Canada Ecological Monitoring and Assessment Network (EMAN).

6. Carder, Judith E. W. *Restoration of Natural Systems Program*, Garry Oak Ecosystems Recovery Team, Research Colloquium 2006, University of Victoria, BC; and Garry Oak Restoration Project (GORP), www.gorpsaanich.com.

7. World Wildlife Fund, "Ecoregions," www.worldwildlife.org/science/ecoregions.

8. Climatographs adapted from Breckle, S. W. (1999) *Walter's vegetation of the Earth: The ecological systems of the geo-biosphere*, 4th ed., Berlin: Springer-Verlag.

9. World Wildlife Fund, "Ecoregions," www.worldwildlife.org/science/ecoregions/nearctic.cfm.

10. World Wildlife Fund, "Ecoregions," www.worldwildlife.org/science/ecoregions

11. World Wildlife Fund, "Ecoregions," www.worldwildlife.org/science/ecoregions/nearctic.cfm.

12. World Wildlife Fund, "Ecoregions," www.worldwildlife.org/science/ecoregions/nearctic.cfm

13. Roberts, Kimberly, Stephanie Koole, and David Clements, Garry Oak Ecosystems Recovery Team—Research Colloquium 2006, Trinity Western University, Langley, BC.

MyEnvironmentPlace

Go to **www.myenvironmentplace.ca** where you will find quizzes, animations, your Pearson eText, and more.

5 Soil Resources

This is the Mer Bleue provincial wetland, near Ottawa, Ontario.

Upon successfully completing this chapter, you will be able to

- Delineate the fundamentals of soil science, including soil-forming processes
- Describe some important properties of soil
- Characterize the role of soils in biogeochemical cycling
- State the importance of soils for agriculture and in supporting plant growth
- Identify the causes and predict the consequences of soil erosion and soil degradation
- Outline the history and explain the basic principles of soil conservation

CANADA

Hudson Bay

Mer Bleue

UNITED STATES

CENTRAL CASE:
MER BLEUE: A BOG OF INTERNATIONAL SIGNIFICANCE

"This soil of ours, this precious heritage, what an unobtrusive existence it leads! To the rich soil let us give the credit due. The soil is the reservoir of life."
—J.A. TOOGOOD, CANADIAN SOIL SCIENTIST

"The nation that destroys its soil destroys itself."
—FORMER U.S. PRESIDENT FRANKLIN D. ROOSEVELT

The Mer Bleue Conservation Area is a 35-km² provincially protected wetland situated just east of Ottawa, Ontario. It is located in an ancient, now-abandoned channel of the Ottawa River (see satellite photo) and hosts a number of plant species that are specially adapted to moist, boggy, acidic conditions, including *Sphagnum* moss, bog rosemary, blueberry, cottongrass, cattails, and tamarack. The area, classified as an open bog, has been recognized under the Ramsar Convention as a wetland of international importance.

The Mer Bleue wetland provides an example of a specific type of soil—peat—that has been accumulating in many northern areas since the end of the last ice age. Canada has some of the most extensive peatlands in the world, covering 14% of our land area, and the peat deposits in some parts of the Mer Bleue bog, which formed over the past 8000 years, are up to 6 m thick.

Northern peatlands are extremely important storage reservoirs for carbon and are thought to hold about one-third of all the carbon stored in soils. Through decomposition of organic matter, peat produces soil gases such as CO_2 and CH_4, which function as greenhouse gases in the atmosphere. Understanding the potential reaction of these very sensitive soils to climate change, particularly changes in water content and temperature, is of great interest to scientists. For example, if warming leads northern peat soils to decompose at faster rates and thus to release more soil gases, it could have a major impact on the concentration of these carbon-based gases in the atmosphere. This could set up a positive feedback loop and have a reinforcing influence on greenhouse warming.

The storage of carbon in peat depends on the balance between net primary production and decomposition. Plants store or sequester carbon as a result of photosynthesis, then contribute the stored carbon to the peat soil, where it accumulates in the form of plant litter. Temperature and light levels are of obvious importance to this balance, because the process of photosynthesis is involved. Moisture is another very important factor. When water levels are high, CH_4, the by-product of anaerobic (reduced) decomposition, is produced in large quantities; when conditions are drier, respiration tends to be aerobic (oxidized), producing less CH_4 but more CO_2.

The Peatland Carbon Study (PCARS) was initiated by a group of Canadian scientists in 1997. Researchers involved in the project, who are linked by an interest in ecosystem structure and function, include soil scientists, microclimatologists, hydrologists, a palynologist (a scientist who studies ancient pollen), plant ecologists, and graduate students from fields as varied as geochemistry, botany, physical geography, and microbial ecology.

The work continues today as part of the Canadian Carbon Project research network, measuring and modelling the influence of climatic and seasonal changes on the carbon balance of peatlands. Scientific activities at the Mer Bleue site include an instrument tower equipped for meteorological measurements, including energy balance, water vapour, and carbon dioxide and methane fluxes, combined with field investigations on plant growth and decomposition, hydrology, and plots for experimentation with factors such as drainage and excess nutrients (see photo).

On the basis of these ongoing measurements, now one of the longest-standing continuous sets of measurements of a northern peatland, scientists are developing a series of comprehensive ecosystem models for peatlands.[1] By studying this typical Canadian ecosystem, these scientists are contributing to our understanding of how soils may behave in a global context, in response to the phenomenon of climate change.

Graduate student Varun Gupta (left) and soil scientist Nate Basiliko use a raised boardwalk to sample sensitive peat soils from Mer Bleue. The experimental plots are being used to study the impacts of changes in nitrogen deposition on biogeochemical cycling.

Soil as a System

We generally overlook the complexity of soil. In everyday language we tend to equate *soil* with *dirt*. **Soil**, however, is not merely loose material derived from rock; it is a complex plant-supporting system that consists of disintegrated rock, organic matter, water, gases, nutrients, and microorganisms (**FIGURE 5.1**). Soil is also fundamental to the support of life on this planet and the provision of food for the growing human population. As a resource it is renewable if managed carefully, but it is easily degraded and is currently at risk in many locations around the world.

Soil is a complex, dynamic mixture

Soil consists very roughly of half solids, mostly mineral matter with varying proportions of organic matter, and the rest is pore space taken up by air, water, and other soil gases. The mineral particles in the soil are mostly

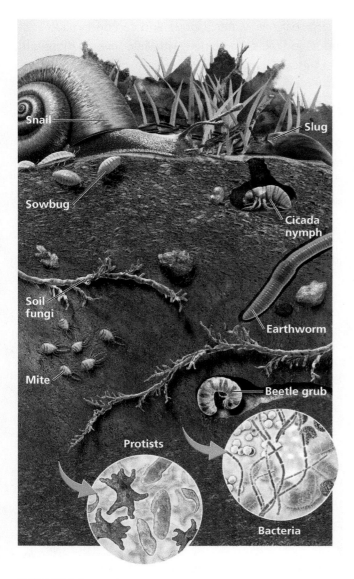

FIGURE 5.1
Soil is a complex mixture of organic and inorganic components and is full of living organisms whose actions help keep it fertile. Entire ecosystems exist in soil. Most soil organisms, from bacteria to fungi to insects to earthworms, decompose organic matter. Many, such as earthworms, also help to aerate the soil.

roots

SOIL

There are a lot of possible pathways that the word **soil** may have taken to arrive at it present-day usage, basically, "earth that plants can grow in." Most recently, it is derived from the Middle English (fifteenth-century) word *soile* (or *soyle*), meaning "ground" or "earth," which came, in turn, from the fourteenth-century Anglo-Norman (French) word *soyl*, "a piece of ground." These are thought to have come originally from the Latin word *solium*, meaning "seat." Another possible contributor is the Latin word *solum*, meaning "soil or ground."

Water partially fills the open spaces, or *pore spaces*, between the mineral grains and particles of organic matter in soils. This is never "pure" water; it contains a variety of dissolved constituents, both minerals and organics, and it is variously referred to as the *soil solution*, *soil water*, or *soil moisture*. These solutions are very important for the support of plant growth because they dissolve and mobilize soil constituents that plants require as nutrients.

Similarly, the "air" that partially fills soil pore spaces is not exactly the same as the air that we normally breathe. Like the atmosphere, *soil gas* contains oxygen and nitrogen, as well as carbon dioxide, methane, and other gases that reflect its chemical equilibrium with the liquid and solid constituents of the soil, including soil organisms. Soils also contain gases that are released from the underlying rock, such as radon, and gases that infiltrate from above, such as volatile constituents derived from spilled gas and oil.

Soil can have as much influence on a region's ecosystems as do the climate, latitude, and elevation. In fact, because soil is composed of living and nonliving components that interact with each other and with their surroundings in complex ways, soil itself meets the definition of an ecosystem. Together the mineral, organic, aqueous, and gaseous components of soil constitute a dynamic, ever-changing system that links the solid geosphere to the atmosphere, hydrosphere, and biosphere.

Soil formation is slow and complex

The formation of soil begins when the parent material is exposed to the effects of the atmosphere, hydrosphere, and biosphere. Parent material can be lava or volcanic

inherited from the **parent material**, the base geological material in a given location, from which the soil is formed. The parent material thus determines the starting composition of the soil.

The organic matter in soil includes living and dead microorganisms as well as decaying material derived from plants and animals. A single teaspoonful of soil can contain 100 million bacteria, 500 000 fungi, 100 000 algae, and 50 000 *protists* (simple eukaryotic microorganisms). Soil also provides habitat for earthworms, insects, mites, millipedes, centipedes, nematodes, sowbugs, and other invertebrates, as well as burrowing mammals, amphibians, and reptiles.

ash; rock or sediment deposited by glaciers; wind-blown dunes; sediments deposited by rivers, in lakes, or in the ocean; or, perhaps most commonly, any type of **bedrock**, the continuous mass of solid rock that makes up Earth's crust.

The processes most responsible for soil formation are weathering, erosion, and the deposition and decomposition of organic matter. **Weathering** describes the physical, chemical, and biological processes that break down rocks and minerals, turning large particles into smaller particles (**FIGURE 5.2**). These small, loose particles of mineral matter—collectively called *regolith*—are the precursors of soils.

Physical or **mechanical weathering** breaks rocks down without triggering a chemical change in the parent material. Temperature, wind, rain, and ice are the main agents of physical weathering. Daily and seasonal temperature variation aids their action by causing the thermal expansion and contraction of parent material; areas with extreme temperature fluctuations experience rapid rates of physical weathering. Flowing water, wind, and glacial ice move rock particles that scrape and abrade other rock surfaces, causing physical weathering. Water freezing and expanding in cracks in rock is another common cause of physical weathering.

Chemical weathering results when water or other substances chemically interact with parent material. If you have ever visited an old cemetery and noticed that some of the headstones seem worn and smooth, this is likely the influence of chemical weathering, slowly dissolving and carrying away the mineral constituents of the headstones. Notice that the headstones made of limestone are the ones that most clearly demonstrate chemical

weathering; limestone dissolves easily in normal, slightly acidic precipitation, whereas granite (the other common material used for headstones) is resistant to chemical weathering. Conditions where precipitation or groundwater are unusually acidic promote chemical weathering, as do warm, wet conditions.

Biological weathering occurs when living things break down parent material by physical or chemical means. For instance, lichens initiate primary terrestrial succession by producing acid, which chemically weathers rock. A tree may accelerate weathering through the physical action of its roots as they grow into fissures in rock. It may also accelerate weathering chemically through the decomposition of its leaves and branches or with chemicals it releases from its roots.

Biological activity further contributes to soil formation through the deposition, decomposition, and accumulation of organic matter. As plants, animals, and microbes die or deposit waste, this material is incorporated into the substrate, mixing with minerals. The deciduous trees of temperate forests, for example, drop their leaves each fall, making leaf litter available to the detritivores and decomposers that break it down and incorporate its nutrients into the soil. In decomposition, complex organic molecules are broken down into simpler ones, including those that plants can take up through their roots.

Partial decomposition of organic matter creates **humus**, a dark, spongy, crumbly mass of material made up of complex organic compounds. Soils with a high humus content hold moisture well and are productive for plant life. Soils that are dominated by partially decayed, compressed organic material—like the soil at Mer Bleue—are called **peat**. Peat is characteristic of (though not exclusive to) northern climates because cool temperatures and saturation by surface water slow the decay process, allowing great thicknesses of organic material to accumulate.

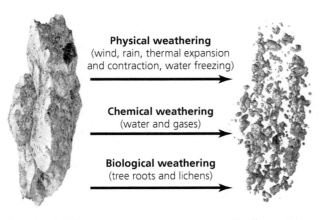

FIGURE 5.2
The weathering of parent material is the first step in soil formation. Rock is broken down into finer particles by physical, chemical, and biological processes.

roots

HUMUS

Humus comes from the Latin word *humus*, meaning "earth" or "soil." It is related to the English word *humility* and possibly even to the word *human*. The Latin probably came originally from the Proto-Indo-European root *dhghem-*, meaning "low" or "on the ground." The term *Proto-Indo-European* (abbreviated *PIE*) refers to the common ancestor of all Indo-European languages.

weighing the issues

EARTH'S SOIL RESOURCES

It can take anywhere from 500 to 10 000 years to produce 1 cm of natural topsoil, depending on local conditions. Much of Canada's land area was scraped free of soil during the last glaciation by the passage of huge ice masses, which retreated about 10 000 years ago. Today much of interior and northern Canada still lacks soil cover. Given this very long renewal time, is soil truly a renewable resource? How should the very long renewal time influence soil management?

Weathering produces fine particles and is the first step in soil formation. Another process often involved is **erosion**, the movement of particles from one location to another. When soil or regolith is transported by wind, water, or ice and then deposited somewhere else, it is generally referred to as **sediment**. The transport process itself can promote physical weathering as the transported particles collide and scrape against one another. Erosion is particularly prevalent when soil is denuded of vegetation, leaving the surface exposed to water and wind that may wash or blow it away.

Weathering, erosion, the accumulation and transformation of organic matter, and the other processes that contribute to soil formation are all influenced by environmental factors. Soil scientists cite five primary factors that influence the formation of soil (TABLE 5.1).

A soil profile consists of layers known as horizons

Once weathering has produced an abundance of small mineral particles, wind, water, and organisms begin to move and sort them, and water moves through, picking up and transporting soluble materials. Eventually, distinct layers develop. Each layer of soil is known as a **horizon**, and the cross-section as a whole, from surface to bedrock, is known as a **soil profile**.

Minerals are carried downward through the developing soil profile as a result of **leaching**, a process in which materials suspended or dissolved in liquid are transported through the subsurface. Soil that undergoes leaching is a bit like coffee in a drip filter. When it rains, water infiltrates the soil (just as it infiltrates coffee grounds), dissolves some of its components, and carries them downward into the deeper horizons. At depth in the soil profile, some of this material may be deposited

Table 5.1   The Five Factors That Influence Soil Formation

Factor	Effects
Climate	Soil forms faster in warm, wet climates. Heat speeds chemical reactions and accelerates weathering, decomposition, and biological growth. Moisture is required for many biological processes and can speed weathering.
Organisms	Earthworms and other burrowing animals mix and aerate soil, add organic matter, and facilitate microbial decomposition. Plants add organic matter and affect a soil's composition and structure.
Topography	Hills and valleys affect exposure to sun, wind, and water, and they influence where and how soil and water move. Steeper slopes result in more runoff and erosion and in less leaching, slower accumulation of organic matter, and less differentiation of soil layers.
Parent material	Chemical and physical attributes of the parent material influence properties of the resulting soil.
Time	Soil formation takes decades, centuries, or millennia. The four factors above change over time, so the soil we see today may be the result of multiple sets of factors.

in zones of *accumulation*. Minerals that are commonly leached are those that are the most *soluble* (easily dissolvable), including various iron, aluminum, and silicate minerals. In some soils, minerals may be leached so rapidly that plants are deprived of nutrients. Minerals that leach rapidly from soils may be carried into groundwater, where they can affect water quality.

Soil scientists subdivide horizons according to their characteristics and the processes that take place within them. For our purposes we will discuss five major horizons, known as the O, A, B, C, and R horizons (FIGURE 5.3). Soils from different locations vary, and few soil profiles contain all of these horizons, but any given soil contains at least some of them. Generally, the degree of weathering and the concentration of organic matter decrease downward in the soil profile.

Peat deposits are classified as **O horizons**, whereas surface deposits of leaves, branches, mosses, animal waste, collectively termed **litter**, form another type of organic horizon in upland forests. These surface deposits (including *L*, *F*, and *H* horizons) are classified and subdivided on the basis of their degree of decomposition.

Just below the litter layer lies the **A horizon**, the uppermost mineral horizon, which consists of inorganic mineral components with organic matter and humus

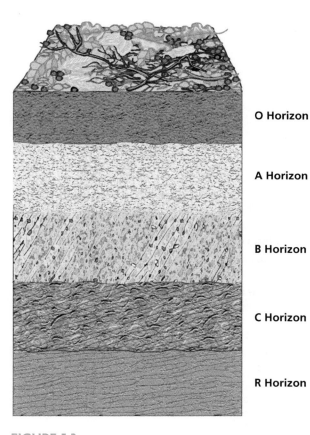

FIGURE 5.3
Mature soil consists of layers, or horizons, that have different compositions and characteristics. The number and depth of horizons vary from place to place as a result of the mix of soil-forming factors at the location, producing different soil profiles. The O horizon consists mostly of organic matter deposited by organisms. The A horizon (or *topsoil*), is the uppermost mineral horizon and consists of some organic material mixed with mineral components. Materials tend to be leached from the A horizon and deposited in the B horizon. The C horizon consists largely of weathered material that is still identifiable as parent rock, and which may overlie an R horizon of pure parent material.

from above mixed in. The A horizon is often referred to as **topsoil**, that portion of the soil that is most nutritive for plants and therefore most vital to ecosystems and agriculture. Topsoil takes its loose texture and dark colour from its humus content. The A horizon is home to most of the countless organisms that give life to soil.

Minerals and organic matter that are leached from the topsoil move down into the **B horizon**, or *subsoil*, where they accumulate. If leached minerals are deposited in the B horizon, they can lead to the development of hard, mineral-rich layers that are variously called *hardpan*, *claypan*, *duripan*, or *caliche*, depending on their specific composition and structure. These hard layers can cause problems for plant growth because they interfere with drainage and prevent plant roots from penetrating to lower, nutrient-rich layers of the soil.

The **C horizon**, if present, is a transition zone located below the B horizon. It consists of broken-up parent

material only slightly altered by the processes of soil formation, and contains rock particles that are larger and less weathered than the layers above. The C horizon may sit directly above an **R horizon** of unaltered parent material (*R* for *rock*). Some soils also are characterized by the presence of a distinct layer of water, called a *W horizon*, and some arctic soils contain a perennially frozen layer called **permafrost**.

Soils vary in colour, texture, structure, and pH

The horizons presented above depict an idealized, "typical" soil, but soils display very great variety. Young soils tend to be thin, and not all horizons are present in all soils. Canadian soil scientists classify soils into 10 major groups, based largely on the processes through which the soils are formed (**TABLE 5.2**). Within these 10 *soil orders*, there are dozens of "great groups," hundreds of "subgroups," and thousands of soils belonging to lower categories, all arranged in a hierarchical or taxonomic system. Scientists classify soils into these various categories using properties such as colour, texture, structure, and pH.

Soil colour The colour of soil (**FIGURE 5.4**) can indicate its composition and sometimes its fertility. For example, the famously red colour of soils on Prince

Clay

Peat

Chalk

Iron-rich

FIGURE 5.4
The colour of soil can vary drastically from one location to another. A soil's composition affects its colour; for instance, soils high in organic matter tend to be dark brown or black, light grey soils are often chalky in composition. Iron-rich soil, such as the one seen here in Central Australia, is often bright red in colour.

Table 5.2   The Canadian System of Soil Classification

Categories, or "Taxa," in the Canadian System of Soil Classification

Taxa	Principles used	No. of classes
Order	Dominant soil-forming process	10
Great group	Strength of soil-forming	31
Subgroup	Kind and arrangement of horizons	231
Family	Parent material characteristics	about 10 000
Series	Detailed features of the soil	about 100 000

Orders in the Canadian System of Soil Classification

Regosolic	Weakly developed soils, lacking a B horizon and typically forming in recent deposits.
Brunisolic	Poorly developed soils (i.e., lacking in horizon development, sometimes only lightly weathered, but slightly more developed than regosols, see below) that typically form under boreal forests.
Chernozemic	Well-drained to imperfectly drained soils with surface horizons darkened by the accumulation of organic matter from the decomposition of grasses; typical of the Interior Plains of Western Canada.
Luvisolic	Soils with light-coloured eluvial (E, or leached) horizons and B horizons in which clay has accumulated; characteristic of well-drained to imperfectly drained sites; in sandy loam to clay, base-saturated parent materials under forest vegetation in subhumid to humid and mild to very cold climates; from the southern extremity of Ontario to the zone of permafrost and from Newfoundland to British Columbia.
Vertisolic	Unstable soils with high clay contents, characterized by shrinking-swelling or wetting-drying cycles that either disrupt or inhibit the formation of soil horizons.
Solonetzic	Soils with a B horizon that is very hard when dry and swells to a sticky mass of very low permeability when wet; occur on saline parent materials in some areas of the Interior Plains in association with Chernozemic soils, mostly associated with a vegetative cover of grasses.
Podzolic	Soils with a B horizon in which the dominant accumulation product is amorphous material composed mainly of humified organic matter combined in varying degrees with Al and Fe; typically form in coarse soils under forest or heath vegetation in cool to very cold climates.
Gleysolic	Soils that are mottled (i.e., patchy) in colour, as a result of intermittent or continuous saturation with water and reducing (i.e., nonoxygenated) conditions; saturation may result from either a high ground-water table or temporary accumulation of water, or both.
Organic	Soils that are composed largely of organic materials, including soils commonly known as peat, muck, or bog and fen soils; commonly saturated with water for prolonged periods.
Cryosolic	Soils that form in either mineral or organic materials that have permafrost within 1 m of the surface; occupy much of the northern third of Canada.

Source: Based on Soil Classification Working Group (1998) The Canadian System of Soil Classification, 3rd ed. Agriculture and Agri-Food Canada Publication 1646, 187 pp. (available online through the National Land and Water Information Service, http://sis.agr.gc.ca/cansis/references/1998sc_a.html)

Edward Island is a result of the high iron content of the soil. Black or dark brown soils are usually rich in organic matter, whereas a pale grey to white colour often indicates a chalky composition, leaching, or low organic content. This colour variation occurs among soil horizons in any given location and also among soils from different geographic locations. Long before modern analytical tests of soil content were developed, the colour of topsoil provided farmers and ranchers with information about a region's potential to support crops and provide forage for livestock.

Soil texture   **Soil texture** is determined by the size of particles and is the basis on which soils are assigned to one of three general categories (FIGURE 5.5). **Clay** consists of particles less than 0.002 mm in diameter, **silt** of particles 0.002 to 0.05 mm, and **sand** of particles 0.05 to 2 mm. Sand grains, as any beachgoer knows, are large enough to see individually and do not adhere to one another. Clay particles, in contrast, readily adhere to one another and give clay a sticky feeling when moist. Soil with a relatively even mixture of the three particle sizes is known as **loam**.

For a farmer, soil texture influences a soil's *workability*, its relative ease or difficulty of cultivation. Texture influences the soil's **porosity**, a measure of the relative volume of spaces within the soil, as well as its **permeability**, a measure of the interconnectedness of the spaces and the ease with which fluids can move around in the

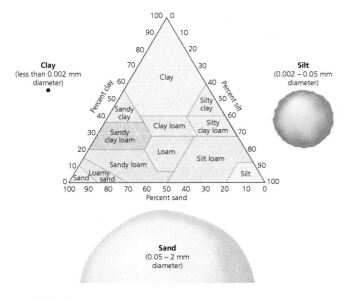

FIGURE 5.5
The texture of soil depends on its mix of particle sizes. Scientists classify soil texture according to the relative proportions of sand, silt, and clay. After measuring the percentage of each type of particle size in a soil sample, a scientist can trace the appropriate white lines extending inward from each side of the triangular graph to determine what type of soil texture that particular combination of values creates.

material. In general, the finer the texture of a sediment or soil, the smaller the pores. The smaller the pores, the harder it is for water and air to travel through the soil, slowing infiltration and reducing the amount of oxygen available to soil biota.

It is possible for a material to have a fairly high porosity but low permeability. This is typical of soils with high clay content. Conversely, soils with large particles tend to have larger spaces that are highly interconnected, allowing water to pass through (and beyond the reach of plant roots) too quickly. Thus, crops planted in sandy soils require frequent irrigation. For this reason, silty soils with medium-sized pores, or loamy soils with mixtures of pore sizes, are generally best for plant growth and crop agriculture.

Soil structure   **Soil structure** is a measure of the organization or "clumpiness" of soil. Some degree of structure encourages soil productivity, and organic matter, biological activity, and clay help promote this structure. However, soil clumps that are too large can discourage plant roots from establishing if soil particles are compacted too tightly together. Repeated tilling can compact soil and make it less able to absorb water. When farmers repeatedly till the same field at the same depth, they may end up forming a hardpan or *ploughpan* layer that resists the infiltration of water and the penetration of roots.

Soil pH   The degree of acidity or alkalinity of a soil influences the soil's ability to support plant growth. Plants can die in soils that are too acidic (low pH) or too alkaline (high pH), but even a moderate variation can influence the availability of nutrients for plants' roots. During leaching, for instance, acids from organic matter may remove some nutrients from the sites of exchange between plant roots and soil particles. Water leaches these nutrients, carrying them to deeper levels and making them less available for plants.

Biogeochemical Cycling in Soil

You have learned that soil is a complex mixture of organic and inorganic, living and nonliving, solid, liquid, and gaseous components. Soil and regolith physically blanket Earth's surface, and act as an important interface for exchanges of material through biological, geological, chemical, atmospheric, and hydrologic processes.

Soils support plant growth through ion exchange

Materials move through soils and plants gain many of their nutrients through a set of processes called **ion exchange** (FIGURE 5.6), in which positively charged particles (*cations*) and negatively charged particles (*anions*) are exchanged between the soil and the soil solution. Nutrients are held on *exchange sites*, along the positively or negatively charged edges of soil particles; in

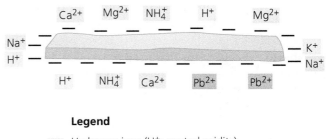

Legend

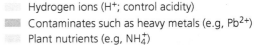
Hydrogen ions (H^+; control acidity)
Contaminates such as heavy metals (e.g, Pb^{2+})
Plant nutrients (e.g, NH_4^+)

FIGURE 5.6
Negatively charged soil solids (mainly clay or humus, shown in brown here) in soils attract positively charged nutrients (cations), such as Ca^{2+}, NH_4^+, Mg^{2+} and K^+, making them available when needed for plant growth. Heavy metals such as lead (Pb^{2+}) can also be attracted to negatively charged soil particles, making it challenging to clean up contaminated soils.

clay and humus particles, negatively charged sites prevail. Soil particle surfaces that are negatively charged hold on to positively charged nutrients, such as calcium (Ca^{2+}), magnesium (Mg^{2+}), potassium (K^+), and ammonium (NH_4^+). Cations and anions move from the exchange sites into the soil solution; from there they are taken up by roots and other soil organisms. Nutrients are resupplied to the exchange sites and the soil solution by weathering of minerals and the decomposition of organic matter.

Cation exchange capacity is a measure of a soil's ability to hold cations, preventing them from leaching away, and thus making them available to plants. It is thus a useful indicator of *fertility*, the soil's ability to support plant growth. Soils with fine texture (lots of clay particles) and soils rich in organic matter have the greatest cation exchange capacity. As soil pH becomes lower (more acidic), cation exchange capacity diminishes, nutrients leach away, and soil instead may supply plants with harmful aluminum ions. This is one way in which acid precipitation can harm soils and plant communities.

Many pollutants are also positively charged, notably heavy metals such as cadmium, lead, arsenic, and mercury. These cations are attracted to the negatively charged clay and humus particles in soil, which can make it difficult to remediate soil that has been contaminated with heavy metals. It also can mean that heavy metal contaminants are held in soil instead of being released into aquatic ecosystems, which can be beneficial.

Soil is a crucial part of the nitrogen cycle

Soil is the locus for a crucial set of processes that are part of the global biogeochemical cycle of nitrogen. Nitrogen gas (N_2)—the most abundant component of the atmosphere—is chemically inert and must undergo a series of chemical changes in order to become biologically available to the organisms that need it. In its biologically active form, nitrogen is a powerful plant nutrient; its scarcity makes it a limiting factor for plant growth.

Nitrogen fixation   To become biologically available, inert nitrogen gas (N_2) from the atmosphere must be "fixed"—that is, combined with hydrogen to form ions of ammonium (NH_4^+). This transformation, called **nitrogen fixation**, can be accomplished when air in the top layer of soil comes in contact with various specialized nitrogen-fixing bacteria. Some of these bacteria are free-living in the soil. Others live in a symbiotic, mutualistic relationship with plants, particularly *leguminous* plants such as beans, peas, and clover, which host nitrogen-

fixing bacteria in nodules attached to their roots. Farmers routinely promote this process by planting leguminous crops to boost soil fertility.

Other natural processes that lead to nitrogen fixation are combustion (such as in forest fires) and lightning strikes. A significant amount of nitrogen is also fixed by the industrial production of nitrate fertilizers, using the *Haber-Bosch process*. However, the most important nitrogen-fixing process—natural or anthropogenic—is still biologically mediated nitrogen fixation by soil- and root-dwelling bacteria. These microorganisms thus play a crucial role in supporting life.

Nitrification   Once atmospheric N_2 has been converted into ammonium, other specialized bacteria perform a process known as **nitrification**. In this process, ammonium ions are first converted into nitrite ions (NO_2^-), then (by yet another group of specialized microorganisms) into nitrate ions (NO_3^-). Plants can take up nitrate ions as nutrients, through their roots. The microorganisms that perform the task of nitrification are *chemoautotrophs*, because they are producing their own food energy (*autotroph*), not through photosynthesis but through chemical reactions.

Animals, in turn, obtain the nitrogen they need by consuming plants or other animals. Decomposers obtain nitrogen from dead and decaying plant and animal matter, and from animal urine and feces (as shown in **FIGURE 5.7**). Once decomposers process the nitrogen-rich compounds they take in, they release ammonium ions, again making these available to nitrifying bacteria to convert into nitrates and nitrites for plant use.

Denitrification   The next step in the nitrogen cycle is **denitrification**, which occurs when bacteria convert nitrates in soil or water into gaseous forms of nitrogen (either N_2, nitrous oxide, or nitric oxide). This, too, is a multistep process that is carried out by several varieties of microorganisms in anaerobic (nonoxygenated) conditions in soil. Denitrification thereby completes the cycle and balances the nitrogen-fixation process by releasing nitrogen back to the atmosphere.

Soil is an important terrestrial reservoir for carbon

The global carbon cycle is of considerable interest today, primarily because of its role in controlling climate. In studies of the carbon cycle, much attention is justifiably paid to the role of forests and the atmospheric and oceanic carbon reservoirs. However, it is also important to

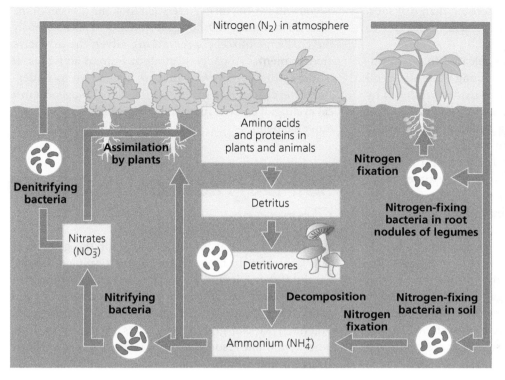

FIGURE 5.7
Specialized bacteria in soils convert atmospheric nitrogen into ammonium through the process of nitrogen fixation. Ammonium is transformed into nitrate, useable as a plant nutrient, by the process of nitrification. Finally, excess nitrate is converted back to the atmospheric gas N_2 through the process of denitrification. All of these processes are biologically mediated by microorganisms that live in soils and among the roots of certain plants.

recognize that soils play a crucial role in the global carbon cycle. Soil represents the largest terrestrial reservoir for carbon—about four times as large as the entire reservoir in terrestrial biota, including forests (FIGURE 5.8). The rock reservoir (below a depth of 1 metre or so) is considerably larger; however, carbon sequestered in rock is generally not active in the short-term carbon cycle unless it has been remobilized as a result of human activities, mainly through the burning of fossil fuels and manufacture of cement from carbonate rocks. (See The Science Behind the Story: "Dark Earth: A New (Old) Way to Sequester Carbon" for further discussion about carbon sequestration in soils.)

The main carbon fluxes in which soil is involved are driven by photosynthesis and the production of organic matter, followed by respiration and decay of organic matter. Carbon fluxes from the atmosphere to soils therefore generally pass through photosynthetic plants, which contribute litter and other organic matter to soils, either directly or via consumption by animals. The subsequent alteration of litter, animal waste, and soil organic matter results in the production of humus and the accumulation of carbon, especially in organic-rich soils such as peat.

In addition to producing humus, the decay of soil organic matter produces soil gas that contains carbon species. These decay processes are complex, and their specific chemistry depends on the decomposing microorganisms that are involved and on the physical-

chemical conditions within the soil. For example, the decay of organic matter in aerobic (oxygenated) conditions typically produces soil gas with a higher concentration of carbon dioxide (CO_2), whereas decay in anaerobic conditions tends to be slower and produces soil gas with a higher concentration of methane (CH_4).

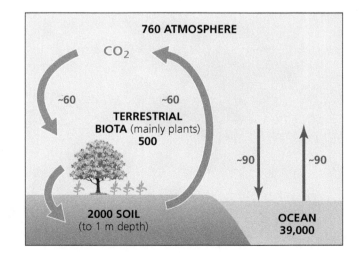

FIGURE 5.8
Soil is the largest active terrestrial reservoir for carbon. (The rock reservoir is considerably larger, but carbon in the rock reservoir is not active in the short-term global carbon cycle unless it is remobilized by human activity, mainly through the burning of fossil fuels and manufacture of cement from carbonate rocks.) Reservoir contents are shown in gigatonnes, and fluxes are shown in gigatonnes of carbon per year.

Wet soils are more likely to be anaerobic than dry soils, so the soil moisture conditions are also important to consider.

Carbon-bearing soil gases are released to the atmosphere (as shown in FIGURE 5.8) along with other soil gases, including the N_2 and nitrous oxides produced by denitrification, and radon produced by the radioactive decay of uranium in underlying bedrock. Both carbon dioxide and methane are greenhouse gases, so these fluxes are of significance in understanding the global climate system. In fact, methane is many times more effective than carbon dioxide as a greenhouse gas, so the specific conditions in which methane is produced in soils are of particular interest.

For example, soils in wetlands—which are (by definition) water-saturated for at least part of the year—vary both spatially and temporally in the relative proportions of carbon dioxide and methane gas they produce and in their ability to store and release carbon. Many perennially frozen soils (permafrost) are peat soils, which are significant reservoirs of carbon; scientists are beginning to investigate the potential consequences for the climate system if these carbon-rich soils were to thaw in a warming climate.

In short, most people recognize the importance of soils in supporting plant growth, particularly in the agricultural context (although this was not always the case—

as you will see, in North America it took the disaster of the Dust Bowl in the 1930s for governments to take seriously the challenge of soil conservation). Given the extensive environmental impacts of modern human activities, it is increasingly important that we also strive to understand the crucial role of soils in the global biogeochemical cycling of carbon, nitrogen, phosphorus, sulphur, and other elements.

Soil Degradation: A Global Concern

Healthy soil is vital for agriculture, for the growth of forests, and for the biogeochemical functioning of Earth's natural systems, including the climate system. Productive soil is a renewable resource, but not on a human time scale. If we abuse it through careless or uninformed practices, we can greatly reduce its productivity. Like other renewable resources, if soil is degraded or depleted at a rate that is faster than the rate at which it can be renewed, it effectively becomes nonrenewable.

Throughout the world, especially in drier regions, soils have become eroded and degraded (FIGURE 5.9). **Soil degradation**, that is, damage to or loss of soil, worldwide has resulted from erosion caused by roughly

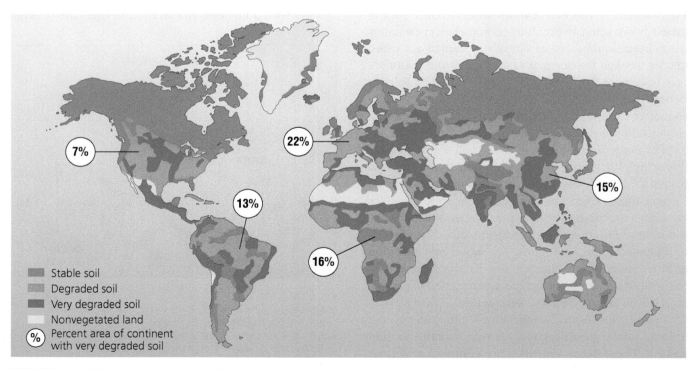

FIGURE 5.9   Soils are becoming degraded in many areas worldwide. Europe currently has a higher proportion of degraded land than other continents because of its long history of intensive agriculture, but degradation is rising quickly in developing countries in Africa and Asia. *Source: Data from United Nations Environment Programme (UNEP), 2002. Global Environmental Outlook 3. London: UNEP and Earthscan Publ.*

equal parts forest removal, poorly managed cropland agriculture, and over-grazing of livestock, with a much smaller (but still significant) contribution from industrial contamination (FIGURE 5.10A). Additional causes of soil degradation include mining, construction, acid rain, and other sources of chemical contamination; we will consider all of these in subsequent chapters.

Scientists' studies of soil and the practical experience of farmers have shown that the most desirable soil for agriculture is a loamy mixture with a pH close to neutral, which is workable and capable of holding nutrients. Many soils deviate from this ideal and prevent land from being arable or limit the productivity of arable land (FIGURE 5.10B). Increasingly, limits to productivity are being set by human impact that has degraded many once-excellent soils. Common problems affecting soil productivity include erosion, desertification, salinization, waterlogging, nutrient depletion, structural breakdown, and pollution.

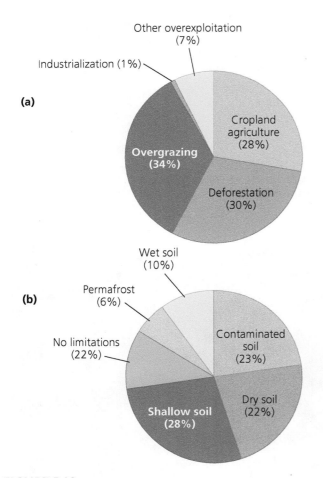

FIGURE 5.10
(a) Most of the world's soil degradation results from cropland agriculture, over-grazing by livestock, and deforestation. Data based on information from UNEP. **(b)** Various factors limit the agricultural productivity of soil, as shown in this diagram based on information from the United Nations Food and Agriculture Organization.

Regional differences affect soil productivity

The characteristics of soil and soil profiles vary from place to place. One striking example is the difference between soils of tropical rainforests and those of temperate grasslands. Although rainforest ecosystems have high primary productivity, most of their nutrients are tied up in plant tissues and are not in the soil (FIGURE 5.11). For example, the soil of Amazonian rainforest is much less productive than the soil of the grasslands in Saskatchewan.

To understand how this can be, consider the main differences between the two regions: temperature and rainfall. The enormous amount of rain that falls in the Amazon readily leaches minerals and nutrients out of the topsoil. Those not captured by plants are taken quickly down to the water table, out of reach of most plants' roots. High temperatures speed the decomposition of leaf litter and the uptake of nutrients by plants, so amounts of humus remain small, and the topsoil layer remains thin.

This means that most of the organic matter in the tropical rainforest environment is thus held in the above-ground plant biomass (as shown in FIGURE 5.11). Thus when forest is cleared for farming, cultivation quickly depletes the soil's fertility. This is why the traditional form of agriculture in tropical forested areas is *swidden* agriculture, in which the farmer cultivates a plot for one to a few years and then moves on to clear another plot, leaving the first to grow back to forest (FIGURE 5.12). This method may work well at low population densities, but with today's high human populations, soils may not be allowed enough time to regenerate. As a result, intensive agriculture has ruined the soils and forests of many tropical areas.

In temperate grassland areas such as the Saskatchewan prairies, in contrast, rainfall is low enough that leaching is reduced and nutrients remain high in the soil profile,

roots

SWIDDEN

Swidden agriculture is a practice where an area of forest is cleared and cultivated for a few years and then left to regrow while farmers move on to clear a new area for agriculture. The word **swidden**, first used around 1868, derives from the Old Norse word *svithinn* (from the verb *svitha*), meaning "to burn or singe," and therefore refers to land made available by burning.

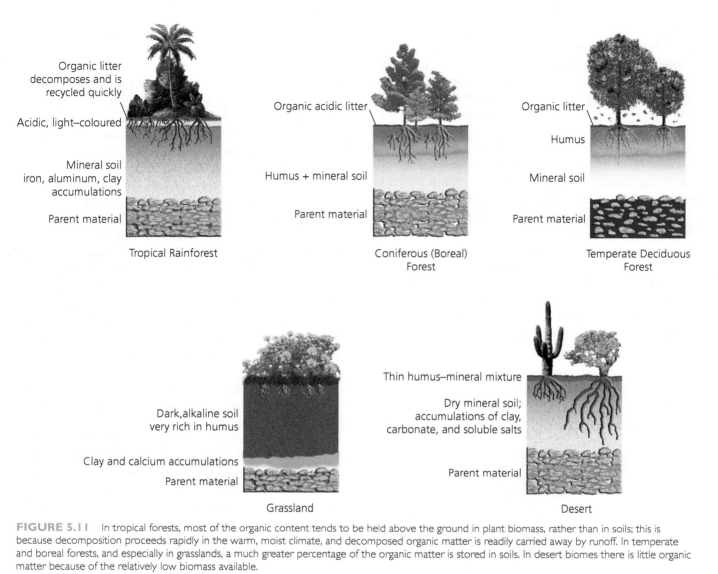

FIGURE 5.11   In tropical forests, most of the organic content tends to be held above the ground in plant biomass, rather than in soils; this is because decomposition proceeds rapidly in the warm, moist climate, and decomposed organic matter is readily carried away by runoff. In temperate and boreal forests, and especially in grasslands, a much greater percentage of the organic matter is stored in soils. In desert biomes there is little organic matter because of the relatively low biomass available.

FIGURE 5.12

In tropical forested areas, the traditional form of farming is swidden agriculture, as seen here in Surinam. In this practice, forest is cleared, often by burning; the plot is farmed for one to a few years; and the farmer then moves on to clear another plot, leaving the first to regrow into forest. Frequent movement is necessary because tropical soils are nutrient-poor, with nearly all nutrients held in the vegetation. Burning the cut vegetation adds nutrients to the soil, which is why this practice is often called "slash-and-burn" agriculture. At low population densities, this form of farming had little large-scale impact on forests, but at today's high population densities, it is a leading cause of deforestation.

within reach of plants' roots. Plants take up nutrients and then return them directly to the topsoil when they die; this cycle maintains the soil's fertility. In addition, cool temperatures slow the rate of decomposition of organic matter. Most of the organic matter in this system is stored below ground, in the soil (as shown in FIGURE 5.11), and the thick, rich topsoil of temperate grasslands can be farmed repeatedly with minimal loss of fertility if proper farming techniques are used.

However, even in the rich soils of temperate grasslands, growing and harvesting crops without returning adequate organic matter to the soil gradually depletes soil organic matter. Leaving soil exposed to the elements also increases the rate of erosion of topsoil. It is such consequences that farmers in many locations around the world have sought to forestall through the use of agricultural approaches to soil conservation.

Erosion can degrade ecosystems and agriculture

Erosion, as we have noted, is the removal of weathered material from one place and its transport to another by the action of wind, water, or (in some cases) glacial ice. **Deposition** of sediment is the other end of this process—the arrival of the eroded material at its new location. Erosion and deposition are natural processes that in the long run can help create soil. Flowing water can deposit eroded sediment in river valleys and deltas, producing rich and productive soils. This is why floodplains are excellent for farming and why flood control measures can decrease the productivity of agriculture in the long run.

However, accelerated erosion is associated with human activity and is a problem locally for ecosystems and agriculture because it takes place much more quickly than soil is formed. Furthermore, erosion tends to remove topsoil, the most valuable soil layer for living things. People have increased the vulnerability of fertile lands to erosion through three widespread practices:

1. Over-cultivating fields through poor planning or excessive ploughing, particularly when land is left bare of vegetative cover
2. Over-grazing rangelands with more livestock than the land can support, resulting in reduced vegetative cover
3. Clearing forested areas on steep slopes or with large clear-cuts

Erosion can be gradual and hard to detect, but still devastating in the long run. For example, an erosion rate of 12 tonnes/ha/yr removes only a penny's thickness of soil per year. That doesn't seem like much until you

realize that it would have taken anywhere between 75 and 1500 years to produce a layer of soil the thickness of a penny. In many parts of the world, scientists, farmers, and extension agents are measuring erosion rates in hopes of identifying areas in danger of serious degradation before they become too badly damaged.

Soil erodes by several mechanisms

Several types of erosion can occur, including wind erosion and four principal kinds of water erosion (FIGURE 5.13).

Research indicates that rill erosion has the greatest potential to move topsoil, followed by sheet erosion and splash erosion, respectively. All types of water erosion—particularly gully erosion—are more likely to occur where slopes are steeper. In general, steeper slopes, greater precipitation intensities, and sparser vegetative cover all lead to greater water erosion.

The *Universal Soil Loss Equation (USLE)* was developed as a tool for estimating erosion losses by water from cultivated fields and to show how different soil and management factors influence soil erosion (TABLE 5.3). A revised version of the USLE is used in

Table 5.3	Universal Soil Loss Equation	
	A = R K LS C P	
A	Predicted soil loss due to water erosion	Results in t/ha/yr
R	Erosivity factor	Quantifies the erosive energy of rainfall and runoff; takes into account both total amount of rainfall and its intensity.
K	Soil erodibility factor	Represents the ease with which a soil is eroded; based on the cohesiveness of a soil and its resistance to detachment and transport.
LS	Slope length and steepness factor	Steeper slopes lead to higher flow velocities; longer plots accumulate runoff from larger areas and result in higher flow velocities.
C	Vegetative cover and management factor	Considers the type and density of vegetative cover as well as all related management practices such as tillage, fertilization, and irrigation.
P	Erosion control practices factor	Influence of conservation practices such as contour planting, strip cropping, grassed waterways, and terracing relative to the erosion potential of simple up–down slope cultivation.

Source: Based on material from www.landfood.ubc.ca/soil200/soil_mgmt/soil_erosion.htm.

(a) Splash erosion

(c) Rill erosion

(d) Gully erosion

(b) Sheet erosion

FIGURE 5.13   *Splash erosion* **(a)** occurs as raindrops strike the ground with enough force to dislodge small amounts of soil. *Sheet erosion* **(b)** results when thin layers of water traverse broad expanses of sloping land. *Rill erosion* **(c)** leaves small pathways along the surface where water has carried topsoil away. *Gully erosion* **(d)** cuts deep into soil, leaving large gullies that can expand as erosion proceeds.

Canada to estimate losses from soil erosion, mainly for the purpose of soil conservation planning. It utilizes the same variables as the original format, but with refinements for quantifying their values in situations that are more common in Canada (for example, if frost is present, some of the factors will be applied differently).[2]

Wind, like water, is a moving fluid. Wind often flows very quickly over the surface, but it typically does not have the same ability to pick up and transport soil particles that water has. Nevertheless, wind can be a highly effective agent of erosion. Wind erosion, also called *aeolian erosion*, operates mainly by *deflation*, in which all loose, fine-grained material is picked up from the surface and carried away by wind. Another important mechanism of wind erosion is *abrasion*, whereby wind-transported particles become "projectiles," striking other rocks at the surface and causing them to break up.

Table 5.4   Wind Erosion Prediction Equation

$$E = f(I\,C\,K\,L\,V)$$

E	Predicted soil loss due to wind erosion	Results in t/ha/yr
I	Soil erodibility factor	Represents the ease with which a soil is eroded by the abrasive action of wind-carried particles; dependent upon a number of factors including soil texture and aggregation.
C	Local wind erosion climate factor	Quantified as the wind energy available to erode soil; takes into account moisture, wind speed, and wind direction. Wind erosion is most common in arid and semiarid regions.
K	Roughness factor	Describes the surface roughness of the soil; greater roughness indicates greater resistance to erosion.
L	Length of field factor	A measure of the unsheltered length of the field; a longer field will have higher wind velocities and thus greater erosion potential.
V	Vegetative cover factor	Accounts for cover type and density, including cover from crop residues; erosion risk is greatest when there is least cover.

The *Wind Erosion Prediction Equation* shows how wind erosion is a function of five factors and their interactions (**TABLE 5.4**).

Grasslands, forests, and any other healthy plant cover protect soil from both wind and water erosion. Vegetation breaks the wind and slows water flow, and plant roots hold soil in place and take up water. Removing plant cover will nearly always accelerate erosion.

Soil erosion is widespread

In today's world, humans are the primary cause of erosion, and we have accelerated it to unnaturally high rates. In a 2004 study, geologist Bruce Wilkinson analyzed prehistoric erosion rates from the geologic record and compared these with modern rates. He concluded that humans are over 10 times more influential at moving soil than are all other natural processes on the surface of the planet combined.

More than 19 billion ha of the world's croplands suffer from erosion and other forms of soil degradation resulting from human activities. In the last half of the twentieth century, China lost as much arable farmland as exists in Denmark, France, Germany, and the Netherlands combined. In Kazakhstan, industrial cropland agriculture has caused tens of millions of hectares to be degraded by

wind erosion. For Africa, soil degradation over the next 40 years could reduce crop yields by half. Couple these declines in soil quality and crop yields with the rapid population growth occurring in many of these areas, and we begin to see why some observers describe the future of agriculture as a crisis situation.

Erosion of agricultural soil has been a significant concern in Canada for the past 25 years or more, but improvements are occurring. Soil researchers from Agriculture and Agri-Food Canada have determined the on-farm cost of agricultural land degradation in Canada to be almost $670 million per year.[3] However, the same report showed significant reductions in the area of cropland at risk of erosion in recent years. Approximately 85% of cropland area in Canada was deemed to be in the "tolerable" range of risk for water-related erosion as of 1996, a 22% improvement over the situation 15 years earlier. The wind erosion risk improved by 59% over the same period. A combination of reduced tillage, less intensive crop production, and removal of *marginal land* (that is, land ill-suited to agriculture) from production were cited as contributing to lower erosion rates.[4] Other sources[5] also point to changes in farming techniques since the recognition of a soil erosion crisis in the early 1980s; these changes have led to overall improvement in the health and stability of Canada's soils.

Desertification reduces productivity of arid lands

Much of the world's population lives and farms in arid environments, where **desertification** is a concern. This term describes a loss of more than 10% productivity due to erosion, soil compaction, forest removal, over-grazing, drought, salinization, climate change, depletion of water sources, and other factors. The terms *desertification* and *degradation* are often confused, and the United Nations is careful to distinguish them.[6] Land degradation is the reduction or loss of the biological or economic productivity of land. Desertification is a type of land degradation that occurs in arid and semiarid areas and can result from various factors, including climatic variations and human activities.

Severe desertification can result in the expansion of desert areas or creation of new ones in areas that once supported fertile land (**FIGURE 5.14A**). This process has occurred in many areas of the Middle East that have been inhabited, farmed, and grazed for long periods of time. To appreciate the cumulative impact of centuries of traditional agriculture, we need only look at the present desertified state of that portion of the Middle East where agriculture originated, nicknamed the "Fertile Crescent."

FIGURE 5.14
(a) Desertification occurs when formerly productive land turns into desert, as shown here in this photo from Mauritania, Africa. **(b)** Canada is not exempt from the impacts of wind erosion, as shown in this photo from the Dust Bowl of the 1930s.

(a)

(b)

These arid lands—in present-day Iraq, Syria, Turkey, Lebanon, and Israel—are not so fertile anymore.

Arid and semi-arid lands are prone to desertification because their precipitation is too meagre to meet the greater demands in productivity from a growing human population. According to the United Nations Environment Programme (UNEP), 40% of Earth's land surface can be classified as drylands, arid areas that are particularly subject to degradation. Declines of soil quality in these areas have endangered the food supply or well-being of more than 1 billion people around the world.

In the affected lands, most degradation results from wind and water erosion. In recent years, gigantic dust storms from denuded land in China have blown across the Pacific Ocean to North America, and dust storms from Africa's Sahara Desert have blown across the Atlantic Ocean to the Caribbean Sea. Such massive dust storms occurred in the Canadian Prairies and the Great Plains of the United States during the Dust Bowl days of the early twentieth century,

when desertification shook North American agriculture and society to their very roots (**FIGURE 5.14B**).

It has been estimated that desertification affects fully one-third of the planet's land area, impinging on the lives of 250 million people[7] and costing tens of billions of dollars in lost income per year. China alone loses $6.5 billion annually from desertification. In its western reaches, desert areas are expanding and joining one another because of over-grazing from over 400 million goats, sheep, and cattle. In the Sistan Basin, on the border of Iran and Afghanistan, an oasis that supported a million livestock recently turned barren in just five years, and windblown sand buried over 100 villages. In Kenya, over-grazing and deforestation fuelled by rapid population growth has left 80% of its land vulnerable to desertification. In a positive feedback cycle, the soil degradation forces ranchers to crowd onto more marginal land and farmers to reduce fallow periods, both of which further exacerbate soil degradation.

A 2007 United Nations report estimated that desertification, worsened by climate change, could result in the displacement of 50 million people in 10 years. The report suggested that industrialized nations fund reforestation projects in dryland areas of the developing world to slow desertification while gaining carbon credits in emissions trading programs.

The Dust Bowl was a monumental event in North America

Prior to large-scale cultivation of the Prairies and the Great Plains, native prairie grasses of this temperate grassland region held erosion-prone soils in place. The American bison played a significant role as a keystone species in this ecosystem. In the late nineteenth and early twentieth centuries, however, many homesteading settlers arrived with hopes of making a living there as farmers. Between 1879 and 1929, cultivated area in the region soared, driven primarily by rapid increases in the price of wheat. Bison were hunted almost to extinction. Farmers in the region grew abundant wheat, and ranchers grazed many thousands of cattle, sometimes expanding onto unsuitable land. Both types of agriculture contributed to erosion by removing native grasses and breaking down soil structure.

At the end of 1929 the stock market crashed, sending the price of wheat lower than the price of seed; the Great Depression began, and with it an inexorable cycle of poverty and land degradation that would last most of the decade. Starting in the early 1930s, a prolonged period of drought in the region exacerbated the ongoing human impacts on the soil from overly intensive agricultural practices. Strong winds began to carry away millions of tonnes of topsoil, and often newly planted seed, as well. Dust storms travelled up to 2000 km, blackening skies and coating the skins of farm workers. Some areas lost as much as 10 cm of topsoil in a few short years.

The affected region in the Prairies and Great Plains became known as the *Dust Bowl*, a term now also used for the historical event itself. The "black blizzards" of the Dust Bowl (see FIGURE 5.14B) destroyed livelihoods and caused many people to suffer a type of chronic lung irritation and degradation known as dust pneumonia, similar to the silicosis that afflicts coal miners exposed to high concentrations of coal dust. Large numbers of farmers were forced off their land; those who stayed faced infestations of grasshoppers so thick that they clogged car radiators and made the roads slippery. Chickens and turkeys ate the grasshoppers, which caused their meat and eggs to develop a bad taste. There were no pesticides (chemical pesticides had not yet been invented) and no way to control the grasshoppers.

By 1937, Dust Bowl conditions had reached their peak. Since the price of wheat was so low, farmers began to plant alternative crops, such as oats, rye, flax, peas, and alfalfa. They adapted to the dry weather with reduced tilling, crop rotations (to allow the soil a chance to replenish itself), and fertilizer applications. By the end of the decade, the slow recovery from the Dust Bowl had begun.[8]

The Soil Conservation Council emerged from the experience of drought

In 1935 the Prairie Farm Rehabilitation Administration (PFRA) was set up; interestingly, however, it was not until the early 1980s that the issue of soil erosion and the degradation of agricultural soils really took centre stage in Canada on a nationwide basis. This occurred partly as a result of another serious drought in the late 1970s, followed by the publication in 1984 of a book by the federal government titled *Soil at Risk: Canada's Eroding Future*.[9] In that publication, the Standing Committee on Agriculture, Fisheries, and Forestry (also known as the Sparrow Commission) concluded, "Canada risks permanently losing a large portion of its agricultural capability if a major commitment to conserving the soil is not made immediately by all levels of government and by all Canadians." The following year saw the first National Soil Conservation Week and the establishment of the National Soil Conservation Program.

The Soil Conservation Council of Canada was established in 1987, with the following goals:

- To develop a national spirit to foster a feeling of unity among those who are concerned for soil conservation
- To improve the level of understanding and awareness about the causes of soil degradation among all Canadians and to increase their support of soil conservation goals
- To facilitate communication among soil conservation groups, governments, and industry relating to soil conservation needs, programs, and policies
- To communicate to the general public policies, programs, or activities that affect the sustainable use of this country's soil resources
- To encourage the development of policies, production methods, and management systems for agriculture, forestry, and land use that enables sustainable use of our soil and related resources.[10]

Today a number of federal government agencies (as well as provincial and territorial agencies) provide services to assist farmers with all aspects of soil management and conservation in Canada. The PFRA still exists, but it is now one component of a broader organization, the Agri-Environment Services Branch (AESB) of Agriculture and Agri-Food Canada, which was set up specifically to address agricultural and soil-related environmental issues. The organization was an integration of three previously existing federal agencies: the PFRA, the National Land and Water Information Service (NLWIS), and the Agri-Environmental Policy Bureau. The AESB promotes "an integrated approach to sustainable agriculture in Canada which recognizes that environmentally responsible agriculture and competitive agriculture are part of an integrated system."[11]

Internationally, the United Nations promotes soil conservation and sustainable agriculture through a variety of programs of its Food and Agriculture Organization (FAO). The FAO's Farmer–Centred Agricultural Resource Management Program (FAR) is a project that supports innovative approaches to resource management and sustainable agriculture in China, Thailand, Vietnam, Indonesia, Sri Lanka, Nepal, the Philippines, and India. The program studies agricultural success stories and tries to help other farmers duplicate the successful efforts. Rather than following a top-down, government-controlled approach, the FAR program relies on the creativity of local communities to educate and encourage farmers throughout Asia to conserve soils and secure their food supply.

Protecting Soils

As environmental problems go, soil erosion has two good things going for it: most of the approaches that can be used to protect soils are neither technologically sophis-

ticated nor excessively costly. Most often, soil can be protected by modifying practices in farming and forestry.

Erosion-control practices protect and restore plant cover

Farming and forestry methods to control erosion make use of the general principle that maximizing vegetative cover will protect soils, and this principle has been applied widely. It is common to stabilize eroding banks along creeks and roadsides by planting plants to anchor the soil, or in rows to protect open fields from the wind (FIGURE 5.15A). In areas with severe and widespread erosion, some nations have planted vast plantations of fast-growing trees. For example, China has embarked on the world's largest tree-planting program to slow its soil loss (FIGURE 5.15B). Although such reforestation efforts do help slow erosion, they do not at the same time produce ecologically functioning forests, because tree species are selected only for their fast growth and are planted in monocultures.

Several farming techniques can reduce the impacts of conventional cultivation on soils. Such measures have been widely shared and applied in many places around the world, and some have been practised by traditional farmers for centuries.

Crop rotation   The practice of alternating the kind of crop grown in a particular field from one season or year to the next is called *crop rotation* (FIGURE 5.16A). Rotating crops can return nutrients to the soil, break cycles of disease associated with continuous cropping, and minimize erosion that can come from letting fields lie

(a)   (b)

FIGURE 5.15   Rows of trees designed to shelter farm fields against the wind are now common in Canada's Prairie agricultural lands **(a)**. Vast swaths of countryside in western China have been planted with fast-growing poplar trees **(b)**. These reforestation efforts can slow erosion but do not create ecologically functional forests because the plantations are too biologically simple.

exposed. Farmers in Alberta, Prince Edward Island, and elsewhere have returned to an earlier farming approach in which they plant alternating swaths of land each year, but leave the field stubble from the previous year to protect fields from exposure to wind and water erosion. Many farmers rotate between wheat or corn and soybeans from one year to the next. Soybeans are legumes, with nitrogen-fixing bacteria among their roots, so they can revitalize soil that the previous crop had partially depleted of nutrients. Crop rotation also reduces insect pests; if an insect is adapted to feed and lay eggs on one particular crop, planting a different crop will leave its offspring with nothing to eat.

Intercropping and agroforestry   Farmers may also gain protection against erosion by *intercropping*, planting different types of crops in alternating bands or other spatially mixed arrangements (**FIGURE 5.16B**). Intercropping helps slow erosion by providing more complete ground cover than does a single crop. Like crop rotation, intercropping offers the additional benefits of reducing vulnerability to insect and disease incidence, and, when a nitrogen-fixing legume is one of the crops, of replenishing the soil. Cover crops can be physically mixed with primary food crops, which include maize, soybeans, wheat, onions, cassava, grapes, tomatoes, tobacco, and orchard fruit.

When crops are interplanted with trees, in a practice called **agroforestry**, even more benefits can be realized. Agroforestry systems are generally more biologically productive than farm systems in which food crops are grown alone. One reason is that trees draw nutrients and water from deep in the soil through their root systems, cycling them into the shallower layers of soil. They also contribute organic material to the topsoil, in the form of tree litter, such as fallen branches and leaves. Trees can also provide partial shade for crops, although light levels must be managed by appropriate pruning and spacing of the trees. In many agricultural regions, especially in the developing world where small-scale agriculture is still practised, agroforestry provides a low-cost way to close the nutrient cycle and rehabilitate soils while providing other sustainably harvested forest products such as fruits, nuts, and timber.

Contour farming and terracing   Water running down a hillside can easily carry soil away, particularly if there is too little vegetative cover to hold the soil in place. Thus, sloped land is especially vulnerable to erosion. Several methods have been developed for farming on slopes. *Contour farming* (**FIGURE 5.16C**) consists of ploughing furrows sideways across a hillside, perpendicular to its slope, to help prevent formation of rills and

gullies. The technique is so named because the furrows follow the natural contours of the land. In contour farming, the downhill side of each furrow acts as a small dam that slows runoff and catches soil before it is carried away. Contour farming is most effective on gradually sloping land with crops that grow well in rows.

On extremely steep terrain, *terracing* (**FIGURE 5.16D**) is the most effective method for preventing erosion. Terraces are level platforms, sometimes with raised edges, that are cut into steep hillsides to contain water from irrigation and precipitation. Terracing transforms slopes into series of steps like a staircase, enabling farmers to cultivate hilly land without losing huge amounts of soil to water erosion. Terracing is common in ruggedly mountainous regions, such as the foothills of the Himalayas and the Andes, and has been used for centuries by farming communities in such areas. Terracing is labour-intensive to establish but in the long term is likely the only sustainable way to farm in mountainous terrain.

Shelterbelts   A widespread technique to reduce erosion from wind is to establish **shelterbelts** (**FIGURE 5.16E**). Shelterbelts are *windbreaks*—rows of trees or tall shrubs that are planted along the edges of fields to slow the wind. Shelterbelts have been widely planted across the Prairies and the Great Plains, where fast-growing species such as poplars are often used. The Ontario Ministry of Agriculture, Food, and Rural Affairs documents more than 67 000 shelterbelts installations in Ontario alone.[12] They cite up to a 15% increase in crop yield associated with shelterbelt but decline to quantify the amount of soil conserved as a result of the approach. Shelterbelts are combined with intercropping in a practice known as *alley cropping*. In this approach, fields planted in rows of mixed crops are surrounded by or interspersed with rows of trees that provide fruit, wood, or protection from wind. Agroforestry and alley cropping methods are widely used in India, Africa, China, and Brazil, where coffee growers commonly combine farming and forestry.

Reduced tillage   Repeated cycles of ploughing and planting over many decades diminishe the productivity of the soil and render it more susceptible to erosion. To plant using the *reduced-tillage* or *no-till* method (**FIGURE 5.16F**), a tractor pulls a drill that cuts long, shallow furrows through the litter of dead weeds and crop residue and the upper levels of the A horizon. The device drops seeds into the furrow and closes the furrow over the seeds. Often a localized dose of fertilizer is added to the soil along with the seeds. By increasing organic matter and soil biota while reducing erosion, no-till and reduced tillage farming can build soil up, aerate it, restore it, and improve it. Proponents of no-till farming claim that the

(a) Crop rotation

(b) Intercropping

(c) Contour farming

(d) Terracing

(e) Shelterbelts

(f) No-till farming

FIGURE 5.16   The world's farmers have adopted various strategies to conserve soil. Rotating crops such as soybeans and corn **(a)** helps restore soil nutrients and reduce impacts of crop pests. Intercropping **(b)** can reduce soil loss while maintaining soil fertility. Contour farming **(c)** reduces erosion on hillsides, whereas terracing **(d)** is most useful in steep mountainous areas. Shelterbelts **(e)** protect against wind erosion. In **(f)**, corn grows up from amid the remnants of a "cover crop" used in reduced-tillage agriculture.

practice offers a number of benefits, including higher crop yields, reduced erosion, reduced costs of land preparation, and a reduced carbon footprint.

The no-till or reduced-tillage practice has been widely adopted in Canada, but not with unmitigated success.

The Soil Conservation Council of Canada estimates that as much as 50% of some crops in Ontario are now grown using a no-till approach, including wheat and soybeans. However, some crops—notably corn—are not amenable to reduced tillage, which tends to keep the soil colder and moister for longer than conventional tillage methods (because litter mulch is applied).[13] Critics of no-till and reduced-tillage farming also note that these techniques often require substantial use of chemical herbicides (because weeds are controlled chemically rather than physically removed from fields) and synthetic fertilizer (because other plants take up a significant portion of the soil's nutrients).

Irrigation can cause long-term soil problems

Erosion is not the only threat to the health and integrity of soils. Soil degradation can result from other factors as well, such as impacts caused by the application of water to support crop growth—that is, *irrigation*. If the climate is too dry or too much water evaporates or runs off before it can be absorbed into the soil, crops may require irrigation. The soil's ability to hold water and make it available to plant roots also influences the amount of irrigation required. Some crops, such as rice and cotton, require large amounts of water, whereas others, such as beans and wheat, require relatively little.

By irrigating croplands, people have managed to turn previously dry and unproductive regions into fertile farmland. Currently about 70% of all fresh water withdrawn by people is used for irrigation. Irrigated land area increased dramatically around the world starting in the 1950s, reaching almost 2.8 million ha by 2003. Since then, the rate of increase has declined as a result of limited availability of both fresh water and new arable land.

If some water is good for plants and soil, it might seem that more must be better. But this is not necessarily the case; there is indeed such a thing as too much water. Over-irrigation in poorly drained areas can cause or exacerbate certain soil problems. Soils too saturated with water may become waterlogged. When **waterlogging** occurs, the water table is raised to the point that water bathes plant roots, depriving them of access to gases and essentially suffocating them. If it lasts long enough, waterlogging can damage or kill plants.

An even more frequent problem is **salinization** (or *salination*), the buildup of salts in surface soil layers. In dryland areas where precipitation is minimal and evaporation rates are high, water evaporating from the A horizon may pull saline water up from lower horizons by capillary action. As this water rises through the soil, it carries dissolved salts; when the water evaporates at the surface, those salts precipitate and are left at the surface. Eventually, high salinity levels can make the soil inhospitable to plants. Irrigation in arid

FIGURE 5.17
Salinization can result from over-irrigation, especially in arid and semi-arid regions. It is a widespread problem affecting agricultural soils, as shown here in Alberta. The white crust on the surface is a toxic layer of salts.

areas generally hastens salinization, because it provides repeated doses of moderate amounts of water, which dissolve salts in the soil and gradually raise them to the surface. Moreover, because irrigation water often contains some dissolved salt in the first place, irrigation introduces new sources of salt to the soil. In many areas of farmland where over-irrigation has occurred, soils are turning white with encrusted salt (**FIGURE 5.17**).

Salinization now inhibits agricultural production on one-fifth of all irrigated cropland globally, costing more than $11 billion annually. As of 2000, the Food and Agriculture Organization of the United Nations estimated that the total area of salinized soil is 397 million ha. Of 230 million ha of irrigated land, 45 million ha (or 19.5%) of soil were affected by salt, and of 1500 million ha of dryland agriculture, 32 million ha (or 2.1%) of soil were affected by salinization due to human activities.[14]

The remedies for correcting salinization once it has occurred are more expensive and difficult to implement

weighing the issues

MEASURING AND REGULATING SOIL QUALITY

The Government of Canada has adopted comprehensive measures of air quality and water quality and has set legal standards for allowable levels of various pollutants in air and water. Could such standards be developed for soil quality? If so, what properties should be measured to inform the standards?

THE SCIENCE BEHIND THE STORY

Dark Earth: A New (Old) Way to Sequester Carbon

Prof. Johannes Lehmann holds a bowl of wood chips (right), biomass that can be turned into biochar (left).

About 15 years ago, while doing field work in the central Amazon of Brazil, Dr. Johannes Lehmann encountered patches of unusually dark, rich, fertile soil, locally called *terra preta*, or "black earth" in Portuguese. To Dr. Lehmann, a professor in the Department of Crop and Soil Sciences at Cornell University, these dark patches of soil stood out amongst the agriculturally degraded, nutrient-poor soils of the Amazon.

Further research on *terra preta* by Dr. Lehmann and other researchers has revealed that the black soil is a remnant of pre-Columbian indigenous residents of the area, from as long ago as 450 BCE. It is probable that the charcoal-like *terra preta* was not made intentionally, but rather accumulated over time as a black, carbon-rich residue of cooking fires and pottery

kilns. Indigenous farmers are thought to have used this residue as an addition to soils, to increase their fertility. Hundreds and even thousands of years later, the black earth is still in place, an indication of its surprising stability.

Dr. Lehmann, who is particularly interested in nutrient cycling and carbon storage in soils, recognized in *terra preta* the potential for a carbon reservoir that would be significantly longer lasting than trees or even natural soils. He began to research methods for producing black earth. The most promising technology for this has turned out to be *pyrolysis*, which is a relatively straightforward, low-temperature heating process, whereby biomass (either plant or animal matter) is reduced to a black, carbon-rich, charcoal-like residue. This residue has been named *biochar*.

A photomicrograph of biochar **(see photo)** reveals that it is riddled with tiny, micron-sized pore spaces. The complexity of the spaces and surfaces partly explain the efficiency of biochar at holding onto plant nutrients and thus enhancing the fertility of soils. Biochar also appears to be very effective at absorbing and holding some pollutants, notably heavy metals, potentially contributing to improvements in water quality.

But the most exciting prospect of all, according to Professor Lehmann and other biochar reasearchers, is the possibility of using biochar to enhance the ability of soils

to act as long-term reservoirs for carbon. Soils are already the most important terrestrial reservoir for carbon—even larger than forests and grasslands (see "Interpreting Graphs and Data"). If adding biochar could greatly increase the longevity and stability of the soil reservoir, thus sequestering carbon from the atmosphere, it could help in the fight against rising atmospheric carbon and global warming.

The success of biochar as a method of carbon sequestration depends on the

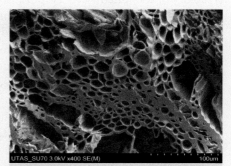

UTAS_SU70 3.0kV x400 SE(M)   100um

Biochar (seen here in a photomicrograph, magnified thousands of times) has many complex, micron-sized pore spaces and surfaces. This partly accounts for some of biochar's properties, such as the capacity to improve water and soil quality by absorbing pollutants and holding on to fertilizers and plant nutrients.

---

than the techniques for preventing it in the first place. The best way to prevent salinization is to avoid planting crops that require a great deal of water in areas that are prone to the problem. A second way is to irrigate with water that is as low as possible in salt content. A third way is to irrigate efficiently, supplying no more water than the crop requires, thus minimizing the amount of water that evaporates and hence the amount of salt that accumulates in the topsoil. This can be accomplished through the use of drip systems that target water directly to the plant roots.

If salinization has occurred, one possible way to mitigate it is to stop irrigating and wait for rain to infil-

trate and leach the salts from the soil. However, this solution is often unfeasible because salinization is mainly a problem in dryland areas, where precipitation is inadequate to flush salts from the soil. A better option may be to plant salt-tolerant plants, such as barley, that can be used as food or pasture. A third option is to bring in large quantities of less-saline water with which to flush the soil; however, using too much water may cause waterlogging. The most effective, but most expensive, option is to install artificial drainage to lower the level of the saline water table below a depth where it can be drawn up to the soil surface. Rain or irrigation can then flush the remaining salts away from the rooting zone.

technologies that are used. They require energy inputs, which contribute to carbon dioxide emissions. The key is to balance the carbon emitted to the atmosphere as a result of the pyrolysis process with the carbon sequestered through the production of biochar. Dr. Lehmann's calculations show that with low-temperature pyrolysis of biomass it should be possible to halve the amount of carbon being released to the atmosphere, as compared to natural decomposition of the biomass.

Using pyrolysis to produce biochar also has an economic cost, which represents a potential barrier to its adoption as an approach for mitigating carbon emissions. One way to improve its economic competitiveness is to promote the use of biochar as an agricultural amendment for the improvement of soil fertility (see diagram). Another is to capture the heat released during the pyrolysis process and use it as a form of bioenergy. One of the most intriguing aspects of biochar is that the technologies are simple and adaptable even in remote settings. It is possible that someday soon farmers all over the world will be enhancing their soils with biochar while capturing and sequestering carbon at the same time.

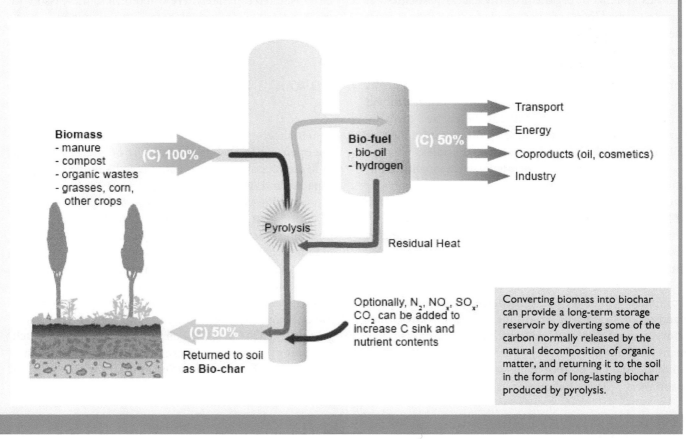

Converting biomass into biochar can provide a long-term storage reservoir by diverting some of the carbon normally released by the natural decomposition of organic matter, and returning it to the soil in the form of long-lasting biochar produced by pyrolysis.

Other chemicals also contribute to soil contamination

Salinization is not the only source of chemical damage to soil. Over-application of fertilizers can also chemically damage soils. Even organic fertilizers such as manure, when applied in amounts needed to supply sufficient nitrogen for a crop, may introduce excess phosphorus that can run off into waterways. Inorganic (mineral-based, industrially produced) fertilizers are generally more susceptible than are organic fertilizers to leaching and runoff, and they are somewhat more likely to cause soil degradation and off-site impacts.

Nitrogen and phosphorus runoff from farms and other sources can lead to phytoplankton (algal) blooms, creating oxygen-depleted "dead zones" in river mouths, lakes, and marine coastal zones throughout the world. Moreover, nitrates readily leach through soil and contaminate groundwater, and components of some nitrogen fertilizers can even volatilize (evaporate) into the air. Nitrate and phosphate buildup in soil and water systems also pose human health risks, including cancer and methemoglobinemia, or "blue-baby" syndrome. Many negative side effects of fertilizer use can be reduced by proper timing and appropriate application methods, and by regular testing of the soil to determine whether, what type, and how much fertilizer is needed, thus matching the fertilizer delivery to the amount that can be utilized by crops.

Pesticides applied to agricultural fields are another important source of soil contamination. These chemicals, designed to attack specific weeds, insect pests, and crop fungi, unfortunately also affect nontarget species, including humans. Most insecticides, for example, are *neurotoxins*, which means that they affect the central nervous systems of organisms. Any excess pesticide that is not absorbed by plants or animals on the field can leave the system via runoff, infiltration into the soil, or volatilization. The amount, type, and timing of application are all crucially important in preventing pesticide-related contamination problems. For example, a pesticide that is water soluble and is applied just before a rainstorm will infiltrate quickly into the soil and be carried away by surface runoff, increasing the risk of contamination of adjacent groundwater and surface water bodies.

A growing problem worldwide is the contamination of soil as a result of industrial activity, particularly from inappropriate disposal or poorly designed storage of hazardous industrial wastes. An example occurred in Elmira, Ontario, in 1988 when a carcinogenic (cancer-causing) chemical, nitrosodimethylamine (NDMA) was found in the town's drinking water supply. The source of the chemical was traced to the Uniroyal Chemical Company, a producer of agrochemicals. The company had been disposing of hazardous chemical wastes in an above-ground storage pond (which met the legal requirements of Ontario's Ministry of Environment, it should be pointed out). The bottom of the pond was lined with clay, a common practice because of its capacity to seal ponds

and absorb contaminants. But when the bottom layers became saturated, the liquid waste began to seep through the soil. It percolated into the underlying groundwater, eventually contaminating several of the town's wells and nearby streams. Water for drinking and cooking had to be trucked in, and local residents were even advised not to bathe in water from the municipal wells.

The example of Elmira illustrates that soil and water contamination are so closely connected that they cannot be considered separately. We will return to these issues in greater detail when we look at freshwater contamination, waste management, and environmental health concerns.

Grazing practices can contribute to soil degradation

When sheep, goats, cattle, or other livestock graze on the open range, they feed primarily on grasses. As long as livestock populations do not exceed a range's carrying capacity and do not consume grasses faster than grasses can be replaced, grazing may be sustainable. However, when too many animals eat too much of the plant cover, impeding plant regrowth and preventing the replacement of biomass, the result is *over-grazing*.

Rangeland scientists have shown that over-grazing causes a number of impacts, some of which give rise to positive feedback cycles that exacerbate damage to soils, natural communities, and the land's productivity for grazing (FIGURE 5.18). When livestock remove too much of an area's plant cover, more soil surface is exposed and made vulnerable to erosion. Soil erosion makes it difficult for vegetation to regrow, perpetuating the lack of cover

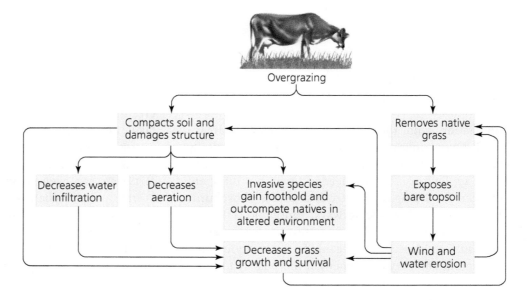

FIGURE 5.18
When grazing by livestock exceeds the carrying capacity of rangelands and their soil, over-grazing can set in motion a series of consequences and positive feedback loops that degrade soils and grassland ecosystems.

CANADIAN ENVIRONMENTAL PERSPECTIVES

Myrna Simpson

Myrna Simpson is a soil scientist, environmental chemist, and professor.

- **Professor** of environmental chemistry
- Soil resource **advocate**
- One of the *Toronto Star*'s **"Top Ten to Watch"** for 2008

Soils are complex, changeable materials. They have many components—organic and inorganic; living and nonliving; microscopic and macroscopic; solid, liquid, and vapour. They also change continually in response to a wide variety of environmental conditions. Dr. Myrna Simpson has spent her research career at the University of Toronto investigating both the detailed characteristics of soil components, and their responses to environmental change.

Dr. Simpson is a professor of environmental chemistry, and co-director (with professor of chemistry André Simpson—and yes, they are married) of the Environmental Nuclear Magnetic Resonance (NMR) Centre at the University of Toronto's Scarborough campus. This is the only NMR facility in Canada that is dedicated specifically to environmental research. (Most are used for health-related applications or for research in chemistry and physics.)

NMR spectroscopy, or *nuclear magnetic resonance spectroscopy*, is a powerful chemistry technique that can be used to identify the properties of matter. In a general sense, *spectroscopy* refers to chemical analytical techniques used to measure the interactions of materials with various forms of energy. In NMR spectroscopy, certain atomic nuclei in the sample—nuclei that have a specific property called *spin*—are aligned in a strong magnetic field and then respond to radiofrequency irradiation in a way that is characteristic of that particular material. By measuring this reaction, which comes in the form of an output of energy in a characteristic frequency, scientists can determine the identity of the material.

NMR works only for analyzing materials whose nuclei possess the property of spin. Luckily, most elements do have naturally occurring isotopes with spin, including hydrogen, nitrogen, phosphorus, and carbon—all of which are important materials in soil. But the real strength of NMR spectroscopy is that it not only identifies the materials present, but also reveals the *form* in which the materials occur, including very detailed information about the molecular structure of the materials, how the atoms in the molecules are bonded, how far apart they are, the three-dimensional shape of the molecules, and the extent to which they are interacting with other materials in the sample.

Dr. Simpson and colleagues use NMR to study environmental and geochemical processes in soils and sediments from terrestrial, freshwater, and marine environments. Part of this work involves characterization of the forms in which organic matter occurs in soils and how soil organic matter interacts with water and minerals. This is fundamentally important because organic matter gives soil its fertility. Organic materials in soil also interact with contaminants, sometimes holding on to them in ways that can hinder efforts to clean up contaminated soil. To improve our capacity to manage contaminated soils, scientists need to develop a better understanding of how these interactions work. NMR can even reveal how metabolic processes in soil organisms, such as earthworms, change in response to environmental changes.

Another extremely important aspect of the work is to study the role of soils in carbon cycling. This involves the identification of environmental "fingerprints," called *biomarkers*, which allow the researchers to track the biogeochemical cycling of carbon as it moves through terrestrial ecosystems. Concerns about changes in our global climate have made it particularly urgent to understand the factors that control carbon cycling, particularly the reservoirs where carbon is sequestered in the global carbon cycle. Soil is one of the most important global carbon reservoirs, and the research of Dr. Simpson and her colleagues is contributing to our scientific understanding of how the soil carbon reservoir might respond to changes in temperature, moisture, and other environmental factors.

"Soil is the world's most underrated resource. Soil contains more than twice the amount of carbon as does the atmosphere; yet, until now, scientists haven't examined this significant carbon pool closely.... Through our research, we've sought to determine what soils are made up of at the molecular level and whether this composition will change in a warmer world."—**Myrna Simpson**

Thinking About Environmental Perspectives

In addition to being a soil scientist and environmental chemist, Professor Simpson is the mother of twins. She says, "As a mother, paving the way for environmental protection and solving environmental problems becomes more relevant and personal. I am constantly striving to ensure that our environment is healthy for my children as well as yours." In what ways do you think Professor Simpson's role as a parent affects her work as an environmental scientist and researcher?

and giving rise to more erosion. Moreover, non-native weedy plants may invade denuded soils. These invasive plants are usually less palatable to livestock and can out-compete native vegetation in the new, modified environment, further decreasing native plant cover.

Over-grazing can also compact soils and alter their structure. Soil **compaction**, in which pore space in the soil is reduced, makes it harder for water to infiltrate, for soils to be aerated, for plants' roots to expand, and for roots to conduct cellular respiration. All of these effects further decrease the growth and survival of native plants. Soil compaction also can be caused by over-tilling, use of heavy agricultural machinery, clear-cut logging, and rapid withdrawal of groundwater.

As a cause of soil degradation, over-grazing is equal to poorly managed cropland agriculture, and it is a greater cause of desertification. Humans keep a total of 3.4 billion cattle, sheep, and goats. Rangeland classified as degraded now adds up to 680 million ha, although some estimates put the number as high as 2.4 billion ha, fully 70% of the world's rangeland area. Rangeland degradation is estimated to cost $23.3 billion per year. Grazing exceeds the sustainable supply of grass in India by 30% and in parts of China by up to 50%. To relieve pressure on rangelands, both nations are now beginning to feed crop residues to livestock.

Range managers do their best to assess the carrying capacity of rangelands and inform livestock owners of these limits, so that herds are rotated from site to site as needed to conserve grass cover and soil integrity. Managers also can establish and enforce limits on grazing on publicly owned land when necessary. Today increasing numbers of ranchers are working cooperatively with government agencies, environmental scientists, and even environmental advocates to find ways to ranch more sustainably and safeguard the health of the soil.

Conclusion

Soil is a complex system, which functions as the interface between the geosphere, hydrosphere, and atmosphere. The importance of soil as a resource is often underestimated, but the preservation of arable soil is crucial for the maintenance of global food security.

Many of the policies enacted and the practices developed to combat soil degradation in Canada and worldwide have been quite successful, particularly in reducing the erosion of topsoil. However, soil is still being degraded at a rate that threatens the sustainability of the resource. Despite all we have learned about soil degradation and conservation, many challenges remain.

The role of soil as a reservoir in biogeochemical cycling is also of increasing interest to scientists. As long ago as 1945, Russian scientist Vladimir Vernadsky, considered to be one of the founders of biogeochemistry, declared that humans had become "a mighty and ever-growing geological force." This has never been truer than it is today, as we race to document, explain, and mitigate the global and potentially permanent environmental impacts of some human actions. Understanding the characteristics and behaviour of soils in this context will be a crucial part of this task.

REVIEWING OBJECTIVES

You should now be able to:

Delineate the fundamentals of soil science, including soil-forming processes

- Soil is a complex system that consists of mineral fragments with varying proportions of organic matter, with the rest of the pore space taken up by soil water and gases.
- The diverse biotic communities in soil include living and dead microorganisms, as well as larger organisms such as earthworms and other invertebrates, burrowing mammals, amphibians, and reptiles.

- Soil formation begins with the breakdown of parent rock by physical (mechanical), chemical, or biological weathering.
- Climate, organisms, relief, parent material, and time are factors that influence soil formation.

Describe some important properties of soil

- Soil profiles consist of distinct horizons that form as a result of weathering combined with leaching.
- Soil can be categorized according to properties such as colour (composition), texture, structure, and pH.

Characterize the role of soils in biogeochemical cycling

- Materials move from soil particles to soil solutions and back again by way of processes such as cation exchange.
- Soils play a crucial role in the nitrogen cycle by hosting free-living and symbiotic microorganisms that mediate nitrogen fixation, nitrification, and denitrification.
- Soils represent the largest terrestrial reservoir for carbon in the active carbon cycle—larger than all terrestrial vegetation and the atmosphere combined.

State the importance of soils for agriculture and in supporting plant growth

- Soil is crucial for providing nutrients for plant growth and, thus, for the support of life on Earth.
- Successful agriculture and a secure food supply require healthy soil.
- Soil properties affect (and may limit) the potential for plant growth and agriculture in any given location.

Identify the causes and predict the consequences of soil erosion and soil degradation

- As the human population grows, pressures from agriculture and other activities are degrading Earth's soil, and we are losing topsoil from productive cropland at an unsustainable rate.

- The main mechanisms of soil loss are splash, sheet, rill, and gully erosion by water, and deflation and abrasion by wind.
- Over-grazing, over-tilling, and careless forestry practices can cause soil degradation and negative impacts to native ecosystems.
- Desertification affects a large portion of the world's soils, especially in arid regions.
- Over-irrigation can cause salinization and water-logging, which lower crop yields and are difficult to mitigate.
- Over-application of fertilizers can cause pollution problems that affect ecosystems and human health.

Outline the history and explain the basic principles of soil conservation

- The Dust Bowl in North America and similar events elsewhere have encouraged scientists and farmers to develop ways of better protecting and conserving topsoil.
- Techniques such as crop rotation, contour farming, intercropping, terracing, shelterbelts, and reduced tillage can help protect soils from erosion.
- In Canada and across the world, governments are devising innovative policies and programs to deal with the problems of soil degradation.

TESTING YOUR COMPREHENSION

1. What is soil?
2. Describe the three types of weathering that may contribute to the process of soil formation.
3. What processes most influence the formation of soil? What is leaching, and what is its role in soil formation?
4. Name the five primary factors thought to influence soil formation, and describe one effect of each.
5. How are soil horizons created? What is the general pattern of distribution of organic matter in a typical soil profile?

6. Why is erosion generally considered a destructive process? Name three human activities that can promote soil erosion.
7. Describe the principal types of soil erosion by water and by wind.
8. How does terracing effectively turn very steep and mountainous areas into arable land?
9. How can fertilizers and irrigation contribute to soil degradation?
10. Describe the effects of over-grazing on soil.

THINKING IT THROUGH

1. How and why might actual soils differ from the idealized five-horizon soil profile presented in the chapter? How might departures from the idealized profile indicate the impact of human activities? Provide at least three examples.

2. Some pollutants, such as heavy metals, are positively charged and adhere to negatively charged soil particles. This can make it difficult to clean up contaminated soils and can reduce nutrient availability for plants. Explain why this is so, making reference to the process of cation exchange in soils.

3. How do you think a farmer can best help to conserve soil? How do you think a scientist can best help to conserve soil? How do you think a national government can best help to conserve soil?

4. Wetlands, with their highly organic-rich soils, are important reservoirs for carbon in the terrestrial ecosystem. Global warming may cause some wetlands to dry up or cause seasonally fluctuating water levels. What might be the impacts of these changes on the capacity of wetlands to store carbon and on the rate of flux of greenhouse gases to the atmosphere from wetlands? (If you cannot find a simple answer to this question, do not worry; scientists also do not yet know what the final answer is.)

5. You are a land manager with your provincial government and you have just been put in charge of 200 000 ha of public lands that have been severely degraded by over-grazing. Soil is eroding, creating large gullies. Shrubs have encroached on grassland areas because fire was suppressed. Environmentalists want an end to ranching on the land, and they want to bring back wolves and other endemic species. Ranchers want continued grazing and are strongly opposed to the reintroduction of native species, especially wolves. However, the ranchers are concerned about the land's condition and are willing to entertain new ideas. What steps would you take to assess the land's condition and begin restoring its soil and vegetation? Would you allow grazing, and if so, would you set limits on it? Would you try to reintroduce wolves to the area?

6. You are the head of an international granting agency that assists farmers with soil conservation and sustainable agriculture. You have $10 million to disburse. Your agency's staff has decided that the funding should go to (1) farmers in an arid area of Africa prone to salinization, (2) farmers in a fast-growing area of Indonesia where swidden agriculture is practised, (3) farmers in southern Brazil practising no-till agriculture, and (4) farmers in a dryland area of Mongolia undergoing desertification. What types of projects would you recommend funding in each of these areas, how would you apportion your funding among them, and why?

INTERPRETING GRAPHS AND DATA

Dr. Henry Janzen is a soil scientist at the Lethbridge Research Centre in Alberta and an adjunct professor at the University of Manitoba. He is an expert on carbon cycling and the emission of greenhouse gases from soils, and he carries out research on the effects of different management approaches on carbon storage in agricultural soils. In a 2004 paper in the journal *Agriculture, Ecosystems and Environment*, Dr. Janzen summarized many of the main scientific questions concerning carbon storage in terrestrial reservoirs.

One concern outlined in Dr. Janzen's study was the impact of land-use changes on carbon storage in terrestrial reservoirs. The following figure from the paper summarizes major land-use changes since 1700:

1. On the basis of this graph, which of the biomes or managed ecosystems (forest/woodland, steppe/savannah/grassland/shrubland, tundra/desert, or pasture/cropland) *increased* the most, in terms of percentage increase, from 1700 to 1990? Which one of them *decreased* the most, in terms of percentage

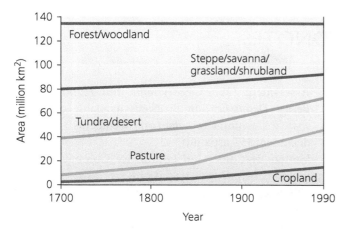

This graph shows the change in terrestrial area for three groups of major biome types and the increase in area of pasture and croplands since 1700.
Source: Figure 2 from Janzen, H.H. (2004) Carbon cycling in earth systems—a soil science perspective. Agriculture, Ecosystems and Environment *104, 399–417, plotted from values in Goldewijk, K.K. (2001) Estimating global land use change over the past 300 years: the HYDE database.* Global Biogeochem. Cycles *15(2), 417–433.

decrease? What happened to the area covered by tundra/desert over the time period represented on the graph?

2. The table below presents some information about carbon storage in various terrestrial reservoirs, based on data from Janzen's study. It also provides the current total area occupied by each of the biome types. For each biome type and pasture/cropland, calculate and fill in the last column of the table, which shows the amount of carbon stored per hectare (in units of t/ha, or tonnes per hectare). One calculation (for the steppe/savannah grouping) has been completed as an example.

3. From the calculations you made and the information that is now in the final column of your table, which biome type stores the *most* carbon per hectare? Which stores the *least* carbon per hectare? How does the pasture/cropland carbon storage per hectare compare to that in the natural ecosystems?

4. Based on the data provided in the table, which of the natural ecosystems stores the highest proportion of its carbon in *plants*? Which of the natural ecosystems stores the highest proportion of its carbon in the *soil*? How does the proportion of carbon stored in plants vs. soils in pasture/cropland compare to the natural systems? Do these results surprise you? (Why or why not?)

5. In terms of carbon storage in terrestrial reservoirs, what do you think would be the overall result of the shift, shown in the graph (above), to increasing pasture/cropland at the expense of forests and grasslands?

Biome type	Global Carbon Reservoir (in Gt, or tonnes × 10⁹)			Current total area (ha × 10⁹)	C stored per hectare (t/ha)
	In Plants	In Soils	Total		
Forest/woodland	359	787	1146	4.17	
Steppe/savannah/grassland/shrubland	75	559	634	3.50	181.1
Tundra/desert (incl. ice-covered)	14	312	326	5.50	
Pasture/cropland	3	128	131	1.60	

This table shows the approximate area of three sets of biome types and pasture/cropland, in billions of hectares (ha × 10⁹), and the size of the carbon stock in each of them, in gigatonnes (Gt, or tonnes × 10⁹).
Source: Based on information in Table 1 from Janzen, H.H. (2004) Carbon cycling in earth systems—a soil science perspective. Agriculture, Ecosystems and Environment *104, 399–417.*

CHAPTER ENDNOTES

1. Based on information from www.trentu.ca/academic/bluelab/research_merbleue.html and personal communications with Nigel Roulet, Tim Moore, and Nathan Basiliko, August, 2008.

2. Wall, G.J., D.R. Coote, E.A. Pringle, and I.J. Shelton (eds.) (2002) *RUSLEFAC—Revised Universal Soil Loss Equation for Application in Canada: A Handbook for Estimating Soil Loss from Water Erosion in Canada.* Research Branch, Agriculture and Agri-Food Canada, Ottawa, Contribution No. AAFC/AAC2244E. 117 pp.

3. Agriculture and Agri-Food Canada (1997) *Profile of Production Trends and Environmental Issues in Canada's Agriculture and Agri-food Sector* http://www4.agr.gc.ca/resources/prod/doc/policy/environment/pdfs/sds/profil_e.pdf

4. van Vlietl, L.J.P, G.A. Padbury, and D.A. Lobb (2003) Soil erosion risk indicators used in Canada. Paper presented at the OECD Expert Meeting on Soil Erosion and Biodiversity.

5. Agriculture and Agri-Food Canada (1997) *Profile of Production Trends and Environmental Issues in Canada's Agriculture and Agri-food Sector, 1997.*

6. From the U.N. Convention to Combat Desertification, as cited in the Millennium Ecosystem Assessment (2005) *Ecosystems and Human Well-Being: Desertification Synthesis* available online at www.millenniumassessment.org/documents/document.355.aspx.pdf

7. United Nations Convention to Combat Desertification, http://www.unccd.int/

8. CBCRadiowww.cbc.ca/news/background/agriculture/drought1930s.html

9. Government of Canada (1984) *Soil at Risk: Canada's Eroding Future.*

10. Soil Conservation Council of Canada, www.soilcc.ca.

11. Agriculture and Agri-Food Canada, Agri-Environmental Services Branch, www4.agr.gc.ca/AAFC-AAC/display-afficher.do?id=1187362338955&lang=eng

12. Ontario Ministry of Agriculture, Food, and Rural Affairs, Agroforestry Statistics, www.omafra.gov.on.ca/english/crops/facts/info_statistics.htm.

13. Soil Conservation Council of Canada, www.soilcc.ca

14. FAO Land and Plant Nutrition Management Service, Global Network on Integrated Soil Management for Sustainable Use of Salt-Affected Soils, http://193.43.36.103/ag/AGL/agll/spush/intro.htm

MyEnvironmentPlace

Go to **www.myenvironmentplace.ca** where you will find quizzes, animations, your Pearson eText, and more.

6

Agriculture, Food, and Biotechnology

For a farm to be certified as organic, the farmer must adhere to strict regulations.

Upon successfully completing this chapter, you will be able to

- Outline the historical development of agriculture and the transition to industrialized agriculture
- Explain the challenge of feeding a growing human population
- Identify the main approaches and summarize the environmental impacts of the Green Revolution
- Summarize the strategies and impacts of pest management and the importance of pollination
- Describe the science and evaluate the controversies associated with genetically modified food

- State the importance of crop diversity and some approaches to preservation
- Assess the positive and negative aspects of feedlots and aquaculture for raising animals for food
- Summarize the main goals of sustainable agriculture

Farmer in maize field in Oaxaca, Mexico.

MEXICO

Oaxaca

CENTRAL CASE:
GM MAIZE AND ROUNDUP-READY CANOLA

"If you desire peace, cultivate justice, but at the same time cultivate the fields to produce more bread; otherwise there will be no peace."

—NORMAN BORLAUG, CONSIDERED TO BE THE FATHER OF THE GREEN REVOLUTION

"Worrying about starving future generations won't feed them. Food biotechnology will . . . . At Monsanto, we now believe food biotechnology is a better way forward."

—MONSANTO COMPANY ADVERTISEMENT

"I never put those plants on my land. The question is, where do Monsanto's rights end and mine begin?"

—PERCY SCHMEISER

Corn is a staple grain of the world's food supply. We can trace its ancestry back roughly 5500 years, when people in the highland valleys of what is now the state of Oaxaca in southern Mexico first domesticated that region's wild maize plants. The corn we eat today arose from some of the many varieties that evolved from the early selective crop breeding conducted by the people of this region.

Today Oaxaca remains a world centre of biodiversity for maize, with many native varieties growing in the rich soil (see photo). Preserving such varieties of crops in their ancestral homelands is important for securing the future of our food supply, scientists maintain, because these varieties serve as reservoirs of genetic diversity—reservoirs we may need to draw on to sustain or advance our agriculture.

In 2001, Mexican government scientists conducting routine genetic tests of Oaxacan farmers' maize announced that they had turned up DNA that matched *transgenes*, that is, genes transferred from genetically modified (GM) corn, even though Mexico had banned its cultivation since 1998. Corn is one of many crops that scientists have genetically engineered to express desirable traits such as large size, fast growth, and resistance to insect pests.

Activists opposed to GM food trumpeted the disturbing news and urged a ban on imports of transgenic crops from producer countries such as the United States into developing nations. The agrobiotech industry defended the safety of its crops and questioned the validity of the research. Further research by Mexican government scientists confirmed the presence of transgenes in Mexican maize. Those studies were controversial and still have not been definitively verified, although the findings were accepted by a special commission of experts convened under the North American Free Trade Agreement (NAFTA). The commission concluded that corn imported from the United States was the source for the transgenes, which spread by wind pollination and interbreeding with native cultivars once in Mexico.

Meanwhile, back in Canada, Monsanto, a producer of GM foods, was engaged in a high-publicity battle with 74-year-old Saskatchewan farmer Percy Schmeiser (see photo) over Schmeiser's canola crop. Canola is an edible oil derived from rapeseed. It is widely grown throughout the Canadian prairies, and 80% of the rapeseed grown in Canada is genetically modified.

Schmeiser maintained that pollen from Monsanto's Roundup-Ready canola had blown from a neighbouring farm onto his land and pollinated his non-GM canola. Schmeiser had not purchased the patented seed and did not want the crossbreeding. Monsanto investigators took seed samples from his plants and charged him with violating a Canadian law that makes it illegal for farmers to reuse or grow patented seed without a contract. The courts sided with Monsanto, ordering the farmer to pay the corporation $238,000. Schmeiser appealed to the Supreme Court of Canada, which ruled that Monsanto's patent had indeed been violated but acknowledged that the farmer had not benefited from the GM seeds and had not intended their use. The Court exempted him from paying any fines or fees to the company.

Saskatchewan farmer Percy Schmeiser was accused by the Monsanto Company of planting its patented canola without a contract with the company. Schmeiser said his non-GM plants were contaminated with Monsanto's transgenes from neighbouring farms, and he became a hero to small farmers and anti–GM food activists worldwide.

In spite of the Supreme Court loss, Schmeiser received wide public support. He and his wife, Louise, were given the 2007 Right Livelihood Award in recognition of their struggle. A government committee sought a revision in the patent law, and the National Farmers Union of Canada called for a moratorium on GM food. Schmeiser says that the most difficult part of the entire saga was the loss, through contamination by transgenes, of the local variety of rapeseed that he had planted throughout his 60-year farming career.[1]

The larger question of the legality of holding patents on living organisms remains unresolved. In 2002, Canada became the first nation in the industrialized world to prohibit the holding of patents on higher organisms (a genetically modified mouse was the organism in question). Monsanto continues to demand that farmers heed patent laws and is continuing with several similar lawsuits. In a fascinating turn of events, Percy Schmeiser reached an out-of-court settlement with Monsanto in March of 2008, in which the company admitted that contamination had occurred and agreed to pay all costs of remediating it.

The Race to Feed the World

Although human population growth has slowed, we can still expect our numbers to swell to 9 billion by the middle of this century. For every two people living in the year 2000, there will likely be three in 2050. Feeding 50% more mouths will require significant advances in agricultural technology and food distribution processes; doing all of this while protecting the integrity of soil, water, and ecosystems will require that sustainability be a guiding principle of these advances.

As the human population has increased, so have the amounts of land and resources we devote to agriculture, which currently covers 38% of Earth's land surface. We can define **agriculture** as the practice of raising crops and livestock for human use and consumption. We obtain most of our food, fibre, and (increasingly) biofuels from **cropland**, land used to raise plants for human use, and **rangeland**, land used for grazing livestock.

Agriculture is not something that people have "always done." The development of agriculture was a major achievement—perhaps the most important technological leap forward by humans in our history as a species. In the past 60 years or so, agricultural technology has undergone massive, rapid changes. These changes have allowed food production to keep pace with population growth, more or less, but they have led to some unanticipated environmental impacts. In this chapter we look at the development of agricultural technologies over time and in recent decades, the challenge of offering food security to the world's population, and the environmental implications of both.

Agriculture first appeared around 10 000 years ago

During most of our species' 200 000-year existence[2] we were hunter-gatherers, dependent on wild plants and animals. Then about 10 000 years ago, as the climate

roots

AGRICULTURE

The word **agriculture** comes from the Latin *agricultura*, a combination of *ager*, "field," and *cultura*, "to cultivate." *Cultivar*—a cultivated plant that has been selected for specific desirable traits—is a term that was coined in 1923 by an American horticulturalist by combining the terms *cultivated* and *variety*.

warmed following a period of glaciation, people in some cultures began to **cultivate**, or raise plants (*cultivars*) from seeds, and to **domesticate** animals as a source of both food and labour.

Agriculture most likely began as hunter-gatherers brought back to their encampments wild fruits, grains, and nuts. Some of these foods fell to the ground, were thrown away, or were eaten and survived passage through the digestive system. The plants that grew from these seeds near human encampments likely produced fruits that were on average larger and tastier than those in the wild because they sprang from seeds of fruits people selected for their size and flavour. As these plants bred with others nearby that shared their characteristics, they gave rise to subsequent generations of plants with large and flavourful fruits.

Eventually, people realized that they could guide this process and began intentionally planting seeds from the plants whose produce was most desirable. This is *artificial selection*, or *selective breeding*, at work. The practice of selective breeding continues to the present day and has produced the many hundreds of crops we enjoy, all of which are artificially selected versions of wild plants. People followed the same process of selective breeding with animals, creating domesticated livestock from wild species—by accident at first, then by intention.

Evidence from archaeology and paleoecology suggests that agriculture was invented independently by different cultures in at least 5 and possibly 10 or more areas of the world at around the same time (**FIGURE 6.1**). The earliest widely accepted archaeological evidence for plant domestication is from the "Fertile Crescent" region of the Middle East about 10 500 years ago, and the earliest evidence for animal domestication, also from that region, just 500 years later. Crop remains have been dated using radiocarbon dating and similar methods. Wheat and barley originated in the Fertile Crescent, as did rye, peas, lentils, onions, garlic, carrots, grapes, and other food plants familiar to us today. The people of this region also domesticated goats and sheep. Meanwhile, in China, domestication began as early as 9500 years ago, leading eventually to the rice, millet, and pigs we know today. Agriculture in Africa (coffee, yams, sorghum, and more) and the Americas (corn, beans, squash, potatoes, llamas, and more) developed later in several areas, 4500 to 7000 years ago.

Once our ancestors learned to cultivate crops and domesticate animals, they began to settle in more permanent camps and villages near water sources. Agriculture and a *sedentary* (that is, settled) lifestyle likely reinforced one another. The need to harvest crops kept people sedentary, and once they were sedentary it was necessary to plant more crops to support the population.

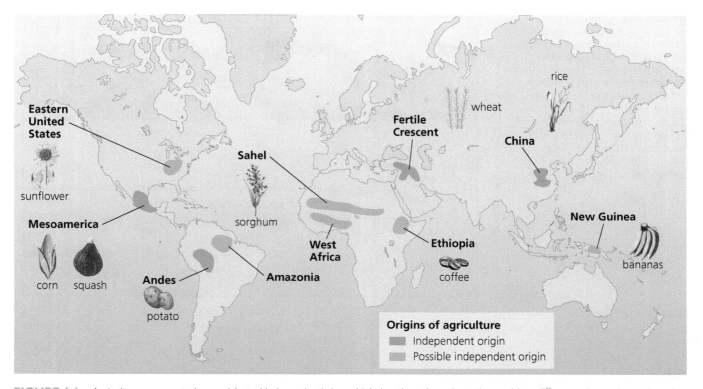

FIGURE 6.1   Agriculture appears to have originated independently in multiple locations throughout the world, as different cultures domesticated certain plants and animals from wild species living in their environments. This map summarizes conclusions from diverse sources of research on evidence for early agriculture. Areas where people are thought to have independently invented agriculture are coloured green. (China may represent two independent origins.) Areas coloured blue represent regions where people either invented agriculture independently or obtained the idea from cultures of other regions. A few of the many crop plants domesticated in each region are shown.   *Source: Data from syntheses in Diamond, J. (1997)* Guns, Germs, and Steel. *New York: W.W. Norton; and Goudie, A. (2000)* The Human Impact, *5th ed. Cambridge, MA: MIT Press.*

Population increase resulted from these developments and further promoted them, in a positive feedback cycle.

Agriculture is a form of **intensification**—a way to increase the productivity and carrying capacity of a given unit of land. A hunter-gatherer lifestyle requires a very large land area to support a given population; switching to a sedentary lifestyle based on agriculture increased the carrying capacity and allowed for larger groups to be supported on much smaller areas of land. The development of agriculture thus permitted—or possibly caused—a sudden dramatic increase in population. The ability to grow excess farm produce enabled some people to leave farming and to live off the food that others produced. This led to the development of professional specializations, commerce, technology, densely populated urban centres, social stratification, and politically powerful elites. For better or worse, the advent of agriculture eventually brought us the civilization we have today.

For thousands of years, crops were cultivated, harvested, stored, and distributed by human and animal muscle power, using hand tools and simple machines (**FIGURE 6.2**). This biologically powered agriculture is known as **traditional agriculture**. In the oldest form of traditional agriculture, known as **subsistence agriculture**, farming families produce only enough food for themselves and do not make use of large-scale irrigation, fertilizer, farm machinery, or teams of labouring animals. Intensive traditional agriculture sometimes uses draft animals and employs significant quantities of irrigation water and fertilizer, but stops short of using fossil fuels. This type of agriculture aims to produce food for the farming family, as well as extra food to sell in the market. Today there are still many subsistence farmers, especially in the developing world.

Industrialized agriculture is more recent

The Industrial Revolution introduced large-scale mechanization and fossil fuels to agricultural fields, enabling farmers to replace horses and oxen with faster and more powerful means of cultivating, harvesting, transporting, and processing crops. Other advances facilitated irrigation and fertilization, while the invention of chemical pesticides reduced competition from weeds and herbivory by insects and other crop pests.

FIGURE 6.2
Hunting and gathering was the predominant human lifestyle until the onset of agriculture and sedentary lliving, which centred on farms, villages, and cities, beginning around 10 000 years ago. Over the millennia, societies practicing traditional agriculture gradually replaced hunter-gatherer cultures. Within the past century and a half, industrialized agriculture has spread, replacing much traditional agriculture.

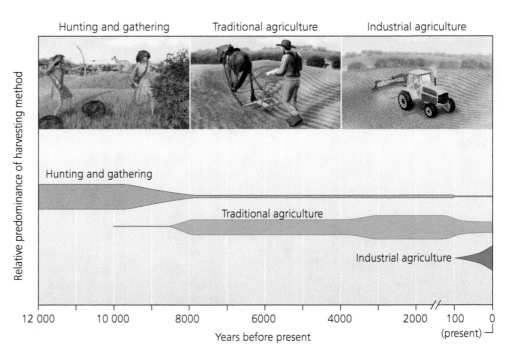

To be efficient, modern **industrialized agriculture** requires that vast fields be planted with single types of crops. The uniform planting of a single crop type over a large expanse of land, termed **monoculture**, is distinct from the *polyculture* approach of much traditional agriculture, such as Native American farming systems that mixed maize, beans, squash, and peppers in the same fields. Today, industrialized agriculture, characterized by monoculture, occupies about 25% of the world's cropland.

We are producing more food per person

Over the past half century, our ability to produce food has grown even faster than population (**FIGURE 6.3**). However, largely because of political obstacles and inefficiencies in distribution, today over 900 million people in the world still do not have enough to eat. Every five seconds, somewhere in the world, a child starves to death.

Agricultural scientists and policy makers pursue the goal of **food security**—the guarantee of an adequate and acceptable food supply to all people at all times. Making a food supply sustainable depends on maintaining healthy soil, water, and biodiversity, but careless agricultural practices can have devastating effects on the environment and the long-term ability of the world's soils to support crops and livestock.

In the 1960s there were predictions of widespread starvation and catastrophic failure of agricultural systems,

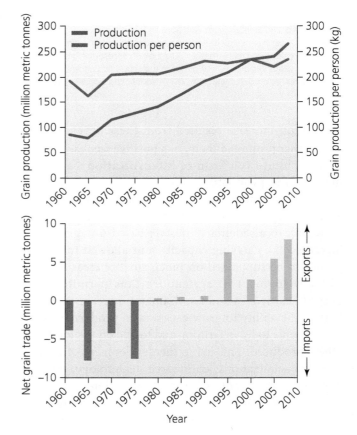

FIGURE 6.3
India increased its grain production even faster than its population grew during the years of the Green Revolution, so grain per person also increased (upper graph). As production rose, India began exporting grain to other nations (lower graph). The same trends can be seen in global grain production over this period.
Source: Data from U.N. Food and Agriculture Organization (FAO).

amidst concerns that the human population could not continue to grow without outstripping its food supply. However, the population has continued to increase well past the predictions. It is tragic that more than 900 million people are still chronically hungry today, but in percentage terms hunger has been reduced by half—from 26% of the population in 1970 to 13% today.

Although agricultural production has so far outpaced population growth, there is no guarantee that it will continue to do so. Already with grain crops, the world's staple foods, we are producing less food per person each year. Since 1985, world grain production per person has fallen by 9%. Moreover, the world's soils are in decline, and a significant portion of the planet's **arable** land (land that is suitable for the annual planting of crops) has already been brought into production.

We face undernourishment, overnutrition, and malnutrition

Although many people lack access to adequate food, others are affluent enough to consume more than is healthy. People who are *undernourished*, receiving less than 90% of their daily caloric needs, mostly live in the developing world. Meanwhile, in the developed world, many people suffer from *overnutrition*, taking in too many calories each day. In Canada, where food is available in abundance and people tend to lead sedentary lives with little exercise, 48% of adults exceed healthy weight standards, and 14% are obese (according to World Health Organization standards).[3]

For most people who are undernourished, the reasons are economic. One-fifth of the world's people live on less than $1 per day, and over half live on less than $2 per day, the World Bank estimates. Hunger is a problem even in Canada, where over 850 000 people used the services of a food bank during a typical month in 2010, according to Food Banks Canada;[4] almost 40% of them were children. This measure underrepresents the true situation, particularly for rural areas that lack access to food banks. The National Population Health Survey has estimated that *food insecurity*—the inability to procure sufficient food when needed—is a factor in 10.2% of Canadian households, affecting well over 3 million people.[5]

In a wealthy, food-producing nation such as Canada, the cause of hunger is more than just a lack of available food. Many factors coalesce to cause hunger insecurity around the world, and these factors have as much to do with poverty and the weaknesses of our food delivery systems as with the abundance and availability of food.

Just as the *quantity* of food a person eats is important for health, so is the *quality* of food. **Malnutrition**,

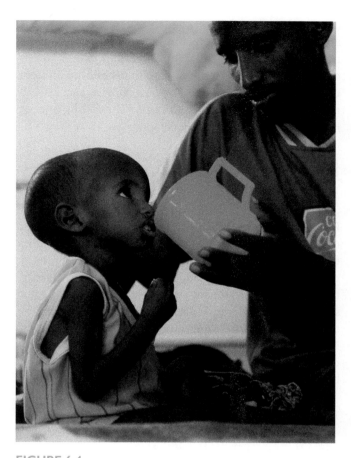

FIGURE 6.4
Millions of children, including this child in Somalia, suffer from forms of malnutrition such as marasmus.

a shortage of nutrients the body needs, including a complete complement of vitamins and minerals, can occur in both undernourished and overnourished individuals. Malnutrition can lead to disease (**FIGURE 6.4**). A diet without enough protein or essential amino acids

roots

KWASHIORKOR AND MARASMUS

The disease **kwashiorkor** is common in children who eat a diet high in starch but low in protein or essential amino acids. The word *kwashiorkor* derives from one of the languages of coastal Ghana. It literally means "first-second," but is commonly translated as "rejected one." It refers to the first child, who is weaned off breast milk when the second child is born and therefore loses that important source of nutrition. The word **marasmus**, which refers to a disease caused by protein deficiency and low caloric intake, originates from the Greek *marasmus*, meaning "wasting away, withering, decay."

can result in *kwashiorkor*, which causes bloating of the abdomen, deterioration and discolouration of hair, mental disability, anaemia, immune suppression, developmental delays, and reduced growth in children. Protein deficiency together with a lack of calories can lead to *marasmus*, which causes wasting or shrivelling among millions of children in the developing world.

Impacts of the Green Revolution

Beginning around 1950, agricultural advancement allowed new technologies, crop varieties, and farming practices to be exported to the developing world. Although many people saw growth in production and increased agricultural efficiency as the key to ending starvation, hunger still exists in the world. We now realize that boosting agricultural production is only part of the solution to hunger. Nevertheless, technological advances allowed farmers to dramatically increase yields per hectare of cropland and helped millions of people avoid starvation.

The Green Revolution led to dramatic increases in agricultural productivity

The desire for greater quantity and quality of food for the growing human population led directly to a so-called **Green Revolution**, with enormous increases in agricultural productivity during the mid- to late twentieth century. We have increased food production and per capita food consumption worldwide by devoting more energy (especially fossil fuel energy) to agriculture; by planting and harvesting more frequently; by greatly increasing the use of irrigation, fertilizers, and pesticides; by planting monocultures; by increasing the amount of cultivated land; and by developing (through crossbreeding and genetic engineering) more productive crop and livestock varieties.

Prior to the Green Revolution, the best way to increase agricultural productivity was to plant more land with crops or to increase the size of a herd. This is a form of **extensification**—increasing resource productivity by bringing more land into production (as opposed to *intensification*, in which new technologies permit greater resource productivity from each unit of land). Realizing that farmers could not go on indefinitely cultivating more and more land to increase crop output, agricultural scientists consciously worked to develop technologies to increase crop output per unit area of cultivated land. In the end, the Green Revolution was characterized by both extensification *and* intensification of agricultural production.

FIGURE 6.5
Norman Borlaug holds examples of the wheat variety he bred that helped launch the Green Revolution. The high-yielding disease-resistant wheat helped increase agricultural productivity in many developing countries. Borlaug, quoted at the beginning of this chapter, won the Nobel Peace Prize for his work.

The transfer of agricultural technology to the developing world that marked the Green Revolution began in the 1940s, when U.S. agronomist Norman Borlaug introduced Mexico's farmers to a specially bred type of wheat (**FIGURE 6.5**). This strain of wheat produced large seed heads, was short in stature to resist wind, was resistant to diseases, and produced high yields. Within two decades of planting and harvesting this specially bred crop, Mexico tripled its wheat production and began exporting wheat.

The stunning success of this program inspired others. Next were India and Pakistan, and soon many developing countries were increasing their crop yields using selectively bred strains of wheat, rice, corn, and other crops from developed nations. Some varieties yielded three or four times as much per hectare as did their predecessors.

The Green Revolution has had both positive and negative impacts

Along with the new grains, developing nations adopted the methods of modern, industrialized agriculture. They began applying large amounts of synthetic fertilizers and chemical pesticides to their fields, irrigating crops with generous amounts of water, and using heavy equipment powered by fossil fuels. This high-input agriculture allowed farmers to harvest dramatically more corn, wheat, rice, and soybeans from each hectare of land. From 1900 to 2000, humans expanded the world's total cultivated area by 33% but increased energy inputs into agriculture by 800%. Intensive agriculture saved millions in India from starvation in the 1970s and eventually turned that nation into a net exporter of grain.

These developments had mixed impacts on the environment. On the positive side, the intensified use of already-cultivated land reduced pressures to convert additional natural lands for new cultivation. Between 1961 and 2002, food production rose 150% and population rose 100%, while land area converted for agriculture increased only 10%. For this reason, the Green Revolution can be said to have prevented some degree of deforestation and habitat conversion in many countries while those countries were experiencing their fastest population growth rates. In this sense, the Green Revolution was beneficial for natural ecosystems.

However, despite its successes, the Green Revolution has exacted a high price. The intensive cultivation of farmland has created new environmental problems and exacerbated some old ones. Many of these problems pertain to the integrity of soil and water supplies, which are the very foundation of our food supply. The intensive use of water, fossil fuels, and chemical fertilizers and pesticides had negative environmental impacts in the form of pollution, salinization, and desertification. The social and economic impacts of the Green Revolution on small-scale farmers in the developing world—many of whom are disadvantaged by lack of income, lack of education, or both, preventing them from accessing or benefiting from these technologies—are particularly controversial.

Fertilizer impacts. One hallmark of the Green Revolution was greatly increased use of industrial fertilizers. Plants remove nutrients from soil as they grow, and water also carries away nutrients. If agricultural soils come to contain too few nutrients, crop yields decline. Therefore, a great deal of effort has aimed to enhance productivity in nutrient-limited soils by adding **fertilizer**, any of various substances that contain essential nutrients.

There are two main types of fertilizers. **Inorganic** (or industrial) **fertilizers** are mined or synthetically manufactured mineral supplements, mainly various combinations of nitrogen, phosphorus, and potassium. **Organic fertilizers** consist of natural materials (largely the remains or wastes of organisms) and include animal manure; crop residues; fresh vegetation (or "green manure"); and *compost*, a mixture produced when decomposers break down organic matter, including food and crop waste, in a controlled environment. Organic fertilizers offer some benefits that inorganic fertilizers cannot, but they are not a panacea.

Applying substantial amounts of fertilizer to croplands can have impacts far beyond the boundaries of the fields (**FIGURE 6.6**). Nitrogen and phosphorus runoff

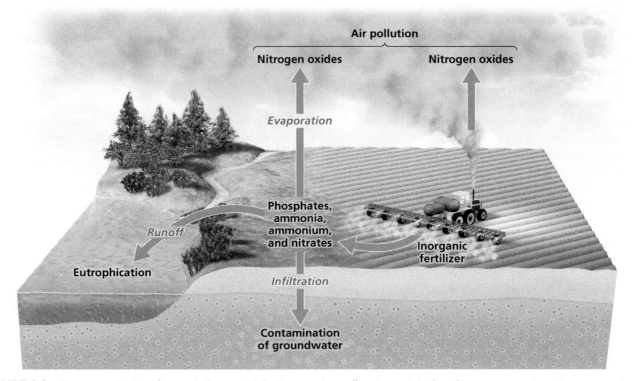

FIGURE 6.6 The overapplication of inorganic (or organic) fertilizers can have effects beyond the farm field because nutrients that are not taken up by plants may end up in other reservoirs. Anthropogenic inputs of nitrogen have greatly modified the nitrogen cycle and now account for one-half the total nitrogen flux on Earth.

from farms and other sources can lead to phytoplankton blooms, creating an oxygen-depleted "dead zone." Such eutrophication occurs at many river mouths, lakes, and ponds throughout the world. Moreover, nitrates readily leach through soil and contaminate groundwater, and components of some nitrogen fertilizers can even volatilize (evaporate) into the air.

Through these processes, unnatural amounts of nitrates and phosphates spread through ecosystems and pose human health risks, including cancer and methemoglobinaemia, or "blue-baby" syndrome. Health Canada and the U.S. Environmental Protection Agency both have determined that nitrate concentrations in excess of 10 mg/L for adults and 5 mg/L for infants in drinking water are unsafe, yet many sources around the world exceed even the looser standard of 50 mg/L set by the World Health Organization. Careful timing and regular soil testing can help to minimize applications of fertilizers that exceed what the plants need and can absorb.

Irrigation impacts.   Another key feature of the Green Revolution was an enormous increase in the amount of irrigated cropland, with the result that agriculture is the main reason for extraction and use of fresh water worldwide. Unfortunately, irrigation efficiency worldwide is quite low; only 43% of the water applied actually gets used by plants. *Drip irrigation* systems (FIGURE 6.7) that target water directly to plants are one solution to the problem. These systems allow more control over where water is aimed and waste far less water. Once considered expensive to install, they are becoming less costly, such that more farmers in developing countries will be able to afford them.

Poorly designed irrigation can also lead to the problems of waterlogging and salinization of soils, especially in hot, dry regions. When croplands are overwatered, soils can become soggy and saturated. As this water evaporates, it moves up through the soil profile, carrying dissolved mineral salts toward the surface. At the surface, only the fresh water evaporates, leaving a concentrated layer of salts encrusting the surface. Salinized agricultural soils are problematic in many parts of the world, and once soil has been degraded in this way it is almost impossible to restore it.

Monoculture impacts.   One key aspect of Green Revolution techniques has had particularly negative consequences for biodiversity and mixed consequences for crop yields. Monoculture, the planting of large expanses of single crop types (FIGURE 6.8), has made planting and harvesting more efficient and has thereby increased output. However, when all plants in a field are genetically similar, all will be equally susceptible to viral diseases,

(a) Conventional irrigation

(b) Drip irrigation

FIGURE 6.7
Currently, plants take up less than half the water we apply in irrigation. Conventional methods lose a great deal of water to evaporation **(a)**. In more-efficient drip irrigation approaches, such as this one watering grape vines **(b)**, hoses are arranged so that water drips from holes in the hoses directly onto the plants that need the water.

fungal pathogens, or insect pests that can spread quickly from plant to plant. For this reason, monocultures require large amounts of pesticides and bring significant risks of catastrophic failure.

Monocultures have also contributed to a narrowing of the human diet. Globally, 90% of the food we consume now comes from only 15 crop species and 8 livestock species—a drastic reduction in diversity from earlier times. The nutritional dangers of such dietary restriction have been alleviated by the fact that expanded global trade has provided many people access to a wider diversity of foods from different locations around the world. However, this effect has benefited wealthy people far more than poor people. One reason that farmers and scientists were so concerned about transgenic contamination of Oaxaca's native maize is that Oaxacan maize varieties serve as a valuable source of genetic variation in a world where so much variation is being lost to monocultural practices.

FIGURE 6.8
Most agricultural production in industrialized countries comes from monocultures—large stands of single types of crop plant, such as this wheat field. Clustering crop types in uniform fields on large scales greatly improves the efficiency of planting and harvesting, but it also decreases biodiversity and makes crops more susceptible to outbreaks of pests that specialize on particular crops.

Pests and Pollinators

Throughout the history of agriculture, the insects, fungi, viruses, rodents, and weeds that eat or compete with our crops have taken advantage of the ways we cluster food plants into agricultural fields. These organisms, in making a living for themselves, cut crop yields and make it harder for farmers to make a living. As just one example of thousands, various species of moth caterpillars known as armyworms decrease yields of everything from beets to sorghum to millet to canola to pasture grasses. Pests and weeds have always caused problems in traditional agriculture; they pose an even greater threat in a monoculture situation, where a pest adapted to specialize on that particular crop can easily move from one individual plant to many others of the same type.

What humans term a **pest** is any organism that damages crops that are valuable to us, and a **weed** is any plant that competes with crops. These are subjective categories that

weighing the issues

WHAT A PEST!

Compare the concept of a pest or weed species with that of alien and invasive species. At what point should a species be considered a pest? Does it have to cause damage to human interests? What if it causes harm only to natural ecosystems? How should pest species be managed?

we define entirely by our own economic interests. There is nothing inherently malevolent in the behaviour of a pest or a weed; the organisms are simply trying to survive and reproduce. From the viewpoint of an insect that happens to be adapted to feed on corn, grapes, or apples, a grain field, vineyard, or orchard represents an endless buffet.

Thousands of chemical pesticides have been developed

To prevent pest outbreaks and to limit competition with weeds, people have developed thousands of artificial chemicals to kill insects (*insecticides*), plants (*herbicides*), and fungi (*fungicides*). Poisons that target pest organisms are collectively termed **pesticides**. Enormous increases in the use of a wide variety of pesticides were another key feature of the Green Revolution.

In Canada today more than 7000 pesticides are registered for use. Many of the over 500 active ingredients in these pesticides have not been evaluated for health or environmental impacts for many years—over 150 were approved for use in Canada prior to 1960. The *Pest Control Products Act*, which came into effect as federal legislation in Canada in 2006, requires products to be reevaluated 15 years after they are initially approved for use, among other provisions designed to improve the safety and minimize the environmental impacts of pesticide use.[6] **TABLE 6.1** shows the main categories of chemical pesticides used in Canada.

Today more than $32 billion is expended annually on pesticides, $1.5 billion of that in Canada. Most pesticides used in Canada are for agricultural purposes (91% of sales), while the remaining nonagricultural pest management products—primarily for domestic use, but also used in the forestry and industrial sectors and for the management of golf courses and other landscapes—represent 9% of total sales. Eighty-five percent of the total pesticides sold in Canada are herbicides, followed by fungicides, insecticides, and other specialty pest-management chemicals such as rodenticides.[7]

Pesticides are, by definition, designed to be toxic to organisms, and the toxic effects may not be limited to the target organisms. Consequently, the application of synthetic pesticides can have health consequences for both humans and other nontarget organisms (see the "Effects" column of **TABLE 6.1**).

Pests evolve resistance to pesticides

Despite the toxicity of these chemicals, their usefulness tends to decline with time as pests evolve resistance to

Table 6.1   Categories of Pesticides Used in Canada

Class of Chemical Pesticide	First Used	Examples	Types	Current Status	Effects
Organochlorines	1942	Aldrin; chlordane; dieldrin; endrin; heptachlor; lindane; methoxychlor; toxaphene; HCB; PCP; DDT	Mostly insecticides	Some registered in Canada; others (such as DDT) discontinued in Canada but still used in developing nations	Persistent; bioaccumulative; affect ability to reproduce, develop, and withstand environmental stress
Organophosphates	Very early 1940s	Schradan; parathion; malathion	Insecticides	Schradan discontinued in 1964, resulting in a move toward less toxic groups (malathion, parathion)	Nonpersistent; systemic; not very selective; toxic to humans
Carbamates	First appeared in 1930; large-scale use in 1950s	Carbaryl; methomyl; propoxur; aldicarb	Fungicides, insecticides	Aldicarb discontinued in 1964; the others are registered in Canada	Nonpersistent; not very selective; toxic to birds and fish
Phenoxy	1946	2,4-D 2,4,5-T	Herbicides	2,4-D is widely used 2,4,5-T banned in Canada	Selective effects on humans and mammals are not well known; some potential to cause cancer in laboratory animals
Pyrethroids	1980	Fenpropanthrin; deltamethrin; cypermethrin	Insecticides	Fenpropanthrin is not registered in Canada, unlike the two other pesticides	Target-specific: more selective than organophosphates or carbamates; not acutely toxic to birds or mammals, but particularly toxic to aquatic species

Source: *Government of Canada*, Pesticides: Making the Right Choice for Health and the Environment. *(2000) Report of the Standing Committee on Environment and Sustainable Development. http://cmte.parl.gc.ca/cmte/CommitteePublication.aspx?COM=173&Lang=1&SourceId=36396*

them. Recall from our discussion of natural selection that organisms within populations vary in their traits. Because most insects and microbes occur in huge numbers, it is likely that a small fraction of individuals may by chance have genes that confer some degree of immunity to a given pesticide. Even if a pesticide application kills 99.99% of the insects in a field, 1 in 10 000 survives. If an insect survives by being genetically resistant to a pesticide, and if it mates with other resistant individuals of the same species, the insect population may grow. This new population will consist of individuals that are genetically resistant to the pesticide. As a result, pesticide applications will cease to be effective (**FIGURE 6.9**).

In many cases, industrial chemists are caught up in an "evolutionary arms race" with the pests they battle, racing to increase or retarget the toxicity of their chemicals while the armies of pests evolve ever-stronger resistance to their efforts. The number of species known to have evolved resistance to pesticides has grown over the decades. As of 2007, there were more than 2700 known cases of resistance by 550 species to over 300 pesticides,

and some species have evolved resistance to multiple pesticides. Resistant pests can take a significant economic toll on crops. In Canada, resistance to herbicides is of great concern; both the number of herbicide-resistant weeds and the area of land covered by such weeds are increasing.[8]

Biological control pits one organism against another

Because of pesticide resistance and the health risks of some synthetic chemicals, agricultural scientists increasingly battle pests and weeds with organisms that eat or infect them. This strategy is called **biological control**, or *biocontrol* for short. For example, parasitoid wasps are natural enemies of many caterpillars. These wasps lay eggs on a caterpillar, and the larvae that hatch from the eggs feed on the caterpillar, eventually killing it. Parasitoid wasps have been used as biocontrol agents in many situations. Some such efforts have succeeded at pest control and have led to steep reductions in chemical pesticide use.

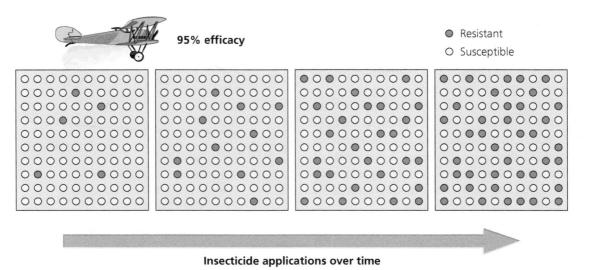

95% efficacy

○ Resistant
○ Susceptible

Insecticide applications over time

FIGURE 6.9   Through natural selection, pests can evolve resistance to the poisons we apply to kill them. This simplified diagram shows that when a pesticide is applied to an outbreak of insect pests, it may kill virtually all individuals except those few with an innate immunity to the poison. Those surviving individuals may found a population with genes for resistance to the poison. Future applications of the pesticide may then be ineffective, forcing us to develop a more potent poison or an alternative means of pest control.

One classic case of successful biological control is the introduction of the cactus moth, *Cactoblastis cactorum*, from Argentina to Australia in the 1920s to control invasive prickly pear cactus that was overrunning rangeland (**FIGURE 6.10**). Within just a few years, the moth managed to free millions of hectares of rangeland from the cactus.

A widespread modern biocontrol tool has been the use of *Bacillus thuringiensis* (Bt), a naturally occurring soil bacterium that produces a protein that kills many caterpillars and the larvae of some flies and beetles. Farmers have used the natural pesticidal activity of this bacterium to their advantage by spraying spores of this bacterium on their crops. If used correctly, Bt can protect crops from pest-related losses.

Biocontrol agents themselves may become pests

In most cases, biological control involves introducing an animal or microbe into a foreign ecosystem. Such relocation helps ensure that the target pest has not already evolved ways to deal with the biocontrol agent, but it also introduces risks. In some cases, biocontrol can produce unintended consequences if the biocontrol agent becomes invasive and

(a) Before cactus moth introduction

(b) After cactus moth introduction

FIGURE 6.10   In one of the classic cases of biocontrol, larvae of the cactus moth, *Cactoblastis cactorum*, were used to clear non-native prickly pear cactus from millions of hectares of rangeland in Queensland, Australia. These photos from the 1920s show an Australian ranch before **(a)** and after **(b)** introduction of the moth.

begins to affect nontarget organisms. Following the cactus moth's success in Australia, for example, it was introduced in other countries to control prickly pear; however, it is now feared that the moth larvae could decimate native and economically important species of cacti.

Scientists debate the relative benefits and risks of bio-control measures. If biocontrol works as planned, it can be a permanent solution that requires no further maintenance and is environmentally benign. However, if the agent has nontarget effects, the harm done may become permanent. Removing the agent from the system once it is established is far more difficult than simply stopping a chemical pesticide application. The potential impacts of releasing a biocontrol agent into the natural environment are basically the same as for any alien or non-native species.

Because of concerns about unintended impacts, researchers now study biocontrol proposals carefully before putting them into action, and government regulators must approve these efforts. Canada has been a world leader in this regard. However, there will never be a sure-fire way of knowing in advance whether a given biocontrol program will work as planned.

IPM combines biocontrol and chemical methods

Since chemical and biocontrol approaches have drawbacks, agricultural scientists and farmers developed a more sophisticated strategy, combining the best attributes of each approach. In **integrated pest management (IPM)**, numerous techniques are integrated to achieve long-term suppression of pests, including biocontrol, use of chemicals, close monitoring of populations, habitat alteration, crop rotation, transgenic crops, alternative tillage methods, and mechanical pest removal. IPM is broadly enough defined that it encompasses a wide variety of strategies.

IPM has now become popular in many parts of the world. Indonesia (FIGURE 6.11) subsidized pesticide use heavily for years, but its scientists came to understand that pesticides were actually making pest problems worse. They were killing the natural enemies of the brown planthopper, which began to devastate rice fields as its populations exploded. Concluding that pesticide subsidies were costing money, causing pollution, and decreasing yields, the Indonesian government in 1986 banned the importation of 57 pesticides, slashed pesticide subsidies, and encouraged IPM. Within 4 years, pesticide production fell to below half its 1986 level, imports fell to one-third, and subsidies were phased out (saving $179 million annually), but rice yields rose by 13%.

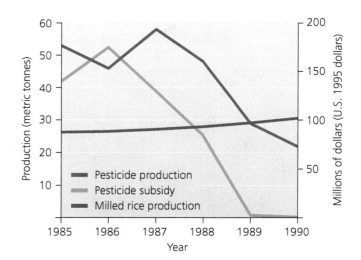

FIGURE 6.11
The Indonesian government threw its weight behind integrated pest management starting in 1986. Within just a few years, pesticide production and pesticide imports were down drastically, pesticide subsidies were phased out, and yields of rice increased slightly.

We depend on insects to pollinate crops

Managing insect pests is such a major issue in agriculture that many people fall into a habit of thinking of all insects as somehow bad or threatening. But in fact, most insects are harmless to agriculture, and some are absolutely essential. The insects that pollinate agricultural crops are one of the most vital, yet least understood and least appreciated, factors in cropland agriculture.

Pollination is the process by which male sex cells of a plant (pollen) fertilize female sex cells of a plant. Without pollination, no plants could reproduce. Many plants achieve pollination by wind distribution. Millions of minuscule pollen grains are blown long distances, and by chance a small number land on the female parts of other plants of their species. The many kinds of plants that sport showy flowers, however, typically are pollinated by animals, such as hummingbirds, bats, and insects (FIGURE 6.12). Flowers are, in fact, evolutionary adaptations that function to attract pollinators. The sugary nectar and protein-rich pollen in flowers serve as rewards to lure these sexual intermediaries, and the sweet smells and bright colours of flowers are signals that advertise these rewards.

Although our staple grain crops are derived from grasses and are wind-pollinated, many other crops depend on insects for pollination. This environmental service has economic, not just ecological, value; the estimated value of pollination services rendered by insects in Canada each year is $1.2 billion.[9] A comprehensive survey by tropical bee biologist Dave Roubik documented 800 species of

FIGURE 6.12
Many agricultural crops depend on insects or other animals to pollinate them. Our food supply, therefore, depends partly on conservation of these vital organisms. These apple blossoms are being visited by a European bee. Plants use flowers with colours and sweet smells to advertise nectar and pollen, enticements that attract pollinators.

cultivated plants that rely on bees and other insects for pollination. An estimated 73% of cultivars are pollinated, at least in part, by bees; 19% by flies; 5% by wasps; 5% by beetles; and 4% by moths and butterflies. In addition, bats pollinate 6.5% and birds 4%. According to Seeds of Diversity and Environment Canada,

Animals pollinate three-quarters of the world's staple crops, 80% of all flowering plants in temperate climates, and 90% globally. One mouthful in three requires insect pollination. Since 25% of all birds eat seeds or fruit, they are also dependent on pollinators. Quite simply, without pollinators, the entire terrestrial globe would look entirely different and would not be able support the number of people that it currently does.[10]

Many pollinating insects are at risk from the same pressures that threaten other species, including habitat loss, land degradation, habitat fragmentation, pesticide use, invasive species, and climate change. These are not new phenomena; for example, habitat destruction in the 1930s caused the failure of native leafcutter bee populations in Manitoba; this, in turn, led to the collapse of alfalfa seed production in the Canadian Prairies (see "The Science Behind the Story: The Alfalfa and the Leafcutter"). Increases in the rate and extent of environmental change now put these ecological relationships at even greater risk. The relationship between flowering plants and insect pollinators is so specific (the precise shape of an insect's appendages can determine its suitability for pollinating a particular plant species) that even minor changes can have devastating impacts.

Conservation of pollinators is vital

Preserving the biodiversity of native pollinators is especially important today. The domesticated workhorse of pollination, the European honeybee *(Apis apis)*, is being devastated by parasites and, more recently, by *Colony Collapse Disorder*, the causes of which are poorly understood but may include pathogens, pesticides, environmental stress, or insect-resistant GM crops. North American farmers regularly hire beekeepers to bring colonies of this introduced honeybee to their fields when it is time to pollinate crops (**FIGURE 6.13**). In recent years, parasitic mites have swept through honeybee populations, decimating hives. Moreover, research indicates that honeybees are sometimes less effective pollinators than many native species but often outcompete them, keeping the native species away from the plants.

Farmers and homeowners can help maintain populations of pollinating insects by reducing or eliminating pesticide use. All insect pollinators, including honeybees, are vulnerable to insecticides that are applied to crops, lawns, and gardens. Some insecticides are designed to specifically target certain types of insects, but many are not. Without full and detailed information on the effects of pesticides, farmers and homeowners trying to control the "bad" bugs that threaten the plants they value all too often kill the "good" insects as well.

Homeowners, even in the middle of a city, can encourage populations of pollinating insects by planting gardens of flowering plants and by providing nesting sites for bees. By allowing noncrop flowering plants (such as clover) to grow around the edges of their fields, farmers

FIGURE 6.13
European honeybees are widely used to pollinate crop plants, and beekeepers transport hives of bees to crops when it is time for flowers to be pollinated. However, honeybees have recently suffered devastating epidemics of parasitism, making it increasingly important for us to conserve native species of pollinators.

THE SCIENCE BEHIND THE STORY

The Alfalfa and the Leafcutter

Leafcutter bee pollinating an alfalfa flower.

In the first half of the twentieth century, land clearing for agriculture destroyed many nesting sites of native leafcutter bees in the Canadian Prairies. As a result, Canadian alfalfa seed production decreased dramatically, virtually collapsing by mid-century. Alfalfa is an important forage crop for livestock, and it is used to control moisture and nutrient levels in agricultural fields. Honeybees are ineffective alfalfa pollinators because they can steal nectar without "tripping" the alfalfa flower, a process that uncovers the plant's stigma and is required for the pollination to be successful. With the loss of the most effective native pollinators, by 1950 Canada was importing alfalfa seed to meet 95% of its domestic needs.

In response to this crisis, the European alfalfa leafcutter bee (*Megachile rotundata*) was introduced to Canada in 1961 (see photo). Scientists, beekeepers, and seed growers worked together to develop a management system for the new bees, which eventually resulted in a six-fold increase in alfalfa yields. By the end of the twentieth century, Canada was meeting or exceeding its demand for alfalfa seed, thanks to the alfalfa leafcutter bee. The bees are now being used by blueberry producers in eastern Canada and to pollinate buckwheat and hybrid canola in the Prairies.

The importation of leafcutter bees also led to a new kind of beekeeper who sells bee larvae to other growers for pollination. The leafcutter bee is gentler than the honeybee and typically will sting only if it is squeezed. Leafcutters are solitary (rather than gregarious, like other kinds of bees) and less likely to wander than honeybees. These characteristics make leafcutters easier to manage and handle than other bees. Management of leafcutters, which do not build colonies or store honey, involves building large nesting arrays of layered, grooved materials. These arrays mimic the sites in which the bees would naturally build their individual nests, in cracks and grooves in soft, decaying wood.

By controlling temperature, the emergence of the adult bees can be synchronized with the alfalfa bloom. The bees are kept dormant at 4°C until about three weeks before the expected crop bloom, when the temperature is turned up to 29°C to trigger the development of adult leafcutter bees. This management system has made Canada the leading producer of alfalfa leafcutters, currently producing 4 billion bees for pollination of domestic and international crops each year.

Interestingly (but not surprisingly, given their name) leafcutters can also become a pest species. To line their nests, the bees carefully incise small, round pieces of leaves and carry them back to the nesting site, which can potentially damage the leaf. The damage is usually minor, unless there is an unusually large population of feral (escaped domesticated) or native leafcutter bees in a small area.[11]

---

can maintain a diverse community of insects—some of which will pollinate their crops.

Genetically Modified Food

The Green Revolution enabled us to feed a greater number and proportion of the world's people, but relentless population growth demands still more. A new set of potential solutions began to arise in the 1980s and 1990s, as advances in genetics enabled scientists to directly alter the genes of organisms, including crop plants and livestock. The genetic modification of organisms that provide us food holds promise for increasing nutrition and the efficiency of agriculture while lessening the impacts of agriculture on the planet's environmental systems.

However, genetic modification of food organisms raises concerns and may pose risks that are not yet thoroughly understood. This has given rise to protest around the globe from consumer advocates, small farmers, opponents of big business, and environmental activists. Because genetic modification of food organisms has generated so much emotion and controversy, it is vital at the outset to clear up the terminology and clarify exactly what is involved in the process.

Genetic modification of organisms depends on recombinant DNA

The genetic modification of crops and livestock is one type of **genetic engineering,** any process whereby scientists directly manipulate an organism's genetic material in the lab by adding, deleting, or changing segments of its DNA. To genetically engineer organisms, scientists extract genes from the DNA of one organism and transfer them into the DNA of another to create a **genetically modified (GM) organism**. The technique uses *recombinant DNA* technology, referring to DNA that has been patched together from the DNA of multiple organisms. In this process, scientists break up DNA from multiple organisms and then splice segments together, trying to place genes that produce certain proteins and code for certain desirable traits (such as rapid growth, disease or pest resistance, or higher nutritional content) into the genetic information, or *genome*, of organisms lacking those traits.

Recombinant DNA technology was developed in the 1970s by scientists studying the bacterium *Escherichia coli*. As shown in FIGURE 6.14, scientists first isolate *plasmids*, small, circular DNA molecules, from a bacterial culture. DNA containing a gene of interest is removed from the cells of another organism. Scientists insert the gene of interest into the plasmid to form recombinant

DNA. This recombinant DNA enters new bacteria, which then reproduce, generating many copies of the desired gene. These copies are then introduced into the cells of the organism that is to be genetically modified.

An organism that contains DNA from another species is called a **transgenic** organism, and the genes that have moved between them are called *transgenes*. The creation of transgenic organisms is one type of **biotechnology**, the application of biological science to create products derived from organisms.

Recombinant DNA and other types of biotechnology have helped us develop medicines; clean up pollution; understand the causes of cancer and other diseases; dissolve blood clots after heart attacks; and make better beer and cheese. FIGURE 6.15 details several notable developments in GM foods. These examples and the stories behind them illustrate both the promises and the pitfalls of food biotechnology.

Genetic engineering is like, and unlike, traditional breeding

The genetic alteration of plants and animals by humans is nothing new; we have been influencing the genetic makeup of our livestock and crop plants for thousands of years. Our ancestors altered the gene pools of domesticated plants and animals through selective breeding by preferentially mating individuals with favoured traits, so that offspring would inherit those traits. Early farmers selected plants and animals that grew faster, were more resistant to disease and drought, and produced large amounts of fruit, grain, or meat.

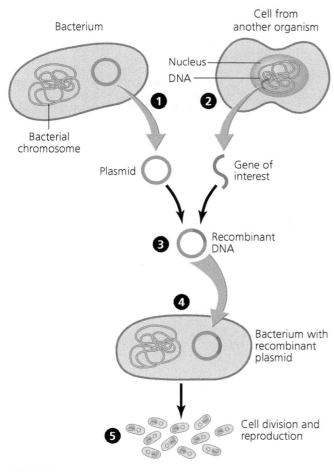

FIGURE 6.14

To create recombinant DNA, a gene of interest is excised from the DNA of an organism and inserted into a stretch of bacterial DNA called a plasmid. The plasmid is then introduced into cells of the organism to be modified. If all goes as planned, the new gene will be expressed in the GM organism as a desirable trait, such as rapid growth or high nutritional content in a food crop.

weighing the issues

GM FOODS AND YOU

Have you ever eaten a food product that contains genetically modified organisms? If you live in North America, the answer is almost certainly "yes." As many as 70% of the food products on shelves in North American grocery stores contain at least some GM ingredients. Check your kitchen for any foods that contain products or ingredients made from corn, soy, or canola. The probability that some of those ingredients came from genetically modified plants is very high. The European Union requires labelling of foods that contain GM ingredients. Do you want your food to be labelled? Would you choose foods based on whether they are organic or genetically modified?

Several Notable Examples of Genetically Modified Food Technology			
Food	**Development**	**Food**	**Development**
Bt crops 	By equipping plants with the ability to produce their own pesticides, scientists hoped to reduce crop losses from insects. Scientists working with *Bacillus thuringiensis* (Bt) pinpointed the genes responsible for producing that bacterium's toxic effects on insects and inserted the genes into the DNA of crops. The USDA and EPA approved Bt versions of 18 crops for field testing, from apples to broccoli to cranberries. Corn and cotton are the most widely planted Bt crops today. Proponents say Bt crops reduce the need for chemical pesticides. Critics worry that they induce insects to evolve resistance to the toxins, cause allergic reactions in people, and harm nontarget species.	Roundup Ready crops 	The Monsanto Company's widely used herbicide, Roundup, kills weeds, but it kills crops, too. So Monsanto engineered soybeans, corn, cotton, and canola to withstand the effects of its herbicide. With these "Roundup Ready crops," farmers can spray Roundup without killing their crops. Of course, this also creates an incentive for farmers to use Roundup rather than a competing brand. Unfortunately, Roundup's active ingredient, glyphosate, is a leading cause of illness for California farm workers, and weeds are starting to evolve resistance to glyphosate.
Golden rice 	Millions of people in the developing world get too little vitamin A in their diets, causing diarrhea, blindness, immune suppression, and even death. The problem is worst with children in east Asia, where the staple grain, white rice, contains no vitamin A. Researchers took genes from plants that produce vitamin A and spliced the genes into rice DNA to create more-nutritious "golden rice" (the vitamin precursor gives it a golden colour). Critics charged that biotech companies over-hyped their product.	Sunflowers and superweeds 	Research on Bt sunflowers suggests that transgenes might spread to other plants and turn them into vigorous weeds that compete with the crop. This is most likely to happen with crops like squash, canola, and sunflowers that can breed with their wild relatives. Researchers bred wild sunflowers with Bt sunflowers and found that hybrids with the Bt gene produced more seeds and suffered less herbivory than hybrids without it. They concluded that if Bt sunflowers were planted commercially, the Bt gene might spread and turn wild sunflowers into superweeds.
Ice-minus strawberries 	Researchers removed a gene that facilitated the formation of ice crystals from the DNA of a bacterium, *Pseudomonas syringae*. The modified, frost-resistant bacteria could then serve as a kind of antifreeze when sprayed on the surface of crops such as strawberries, protecting them from frost damage. However, news coverage of scientists spraying plants while wearing face masks and protective clothing caused public alarm.	StarLink corn	StarLink corn, a variety of Bt corn, had been approved and used in the United States for animal feed but not for human consumption. In 2000, StarLink corn DNA was discovered in taco shells and other corn products. These products were recalled amid fears of allergic reactions. No such health effects were confirmed, but the corn's manufacturer chose to withdraw the product from the market.

FIGURE 6.15   As genetically modified foods were developed, a number of products ran into public opposition or trouble in the marketplace. A selection of such cases serves to illustrate some of the issues that proponents and opponents of genetically modified foods have been debating.

Proponents of GM crops often stress this continuity with our past and say there is little reason to expect that today's GM food will be any less safe than traditionally bred food. However, as biotech's critics are quick to point out, the techniques used to create GM organisms differ from traditional selective breeding in several important ways.

For one, selective breeding generally mixes genes of individuals of the same species, whereas with recombinant DNA technology, scientists mix genes of different species, as different as spiders and goats. For another, selective breeding deals with whole organisms living in the field, whereas genetic engineering involves lab experiments dealing with genetic material apart from the organism. And whereas traditional breeding selects from among combinations of genes that come together on their own, genetic engineering creates novel combinations directly. Thus, traditional breeding changes organisms through the process of selection, whereas genetic engineering is more akin to the process of mutation.

Biotechnology is transforming the products around us

In just three decades, GM foods have gone from science fiction to big business. As recombinant DNA technology was first developed in the 1970s, scientists debated among themselves whether the new methods were safe. They collectively regulated and monitored their own research until most scientists were satisfied that reassembling genes in bacteria did not create dangerous superbacteria. Once the scientific community declared itself confident that the technique was safe in the 1980s, industry leaped at the chance to develop hundreds of applications, from improved medicines to designer plants and animals.

Most GM crops today are engineered to resist herbicides, so that farmers can apply herbicides to kill weeds without having to worry about killing their crops. Other crops are engineered to resist insect attacks. Some are modified for both types of resistance. Crop resistance to herbicides and pests enables large-scale commercial farmers to grow crops more efficiently and economically. As a result, sales of GM seeds to farmers have risen quickly.

Today three-fourths of the world's soybean plants are transgenic, as is one of every four corn plants, one of every five canola plants, and half of all cotton plants. Globally in 2009, 14 million farmers grew GM crops on 134 million ha of farmland—nearly 9% of all cropland in the world. Of the 29 nations growing GM crops in 2009, 6 (Canada, USA, Argentina, Brazil, China, and India), 4 crops (soybean, cotton, maize, and canola), and 2 controlled traits (herbicide tolerance and insect resistance) account for about 99% of the area devoted to the production of transgenic crops worldwide (FIGURE 6.16). Because these nations are major food exporters, much of the produce on the world market is now transgenic, and the market value of GM crops in 2009 was $10.5 billion.

What are the impacts of GM crops?

As GM crops were adopted, as research proceeded, and as biotech business expanded, many citizens, scientists, and policy makers became concerned. Some feared the new foods might be dangerous for people to eat—what if there were unexpected health consequences, such as unanticipated allergic reactions to transgenes in GM foods? Others were concerned that transgenes might escape, pollute ecosystems, and damage nontarget organisms. Still others worried that pests would evolve resistance to the supercrops and become "superpests" or that transgenes would be transferred from crops to other plants

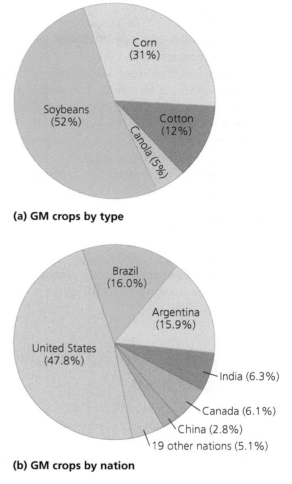

(a) GM crops by type

(b) GM crops by nation

FIGURE 6.16
Of the world's genetically modified crops **(a)**, soybeans now constitute the majority. Of the world's agricultural nations **(b)**, the United States devotes the most land area to GM crops.
Source: Data are for 2009, from the International Service for the Acquisition of Agri-Biotech Applications.

and turn them into "superweeds." Some worried that transgenes might ruin the integrity of native ancestral races of crops.

Because the technology is new and its large-scale introduction into the environment is newer still, there remains a lot scientists don't know about how transgenic crops behave in the field. Millions of North Americans eat GM foods every day without any obvious signs of harm, and evidence for negative ecological effects is limited so far. However, it is still too early to dismiss all concerns without further scientific research. There are numerous mechanisms whereby transgenes can "escape" from the confines of the organism into which they have been implanted and move out into native populations, as well as locations where it is has happened. Therefore, critics argue that we should adopt the **precautionary principle**, the idea that one should not proceed until the ramifications of an action are well understood.

The British government, in considering whether to allow the planting of GM crops, commissioned three large-scale studies between 2003 and 2005. The first study, on economics, found that GM crops could produce long-term financial benefits for Britain, although short-term benefits would be minor. The second study addressed health risks and found little to no evidence of harm to human health, but it noted that effects on wildlife and ecosystems should be tested before crops are approved. The third study looked at effects on bird and invertebrate populations from four GM crops modified for herbicide resistance. Results showed that fields of GM beets and GM spring oilseed rape supported less biodiversity than fields of their non-GM counterparts. Fields of GM maize supported more, however, and fields of winter oilseed rape showed mixed results. Policy makers had hoped that the biodiversity study would end the debate, but the science showed that the impacts of GM crops are complex.

Debate over GM foods involves more than science

Far more than science is involved in the debate over GM foods. Ethical issues have played a large role. For many people, the idea of "tinkering" with the food supply seems dangerous or morally wrong. Even though our agricultural produce is the highly artificial product of thousands of years of selective breeding, people tend to think of food as natural. Furthermore, because every person relies on food for survival and cannot choose *not* to eat, the genetic modification of dietary staples such as corn, wheat, and rice essentially forces people to consume GM products or to go to special effort to avoid them.

The perceived lack of control over one's own food has driven widespread concern about domination of the global food supply by a few large businesses. Gigantic agrobiotech companies, among them Monsanto, Syngenta, Bayer CropScience, Dow, DuPont, and BASF, develop GM technologies. Many activists say these multinational corporations threaten the independence and well-being of the small farmer and raise concerns about the global food supply being dominated by a few large corporations. This perceived loss of democratic control is a driving force in the opposition to GM foods, especially in Europe and the developing world. Critics of biotechnology also voice concern that much of the research into the safety of GM organisms is funded, overseen, or conducted by the corporations that stand to profit if their transgenic crops are approved for human consumption, animal feed, or ingredients in other products.

So far, GM crops have not lived up to their promise of feeding the world's hungry—perhaps because they haven't been allowed to. Nearly all commercially available GM crops have been engineered to express either pesticidal properties (e.g., Bt crops) or herbicide tolerance. Often, these GM crops are tolerant to herbicides that the same company manufactures and profits from (e.g., Monsanto's Roundup Ready crops). Crops with traits that might benefit poor small-scale farmers of developing countries (such as increased nutrition, drought tolerance, and salinity tolerance) have not been widely commercialized, perhaps because corporations have less economic incentive to do so. Similarly, crops such as the infamous "golden rice"—engineered with a higher than usual content of vitamin A and proposed as the solution to vitamin A deficiencies throughout the developing world—have met with limited success.

The development of GM crops has been largely driven by market considerations of companies selling proprietary products. When the U.S.-based Monsanto Company began developing GM products in the mid-1980s, it foresaw public anxiety and worked hard to inform, reassure, and work with environmental and consumer advocates, whom the company feared would otherwise oppose the technology. Monsanto even lobbied the U.S. government to regulate the industry so the public would feel safer about it. These efforts were undermined, however, when the company's first GM product, a growth hormone to spur milk production in cows, alarmed consumers concerned about children's health. Then, when the company went through a leadership change, its new head changed tactics and pushed new products aggressively without first reaching out to opponents. Opposition built, and the company lost the public's trust, especially in Europe and in the developing world.

David-and-Goliath battles that pitted giant Monsanto against lone farmers such as Canadian Percy Schmeiser have not helped to repair the company's public image. As of late 2007, Monsanto had launched 112 such lawsuits against 372 farmers and 49 farm companies in 27 U.S. states, winning judgements averaging $385 000, according to the Center for Food Safety (CFS), a watchdog organization. In addition, Monsanto has forced thousands of other farmers into out-of-court settlements. Monsanto says it is merely demanding that farmers heed the patent laws. North Dakota farmer Tom Wiley, who spoke on behalf of farmers at the World Trade Organization meeting in 2005, sees it differently. Wiley has said, "Farmers are being sued for having GMOs on their property that they did not buy, do not want, will not use, and cannot sell."[12]

Given such developments, the future of GM foods seems likely to hinge on social, economic, legal, and political factors as well as scientific ones. European consumers have been particularly vocal in expressing their unease about the possible risks of GM technologies. Opposition in nations of the European Union resulted in a *de facto* moratorium on GM foods from 1998 to 2003, blocking the importation of hundreds of millions of dollars in agricultural products. This prompted the United States to bring a case before the World Trade Organization in 2003, complaining that Europe's resistance was hindering free trade.

Europeans now widely demand that GM foods be labelled as such and criticize the United States for not joining 100 other nations in signing the Cartagena Protocol on Biosafety (part of the United Nations Convention on Biodiversity), a treaty that lays out guidelines for open information about exported crops. Canada has been a party to the Convention on Biodiversity since 1992 but has never ratified the Cartagena Protocol.[13]

Transnational spats will surely affect the future direction of agriculture, but consumers and the governments of the world's developing nations could exert the most influence in the end. Decisions by the governments of India and Brazil to approve GM crops (following long and divisive debates) are already adding greatly to the world's transgenic agriculture, and China is aggressively expanding its use of transgenic crops.

A counterexample is Zambia, one of several African nations that refused U.S. food aid meant to relieve starvation during a drought in late 2002. The governments of these nations worried that their farmers would plant some of the GM corn seed that was meant to be eaten and that GM corn would thereby establish itself in their countries. They viewed this as undesirable because African economies depend on exporting food to Europe, which has put severe restrictions on GM food. In the end, Zambia's neighbours accepted the grain after it had been milled (so none could be planted), but Zambia held out. Citing health and environmental risks, uncertain science, and the precautionary principle, the Zambian government declined the aid, despite the fact that 2 to 3 million of its people were at risk of starvation (**FIGURE 6.17**). Intense debate followed within the country and around the world. Eventually the United Nations delivered non-GM grain, and in April 2003 the Zambian government announced a plan to coordinate a comprehensive long-term policy on GM foods.

The Zambian experience demonstrates some of the ethical, economic, and political dilemmas modern nations face. The corporate manufacturers of GM crops naturally aim to maximize their profits, but they also aim to develop products that can boost yields, increase food security, and reduce hunger. Although industry, activists,

FIGURE 6.17

Debate over GM foods reached a dramatic climax in Zambia in 2002, when the government refused U.S. shipments of GM corn that were intended to relieve starvation due to drought. Here a Zambian mother and child wait in a line for food assistance.

policy makers, and scientists all agree that hunger and malnutrition are problems and that agriculture should be made environmentally safer, they often disagree about the solutions to these dilemmas and the risks that each proposed solution presents.

Preserving Crop Diversity

One concern many people harbour about GM crops is that transgenes might move, by pollination, into local native races of crop plants. There is certainly now abundant evidence that this has already happened in some localities. The monocultures of modern industrial agriculture essentially place all our eggs in one basket, such that any single catastrophic cause could potentially wipe out entire crops. Preserving crop diversity—domesticated varieties and the wild relatives of crop plants—gives us the genetic diversity that may include ready-made solutions to unforeseen problems.

Crop diversity provides insurance against failure

Preserving the integrity of native variants provides insurance against widespread commercial crop failure. The regions where crops first were domesticated generally remain important repositories of crop biodiversity. Although modern industrial agriculture relies on a small number of plant types, its foundation lies in the diverse varieties that still exist in places like Oaxaca. These varieties contain genes that, through conventional crossbreeding or genetic engineering, might confer resistance to disease, pests, inbreeding, and other pressures that challenge modern agriculture.

Because accidental interbreeding can decrease the diversity of local variants, many scientists argue that we need to protect areas like Oaxaca. For this reason, the Mexican government helped create the Sierra de Manantlán Biosphere Reserve around an area harbouring the localized plant thought to be the direct ancestor of maize. For this reason, too, it imposed a national moratorium in 1998 on the planting of transgenic corn (although that ban was lifted in 2005).

We have lost a great deal of genetic diversity in our crop plants already. The number of wheat varieties in China is estimated to have dropped from 10 000 in 1949 to 1000 by the 1970s, and Mexico's famed maize varieties now number only 30% of what was grown in the 1930s. In the United States, many fruits and vegetables have decreased in diversity by 90% in less than a century. Note, however, that the number of varieties that exist is not, on its own, indicative of the robustness of biodiversity. For example, in recent years the number of wheat varieties in China has actually increased, but the genetic diversity among those varieties has narrowed.[14]

A primary cause of the loss of crop diversity is that market forces discourage diversity in the appearance of fruits and vegetables. Commercial food transporters and processors prefer items to be similar in size and shape, for convenience. Consumers, for their part, have shown preferences for uniform, standardized food products over the years. Now that local organic agriculture is growing in affluent societies, however, consumer preferences for diversity are increasing.

Seed banks are living museums for seeds

Protecting areas with high crop diversity is one way to preserve genetic assets for our agricultural systems. Another is to collect and store seeds from crop varieties and periodically plant and harvest them to maintain a diversity of cultivars. This is the work of **seed banks** and **gene banks**, institutions that preserve seed types as a kind of living museum of genetic diversity (FIGURE 6.18). In total, these facilities hold roughly 6 million seed samples, keeping them in cold, dry conditions to encourage long-term viability. The $300 million in global funding for these facilities is not adequate for proper storage and for the labour of growing out the seed periodically to renew the stocks. Therefore, it is questionable how many of these 6 million seeds are actually preserved.

(a) Traditional food plants of the Desert Southwest

(b) Pollination by hand

FIGURE 6.18
Seed banks preserve genetic diversity of traditional crop plants. Native Seeds/SEARCH of Arizona preserves seeds of food plants important to traditional diets of Native Americans of Arizona, New Mexico, and northwestern Mexico. Beans, chiles, squashes, gourds, maize, cotton, and lentils are all in its collections, as well as less-known plants such as amaranth, lemon basil, and devil's claw **(a)**. Traditional foods such as mesquite flour, prickly pear pads, chia seeds, tepary beans, and cholla cactus buds help fight diabetes, which has become more common in Native Americans since they adopted a Western diet. At the farm where seeds are grown, care is taken to pollinate varieties by hand **(b)** to protect their genetic distinctiveness.

The Royal Botanic Garden's Millennium Seed Bank in Britain holds over 1 billion seeds and aims to bank seed from 20% of the world's plants by 2020. In Arctic Norway, construction has begun on a "doomsday vault" seed bank, intended to hold seeds from around the world as a safeguard against global agricultural calamity. Other major efforts include large seed banks such as the U.S. National Seed Storage Laboratory at Colorado State University, Seed Savers Exchange in Iowa, Plant

Gene Resources of Canada, and the Wheat and Maize Improvement Centre (CIMMYT) in Mexico.

Raising Animals for Food

Food from cropland agriculture makes up a large portion of the human diet, but most people also eat animal products. People don't *need* to eat meat or other animal products to live full, active, healthy lives, but for most people it is difficult to obtain a balanced diet without incorporating animal products. Many of us do eat animal products, and this choice has environmental, social, agricultural, and economic impacts.

Consumption of animal products is growing

As wealth and global commerce have increased, so has our consumption of meat, milk, eggs, fish, and other animal products (FIGURE 6.19). The world population of domesticated animals and animals raised in captivity for food rose from 7.2 billion animals to 24.9 billion animals between 1961 and 2008. Most of these animals are chickens, although the most-eaten meat per unit of weight is pork. Global meat production has increased fivefold since 1950, to approximately 282 000 tonnes as of 2009,[15] and per capita meat consumption has more than doubled over the same period.

Like other domesticated species, livestock and other farm animals can be at risk of biodiversity loss and even extinction. The FAO's Global Databank for Animal Genetic Resources for Food and Agriculture contains information on almost 8000 livestock breeds, of which about 20% are classified as "at risk." During the first six years of the twenty-first century, for example, 62 livestock breeds became extinct, which amounts to a loss of almost one breed per month.[16]

High consumption has led to feedlot agriculture

In traditional agriculture, livestock were kept by farming families near their homes or were grazed on open grasslands by nomadic herders or sedentary ranchers. These traditions have survived, but the advent of industrial agriculture, responding to the pressure of global population growth, has added a new method. **Feedlots**, also known as "factory farms" or *concentrated animal feeding operations (CAFOs)*, are essentially huge warehouses or pens designed to deliver energy-rich food to animals living at extremely high densities (FIGURE 6.20). Today over half of the world's pork and most of the poultry come from feedlots.

Feedlot operations allow for greater production of food and are probably necessary to keep up with levels of meat consumption in Canada and the United States. Feedlots have one overarching benefit for environmental quality: Taking cattle, sheep, goats, and other livestock

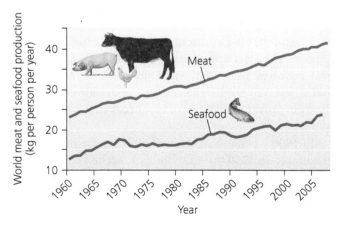

FIGURE 6.19
Per capita consumption of meat from farm animals has increased steadily worldwide over the past few decades, as has per capita consumption of seafood (marine and freshwater, harvested and farmed).
Source: Data from Food and Agriculture Organization of the United Nations (FAO).

FIGURE 6.20
These chickens at a factory farm are housed in crowded conditions and have been "debeaked," the tips of their beaks cut off, to prevent them from pecking one another. The hens cannot leave the cages and spend their lives eating, defecating, and laying eggs, which roll down slanted floors to collection trays. The largest chicken farms house hundreds of thousands of individuals.

off the land and concentrating them in feedlots reduces the impact they would otherwise exert on large portions of the landscape; as you have learned, overgrazing can degrade soils and vegetation, and hundreds of millions of hectares of land are considered overgrazed. Animals that are densely concentrated in feedlots will not contribute to overgrazing and soil degradation.

However, feedlots can have significant environmental impacts. Waste from feedlots emit strong odours and can pollute surface water and groundwater. Livestock produce prodigious amounts of feces and urine; one dairy cow can produce about 20 400 kg of waste in a single year. Greeley, Colorado, is home to North America's largest meatpacking plant and two adjacent feedlots, owned by the agribusiness firm ConAgra. Each feedlot can house 100 000 cattle that are fed surplus grain and injected with anabolic steroids to stimulate growth. During its stay at the feedlot, a typical steer will eat 1360 kg of grain, gain 180 kg in body weight, and generate 23 kg of manure each day.

Poor waste containment practices at some feedlots have been linked to outbreaks of disease, including virulent strains of *Pfiesteria*, a microbe that poisons fish. In 2000 in Walkerton, Ontario, a deadly strain of *E. coli* bacteria, thought to have originated from the contamination of municipal water wells by runoff from factory farms, caused the deaths of seven people and serious illness in hundreds of others.

The crowded and dirty conditions under which animals are often kept at factory farms necessitate the use of antibiotics to control disease. These chemicals can be transferred up the food chain, and their overuse can cause microbes to evolve resistance to them. Crowded conditions also can exacerbate outbreaks of diseases such as *avian influenza* ("bird flu") and *bovine spongiform encephalitis* (*BSE*, or "mad cow" disease), which are now known to be transferable to humans in serious and even deadly forms.

weighing the issues

FEEDLOTS AND ANIMAL RIGHTS

Animal rights activists decry factory farming because they say it mistreats animals. Chickens, pigs, and cattle are kept in crowded pens, fattened up, and slaughtered. Do you think animal rights concerns should be given weight as we determine how best to raise our food? Should we concern ourselves with the quality of life—and death—of the animals that constitute part of our diet?

Feedlot impacts can be minimized when properly managed, and both the federal and provincial governments regulate feedlots in Canada. Feedlot manure can be applied to farm fields, reducing the need for chemical fertilizers. Manure in liquid form can be injected into the ground where plants need it, and farmers can conduct tests to determine amounts that are appropriate to apply.

Our food choices are also energy choices

What we choose to eat has significant ramifications for how we use energy, water, and the land that supports agriculture. Whenever energy moves from one level to the next in a trophic pyramid, as much as 90% of the energy is lost. For example, if we feed grain to a cow and then eat beef from the cow, we lose a great deal of the grain's energy to the cow's digestion and metabolism. Energy is used up when the cow converts the grain to tissue as it grows and as the cow uses its muscle mass on a daily basis to maintain itself. For this reason, eating meat is far less energy-efficient than relying on a vegetarian diet. The lower in the food chain we take our food sources, the greater the proportion of the Sun's energy we put to use as food.

Some animals convert grain feed into milk, eggs, or meat more efficiently than others (FIGURE 6.21). Scientists have calculated relative energy conversion efficiencies for different types of animals. Such energy efficiencies have ramifications for land use—land and water are required to raise food for the animals, and some animals require more than others. FIGURE 6.22 shows the area of land and weight of water required to produce 1 kg of food protein for milk, eggs, chicken, pork, and beef. Producing eggs and chicken meat requires the least space and water, whereas producing beef requires the most. Such differences make clear that when we choose what to eat, we are also indirectly choosing how to make use of resources such as land and water.

In 1900 we fed about 10% of global grain production to animals. In 1950 this number had reached 20%, and by the beginning of the twenty-first century we were feeding 45% of global grain production to animals. Although much of the grain fed to animals is not of a quality suitable for human consumption, the resources required to grow it could have instead been applied toward growing food for people. One partial solution is to feed livestock crop residues, plant matter such as stems and stalks that we would not consume anyway, and this is increasingly being done.

Feed input

Produce output (edible weight)

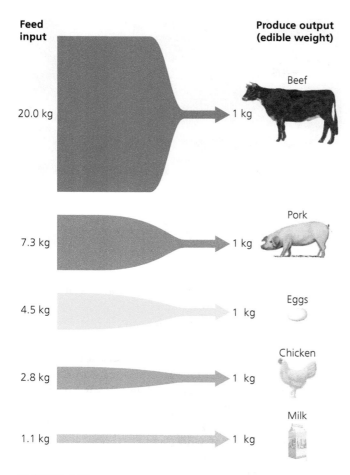

Beef
20.0 kg → 1 kg

Pork
7.3 kg → 1 kg

Eggs
4.5 kg → 1 kg

Chicken
2.8 kg → 1 kg

Milk
1.1 kg → 1 kg

FIGURE 6.21
Different animal food products require different amounts of input of animal feed. Chickens must be fed 2.8 kg of feed for each 1 kg of resulting chicken meat, for instance, whereas 20 kg of feed must be provided to cattle to produce 1 kg of beef.
Source: Data from Smil, V. 2001. Feeding the World: A Challenge for the Twenty-First Century. *Cambridge, MA: MIT Press.*

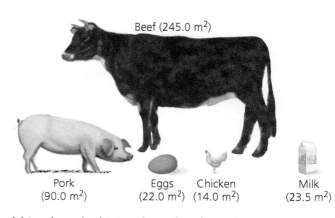

Beef (245.0 m^2)

Pork (90.0 m^2)   Eggs (22.0 m^2)   Chicken (14.0 m^2)   Milk (23.5 m^2)

(a) Land required to produce 1 kg of protein

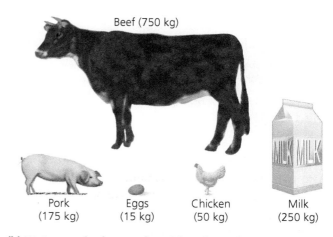

Beef (750 kg)

Pork (175 kg)   Eggs (15 kg)   Chicken (50 kg)   Milk (250 kg)

(b) Water required to produce 1 kg of protein

FIGURE 6.22
Producing different types of animal products requires different amounts of land and water. Raising cattle for beef requires by far the most land and water of all animal products.
Source: Feeding the World: A Challenge for the Twenty-First Century. *Cambridge, MA: MIT Press.*

An additional environmental problem associated with meat production is that the plants required to feed the livestock must be grown on large ranches, which are basically domesticated grasslands. The growth in meat consumption thus requires that forested land worldwide be converted to rangelands in support of livestock production. In the 1970s, this was first dubbed "the hamburger connection"—by purchasing a hamburger made from South American beef, one was unwittingly contributing to the deforestation of tropical rainforests and their conversion into rangelands.

We also raise fish on "farms"

In addition to plants grown on croplands and animals raised on rangelands and in feedlots, we rely on aquatic organisms for food. Wild fish populations are plummeting throughout the world's oceans as increased demand and new technologies have led us to overharvest most marine fisheries. This means that raising fish and shellfish on "fish farms" may be the only way to meet the growing demand for these foods.

Raising aquatic organisms in controlled environments is called **aquaculture**. Many aquatic species are grown in open water in large, floating net-pens. Others are raised in land-based ponds or holding tanks. People pursue both freshwater and marine aquaculture, and both plants and animals are grown. Aquaculture is the fastest-growing type of food production; in the past 20 years, global output has increased sevenfold. Aquaculture today provides a third of the world's fish for human consumption, is most common in Asia, and involves over 220 species (**FIGURE 6.23**). Some, such as carp, are grown for local consumption, whereas others, such as salmon and shrimp, are exported to affluent countries.

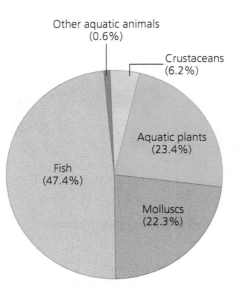

Other aquatic animals
(0.6%)

Crustaceans
(6.2%)

Aquatic plants
(23.4%)

Fish
(47.4%)

Molluscs
(22.3%)

FIGURE 6.23
Aquaculture involves a wide diversity of marine and freshwater organisms, and global production has risen steeply in the past two decades.
Source: Data from FAO 2004. The State of World Fisheries and Aquaculture, 2004.

FIGURE 6.24
Efforts to genetically modify fish have resulted in the creation of transgenic salmon (behind), which can grow considerably faster and larger than wild salmon of the same age and species (front).

Aquaculture has benefits and drawbacks

When conducted on a small scale by families or villages, aquaculture helps ensure people a reliable protein source. Small-scale aquaculture can be sustainable, and it is compatible with other activities. For instance, uneaten fish scraps make excellent fertilizers for crops. Aquaculture on larger scales can help improve a region's or nation's food security by increasing overall amounts of fish available.

Aquaculture on any scale has the benefit of reducing fishing pressure on overharvested and declining wild stocks, as well as providing employment for fishers who can no longer fish from depleted natural stocks. Reducing fishing pressure also reduces *bycatch*, the unintended catch of nontarget organisms that results from commercial fishing. Furthermore, aquaculture relies far less on fossil fuels than do fishing vessels and provides a safer work environment. Fish farming can also be remarkably energy-efficient, producing as much as 10 times more fish per unit area than is harvested from oceanic waters on the continental shelf and up to 1000 times as much as is harvested from the open ocean.

Along with its benefits, however, aquaculture has some serious disadvantages. Counterintuitively, aquaculture can increase the pressure on wild stocks if the feed for the cultured fish is meal made from fish caught in the wild,

which is often the case. Dense concentrations of farmed animals can increase the incidence of disease, which reduces food security, necessitates antibiotic treatment, and results in additional expense. A virus outbreak wiped out half a billion dollars in shrimp in Ecuador in 1999, for instance. If farmed aquatic organisms escape into ecosystems where they are not native, they can spread disease to native stocks or may outcompete native organisms for food or habitat. The opposite has also occurred—recent research suggests that wild Pacific salmon swimming near aquaculture pens have passed on parasites, which then are able to spread rapidly as a result of the high densities of organisms in the pens.

The possibility of competition also arises when farmed animals have been genetically modified. For example, genetic engineering of Pacific salmon has produced transgenic fish that weigh up to 11 times more than nontransgenic ones. Transgenic Atlantic salmon raised in Scotland have been engineered to grow to 5 to 50 times the normal size for their species (**FIGURE 6.24**). GM fish such as these could outcompete their non-GM wild cousins. They may also interbreed with native and hatchery-raised fish and weaken already troubled stocks. Researchers have concluded that under certain circumstances, escaped transgenic salmon may increase the extinction risk that native populations of their species face, in part because the larger male fish have better odds of mating successfully.

Sustainable Agriculture

Post–Green Revolution industrialized agriculture has allowed food production to keep pace with the growing population, but it also has caused negative environmental impacts. These range from the degradation of soils to reliance on fossil fuels to problems arising from pesticide use, genetic modification, and intensive feedlot and aquaculture operations. Although developments in intensive commercial agriculture have alleviated some environmental pressures, they have exacerbated others. Industrial agriculture in some form seems necessary to feed our planet's 7 billion people, but many feel we might be better off in the long run by practicing less-intensive methods of raising animals and crops.

Farmers and researchers have made great advances toward sustainable agriculture in recent years. **Sustainable agriculture** is agriculture that does not deplete soils faster than they form. It is farming and ranching that does not reduce the amount of healthy soil, clean water, and genetic diversity essential to long-term crop and livestock production. It is, simply, agriculture that can be practiced in the same way far into the future. For example, *no-till agriculture*, in which the depth and frequency of ploughing and tilling are kept to a minimum to protect soil moisture and prevent compaction, appears to fit the notion of sustainable agriculture and it can be implemented on the scale of modern agriculture (TABLE 6.2).

Table 6.2   No-Till Farming

Direct benefits of no-till farming

- Conserves biodiversity in soil and in terrestrial and aquatic ecosystems
- Produces sustainable, high crop yields
- Heightens environmental awareness among farmers
- Provides shelter and winter food for animals
- Reduces irrigation demands by 10–20%
- Crop residues act as a sink for carbon (1 metric tonne/ha)
- Reduces fossil fuel use by 40–70%
- Enhances food security by increasing drought resistance
- Reduces erosion by 90%

Indirect benefits arising from the reduction in erosion

- Reduces silt deposition in reservoirs
- Reduces water pollution from chemicals
- Increases groundwater recharge and lessens flooding
- Increases sustained crop yields and lowers food prices
- Lowers costs of treating drinking water
- Reduces costs of maintaining dirt roads
- Eliminates dust storms in towns and cities
- Increases efficiency in use of fertilizer and machinery

Source: Modified from Shaxson, T. F. (1999) The roots of sustainability: Concepts and practice: Zero tillage in Brazil, ABLH Newsletter ENABLE; World Association for Soil and Water Conservation (WASWC) Newsletter.

Sustainable agriculture is closely related to *low-input agriculture*, agriculture that uses smaller amounts of pesticides, fertilizers, growth hormones, water, and fossil fuel energy than are currently used in industrial agriculture. Food-growing practices that use no synthetic fertilizers, insecticides, fungicides, or herbicides—but instead rely on biological approaches such as composting and biocontrol—are termed **organic agriculture**.

As population and consumption increase, soils are being degraded

If we are to feed the world's rising human population, we will need to change our diet patterns or increase agricultural production—and do so sustainably, without degrading the environment and reducing its ability to support agriculture. We cannot simply keep expanding agriculture into new areas because land suitable and available for farming is running out. Instead, we must find ways to improve the efficiency of food production in areas that are already in agricultural use.

Today many lands unsuitable for farming are being farmed, causing considerable environmental damage. Mismanaged agriculture has turned grasslands into deserts and has removed ecologically precious forests. It has extracted nutrients from soils and added them to water bodies, harming both systems. It has diminished biodiversity; encouraged invasive species; and polluted soil, air, and water with toxic chemicals. Poor agricultural practices have allowed countless tonnes of fertile soil to be blown and washed away.

As our planet gains over 80 million people each year, we lose 5 to 7 million ha of productive cropland annually. Throughout the world, especially in drier regions, it has gotten more difficult to raise crops and graze livestock as soils have become eroded and degraded. **Soil degradation**, damage to or loss of soil, around the globe has resulted from roughly equal parts forest removal, cropland agriculture, and overgrazing of livestock, with a much smaller (though still significant) contribution from industrial contamination.

Soil degradation has direct impacts on agricultural production. Scientists estimate that over the past 50 years soil degradation has reduced potential rates of global grain production by 13% on cropland and 4% on rangeland. By the middle of the twenty-first century, there will likely be 3 billion more mouths to feed. For these reasons, it is imperative that we learn to farm in sustainable ways that are gentler on the land and that maintain the integrity of soil.

Organic agriculture is on the increase

Citizens, government officials, farmers, and agricultural industry representatives have debated the meaning of the word *organic* for many years. Experimental organic gardens began to appear in North America in the 1940s, but in Canada the federal Organic Products Regulations only came into effect in December 2006, as a new part of the Canadian Agricultural Products Act. This law establishes national standards for organic products and facilitates the labelling, quality, and sale of organic food. The organic certification logo (FIGURE 6.25) is permitted only on food products that meet specific Canadian standards for organic production, such as using natural fertilizers and raising animals in conditions that mimic nature as much as possible. Multi-ingredient products must also contain at least 95% organic ingredients.

Long viewed as a small niche market, the market for organic foods is on the increase. Although it still accounts for only a small percentage of food expenditures in Canada, sales of organic products are increasing by about 20% annually. Worldwide, sales of organic food tripled between 2001 and 2008, when sales surpassed $50 billion.

Production is increasing along with demand. Although organic agriculture takes up less than 1% of cultivated land worldwide (35 million ha in 2008), this area is rapidly expanding. In North America, the amount of land used in organic agriculture has recently increased 15–20% each year. Today more than 500 000 ha are used to grow organic products in Canada, by almost 4000 producers,[17] and farmers in more than 130 nations practice organic farming commercially to some extent. In addition, 430 000 ha of aquaculture worldwide are now certified as organic.

Several motivating forces have fuelled these trends. Many consumers favour organic products because of better taste, the desire to buy locally, and concern that consuming produce grown with pesticides may pose risks to their health. Consumers also buy organic produce out of a desire to improve environmental quality by reducing chemical pollution and soil degradation (see "The Science Behind the Story: Organic Farming Put to the Test"). Other consumers do not buy organic produce because it usually is more expensive and often looks less uniform and esthetically appealing in the supermarket aisle compared to the standard produce of high-input agriculture.

Overall, though, enough consumers are willing to pay more for organic meat, fruit, and vegetables that businesses are making such foods more widely available. In early 2000, one of Britain's largest supermarket brands announced that it would sell only organic food—and that the new organic products would cost their customers no more than had nonorganic products. In addition to food products, many textile makers (among them The Gap, Levi's, and Patagonia) are increasing their use of organic cotton. (We tend to think of cotton as a "natural" fibre, but it is actually a highly *erosive* crop, meaning that it has an intensive impact on agricultural land. It takes about a half-kilogram of pesticides and fertilizers to grow, by conventional agricultural means, the cotton required to manufacture one T-shirt.[18]) Roots, a company founded in Canada, was one of the first major clothing manufacturers to begin experimenting with large-scale use of organic cotton, in 1989.[19]

Organic agriculture succeeds in part because it alleviates many problems introduced by high-input agriculture, even while passing up many of the benefits. For instance, although in many cases more insect pests attack organic crops because of the lack of chemical pesticides, biocontrol methods can often keep these pests in check. Moreover, the lack of synthetic chemicals maintains soil quality and encourages helpful pollinating insects. In the end, consumer choice will determine the future of organic agriculture. Falling prices and wider availability suggest that organic agriculture will continue to increase. In addition, sustainable agriculture, whether organic or not, will sooner or later need to become the rule rather than the exception.

Government initiatives have also spurred the growth of organic farming. For example, several million hectares of land have undergone conversion from conventional to organic farming in Europe since the European Union

FIGURE 6.25

The new organic certification logo will be used to designate food products that meet the Canadian standards for organic production.

THE SCIENCE BEHIND THE STORY

Organic Farming Put to the Test

Dr. Paul Voroney of the University of Guelph researches the impacts of organic farming methods.

Fields of wheat and potatoes, some grown organically and some cultivated with the synthetic chemicals favoured by industrialized agriculture, stand side by side on an experimental farm in Switzerland. Although conventionally farmed fields receive up to 50% more fertilizer, they produce only 20% more food than organically farmed fields. How are organic fields able to produce decent yields without synthetic agricultural chemicals? The answer, scientists have found, lies in the soil.

Swiss researchers at the Research Institute of Organic Agriculture have been comparing organic and conventional fields since 1978, using a series of growing areas that feature four different farming systems. One group of plots mirrors conventional farms, in which large amounts of chemical pesticides, herbicides, and fertilizers are applied to soil and plants. Another set is treated with a mixed approach of conventional and organic practices, including chemical additives, synthetic sprays, and livestock manure as fertilizer. Organic plots use only manure, mechanical weed-

ing machines, and plant extracts to control pests. A fourth group of plots follows organic practices but also uses extra natural boosts, such as adding herbal extracts to compost. The two organic plots receive about 35–50% less fertilizer than the conventional fields and 97% fewer pesticides.

Over more than 20 years of monitoring, the organic fields yielded 80% of what the conventional fields produced, researchers reported in the journal *Science* in 2002. Organic crops of winter wheat yielded about 90% of the conventional wheat crop yield. Organic potato crops averaged about 68% of the conventional potato yields. The comparatively low potato yield was due to nutrient deficiency and a fungus-caused potato blight.

Scientists have hypothesized that organic farms keep their yields high because organic agricultural practices better conserve soil quality, keeping soil fertile over the long term. Soil scientist Paul Voroney (see photo) from the University of Guelph in Ontario has been looking at the impact of organic methods. Using adjacent fields in nine different locations, he compared the impact of conventional practices with organic practices. On average, organic matter levels were 15% higher in the organically managed fields. There were also better soil structure and a 20% increase in the number of living soil microbes in the top 10 centimetres of the soil profile.[20]

Other researchers have shown that organic farming produces soils that contained more naturally occurring nutrients, held greater quantities of water, and had higher concentrations of microbial life than conventionally farmed soil (see graphs). Organic farms also have deeper nutrient-rich topsoil and greater earthworm activity—all signs of soils healthy enough to

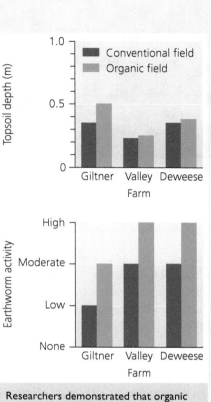

Researchers demonstrated that organic farming at three sites increased topsoil depth moderately and activity of earthworms dramatically.
Source: Data from Liebig, M. A., and J. W. Doran, 1999. Impact of organic production practices on soil quality indicators, Journal of Environmental Quality 28: 1601–1609.

produce crops without help from synthetic chemicals. Increasingly, researchers are concluding that organically managed soil supports a more diverse range of microbial and plant life, which translates into increased biodiversity, self-sustaining fields, and strong crop yields. Such findings may be pivotal as large growers increasingly debate whether to turn to organic farming.

adopted a policy in 1993 to support farmers financially during the first years of conversion. Such support is important because conversion often means a temporary loss in income for farmers. More and more studies, however, suggest that reduced inputs and higher market prices can, in the long run, make organic farming more profitable for the farmer than conventional methods.

Locally supported agriculture is growing

Increasing numbers of farmers and consumers are also supporting local small-scale agriculture. Farmers' markets (**FIGURE 6.26**) are becoming more numerous as consumers rediscover the joys of fresh, locally grown

FIGURE 6.26
Farmers' markets, like this one in Toronto, have become more widespread as consumers have rediscovered the benefits of buying fresh, locally grown produce. There has been farmers' market activity at this particular site, the St. Lawrence Market, since 1803.

produce. The average food product sold in North American supermarkets travels at least 2300 km between the farm and the shelf, and supermarket produce is often chemically treated to preserve freshness and colour. At farmers' markets, consumers can buy fresh produce in season from local farmers and often have a wide choice of organic items and unique local varieties.

Some consumers are partnering with local farmers in a phenomenon called **community-supported agriculture (CSA)**. In this practice, consumers pay farmers in advance for a share of their yield, usually in the form of weekly deliveries of produce. Consumers get fresh seasonal produce, while farmers get a guaranteed income stream up front to invest in their crops—an alternative to taking out loans and being at the mercy of the weather. As of 2005, the CSA network in Québec, alone, counted almost 100 farm members, supplying 20 000 people with local organic meats and produce.[21]

Organic agriculture can even succeed in cities

One surprising place that organic agriculture is making inroads is within cities. Many urban areas now offer community gardens in which residents can grow small plots of fruits and vegetables.

For example, organic agriculture is deeply entrenched in both the cities and the rural areas of Cuba. Long a close ally of the former Soviet Union, Cuba suffered economic and agricultural upheaval following the Soviet Union's dissolution. In 1989, as the USSR was breaking up, Cuba lost 75% of its total imports, 53% of its oil imports, and

80% of its fertilizer and pesticide imports. Faced with such losses, Cuba's farmers had little choice but to "go organic."

Because far less oil was available to fuel Cuba's transportation system, farmers began growing food closer to cities and even within them. By 1998 the Cuban government's Urban Agriculture Department had encouraged the development of more than 8000 gardens in the capital city of Havana (**FIGURE 6.27**). Over 30 000 people, including farmers, government workers, and private citizens, worked in these gardens, which covered 30% of the city's available land. Cuba has also taken steps to compensate for the loss of fossil fuels, fertilizers, and pesticides by, for example, using oxen instead of tractors, using integrated pest management, encouraging people to live outside urban areas and to remain involved in agriculture, and establishing centres to breed organisms for biological pest control.

Cuba's agriculture likely requires more human labour per unit output than do intensive commercial farms of developed nations, and Cuba's economic and agricultural policies are guided by tight top-down control in a rigid state socialist system. Nevertheless, Cuba's low-input farming has produced some positive achievements. The practices have led to the complete control of the sweet-potato borer, a significant pest insect, and in the 1996–1997 growing season the Cuban people produced record yields for 10 crops. Although Cuba's move toward organic agriculture was involuntary, its response to its economic and agricultural crisis illustrates how other nations might, by choice, begin to farm in ways that rely less on enormous inputs of fossil fuels and synthetic chemicals.

FIGURE 6.27
Organic gardening takes place within the city limits of Havana, Cuba, out of necessity. With little money to pay for the large amounts of fertilizers and pesticides required for industrialized agriculture, Cubans get much of their food from local agriculture without these inputs.

CANADIAN ENVIRONMENTAL PERSPECTIVES

Alisa Smith and James MacKinnon

Alisa Smith and J.B. MacKinnon invented the "100-mile diet" concept.

■   **Environmentalists**
■   **Writers** and **bloggers**
■   **Locavores** and inventors of the 100-Mile Diet

One night Alisa Smith and James MacKinnon were expecting company but found that they were out of food. They scrounged outside around their cabin in northern British Columbia and came up with a trout, wild mushrooms, potatoes, garlic, dandelion leaves, apples, sour cherries, and rose hips. Everything tasted so good that the two embarked upon a venture to learn more about the food they ate—specifically, where it comes from and how far it has to travel to get to the dinner table. After learning that food travels almost 2000 km to reach the average North American dinner table, Smith and MacKinnon pledged to spend one year eating only foods that were grown and produced within 100 miles of their Vancouver apartment. They blogged their way through the entire experience, and the result was a book, *The 100-Mile Diet: A Year of Local Eating*, and a new concept in eating.

They were surprised both by the benefits of the 100-mile diet ("It rolls off the tongue easier than 160-km diet") and by the enthusiastic response they received from people around the world. Some of the benefits—on top of the environmental benefits of cutting back on the long-distance transportation of food products—included fresher taste, more fruits and vegetables in a generally healthier diet, seasonal awareness of food, and support of the local economy.[22]

However, there were many challenges. It took a while to figure out how to find some local products and how to tell the provenance of ingredients (which usually don't specify their origin, even if they are listed on food labels). Among the items they could not find in local production were sugar, rice, lemons, ketchup, olive oil, peanut butter, and orange juice.[23] One of the only exceptions, or "cheats," they allowed themselves during that first year was the occasional beer (it may be brewed locally, but the ingredients come from elsewhere).

The 100-mile diet is just one entry—though perhaps the best-known—in the growing movement of local and "slow" food enthusiasts; some are now calling themselves "locavores." MacKinnon and Smith, for their part, are still eating locally—about 85%, by their reckoning—and don't believe they will ever abandon this way of life. They firmly believe that local eating will continue to grow in popularity, especially with rising prices for grains and other basic food products and the rising cost of transporting them. In fact, they believe that local eating will fundamentally transform our approach to food in the coming decades.

"Alisa and I are increasingly convinced that much larger numbers of people could be fed from smaller landscapes than we think; we'd just have to put food closer to the centre of daily life (where it belongs!)." [24]
—J.B. MacKinnon and Alisa Smith

Thinking About Environmental Perspectives

What foods would you have to do without if you decided to try to eat locally? Remember to think about where the individual ingredients come from, as well as where the item is produced. Next time you are in the supermarket read the labels on items that you normally buy, and try to determine their place of origin. (You might have to do some additional research; does this suggest anything to you about how food is labelled?) What are some local substitutions you could make for the "missing" items on your dinner table? What are some of the local specialities that you would be able to enjoy, and how would they vary from season to season?

Conclusion

Many of the intensive commercial agricultural practices we have discussed have substantial negative environmental impacts. At the same time, it is important to realize that many aspects of industrialized agriculture have had positive environmental effects by relieving certain pressures on land and resources.

Whether Earth's natural systems would be under more pressure from 7 billion people practicing traditional agriculture or from 7 billion people living under the industrialized agriculture model is a very complicated question. Additional unanswered questions remain, such as whether genetic modification of food organisms will ultimately prove to be beneficial and whether the environmental and nutritional benefits of locally grown foods will outweigh the efficiencies of modern agriculture.

What is certain is that if our planet is to support 9 billion people by mid-century without further degradation of the soil, water, pollinators, and other ecosystem services that support our food production, we must find ways to shift to more sustainable agricultural practices. Approaches such as biological pest control, organic agriculture, pollinator conservation, preservation of native crop diversity, sustainable aquaculture, and likely some degree of careful and responsible genetic modification of food may all be parts of the game plan we will need to set in motion. What remains to be seen is the extent to which individuals, governments, and corporations will be able to put their own interests and agendas in perspective to work together toward a sustainable future.

REVIEWING OBJECTIVES

You should now be able to:

Outline the historical development of agriculture and the transition to industrialized agriculture

- Agriculture emerged as a human technology about 10 000 years ago.
- The transition to a sedentary lifestyle based on agriculture increased the carrying capacity of land and led to a significant increase in population.
- The Industrial Revolution brought mechanization to farming, along with advances in farm equipment and artificial selection.
- Although there are still many traditional and subsistence farmers, much of the world's cropland is now devoted to modern, industrialized farming.

Explain the challenge of feeding a growing human population

- Food production has outpaced the growth of our population, yet there are still over 900 million hungry people in the world.
- Ensuring food security for all people requires a combination of increased agricultural productivity, a decrease in poverty, and better food distribution methods.

Identify the main approaches and summarize the environmental impacts of the Green Revolution

- The goal of the Green Revolution was to increase agricultural productivity per unit area of land to feed the world's people.
- Agricultural scientists used selective breeding to develop strains of crops that grew quickly, were more nutritious, or were resistant to disease or drought.
- The greatly expanded use of fossil fuels, chemical fertilizers, and irrigation led to enormous increases in productivity, but also caused unintended environmental consequences, including pollution and soil degradation.
- Monoculture—the planting of large tracts of a single crop type—is a hallmark of the Green Revolution that greatly increased agricultural efficiency but reduced crop diversity.

Summarize the strategies and impacts of pest management and the importance of pollination

- Most "pests" and "weeds" are killed with synthetic chemicals that also can pollute the environment and pose health hazards.
- Pests tend to evolve resistance to chemical pesticides, forcing chemists to design ever more toxic poisons.
- Natural enemies of pests can be employed against them in the practice of biological control.
- Integrated pest management includes a combination of techniques, and attempts to minimize use of synthetic chemicals.
- Insects and other organisms are essential for ensuring the reproduction of many of our crop plants.
- Conservation of native pollinating insects is vitally important to our food supply.

Describe the science and evaluate the controversies associated with genetically modified food

- Genetic modification depends on the technology of recombinant DNA. Genes containing desirable traits are moved from one type of organism into another.
- Modification through genetic engineering is both like and unlike traditional selective breeding.
- GM crops may have ecological impacts, including the spread of transgenes and indirect impacts on biodiversity. More research is needed to determine how widespread or severe these impacts may be.
- Little evidence exists so far for human health impacts from GM foods, but anxiety over health impacts inspires wide opposition to GM foods.
- Many people have ethical qualms about altering the food we eat through genetic engineering, and opponents view multinational biotechnology corporations as a threat to the independence of small farmers.

State the importance of crop diversity and some approaches to preservation

- Protecting regions of diversity of native crop varieties, such as Oaxaca, can provide insurance against failure of major commercial crops.

- Seed banks preserve rare and local varieties of seed, acting as storehouses for genetic diversity.

Assess the positive and negative aspects of feedlots and aquaculture for raising animals for food

- Increased consumption of animal products has driven the development of high-density feedlots.
- Feedlots create tremendous amounts of waste and other environmental impacts, but they also relieve pressure on lands that could otherwise be overgrazed.
- Aquaculture provides economic benefits and food security, can relieve pressures on wild fish stocks, and can be sustainable.

- Aquaculture also creates pollution, habitat loss, and other environmental impacts.

Summarize the main goals of sustainable agriculture

- Organic agriculture has fewer environmental impacts than industrial agriculture. It is a small part of the market but is growing rapidly.
- Locally supported agriculture, as shown by farmers' markets and community-supported agriculture, is also growing.

TESTING YOUR COMPREHENSION

1. What kinds of techniques have people employed to increase agricultural food production? How did agricultural scientist Norman Borlaug help inaugurate the Green Revolution?
2. Explain how pesticide resistance occurs.
3. Explain the concept of biocontrol. List several components of a system of integrated pest management (IPM).
4. About how many and what types of cultivated plants are known to rely on insects for pollination? Why is it important to preserve the biodiversity of native pollinators?
5. What is recombinant DNA? How is a transgenic organism created? How is genetic engineering different from traditional agricultural breeding? How is it similar?

6. Describe several reasons why many people support the development of genetically modified organisms, and name several uses of such organisms that have been developed so far.
7. Describe the scientific concerns of those opposed to genetically modified crops. Describe some of the other concerns.
8. Name several positive and negative environmental effects of feedlot operations. Why is beef an inefficient food from the perspective of energy consumption?
9. What are some economic benefits of aquaculture? What are some negative environmental impacts?
10. What are the objectives of sustainable agriculture? What factors are causing organic agriculture to expand?

THINKING IT THROUGH

1. Assess several ways in which high-input agriculture can be beneficial for the environment and several ways in which it can be detrimental to the environment. Now suggest several ways in which we might modify industrial agriculture to lessen its environmental impact.
2. What factors make for an effective biological control strategy of pest management? What risks are involved in biocontrol? If you had to decide whether to use biocontrol against a particular pest, what questions would you want to have answered before you decide?
3. Those who view GM foods as solutions to world hunger and pesticide overuse often want to speed

their development and approval. Others adhere to the precautionary principle and want extensive testing for health and environmental safety. How much caution do you think is warranted before a new GM crop is introduced?

4. Can we call the Green Revolution a success? Has it solved problems, or delayed our resolution of problems, or just created new ones? How sustainable are Green Revolution approaches? Norman Borlaug hoped that the Green Revolution would give us "breathing room" in which to deal with what he called "the Population Monster." Have we dealt effectively with population during the breathing

room that the Green Revolution has given us?

5. Imagine that it is your job to make the regulatory decision as to whether to allow the planting of a new genetically modified strain of cabbage that produces its own pesticide and has twice the vitamin content of regular cabbage. What questions would you ask of scientists before deciding whether to approve the new crop? What scientific data would you want to see, and how much would be enough? Would you also consult nonscientists or take ethical, economic, and social factors into consideration?

6. Cuba adopted low-input organic agriculture out of necessity. If the country were to become economically prosperous once more, do you think Cubans would maintain this form of agriculture, or do you think they would turn to intensive, high-input farming instead? What path do you think they should pursue, and why?

INTERPRETING GRAPHS AND DATA

In the year 2000, over 80 million metric tonnes of nitrogen fertilizer was used in producing food for the world's 6 billion people. Food production, use of nitrogen fertilizers, and world population all had grown over the preceding 40 years, but at somewhat different rates. Food production grew slightly faster than population while relatively little additional land was converted to agricultural use during this time. Fertilizer use grew most rapidly.

1. Express the year 2002 values of the four graphed indices as percentages of the value of each index in 1961.

2. Calculate the ratio of the food production index to the nitrogen fertilizer use index in 1961 and in 2002. What does comparing these two ratios tell you about how the efficiency of nitrogen use in agriculture has changed? Is this an example of the law of diminishing returns?

3. As world population has grown, so has the demand for food, yet little additional land has been devoted to food production. Calculate the ratio of the agricultural land index to the population index for 1961

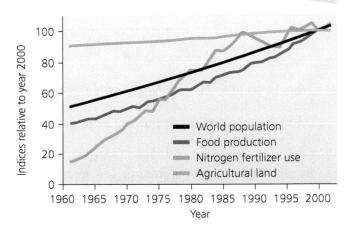

Global food production, nitrogen fertilizer use, human population, and land converted to agriculture, 1961–2002, relative to 2000 levels (2000 = 100). Data from Food and Agriculture Organization of the United Nations.

and 2002. What does comparing these two ratios tell you about how the per capita demand on agricultural land has changed over the years? To what factors can you attribute this change?

CHAPTER ENDNOTES

1.   www.percyschmeiser.com

2.   The species *Homo sapiens* is thought to have originated in Africa approximately 200 000 years BP (before present). The modern human subspecies, *H. sapiens sapiens*, which is the only subspecies of *H. sapiens* that survives today, probably originated about 130 000 BP. Smithsonian Institution Human Origins Project, www.mnh.si.edu/anthro/humanorigins/

3.   Canadian Institute for Health Information (2004) *Overweight and Obesity in Canada: A Population Health Perspective, 2004,* http://secure.cihi.ca/cihi-web/dispPage.jsp?cw_page=GR_1130_E

4.   Food Banks Canada (2011) *Hunger Count 2010: A Comprehensive Report on Hunger and Food Bank Use in Canada, and Recommendations for Change,* www.foodbankscanada.ca/documents/HungerCount2010_web.pdf

5.   Rainville, B., and S. Brink (2001) Food Insecurity in Canada, 1998–1999. Research paper R-01-2E. Ottawa: Applied Research Branch, Human Resources Development Canada.

6.   Health Canada, Pest Management Regulatory Agency, www.pmra-arla.gc.ca/english/legis/pcpa-e.html

7. Government of Canada (2000) *Pesticides: Making the Right Choice for Health and the Environment.* Report of the Standing Committee on Environment and Sustainable Development. http://cmte.parl.gc.ca/cmte/CommitteePublication.aspx?COM=173&Lang=1&SourceId=36396

8. McEwan, K. and W. Deen (1997) *A Review of Agricultural Pesticide Pricing and Availability in Canada,* prepared for Saskatchewan Agriculture and Food; the Ontario Ministry of Agriculture, Food and Rural Affairs; and Agriculture and Agri-Food Canada.

9. Kevan, P. G., E. A. Clark, and V. G. Thomas (1990) Pollinators and sustainable agriculture. *American Journal of Alternative Agriculture.* 5(1): 13–22.

10. Dyer, J. S. (2006) Raising awareness among Canadians about plant pollinators and the importance of monitoring and conserving them. Published electronically by Seeds of Diversity Canada (SoDC) for the Ecological Monitoring and Assessment Network Coordinating Office (EMAN CO) of Environment Canada, www.pollinationcanada.ca/lit/Pollinator%20Awareness%20Paper.pdf

11. Based on information from Kevan, P. G., E. A. Clark, and V. G. Thomas (1990) Pollinators and sustainable agriculture. *American Journal of Alternative Agriculture.* 5(1): 13–22.

12. Leah, S. (2004) Monsanto "Seed Police" Scrutinize Farmers *Inter Press Service,* http://www.commondreams.org/headlines05/0115-04.htm

13. Convention on Biological Diversity, www.cbd.int/default.shtml

14. Eaton, D., J. Windig, S. J. Hiemstra, and M. van Veller (2006) *Indicators for Livestock and Crop Diversity, North-South Policy Brief 2006-1.* Programme International Cooperation, Wageningen International, www.wi.wur.nl/NR/rdonlyres/FADBC382-F7C9-4D2E-B39D-E209AF3C32D2/42280/Policybrief20061.pdf

15. Food and Agriculture Organization of the United Nations (2011) *FAOSTAT: Livestock Primary Production—World Total.* http://faostat.fao.org/site/569/DesktopDefault.aspx?PageID=569#ancor, accessed January 13, 2011.

16. Commission on Genetic Resources for Food and Agriculture, Food and Agriculture Organization of the United Nations (2007) *The State of the World's Animal Genetic Resources for Food and Agriculture.*

17. Canadian Organic Growers. *Quick Facts About Canada's Organic Sector,* www.cog.ca/orgquickfacts.htm

18. Sustainable Cotton Project. www.sustainablecotton.org/

19. Roots, Organic Cotton. www.roots.com

20. Carter, J. (2006) Researchers show soil microbes increase in organic fields—Timing of cover crop planting is important to good performance, depending on variety, *Ontario Farmer*, February 7, 2006, as reported by Ontario Agriculture Centre of Canada, www.organicagcentre.ca/ResearchDatabase/res_microbes_covercrop_of.asp

21. Equiterre. www.equiterre.org/en/agriculture/paniersBios/index.php

22. Smith, A., and J. MacKinnon (2007) *100-Mile Diet: Local Eating for Global Change,* http://100milediet.org/home/

23. Smith, A., and J. MacKinnon (2007) *The 100-Mile Diet: A Year of Local Eating.* Random House Canada.

24. MacKinnon, J. *The 100-Mile Diet: Blog.* http://100milediet.org/category/the-latest

MyEnvironmentPlace

Go to **www.myenvironmentplace.ca** where you will find quizzes, animations, your Pearson eText, and more.

Conservation of Species and Habitats

7

The polar bear (*Ursus maritimus*) is native to the Arctic Circle and depends on sea ice for hunting its main prey, seals.

Upon successfully completing this chapter, you will be able to

- Characterize the scope and value of biodiversity on Earth
- Describe ways to measure biodiversity
- Evaluate the primary causes of biodiversity loss
- Specify the benefits and challenges of conserving habitat and the role of habitat fragmentation

- Contrast *in situ* and *ex situ* conservation approaches
- Compare and contrast traditional and innovative conservation efforts
- Outline reasons for setting aside parks, reserves, and other protected areas

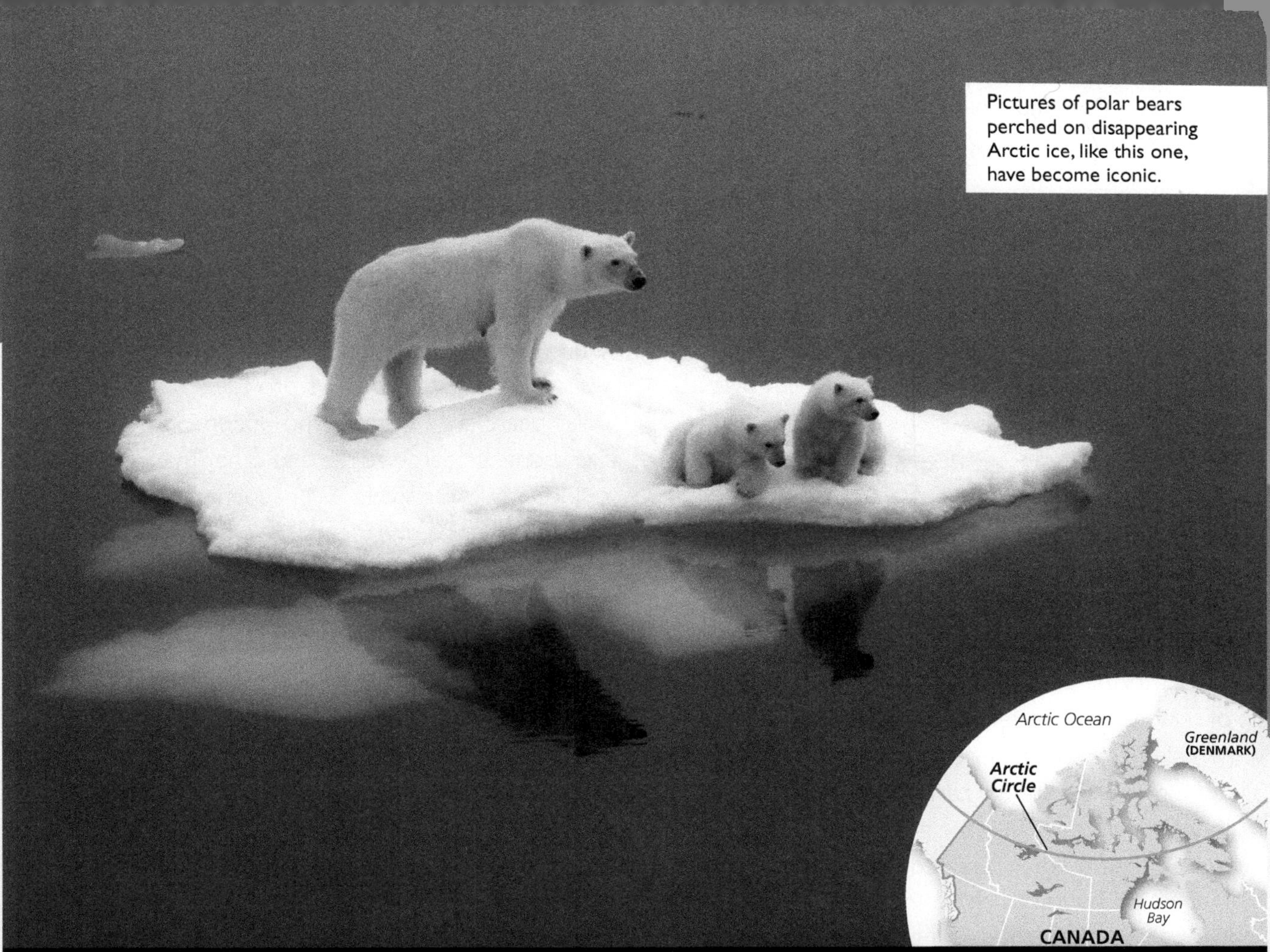

Arctic Ocean
Greenland
(DENMARK)
Arctic
Circle
Hudson
Bay
CANADA

Pictures of polar bears perched on disappearing Arctic ice, like this one, have become iconic.

CENTRAL CASE:
SAVING THE POLAR BEAR: WHAT WILL IT TAKE?

"There will be no polar ice by 2060. Somewhere along that path, the polar bear drops out."

—LARRY SCHWEIGER, PRESIDENT AND CHIEF EXECUTIVE OFFICER OF THE NATIONAL WILDLIFE FEDERATION

"Polar bears are constrained in that the very existence of their habitat is changing and there is limited scope for a northward shift in distribution. Due to the long generation time of polar bears and the current pace of climate warming, we believe it unlikely that polar bears will be able to respond in an evolutionary sense...We conclude that the future persistence of polar bears is tenuous."

—ANDREW DEROCHER, PROFESSOR OF BIOLOGICAL SCIENCE, UNIVERSITY OF ALBERTA (WITH CO-AUTHORS)[1]

"Scientists saying that the polar bear population is decreasing are just taking advantage of the Inuit. Scientists come here for just a few days and don't know everything...There are more bears now. [We] hear about global warming, but [we] see more polar bears. There are more bears on land as well as on sea ice. You can see polar bear tracks in any direction from Arctic Bay."

—COMMENTS MADE AT A PUBLIC CONSULTATION IN ARCTIC BAY, NUNAVUT (CONSULTATIONS ON THE PROPOSED LISTING OF THE POLAR BEAR AS SPECIAL CONCERN UNDER THE *SPECIES AT RISK ACT*, CONDUCTED FEBRUARY–APRIL 2009 BY THE CANADIAN WILDLIFE SERVICE)

"There aren't just a few more bears. There are a hell of a lot more bears. Scientific knowledge has demonstrated that Inuit knowledge was right... Right now, the bears are so abundant there's a public safety issue."

—MITCHELL TAYLOR, POLAR BEAR BIOLOGIST WITH THE GOVERNMENT OF NUNAVUT, CLYDE BAY

The year 2008 was an interesting one for polar bears. That year, partly in response to a lawsuit by environmental groups, the U.S. Fish and Wildlife Service asked the Secretary of the Interior to add the polar bear to the Endangered Species List as a "threatened" species. The official reason was the recognition that the survival of polar bears depends on sea ice for hunting. Arctic sea ice has receded dramatically over the past decade (see graph). Climate models predict that this trend will continue, ending with a largely ice-free Arctic Ocean well before the end of this century. The FWS also recognized the ingestion of or exposure to toxic contaminants, mostly transported from lower latitudes, as a threat to the polar bear's survival.[2] The IUCN Red List of Threatened Species recognizes the polar bear as "vulnerable" (one category below "endangered") on the basis of a global assessment carried out in 2008.[3]

In that same year, 2008, the government of Nunavut announced that it would proceed to allow a cull of 105 polar bears by hunters. The Committee on the Status of Endangered Species in Canada (COSEWIC) also reconfirmed that the polar bear would not be listed as a "threatened" species, but would retain its previous status as a species of "special concern."

The polar bear (*Ursus maritimus*), native to sea ice and land masses within the Arctic Circle, is uniquely adapted to life on the ice. The individual hairs of its outer fur layer are hollow, providing both waterproofing and insulation against the cold. They have a thick layer of blubber that contributes to their ability to retain heat. The fur, which is actually transparent, appears white against their underlying black skin, providing camouflage. On the pads of their paws are small bumps which, along with their thick, strong claws, provide traction on the ice. Polar bears are born on land but spend most of their lives hunting bearded seals and other marine prey from sea ice platforms. What will happen to this animal if its habitat of sea ice disappears?

Also native to the Arctic in Canada, Greenland, Russia, and Alaska are the Inuit, a group of culturally similar indigenous peoples and one of the three Aboriginal groups officially recognized by Canadian law. The Inuit traditionally hunt polar bears, as well as seals, walrus, narwhals, and whales (see painting). They also eat various seabirds, fish, and land mammals such as caribou and Arctic hares. Arctic plants such sorrel, willow, blueberry, soapberry, wintergreen, and lichens complete the traditional diet, which varies seasonally. Inuit hunters seek to maintain an ecological balance between hunting on the sea and on the land. They believe that if this balance is not maintained, and if they do not respect the animals they are hunting, the resource may disappear.[4] They also carefully use all parts of the organisms they harvest.

The right of the Inuit to carry out subsistence hunting in support of their traditional way of life is protected by federal law in Canada, as well as in Alaska. However, other laws, both federal and provincial, are in place to protect wildlife and other aspects of the environment, and this is where the complications begin. There are about 20 polar bear populations in the world, 14 of which have been identified for management purposes in Canada; most of these populations lack long-term monitoring data.[5] The total population of polar bears globally is around 20 000 to 25 000, as of 2011.[6]

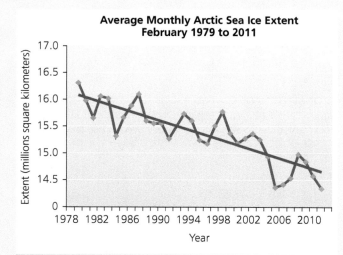

Average Monthly Arctic Sea Ice Extent February 1979 to 2011

Sea ice, which is monitored by satellite, has been declining rapidly for the past couple of decades. February 2011 tied with February 2005 for the lowest extent of sea ice ever recorded.
Source: Data from U.S. National Sea Ice Data Center http://nsidc.org/ arcticseaicenews/2011/030211.html.

Polar bear is a traditional staple in the winter diet of Inuit people in Canada's North.

Canada cooperates with other national governments, state and provincial governments, international organizations, and Aboriginal groups in setting harvest quotas for the polar bear by mutual agreement. Some of these agreements are internal, some are international, and some are bilateral. In Canada, traditional hunters must deal with a confusing bureaucratic landscape to find out what their annual hunting quota will be. For example, early in 2011 the Amarok Hunters and Trappers Association in Iqaluit announced that its members would be allowed a significant increase, from the usual quota of 23 bears to 41, on the basis of accumulated hunting credits. The Qikiqtaaluk Wildlife Board subsequently announced that the hunters would not be allowed to use all of the credits, and it approved an increase of only 10 polar bears to the annual hunt. This came in the context of a decision in 2010 by the Government of Nunavut Environment Minister to *reduce* the total allowable harvest by 10 bears per year. Final approval for the annual quota comes from the Nunavut Wildlife Management Board.[7] The management system in Nunavut was established in 1970, when quotas were first introduced.

The complexity of this situation is hard to grasp. Fundamentally, the prospect of an ice-free Arctic Ocean calls into question the ability of the polar bear to survive as a species. If sea ice continues to deteriorate, polar bear populations will be forced to migrate and possibly even merge. With warming, sea ice is also changing in its physical character, making hunting more precarious. As the bears migrate they are encountering other types of bears, such as brown bears and grizzlies, with which they are interbreeding; this, too, may affect the survival chances of the species.

Meanwhile, polar bears are appearing more frequently in human settlements, necessitating the killing of nuisance bears for public safety. Most scientists interpret the appearance of the bears in settlements as a sign of their increasing stress and desperation for food; many Inuit interpret it as a sign that the number of bears is increasing. This is indicative of a fundamental mistrust that many Inuit hold for scientists, whom they feel do not spend sufficient time on the land to understand the real status of polar bears.

At the same time, traditional Inuit hunting practices are being affected by the loss of sea ice; some hunters have changed their patterns, or the timing of the hunt, in response to these changes. This will eventually affect bear populations but also impacts the survival of traditional Inuit cultures. Many Inuit feel that global warming is not a problem of their making and that finding a solution to the problem should not come at the risk of their cultural survival.

What will it take to save the polar bear? This case illustrates some of the complexity inherent in challenges related to the conservation of species, which almost never present simple solutions. Conservation entails not only ecological concerns, but political, legal, economic, social, and ethical concerns that cross jurisdictional boundaries. As of 2011 the legal status of the polar bear remains unchanged: "threatened" in the United States, but not in Canada.

Our Planet of Life

Changes in biological populations and communities have been taking place naturally as long as life has existed. But today, as never before in the history of this planet, population pressure, human development, and resource extraction are speeding the rate of change and altering the types of changes being imposed on Earth's flora and fauna. Some of our actions are diminishing Earth's diversity of life, the very quality that makes our planet so special. Fortunately, there are steps that we can take to safeguard the diversity of species and habitats, and the ecological and evolutionary processes that make Earth such a unique place.

The ways in which we modify our environment, the impacts of these modifications on species, and the steps we take to mitigate our impacts cannot be understood in a scientific vacuum. Actions that threaten species and habitats have complex social, economic, and political roots, as you have seen in the case of the polar bear. Environmental scientists appreciate that we must understand all of these aspects if we are to develop viable solutions that will contribute to the conservation of species and habitats.

Previously we introduced the concept of **biological diversity**, or **biodiversity**, and defined it as the sum total of all organisms in an area, taking into account the diversity of species, their genes, their populations, and their communities. In this chapter we will refine this definition and examine current biodiversity trends and their relevance to our lives. We will then explore some solutions to biodiversity loss and consider some modern approaches to the conservation and preservation of species and habitats.

Biodiversity encompasses several levels

Biodiversity is a concept as multifaceted as life itself, and definitions of the term are plentiful. Different biologists use different working definitions according to their own aims, interests, and values. Nonetheless, there is broad agreement that the concept applies across several major levels in the organization of life (FIGURE 7.1). We will look, in turn, at the concepts of species diversity, genetic diversity, and ecosystem and habitat diversity.

Species diversity　As you will recall from previous discussions, a *species* is a distinct type of organism, a set of individuals that uniquely share certain characteristics and can breed with one another to produce fertile offspring. Biologists use differing criteria to delineate species boundaries; some emphasize characteristics shared because of common ancestry, whereas others emphasize ability to interbreed. In practice, however, scientists broadly agree on species identities.

We can express **species diversity** in terms of the number and the variety of species in the world, or in a particular region (FIGURE 7.2). One component of species diversity is **species richness**, the number of species in a particular area. Another is **evenness** or **relative abundance**, the extent to which the population numbers of individuals of each different species are equal or skewed.

Speciation generates new species, adding to global species richness. *Extinction*, the disappearance of a species, decreases species richness. *Immigration* (the in-

Ecosystem diversity

Species diversity

Genetic diversity

FIGURE 7.1

The concept of biodiversity encompasses several levels in the hierarchy of life. *Species diversity* refers to the number or variety of species. *Genetic diversity* refers to variety of genes among individuals within a given population or species. *Ecosystem diversity* and related concepts refer to variety at levels above the species level, such as ecosystems, communities, habitats, and landscapes.

roots

BIODIVERSITY

The word *biodiversity* was first used in the 1960s by wildlife conservationist Raymond Dasmann. It was not widely adopted by the scientific community until the 1980s, when it was introduced by conservation biologist Thomas Lovejoy, now the Chief Biodiversity Advisor to the World Bank, who is often credited with having coined the term. The word is a combination of the Greek *bios*, "life," and the Old French *diversité*, "difference, uniqueness," originally from the Latin *diversitas*.

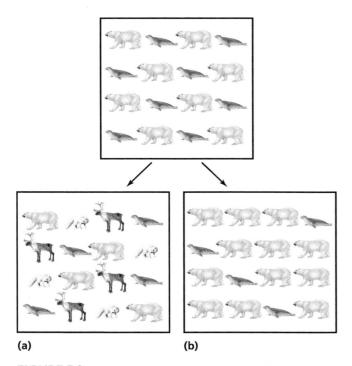

(a)   **(b)**

FIGURE 7.2
Compared with the boxed area at the top, which has an even number of individuals of each of the two species, **(a)** has greater species richness because it contains four species instead of just two. In contrast, **(b)** has the same species richness as the top box but reduced evenness, because one species shows a greater relative abundance than the other.

migration of a species to an area), *emigration* (the out-migration of a species from an area), and *extirpation* (the local extinction of a species) may increase or decrease species richness locally; however, only speciation and extinction change it in an overall sense.

Taxonomists, scientists who classify species, use an organism's physical appearance and genetic makeup to determine its species. Taxonomists also group species by their similarities, into a hierarchy of categories meant to reflect evolutionary relationships. Related species are grouped together into *genera* (singular: *genus*). Related genera are grouped into *families*, which are grouped into *orders*, and so on (**FIGURE 7.3**).

Every species is given a two-part Latin-based scientific name denoting its genus and species. The polar bear, *Ursus maritimus*, differs from other species of bear, such as the brown bear (*Ursus arctos*, of which the grizzly is a subspecies), the American black bear (*Ursus americanus*), and the Asian black bear (*Ursus thibetanus*). These four species are closely related in evolutionary terms, as indicated by the genus name they share, *Ursus*. They are more distantly related to species such as the giant panda (*Ailuropoda melanoleuca*) and the spectacled bear (*Tremarctos ornatus*), even though they are all classified together in the family Ursidae.

Biodiversity exists below the species level in the form of *subspecies*, populations of a species that occur in

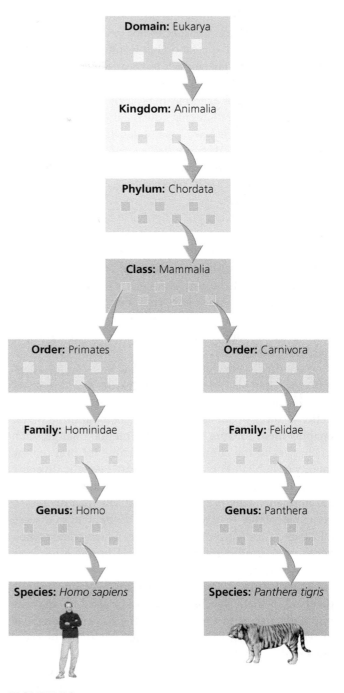

FIGURE 7.3
Taxonomists classify organisms using a hierarchical system meant to reflect evolutionary relationships. Species that are similar in appearance, behaviour, and genetics are placed in the same genus. Organisms of similar genera are placed within the same family. Families are placed within orders, orders within classes, classes within phyla, phyla within kingdoms, and kingdoms within domains. For instance, humans (*Homo sapiens*, a species in the genus *Homo*) and polar bears (*Ursus maritimus*, a species in the genus *Ursus*) are both in the class Mammalia. However, the differences between our two species, which have evolved over millions of years, are great enough that we belong to different orders and families.

different geographic areas and differ from one another in some characteristics. Subspecies are formed by the same processes that drive speciation but result when divergence does not proceed far enough to create separate species. Scientists denote subspecies with the addition of a third scientific name. For example, the grizzly is a subspecies of the brown bear (*Ursus arctos*, which has a large number of subspecies), classified as *Ursus arctos horribilis*. Grizzlies have recently been documented as breeding successfully with polar bears, producing offspring colloquially (and somewhat unattractively) referred to as "pizzlies."

Genetic diversity

Scientists designate subspecies when they recognize substantial genetic differences among individuals from different populations of a species. However, all species consist of individuals that vary genetically from one another to some degree, and this diversity is another important component of biodiversity. **Genetic diversity** encompasses the varieties in DNA present among individuals within species, subspecies, and populations.

Genetic diversity provides the raw material for adaptation to changes in local conditions. In the long term, populations with more genetic diversity may stand better chances of persisting because their variation better enables them to cope with environmental change, such as changes in the climate, the availability of prey, or the quality of habitat. Populations with little genetic diversity are vulnerable to environmental change for which they are not genetically prepared. Populations with depressed genetic diversity may also be more vulnerable to disease and may suffer *inbreeding depression*, which occurs when genetically similar parents mate and produce weak or defective offspring.

Scientists have sounded warnings over low genetic diversity in many species that have dropped to very low population sizes in the past, but the full consequences of reduced diversity in these species remain to be seen. For example, northern elephant seals were hunted almost to extinction by the end of the nineteenth century. They were decreased to one breeding population, and the global number may have fallen to as low as 20 individuals. Since the early twentieth century they have been protected by law, and through various conservation efforts their numbers have recovered to over 100 000. Nevertheless, the existing population is extremely limited in genetic diversity, because all individuals are descended from the 20 individuals that survived the dramatic population decline.

A dramatic decrease in population can cause a **genetic bottleneck**, in which a limited variety of genetic material is available to be passed along by the small number of surviving individuals to their descendants. Even if the population number rebounds, as in the case of the northern elephant seal, the basic genetic diversity of the population will be limited. This limits the ability of the organism to adapt, and can cause it to be vulnerable to environmental changes.

Ecosystem and habitat diversity

Biodiversity also encompasses levels above the species level. **Ecosystem diversity** refers to the number and variety of ecosystems in a given area, based on variations in climate, topography, soil type, and other physical factors. Ecosystem diversity is directly related to the community types and habitat availability within the specified area, so some scientists prefer to call it *habitat diversity*. If the area is large, scientists may also consider the geographic arrangement of habitats, communities, or ecosystems at the landscape level, including the sizes, shapes, and interconnectedness of patches of these entities. Ecosystem diversity has a direct influence on species richness, because a wide range and variety of habitats provide opportunities for species to specialize.

Generally, habitats that are structurally diverse allow for more ecological niches and support greater species richness and evenness. In any given geographic area, species diversity tends to increase with diversity of habitats, because each habitat supports a somewhat different community of organisms. Thus, *ecotones*, where different types of habitat intermix, often have high biodiversity. Because human disturbance (such as clearing plots of forest) can sometimes increase habitat diversity (which ecologists call *habitat heterogeneity*), species diversity may be higher in disturbed areas. However, this is true only at local scales. At larger scales, human disturbance decreases diversity because species that rely on large unbroken expanses of single habitat will disappear.

Some groups hold more species than others

Species are not evenly distributed among taxonomic groups. In terms of number of species, insects show a staggering predominance over all other forms of life (**FIGURE 7.4** and **FIGURE 7.5**). Within insects, about 40% are beetles. Beetles outnumber all non-insect animals and all plants. No wonder the twentieth-century British biologist J. B. S. Haldane famously quipped that God must have had "an inordinate fondness for beetles."

Some groups have given rise to many species in a relatively short period of time (geologically speaking), through the process of *adaptive radiation*. Others have

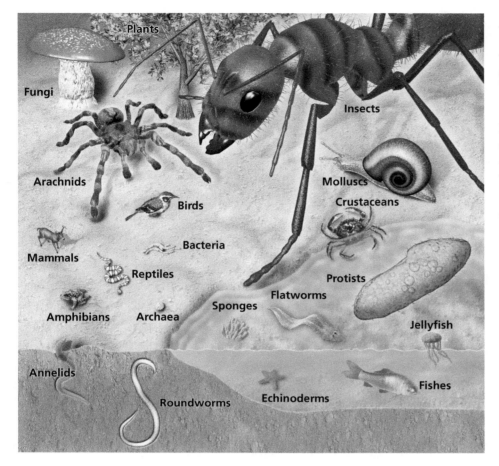

FIGURE 7.4
This illustration shows organisms scaled in size to the number of species known from each major taxonomic group. This gives a visual sense of the disparity in species richness among groups. Because most species are not yet discovered or described, some groups (such as bacteria, archaea, insects, nematodes, protists, and fungi) may contain far more species than we now know of.
Source: Data from Groombridge, B., and M. D. Jenkins (2002) Global Biodiversity: Earth's Living Resources in the 21st Century. UNEP-World Conservation Monitoring Centre. Cambridge, U.K.: Hoechst Foundation.

diversified as a result of having been separated by barriers that promote *allopatric speciation*. Still other groups have accumulated species through time simply because of low rates of extinction.

Measuring biodiversity is not easy

Coming up with precise quantitative measurements to express a region's biodiversity is difficult. This is partly why scientists often express biodiversity in terms of its most easily measured component, species diversity, especially species richness. Species richness is a good gauge for overall biodiversity, but we still are profoundly ignorant of the number of species that exist worldwide. So far, scientists have identified and described about 1.8 million species of plants, animals, and microorganisms. Estimates for the actual total number of species range from 3 million to 100 million, with the most widely accepted estimates in the region of 14 million.

Our knowledge of species numbers is incomplete for several reasons. First, some areas of Earth remain little explored. We have barely sampled the ocean depths, hydrothermal vents, or the tree canopies and soils of tropical forests. Second, many species are tiny and easily overlooked. These inconspicuous organisms include bacteria, nematodes (roundworms), fungi, protists, and soil-dwelling arthropods. Third, many organisms are so difficult to identify that ones thought to be identical sometimes turn out, once biologists look more closely, to be multiple species. This is frequently the case with microbes, fungi, and small insects, but also sometimes with organisms as large as birds, trees, and whales.

Smithsonian Institution entomologist Terry Erwin pioneered one method of estimating species numbers. In 1982, Erwin's crews fogged rainforest trees in Central America with clouds of insecticide and then collected insects, spiders, and other arthropods as they died and fell from the treetops. Using this method, Erwin concluded that 163 beetle species specialized on the tree species *Luehea seemannii*. If this were typical, he calculated,

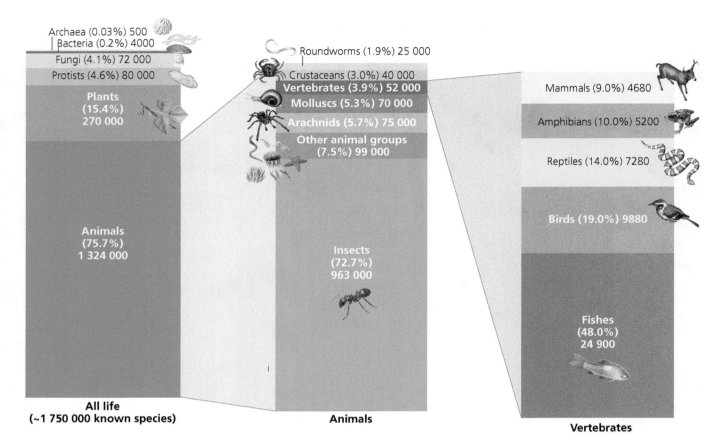

FIGURE 7.5   In the left portion of the figure, we see that three-quarters of known species are animals. The central portion subdivides animals, revealing that nearly three-quarters of animals are insects and that vertebrates comprise only 3.9% of animals. Among vertebrates (right), nearly half are fishes, and mammals comprise only 9%. Most species are not yet discovered or described, so some groups may contain far more species than we now know of.   *Source: Data from Groombridge, B., and M. D. Jenkins (2002) Global Biodiversity: Earth's Living Resources in the 21st Century. UNEP-World Conservation Monitoring Centre. Cambridge, U.K.: Hoechst Foundation.*

then the world's 50 000 tropical tree species would hold 8 150 000 beetle species and—since beetles represent 40% of all arthropods—20 million arthropod species. If canopies hold two-thirds of all arthropods, then arthropod species in tropical forests alone would number 30 million. Many assumptions were involved in this calculation, and several follow-up studies have revised Erwin's estimate downward, but it remains one of the most robust methods for estimating numbers of species.

Measuring and quantifying biodiversity also requires weighting the relative importance of different types of diversity. For example, which would you consider to be more biologically diverse: (1) a region that has high species diversity (lots of different species), in which one species is overwhelmingly dominant and the others are present in vanishingly small numbers; or (2) a region with lower species diversity (a smaller number of species), but in which each species is well represented with numerous individuals? Scientists have devised a number of indices in their attempts to quantify these differences in meaningful ways, but none of them conveys a complete picture of biodiversity.

Biodiversity is unevenly distributed on the planet

Living things are distributed across our planet unevenly, and scientists have long sought to explain the distributional patterns they see. For example, species richness generally increases as one approaches the equator (**FIGURE 7.6**). This pattern of variation with latitude, called the *latitudinal gradient*, is one of the most obvious patterns in ecology, but it also has been one of the most difficult ones for scientists to explain.

Hypotheses abound for the cause of the latitudinal gradient in species richness. It seems likely that plant productivity and climate stability play key roles (**FIGURE 7.7**). Greater amounts of solar energy, heat, and humidity at tropical latitudes lead to more plant growth, making areas nearer the equator more biologically productive and able to support larger numbers of animals. In addition, the relatively stable climates and *aseasonality* of equatorial regions help ensure that single species won't dominate ecosystems, but instead that numerous species can coexist. Variable environmental conditions favour *generalists*—species that can deal with a wide range of circumstances but that do no single thing extremely well. In contrast, stable conditions favour *specialists*—organisms with very specialized niches that do particular things very well.

Another reason that polar and temperate regions may be relatively lacking in species is that glaciation events repeatedly forced organisms out of these regions and toward more tropical latitudes. In other words, species in the tropics have simply had a longer period of geological and climatic stability in which to evolve.

The latitudinal gradient influences the species diversity of Earth's biomes overall. Tropical dry forests and rainforests tend to support far more species than tundra and boreal forests, for instance. Tropical biomes typically show more evenness, as well, whereas in high-latitude biomes with low species richness, particular species may greatly outnumber others. For example, the Canadian boreal forest is characterized by immense expanses dominated by black spruce, whereas Panamanian tropical forest contains hundreds of tree species, no one of which greatly outnumbers the others. Understanding such patterns of biodiversity is vital for landscape ecology, regional planning, and forest management, as well as for the conservation of species and habitats.

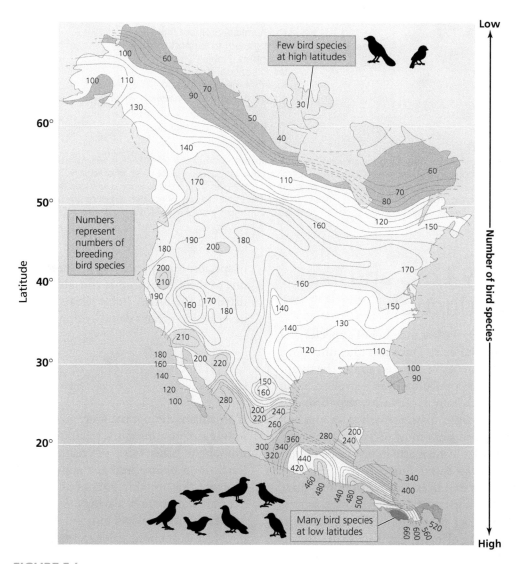

FIGURE 7.6

For many types of organisms, the number of species per unit area tends to increase toward the equator. This trend, the latitudinal gradient in species richness, is one of the most readily apparent—yet least understood—patterns in ecology. One example is bird species in North and Central America: In any one spot in arctic Canada and Alaska, 30 to 100 species can be counted; in areas of Costa Rica and Panama, the number rises to over 600.

Source: Adapted from Cook, R. E. (1969) Variation in species density in North American birds. Systematic Zoology 18: 63–84.

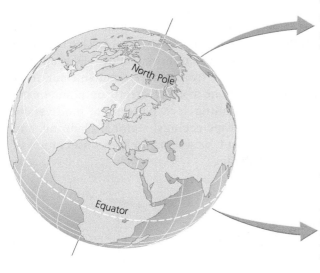

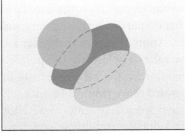

Temperate and polar latitudes
Variable climate favours fewer species, and species that are widespread generalists.

Tropical latitudes
Greater solar energy, heat, and humidity promote more plant growth to support more organisms. Stable climate favours specialist species. Together these encourage greater diversity of species.

FIGURE 7.7   There are many hypotheses for the latitudinal gradient in species richness; one set of ideas is summarized here. The variable climates (days, seasons, and years) of polar and temperate latitudes favour organisms that can survive a wide range of conditions. Such generalist species have expansive niches; they can do many things well enough to survive, and they spread over large areas. In tropical latitudes, the abundant solar energy, heat, and humidity induce greater plant growth, which supports more organisms. The stable climates of equatorial regions favour specialist species, which have restricted niches but do certain things very well. Together these factors promote greater species richness in the tropics.

Biodiversity Loss and Species Extinction

Extinction occurs when the last member of a species dies and the species ceases to exist. Once lost to extinction, a species can never return. As mentioned above, the disappearance of a particular population from a given area, but not the entire species globally, is termed **extirpation**. For example, the Siberian tiger, once native across much of Asia, has been extirpated from most of its historic range, but it is not yet extinct—it still exists in one small mountainous location in the far east of Russia.

Although a species that is extirpated from one place may still exist in others, extirpation is an erosive process that can, over time, lead to extinction. A species that is in imminent danger of extirpation or extinction is referred to as **endangered**. One that is likely to become endangered in the near future, if limiting factors are not reversed, is called **threatened**. These categories—threatened, endangered, extirpated, and extinct—are the main classifications used by the Canadian *Species-At-Risk Act* (also known as **SARA**), and, with some variations in definition, by most organizations that keep track of that status

of species. Any species that is agreed to have fallen within one of these categories is considered to be *at risk*, and is listed on the SARA Public Registry, by a process that is described in greater detail later in this chapter.

Extinction and extirpation occur naturally

If organisms did not naturally go extinct, we would be up to our ears in dinosaurs, trilobites, ammonites, and the millions of other types of creatures that vanished from Earth long before humans appeared. Palaeontologists estimate that roughly 99% of all species that have ever lived are now extinct, leaving only about 1% as the wealth of species on our planet today.

Most extinctions prior to the appearance of humans occurred one by one for independent reasons, at a rate that palaeontologists refer to as the *background rate of extinction*. The fossil record indicates that for mammals and marine animals, one species out of 1000 would typically become extinct every 1000 to 10 000 years. This translates to a background rate of about one extinction per 1 to 10 million species per year.

In the past 440 million years, our planet has experienced five distinct episodes of *mass extinction* (FIGURE 7.8), each of which has eliminated at least half of existing species. There is evidence for further mass extinctions in the Cambrian period and earlier, more than half a billion years ago. The best-known episode of mass extinction occurred at the end of the Cretaceous period, 65 million years ago, when the global side-effects of a large asteroid impact drove the dinosaurs and many other groups to extinction. The most severe episode occurred at the end of the Permian period, 248 million years ago, when close to 54% of all families, 90% of all species, and 95% of marine species went extinct. The cause of this extinction is still being researched.

Some species are more vulnerable to extinction than others

In general, extinction occurs when environmental conditions change rapidly or severely enough that a species cannot adapt genetically to the change; natural selection simply does not have enough time to work. All manner of environmental events can lead to extinction, from climate change to the rise and fall of sea level, to the arrival of new harmful species, to severe weather events such as extended droughts. In general, small populations and species narrowly specialized on a particular resource or way of life are most vulnerable to extinction from environmental change. Thus, **vulnerable** is yet another SARA category, referring to species that are of particular concern because of characteristics that make them particularly sensitive to human activities or natural events.

The golden toad was a prime example of a vulnerable species that did, eventually, become extinct (see "Central Case: Striking Gold in a Costa Rican Cloud Forest"). The golden toad was **endemic** to the Monteverde cloud forest in Costa Rica, meaning that it occurred nowhere else on the planet. Endemic species face relatively high risks of extinction because all of their members belong to a single, sometimes small, population. At the time of its discovery in 1964, the golden toad was known in an area of only 4 km². It required very specific conditions to breed successfully. The golden toads gathered to breed in springtime in small, root-bound pools. Monteverde provided an ideal living environment for the golden toad, but the minuscule extent of that environment meant that any stresses that deprived the toad of the resources it needed might doom the entire world population of the species. Less than 25 years after its discovery by biologist Jay Savage and colleagues, the golden toad was extinct, probably because of several factors including climate change, habitat alteration, and disease.

Today many amphibian species around the globe are at a high level of risk of vulnerability and risk of extinction, in some cases because of specialized habitat and breeding requirements, in others because of exposure to contaminants or disease. The Global Amphibian Assessment ranked nearly one-third (32%) of the world's amphibians as "threatened," compared with 23% of mammal species and 12% of bird species. Of Canada's 45 amphibian species, 16 (35%) are designated as "at risk" or "sensitive."[8]

Vulnerability resulting from restricted or specialized habitat, lifestyle, or resource requirements is certainly not limited to amphibians. Consider the Vancouver Island marmot (*Marmota vancouverensis*),

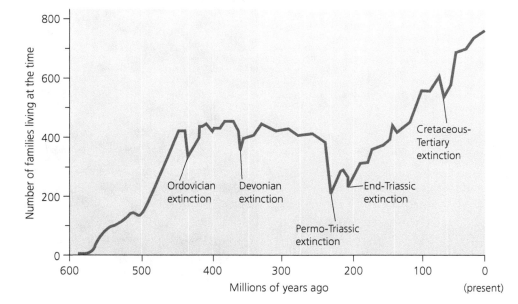

FIGURE 7.8
The fossil record shows evidence of five mass extinctions during the past half-billion years of Earth history. At the end of the Ordovician, Devonian, Permian, Triassic, and Cretaceous periods, 50–95% of the world's species became extinct. Each time, biodiversity later rebounded to equal or higher levels, but the rebound required millions of years in each case. *Source: Data from Raup, D. M., and J. J. Sepkoski (1982) Mass extinctions in the marine fossil record. Science 215: 1501–1503.*

one of the rarest mammals in North America, and one of only five species of mammals whose natural range is entirely within Canada. Marmots require small patches of south- to southwest-facing, steeply sloping, boulder-filled meadow, between 800 and 1500 m in altitude—pretty specific! The marmot's range has been drastically reduced over the past few decades, primarily by habitat alteration resulting from logging. As of 2010 only about 300 individuals of this species were alive in the wild, with only a handful of colonies in a few locations in southern Vancouver Island (FIGURE 7.9). This number has increased over the past few years from near-extinction (as few as 21 individuals in 2003). The increase was the result of conservation efforts, including captive breeding programs at the Toronto Zoo, Calgary Zoo, and Mountainview Conservation and Breeding Centre in Langley, B.C. The Vancouver Island marmot is listed as endangered on the SARA Registry.

Humans may have started a sixth mass extinction

Biodiversity at all levels is currently being lost as a result of human impacts, most irretrievably in the extinction of species. If the current trend continues, the modern era may see the extinction of more than half of all species. Although similar in scale to previous mass extinctions, today's ongoing mass extinction is different in three primary respects. First, humans are causing it. Second, humans will suffer as a result of it. And third, it may be happening even more rapidly than the previous "Big Five" mass extinctions.

There have been many instances of human-induced species extinction over the past few hundred years. Sailors documented the extinction of the dodo on the Indian Ocean island of Mauritius in the seventeenth century, and we still have a few of the dodo's body parts in museums. Among North American birds in the past two centuries, we have driven into extinction the Carolina parakeet, great auk, Labrador duck, and passenger pigeon, and probably the Bachman's warbler, Eskimo curlew, and ivory-billed woodpecker. Several more species, including the whooping crane, California condor, and Kirtland's warbler are teetering on the brink of extinction.

However, species extinctions caused by humans precede written history. Indeed, people may have been hunting and out-competing species into extinction for thousands of years. Archaeological evidence shows that in case after case, a wave of extinctions followed close on the heels of human arrival on islands and continents (FIGURE 7.10). After Polynesians reached Hawaii, half of its birds went extinct. Birds, mammals, and reptiles vanished following human arrival on many other oceanic islands, including large islands such as New Zealand and Madagascar. Dozens of species of large vertebrates died off in Australia after Aborigines arrived roughly 50 000

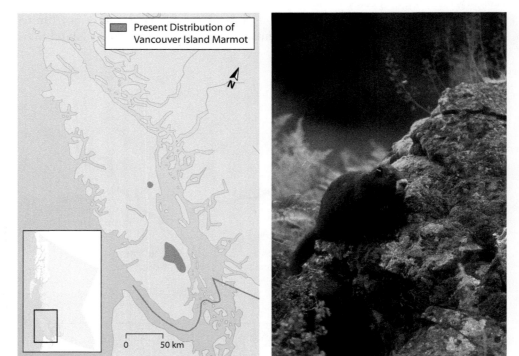

FIGURE 7.9
An extremely restricted natural range with very specific habitat requirements can leave some species highly vulnerable, especially if local environmental changes occur. The Vancouver Island marmot, seen here, is one of the rarest mammals in North America, and one of only five species of mammals that are found only in Canada. This marmot's range (shown in purple on the map) has been drastically reduced to only a few locations with a handful of colonies, primarily as a result of logging.

years ago, and North America lost 33 genera of large mammals after people arrived on the continent about 10 000 years ago.

Today, species loss is accelerating as our population growth and resource consumption put increasing strain on habitats and wildlife. In 2005, scientists with the Millennium Ecosystem Assessment calculated that the current global extinction rate is 100 to 1000 times greater than the background rate. They noted a decrease in genetic diversity as well as declining population sizes and numbers of species, accompanied by greater demands on ecosystem services in the past few decades. Moreover, they projected that the rate of species extinctions would increase tenfold or more in future decades.[9]

To keep track of the current status of endangered species, the *World Conservation Union* (or *IUCN*), a non-governmental organization, maintains the **Red List**, a regularly updated list of species facing high risks of extinction. The 2011 Red List reports that at least 21% (1134) of mammal species and 12.5% (1240) of bird species are threatened. (On the Red List, Threatened species include species that are Critically Endangered, Endangered, or Vulnerable.) Among other major groups (for which

assessments are not fully complete), estimates of the percentage of threatened species range from 17% to 75%.[10] For all of these figures, the *actual* numbers of threatened species extinct, like the actual number of total species in the world, are doubtless greater than the *known* numbers.

In 2011, Anthony Barnosky of the University of California at Berkeley and colleagues carried out a detailed statistical comparison of the current rate of species extinction with the rates of extinction during the "Big Five" mass extinctions. They published their findings in the journal *Nature*. It was an extremely complex undertaking; data limitations and complexities make the analysis very difficult. For example, as the authors pointed out, some 49% of bivalves went extinct at the end of the Cretaceous, but only 1% of the bivalve species alive today have even been assessed, making meaningful comparison difficult. Furthermore, some assessments of threatened and extinct species are inflated because endangered species tend to be assessed first, whereas others are probably grossly underestimated because so few living species have been assessed. The authors concluded from their study that extinctions in the past 500 years do not yet constitute a mass extinction, but they also concluded that rates of

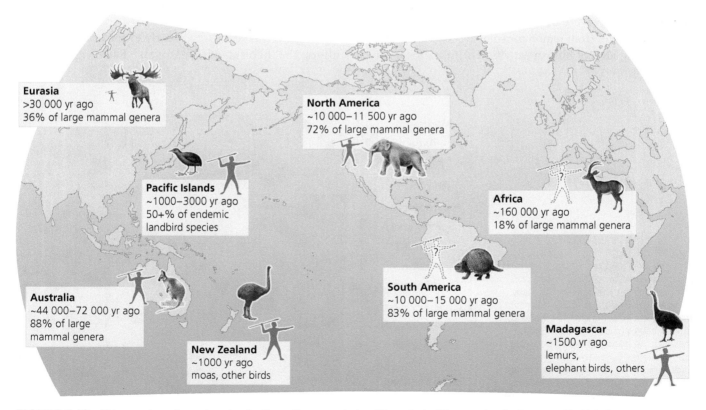

FIGURE 7.10   This map shows for each region the time of human arrival and the extent of the recent extinction wave. Illustrated are representative extinct megafauna from each region. The human hunter icons are sized according to the degree of evidence that human hunting was a cause of extinctions; larger icons indicate more certainty that humans (as opposed to climate change or other forces) were the cause. Data for South America and Africa are too sparse to be conclusive; future archaeological and palaeontological research could alter these interpretations.   Source: *Adapted from Barnosky, A. D., et al. (2004) Assessing the causes of late Pleistocene extinctions on the continents. Science 306: 70–75; and Wilson, E. O. (1992) The Diversity of Life. Cambridge, MA: Belknap Press.*

extinction today are much higher than in similar periods during the "Big Five" (FIGURE 7.11) and that conservation efforts are urgently needed.[11]

Extinction is only part of the story of biodiversity loss. The larger part of the story is the decline in population sizes of many organisms. Declines in numbers are accompanied by shrinkage of species' geographical ranges. Thus, many species today are less numerous and occupy less area than they once did. Tigers numbered well over 100 000 worldwide in the nineteenth century but number only about 5000 today. The Vancouver marmot population dipped to 21 in a greatly reduced geographical range, making a comeback only as a result of captive breeding. The northern elephant seal population may have been as low as 20 at the end of the nineteenth century, in just one breeding population.

To measure and quantify this degradation, scientists at the World Wildlife Fund and the United Nations Environment Programme (UNEP) developed a metric called the *Living Planet Index*. This index summarizes trends in 7953 different populations of 2544 species of mammals, birds, amphibians, fish, and reptiles that are well enough monitored to provide reliable data. Between 1970 and 2007, the Living Planet Index fell by roughly 30%. This means that the monitored populations are roughly 30% smaller than they were in 1970 (FIGURE 7.12), although the decline varies from region to region, species to species, and differing level of human activity. The index for fresh-

water species fell by 35%, the index for tropical species fell by 60%, and the index for low-income regions fell by 58% (as compared to 5% in high-income regions).[12]

There are several major causes of biodiversity loss

Reasons for the decline of any given species are often multifaceted and complex, so they can be difficult to determine. The current precipitous decline in populations of amphibians throughout the world provides an example. Frogs, toads, and salamanders worldwide are decreasing drastically in abundance. Many have already gone extinct, and scientists are struggling to explain why. Recent studies have implicated a wide array of factors, and most scientists now suspect that such factors may be interacting synergistically (see "The Science Behind the Story: Amphibian Diversity and Decline").

Overall, scientists have identified four primary causes of population decline and species extinction: habitat alteration, invasive species, pollution, and overharvesting. Global climate change is becoming the fifth. Each of these factors is intensified by human population growth and by our increase in per capita consumption of resources.

Habitat alteration   Nearly every human activity alters the habitat of organisms. Farming replaces

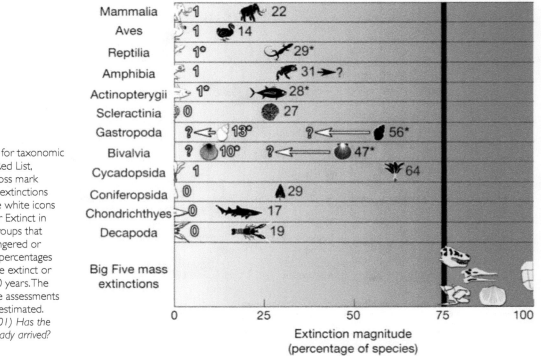

FIGURE 7.11
This diagram shows extinctions for taxonomic groups assessed by the IUCN Red List, compared to the 75% species-loss mark that defines the "Big Five" mass extinctions (red line, and bottom right). The white icons show species that are Extinct or Extinct in the Wild. The black icons add groups that are Threatened (Critically Endangered or Endangered). The numbers are percentages of each group that have become extinct or endangered during the past 500 years. The arrows indicate cases where the assessments may be either inflated or underestimated.
Source: From Barnosky, et al. (2001) Has the Earth's sixth mass extinction already arrived? Nature, 471: 51.

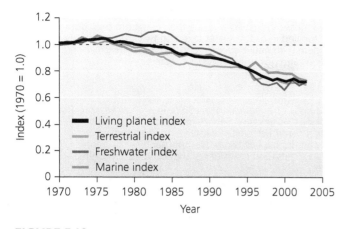

FIGURE 7.12
The Living Planet Index is calculated from trends in populations of individual species. As shown here, some species have increased over the time they have been monitored, but more have decreased; thus, the Living Planet Index overall declined globally. From World Wildlife Fund (2010) *2010 Living Planet Report.*

diverse natural communities with simplified ones of only one or a few plant species. Grazing modifies the structure and species composition of grasslands. Either type of agriculture can lead to desertification. Clearing forests removes the food, shelter, and other resources that forest-dwelling organisms need to survive. Hydroelectric dams turn rivers into reservoirs upstream and affect water conditions and floodplain communities both upstream and downstream. Urbanization and suburban sprawl supplant diverse natural communities with simplified human-made ones, driving many species from their homes.

Because organisms are adapted to the habitats in which they live, any major change is likely to render it less suitable for them. Of course, human-induced habitat change benefits some species. Animals such as starlings, house sparrows, pigeons, raccoons, and grey squirrels do very well in urban and suburban environments and benefit from our modification of natural habitats. However, the species that benefit are relatively few; for every species that gains, more lose. Furthermore, the species that do well in our midst tend to be weedy, cosmopolitan generalists that are in little danger of disappearing any time soon.

Habitat alteration is by far the greatest cause of biodiversity loss today. It is the primary source of population declines for 83% of threatened mammals and 85% of threatened birds, according to UNEP data. As just one example of thousands, the prairies native to central North America have been almost entirely converted to agriculture, especially south of the border in the United States, where the area of prairie habitat has been reduced by more than 99%. As a result, grassland bird populations have declined by an estimated 82–99%. Many grassland species have been extirpated from large areas, and the two species of prairie chickens still persisting in pockets of the Great Plains could soon go extinct.

Habitat destruction has occurred widely in every biome. Over half of temperate forests, grasslands, and shrublands had been converted by the year 1950 (mostly for agriculture). Today habitat is being lost most rapidly in tropical rainforests, tropical dry forests, and savannas. And the Arctic sea ice habitat required by polar bears is disappearing faster than ever in the history of scientific monitoring of its extent.

Invasive species   Our introduction of non-native species to new environments, where some may become invasive (**FIGURE 7.13**), has also pushed native species toward extinction. Some introductions have been accidental. Examples include aquatic organisms such as the zebra mussel, transported among continents in the ballast water of ships; animals that have escaped from the pet or food trade; and weed seeds that cling to us as we travel from place to place. Many other introductions have been intentional. People have brought with them food crops, domesticated animals, and other organisms as they colonized new places, generally unaware of the ecological consequences that could result.

Species native to islands are especially vulnerable to disruption from introduced species because native species have been in isolation for so long with relatively few parasites, predators, and competitors. As a result, they have not evolved the defences necessary to resist invaders that are better adapted to these pressures.

Most organisms introduced to new areas perish, but the few types that survive may do very well, especially if they find themselves without the predators and parasites that attacked them back home or without the competitors that had limited their access to resources. Once released from the limiting factors of predation, parasitism, and competition, an introduced species may increase rapidly, spread, and displace native species. Invasive species cause billions of dollars in economic damage each year.

Pollution   Pollution can harm organisms in many ways. Air pollution can degrade forest ecosystems; water pollution can adversely affect fish and amphibians; agricultural runoff (including fertilizers, pesticides, and sediments) can harm many terrestrial and aquatic species. Heavy metals, PCBs, endocrine-disrupting compounds, and various other toxic chemicals can poison both people and wildlife, and the effects of oil and chemical spills on wildlife are dramatic and well known.

Invasive Species			
Species	**Native to...**	**Invasive in...**	**Effects**
Zebra mussels (*Dreissenna polymorpha*) 	Caspian Sea	Freshwater ecosystems including the Great Lakes of Canada and the United States	Zebra mussels most likely made their way from their home by travelling in ballast water taken on by cargo ships. They compete with native species and clog water treatment facilities and power plant cooling systems.
Kudzu (*Pueraria montana*) 	Japan	Southeastern United States	Kudzu is a vine that can grow 30 m in a single season. The U.S. Soil Conservation Service introduced kudzu in the 1930s to help control erosion. Adaptable and extraordinarily fast-growing, kudzu has taken over thousands of hectares of forests, fields, and roadsides in the southeastern United States.
Asian long-horned beetles (*Anoplophora glabripennis*) 	Asia	United States	Having first arrived in the United States in imported lumber in the 1990s, these beetles burrow into hardwood trees and interfere with the trees' ability to absorb and process water and nutrients. They may wipe out the majority of hardwood trees in an area. Several U.S. cities, including Chicago in 1999 and Seattle in 2002, have cleared thousands of trees after detecting these invaders.
Cane toad (*Bufo marinus*) 	Southern United States to tropical South America	Northern Australia and other locations	Since being introduced 70 years ago to control insects in sugarcane fields, the cane toad has wreaked havoc across northern Australia (and other locations). The skin of this tropical American toad can kill its predators, and the cane toad outcompetes native amphibians.
Gypsy moth (*Lymantria dispar*) 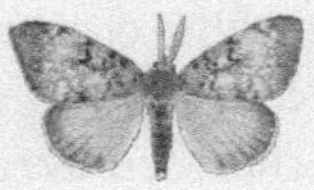	Eurasia	Northeastern United States	In the 1860s, a scientist introduced the gypsy moth to Massachusetts in the mistaken belief that it might be bred with others to produce a commercial-quality silk. The gypsy moth failed to start a silk industry, and instead spread through the northeastern United States and beyond, where its outbreaks defoliate trees over large regions every few years.
European starling (*Sturnus vulgaris*) 	Europe	North America	The bird was first introduced to New York City in the late nineteenth century by Shakespeare devotees intent on bringing every bird mentioned in Shakespeare's plays to the new continent. It took only 75 years for the birds to spread to the Pacific coast, Alaska, and Mexico, becoming one of the most abundant birds on the continent. Starlings are thought to outcompete native birds for nest sites.
Indian mongoose (*Herpestes auropunctatus*) 	Southeast Asia	Hawaii	Rats that had invaded the Hawaiian islands from ships in the seventeenth century were damaging sugarcane fields, so in 1883 the Indian mongoose was introduced to control rat populations. Unfortunately, the rats were active at night and the mongooses fed during the day, so the plan didn't work. Instead mongooses began preying on native species like ground-nesting seabirds and the now-endangered Nene or Hawaiian goose (*Branta sandvicensis*).
A green alga (*Caulerpa taxifolia*) 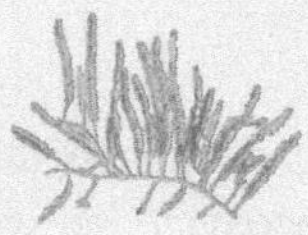	Tropical oceans and seas	Mediterranean Sea	Dubbed the "killer algae," *Caulerpa taxifolia* has spread along the coasts of several Mediterranean countries since it apparently escaped from Monaco's aquarium in 1984. Creeping underwater over the sand and mud like a green shag carpet, it crowds out other plants, is inedible to most animals, and tangles boat propellers. It has been the focus of intense eradication efforts since arriving recently in Australia and California.
Cheatgrass (*Bromus tectorum*) 	Eurasia	Western United States	In just 30 years after its introduction to Washington state in the 1890s, cheatgrass has spread across much of the western United States. Its secret: fire. Its thick patches, which choke out other plants and use up the soil's nitrogen, burn readily. Fire kills many of the native plants, but not cheatgrass, which grows back even stronger amid the lack of competition.

FIGURE 7.13 Invasive species are species that thrive in areas where they are introduced, outcompeting, preying on, or otherwise harming native species. Of the many thousands of invasive species, this chart shows just a few.

Exposure to contaminants, almost exclusively transported by atmospheric and oceanic processes from low latitudes, was cited by the U.S. Fish and Wildlife Service as one of the potential threats to the survival of the polar bear. The damage to wildlife and ecosystems caused by pollution can be severe, but it tends to be less than the damage caused by habitat alteration or invasive species.

Overharvesting   For most species, a high intensity of hunting or harvesting by humans will not *in itself* pose a threat of extinction, but for some species it can. The polar bear is one such species. Large in size, few in number, long-lived, and raising few young in its lifetime—a classic *K-strategist* species—the polar bear is just the type of animal to be vulnerable to population reduction by hunting. Inuit traditional hunters have always carefully balanced and monitored their harvest, informed by their deep ecological knowledge of the environment. The traditional and sport hunt for polar bears is now closely monitored and limited by governments in Canada, the United States, Russia, and other Arctic nations, in conjunction with Aboriginal groups. Whether the balance of sustainable harvesting will be tipped by the impacts of climate change on the polar bear's habitat remains to be seen.

Over the past century, hunting has led to steep declines in the populations of many other K-selected animals. The Atlantic grey whale has gone extinct, and several other whales remain threatened or endangered. Illegal harvesting, poaching, and the sale of contraband wildlife products on the black market contribute to the problem. For example, three of eight tiger species are now extinct; remaining species (such as the Siberian tiger) have been extirpated from much of their natural range. Tiger body parts fetch a high price on the black market (**FIGURE 7.14**). Gorillas and other primates that are killed

for their meat may be facing extinction soon. Thousands of sharks are killed each year for their fins, which are used in soup. Today the ocean contains only 10% of the large animals it once did.

Climate change   The preceding four types of human impacts affect biodiversity in discrete places and times. In contrast, our manipulation of Earth's climate system is beginning to have global impacts on both habitat and biodiversity. As we will explore in subsequent chapters, our emissions of carbon dioxide and other "greenhouse gases" that trap heat in the atmosphere are causing average temperatures to warm worldwide, modifying global weather patterns and increasing the frequency of extreme weather events. Scientists foresee that these effects, together termed *global climate change*, will accelerate and become more severe in the years ahead until we find ways to reduce our emissions from fossil fuels.

Climate change is beginning to exert effects on plants and animals. Extreme weather events such as droughts put increased stress on populations, and warming temperatures are forcing species to move toward the poles and higher in altitude. Some species will be able to adapt, but others will not. Mountaintop organisms cannot move further upslope to escape warming temperatures, so they will likely perish. Trees may not be able to move poleward fast enough. Polar bears may find their sea ice habitat disappearing altogether, with no available replacement. Animals and plants may find themselves among different communities of prey, predators, and parasites to which they are not adapted. All in all, scientists now predict that a 1.5–2.5° global temperature increase could put 20–30% of the world's plants and animals at increased risk of extinction.

FIGURE 7.14
Body parts from tigers have long been used as medicines or aphrodisiacs in some traditional Asian cultures. Hunters and poachers have illegally killed countless tigers through the years to satisfy market demand for these items. Here a street vendor in northern China displays tiger body parts for sale.

THE SCIENCE BEHIND THE STORY

Amphibian Diversity and Decline

Dr. Madhava Meegaskumbura searches for frogs at night in Sri Lanka.

New species of most vertebrate classes are discovered at a rate of only a few per year, but the number of known amphibian species—6300 as of 2010—has jumped by 38% since 1985. At the same time, over 2500 amphibian species worldwide are in decline. Researchers feel they may be naming some species just before they go extinct, and losing others before they are even discovered. The *Global Amphibian Assessment* ranked nearly one-third of the world's amphibians as threatened, compared with 23% of mammals and 12% of bird species. About 170 species of frogs, toads, and salamanders studied just years or decades ago, including the golden toad, are now gone.

These losses are especially worrying because amphibians are regarded as "biological indicators" of the condition of an ecosystem. Amphibians rely on both aquatic and terrestrial environments, and may breathe and absorb water through their skin, so they are sensitive to environmental stresses. Studying the reasons for their decline can tell us much about the state of our environment. The major threats to amphibians worldwide include habitat loss and degradation, exotic species, overharvesting, increases in UV radiation, pollution, disease, and road mortality. Fungal and viral diseases have been implicated in some amphibian declines. Some of these causes of mortality are exacerbated by climate change.[13]

The status of amphibians in Canada is documented in *Wild Species 2005 Report*, the most recent report from the *National General Status Working Group (NGSWG)*.[14] The Wild Species 2005 Report concluded that habitat loss, especially draining of wetlands, is a leading threat to amphibians in Canada.[15] Wetlands that remain within agricultural or urban landscapes may be polluted. Habitat fragmentation also reduces or prevents the movement of individuals among populations, leading to reduced

Raorchestes manohari is one of many new frog species recently discovered in India and Sri Lanka. Its name means "beautiful" in Malayalam.

population stability and reduced exchange of genes.[16]

In some parts of the world, scientific scrutiny has revealed amphibian "hot spots." In the 1990s, an international team of scientists set out to determine whether Sri Lanka, a large tropical island off the coast of India, held more than the 40 frog species that were already known. Researcher Madhava Meegaskumbura and his team combed through trees, rivers, ponds, and leaf litter for 8 years, collecting

All five of these primary causes of population decline are intensified by human population growth and rising per capita consumption. More people and more consumption mean more habitat alteration, more invasive species, more pollution, more overharvesting, and more climate change. Growth in population and growth in consumption are the ultimate or root causes behind the proximate threats to biodiversity.

Benefits of Biodiversity

Just as we now have a solid scientific understanding of the causes of biodiversity loss, we are also coming to appreciate its consequences as we begin to erode the many benefits that biodiversity brings us. The loss of one species may or may not affect us as individuals in any discernible way, but it is important to consider biodiversity from a holistic perspective. A comparison has been made (probably first

by population biologist Paul Ehrlich) to the rivets in an airplane wing. The loss of one rivet, or two, or three, will not cause the plane to crash. But at some point the structure will be compromised, and the loss of just one more rivet will cause it to fail. If individual species are like the rivets in the airplane wing, then we might well ask how many more we can afford to lose before the structure is compromised.

This suggests the question, "Why does biodiversity matter?" There are many ways to answer this question, but we can begin by considering the ways that biodiversity benefits people. Scientists have offered a number of tangible, pragmatic reasons for preserving biodiversity, showing how biodiversity directly or indirectly supports human society. In addition, many people feel that organisms have an intrinsic right to exist and that ethical and aesthetic dimensions to biodiversity preservation cannot be ignored. (We will consider these questions in greater detail in subsequent chapters.)

more than 1400 frogs at 300 study sites. They analyzed the frogs' physical appearance, habitat use, and vocalizations, as well as their genes.

The studies led to the discovery, on this one island, of more than 100 previously unknown species of frogs. Some of these unusual animals live on rocks and have leg fringes and markings that help disguise them as clumps of moss. Others are tree frogs that lay their eggs in baskets they construct. These discoveries, however, come against the backdrop of distressing amphibian declines worldwide. Most worrisome is that populations are vanishing even when no direct damage to habitat is apparent. Researchers surmised that a combination of factors might be at work.

In one study, researchers presented young frogs with two common dangers—pesticides and predators—to see how the mix affected their survival. Groups of tadpoles were put in different tubs of water. Some tubs contained pure water, others contained varying levels of the pesticide carbaryl (a popular lawn care pesticide in Canada), and others contained a harmless solvent as a control. To some of the tubs, the researchers added a hungry predator—a young salamander. The salamander was caged and couldn't reach the tadpoles, but they were aware of its presence. Researchers watched to see how many tadpoles survived the different combinations of stress factors.

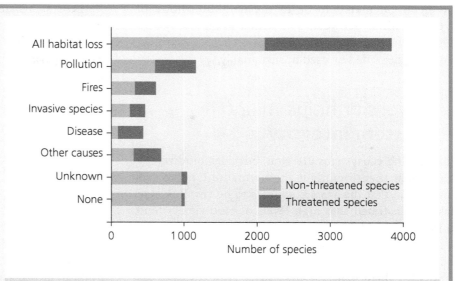

Habitat loss is the main cause of population decline for the world's amphibian species. Pollution is second in importance, but many declines are not yet attributable to cause. *Source: Data from IUCN (2008) Global Amphibian Assessment.*

Their results revealed that tadpoles that withstood one type of stress might not survive two. All tadpoles in clean water with no predators survived, and all tadpoles exposed to high concentrations of carbaryl died within several days, regardless of predator presence. But when carbaryl levels were lower, the presence of the salamander made a noticeable difference. In one trial, 75% of tadpoles survived the pesticide if no predator was present, but in the presence of the salamander, survival rates dropped to 25%. Thus when both stresses were present, death rates increased by two to four times.

As scientists learn more about how factors combine to threaten amphibians, they are gaining a clearer picture of how the fate of these creatures may foreshadow the future for other organisms.

Biodiversity provides ecosystem services

Contrary to popular opinion, some things in life can indeed be free, as long as we choose to protect the living systems that provide them. Intact forests provide clean air and buffer hydrologic systems against flooding and drought. Native crop varieties provide insurance against disease and drought. Abundant wildlife can attract tourists and boost the economies of developing nations. Intact ecosystems provide these and other valuable processes, known as *ecosystem services*, for all of us, free of charge.

Maintaining these ecosystem services is one clear benefit of protecting biodiversity. According to the United Nations Environment Programme (UNEP), biodiversity:

- Provides food, fuel, and fibre
- Provides shelter and building materials
- Purifies air and water
- Detoxifies and decomposes wastes
- Stabilizes and moderates Earth's climate
- Moderates floods, droughts, wind, and temperature extremes
- Generates and renews soil fertility and cycles nutrients
- Pollinates plants, including many crops
- Controls pests and diseases
- Maintains genetic resources as inputs to crop varieties, livestock breeds, and medicines
- Provides cultural and aesthetic benefits
- Gives us the means to adapt to change

Organisms and ecosystems support a vast number of vital processes that humans could not replicate or would need to pay for if nature did not provide them. The annual value of just 17 of these ecosystem services has been calculated to be in the neighbourhood of $16–54 trillion per year. The Millennium Ecosystem Assessment estimated that 60% of ecosystem services are being degraded or used unsustainably.[17]

Biodiversity helps maintain ecosystem integrity

Functioning ecosystems are vital, but does biodiversity really help them maintain their function? Ecologists have found that the answer appears to be yes. Research has demonstrated that high levels of biodiversity tend to increase the *stability* of communities and ecosystems. Research has also found that high biodiversity tends to increase the *resilience* of ecological systems—their ability to weather disturbance, bounce back from stresses, and adapt to change. Most of this research has dealt with species diversity, but new work is finding similar effects for genetic diversity. Thus, a decrease in biodiversity could diminish a natural system's ability to function and to provide services to our society.

What about the extinction of individual species, however? Sceptics have asked whether the loss of a few endangered species will really make much difference in an ecosystem's ability to function. Ecological research suggests that the answer to this question depends on which species are removed. Removing a species that can be functionally replaced by others may make little difference.

Recall, however, our previous discussion of *keystone species*. Like the keystone that holds together an arch, a keystone species is one whose removal results in significant changes in an ecological system. If a keystone species is extirpated or driven extinct, other species may disappear or experience significant population changes as a result.

Top predators such as polar bears and tigers are often considered keystone species. A single top predator may prey on many other carnivores, each of which may prey on many herbivores, each of which may consume many plants. Thus the removal of a single individual at the top of a food chain can have impacts that multiply as they cascade down the food chain. Moreover, top predators such as tigers, wolves, and grizzly bears are among the species most vulnerable to human impact. Large animals are frequently hunted, and also need large areas of habitat, making them susceptible to habitat loss and fragmentation. Top predators are also vulnerable to the buildup of toxic pollutants in their tissues through the process of biomagnification, as seen in the example of beluga whales in the St. Lawrence estuary and polar bears in the Arctic.

Ecosystems are complex, though, and it is difficult to predict which particular species may be important. The influence of tiny "ecosystem engineers," such as ants and earthworms, can be every bit as far-reaching as those of keystone species. Thus, many people prefer to apply the precautionary principle in the spirit of ecologist Aldo Leopold, who advised, "To keep every cog and wheel is the first precaution of intelligent tinkering."[18]

Biodiversity enhances food security

Biodiversity benefits agriculture, as well. Genetic diversity within crop species and their ancestors is enormously valuable. California's barley crops annually receive $160 million in disease resistance benefits from Ethiopian strains of barley. During the 1970s a researcher discovered a maize species in Mexico known as *Zea diploperennis*. This maize is highly resistant to disease, and it is a perennial, meaning it will grow back year after year without being replanted. Yet this valuable plant had almost been lost; at the time of its discovery, its entire range was limited to a 10-ha plot of land in the mountains of the Mexican state of Jalisco.

Other potentially important food crops await utilization (FIGURE 7.15). The babassu palm (*Orbignya phalerata*) of the Amazon produces more vegetable oil than any other plant. The serendipity berry (*Dioscoreophyllum cumminsii*) produces a sweetener that is 3000 times sweeter than table sugar. Several species of salt-tolerant grasses and trees are so hardy that farmers can irrigate them with saltwater. These same plants also produce animal feed, a substitute for conventional vegetable oil, and other economically important products. Such species could be immeasurably beneficial to areas undergoing soil salinization due to poorly managed irrigation.

Biodiversity provides drugs and medicines

People have made medicines from plants for centuries, and many of today's widely used drugs were discovered by studying chemical compounds present in wild plants, animals, and microbes (FIGURE 7.16). Each year pharmaceutical products owing their origin to wild species generate up to $150 billion in sales and save thousands of lives.

It can truly be argued that every species that goes extinct represents one lost opportunity to find a cure

Food Security and Biodiversity: Potential new food sources

Species	Native to...	Potential uses and benefits
Amaranths (three species of *Amaranthus*) 	Tropical and Andean America	Grain and leafy vegetable; livestock feed; rapid growth, drought resistant
Buriti palm (*Mauritia flexuosa*) 	Amazon lowlands	"Tree of life" to Amerindians; vitamin-rich fruit; pith as source for bread; palm heart from shoots
Maca (*Lepidium meyenii*) 	Andes Mountains	Cold-resistant root vegetable resembling radish, with distinctive flavour; near extinction
Tree tomato (*Cyphomandra betacea*) 	South America	Elongated fruit with sweet taste
Babirusa (*Babyrousa babyrussa*) 	Indonesia: Moluccas and Sulawesi	A deep-forest pig; thrives on vegetation high in cellulose and hence less dependent on grain
Capybara (*Hydrochoeris hydrochoeris*) 	South America	World's largest rodent; meat esteemed; easily ranched in open habitats near water
Vicuna (*Lama vicugna*) 	Central Andes	Threatened species related to llama; valuable source of meat, fur, and hides; can be profitably ranched
Chachalacas (*Ortalis*, many species) 	South and Central America	Birds, potentially tropical chickens; thrive in dense populations; adaptable to human habitations; fast-growing
Sand grouse (*Pterocles*, many species) 	Deserts of Africa and Asia	Pigeon-like birds adapted to harshest deserts; domestication a possibility

FIGURE 7.15
By protecting biodiversity, we can enhance food security. The wild species shown here are a tiny fraction of the many plants and animals that could someday supplement our food supply.
Source: Adapted from Wilson, E. O. (1992) The Diversity of Life. Cambridge, MA: Belknap Press.

Medicines and Biodiversity: Natural sources of pharmaceuticals

Plant	Drug	Medical application
Pineapple (*Ananas comosus*)	Bromelain	Controls tissue inflammation
Autumn crocus (*Colchicum autumnale*)	Colchicine	Anticancer agent
Yellow cinchona (*Cinchona ledgeriana*)	Quinine	Antimalarial
Common thyme (*Thymus vulgaris*)	Thymol	Cures fungal infection
Pacific yew (*Taxus brevifolia*)	Taxol	Anticancer (especially ovarian cancer)
Velvet bean (*Mucuna deeringiana*)	L-Dopa	Parkinson's disease suppressant
Common foxglove (*Digitalis purpurea*)	Digitoxin	Cardiac stimulant

FIGURE 7.16
By protecting biodiversity, we can enhance our ability to treat illness. Shown here are just a few of the plants that have so far been found to provide chemical compounds of medical benefit.
Source: Adapted from Wilson, E. O. (1992) The Diversity of Life. Cambridge, MA: Belknap Press.

for cancer or AIDS. The rosy periwinkle (*Catharanthus roseus*) produces compounds that treat Hodgkin's disease and a particularly deadly form of leukemia. Had this native plant of Madagascar become extinct prior to its discovery by medical researchers, two deadly diseases would have claimed far more victims than they have to date. In Australia, where the government has placed high priority on research into products from rare and endangered species, a rare species of cork, *Duboisia leichhardtii*, now provides hyoscine, a compound that physicians use to treat cancer, stomach disorders, and motion sickness. Another Australian plant, *Tylophora*, provides a drug that treats lymphoid leukemia. Researchers are now exploring the potential of the compound prostaglandin E2 in treating gastric ulcers. This compound was first discovered in two frog species unique to the rainforest of Queensland, Australia. Scientists believe that both species are now extinct.

A compound that forms the basis for the anticancer drug Taxol is derived from the bark of the Pacific yew (genus *taxus*), native to British Columbia. At first, over-harvesting threatened not only the very slow-growing yew but also another endangered species, the spotted owl, which relies on the yew as part of its natural habitat. Today the basic ingredient for Taxol is still extracted from the bark of the Pacific yew, but the tree is cultivated specifically for this purpose.

Biodiversity provides additional economic benefits

Besides providing products and contributing to our food security and health, biodiversity can represent a direct source of income through tourism, particularly for developing countries in the tropics that have impressive species diversity. Many people like to travel to experience protected natural areas, and in so doing they create economic opportunity for residents living near those natural areas. Visitors spend money at local businesses, hire local people as guides, and support the parks that employ local residents.

Costa Rica is an example of a country that has benefited in this way. Between 1945 and 1995, the population of Costa Rica grew from 860 000 to 3.34 million, and the percentage of land devoted to pasture increased from 12% to 33%. With much of the formerly forested land converted to agriculture, the proportion of the country covered by forest decreased from 80% to 25%. In 1991, Costa Rica was losing its forests faster than any other country in the world—nearly 140 ha per day. As a result, populations of innumerable species were declining, and some were becoming endangered (FIGURE 7.17). Few people foresaw the need to conserve biological resources until it became clear that they were being rapidly lost.

weighing the issues

BIOPROSPECTING IN COSTA RICA

Bioprospectors for pharmaceutical companies scour biodiversity-rich countries, searching for organisms that might provide new drugs, foods, or other valuable products. Many have been criticized for harvesting indigenous species to create commercial products that do not benefit the country of origin. To make sure it would not lose the benefits of its own biodiversity, Costa Rica reached an agreement with the Merck pharmaceutical company in 1991. The nonprofit National Biodiversity Institute of Costa Rica (INBio) allowed Merck to evaluate a limited number of Costa Rica's species for their commercial potential in return for $1.1 million, a small royalty rate on any products developed, and training for Costa Rican scientists.

Do you think both sides won in this agreement? What if Merck discovers a compound that could be turned into a billion-dollar drug? Does this provide a good model for other countries, and for other companies?

In 1970, the Costa Rican government and international representatives came together to create the country's first national parks and protected areas. In 1972 the efforts of local residents, along with contributions from interna-

(a) Green sea turtle

(b) Red-backed squirrel monkey

FIGURE 7.17
Costa Rica is home to a number of species classified as globally threatened or endangered. The green sea turtle (*Chelonia mydas*) **(a)**, which lays its eggs on beaches in Costa Rica, has undergone steep population declines. The red-backed squirrel monkey (*Saimiri oerstedii*) **(b)** is endemic to a tiny area in Costa Rica and is vulnerable to forest loss because of its small geographic range.

tional conservation organizations, provided the beginnings of what is today the Monteverde Cloud Forest Biological Reserve. This privately managed reserve, which occupies 10 500 ha, was established to protect the forest and its populations of 2500 plant species, 400 bird species, 500 butterfly species, 100 mammal species, and 120 reptile and amphibian species, including the golden toad.

Costa Rica and its citizens are now reaping the benefits of their conservation efforts—not only ecological benefits, but also economic ones. Because of its parks and its reputation for conservation, tourists from around the world now visit Costa Rica for **ecotourism** (FIGURE 7.18). The ecotourism industry draws more than 1 million visitors to Costa Rica each year, provides thousands of jobs, and is a major contributor to the country's economy. Today the Costa Rican economy is fuelled in large part by commerce and ecotourism, whose contributions outweigh those of industry and agriculture combined.

It remains to be seen how effectively ecotourism can help preserve natural systems in Costa Rica in the long term. As forests outside the parks disappear, the parks are beginning to suffer from illegal hunting and timber extraction. Conservationists say the parks are poorly protected and underfunded. Ecotourism will likely need to generate still more money to preserve habitat, protect endangered species, and restore altered communities to their former condition. In the meantime, ecotourism has become a vital source of income for Costa Rica, with its rainforests; Australia, with its Great Barrier Reef; Belize, with its reefs, caves, and rainforests; and Kenya and Tanzania, with their savannah wildlife. Canada, too, benefits from ecotourism; our national and provincial parks draw millions of visitors annually. Ecotourism provides a financial incentive to preserve natural areas and reduce impacts on the landscape and on native species.

As ecotourism increases in popularity, however, critics warn that too many visitors to natural areas can degrade the outdoor experience and disturb wildlife. Anyone who has been to Yellowstone Park on a crowded summer weekend can attest to this. As ecotourism continues to increase, so will the debate over its costs and benefits for local communities and for biodiversity.

People value and seek out connections with nature

Not all of the benefits of biodiversity to humans can be expressed in the hard numbers of economics or the day-to-day practicalities of food and medicine. Some scientists and philosophers argue that there is a deeper importance to biodiversity. E. O. Wilson (FIGURE 7.19)

FIGURE 7.18
Costa Rica has protected a wide array of its diverse natural areas. This protection has stimulated the nation's economy through ecotourism. Here, visitors experience a walkway through the forest canopy in one of the nation's parks.

FIGURE 7.19
Edward O. Wilson is the world's most recognized authority on biodiversity and its conservation and has inspired many people who study our planet's life. A Harvard professor and world-renowned expert on ants, Wilson has written over 20 books and has won two Pulitzer prizes. His books *The Diversity of Life* and *The Future of Life* address the value of biodiversity and its outlook for the future.

has described a phenomenon he calls **biophilia**, "the connections that human beings subconsciously seek with the rest of life."[19] Wilson and others have cited as evidence of biophilia our affinity for parks and wildlife, our keeping of pets, the high value of real estate with a view of natural landscapes, and our interest—despite being far removed from a hunter-gatherer lifestyle—in hiking, bird-watching, fishing, hunting, backpacking, and similar outdoor pursuits.

In a 2005 book, writer Richard Louv adds that as today's children are increasingly deprived of outdoor experiences and direct contact with wild organisms, they suffer what he calls "nature-deficit disorder."[20] Although it is not a medical condition, this alienation from biodiversity and the natural environment, Louv argues, may damage childhood development and lie behind many of the emotional and physical problems young people in developed nations face today.

If Wilson, Louv, and others are right, then biophilia may not only affect ecotourism and real estate prices, but also may influence our ethics. We humans are part of nature, and like any other animal we need to use resources and consume other organisms to survive. In that sense, there is nothing immoral about our doing so. However, we have reasoning ability and are able to control our actions and make conscious decisions. Our ethical sense has developed from this intelligence and ability to choose. As our society's sphere of ethical consideration has widened over time, more people have come to believe that other organisms have intrinsic value and an inherent right to exist.

Despite our ethical convictions, however, and despite biodiversity's many benefits—from the pragmatic and economic to the philosophical and spiritual—the future of biodiversity is far from secure. Even our protected areas and parks are not big enough or protected well enough to ensure that biodiversity is fully safeguarded within their borders. The search for solutions to today's biodiversity crisis is an exciting and active one, and scientists are playing a leading role in developing innovative approaches to maintaining the diversity of life on Earth.

Approaches to Conservation

In his 1994 autobiography, *Naturalist*, E. O. Wilson wrote, "In one lifetime exploding human populations have reduced wildernesses to threatened nature reserves. Ecosystems and species are vanishing at the fastest rate in 65 million years. Troubled by what we have wrought, we have begun to turn in our role from local conqueror to global steward."[21] Today, more and more scientists and

roots

CONSERVATION AND PRESERVATION

The word **conservation**, used in reference to the environment since 1922, comes from the Latin *conservationem*, "keeping, conserving." The word **preservation** comes from the Latin *preservationem*, "keeping safe, preserving."

citizens perceive a need to do something to stem the loss of biodiversity.

In theory, there is a distinction between the concepts of conservation and preservation. *Preservation* implies the maintenance of a natural area or species in a pristine or unaltered state, or as close to it as possible. *Conservation* implies that natural habitat and species should be cared for and maintained for multiple purposes, and that they have not only their own intrinsic value, but also multiple values (potential or actual) for people. You will learn more about these distinctions, and the modern history of these concepts in environmental and resource management, in the chapter on environmental ethics and economics. For now, let's look at some of the approaches that environmental scientists and managers have developed to help us conserve both habitats and species.

Conservation biology addresses habitat degradation and species loss

The loss of biodiversity, the urge to act as responsible stewards of natural systems, and the desire to use science as a tool in that endeavour helped spark the rise of conservation biology. **Conservation biology** is a scientific discipline devoted to understanding the factors, forces, and processes that influence the loss, protection, and restoration of biological diversity. It arose as scientists became increasingly alarmed at the degradation of the natural systems they had spent their lives studying.

Conservation biologists choose questions and pursue research with the aim of developing solutions to the problems of habitat degradation and species loss (**FIGURE 7.20**). Conservation biology is thus an applied and goal-oriented science, with implicit values and ethical standards. This perceived element of advocacy sparked some criticism of conservation biology in its early years. However, as scientists have come to recognize the scope of human impact on the planet, more of them have directed their work to address environmental problems. Today conservation biology is a thriving pursuit that is

FIGURE 7.20
Conservation biologists integrate lab and field research to develop solutions to biodiversity loss. Here, a conservation biologist checks on a jabiru stork nest in the Pantanal region of Brazil.

central to environmental science and to achieving a sustainable society.

Conservation biologists integrate an understanding of evolution and extinction with ecology and the dynamic nature of environmental systems. They use field data, lab data, theory, and experiments to study the impacts of humans on other organisms. They also attempt to design, test, and implement ways to mitigate human impact.

These researchers address the challenges facing biological diversity at all levels, from genetic diversity to species diversity to ecosystem diversity. At the genetic level, *conservation geneticists* study genetic attributes of organisms, to infer the status of their populations. If two populations of a species are found to be genetically distinct enough to be considered subspecies, they may have different ecological needs and may require different types of management. Conservation geneticists also ask how small a population can become and how much genetic variation it can lose before running into problems such as inbreeding depression. By determining a minimum viable population size for a given population, conservation geneticists and population biologists provide wildlife managers with an indication of how important it may be to increase the population.

Many conservation research efforts also revolve around habitats, communities, ecosystems, and landscapes. Organisms are sometimes distributed across a landscape as a network of subpopulations. Because small and isolated subpopulations are most vulnerable to extirpation, conservation biologists pay special attention to them. By examining how organisms disperse from one habitat patch to another, and how their genes flow among subpopulations, conservation biologists try to learn how likely a population is to persist or succumb in the face of habitat change or other threats.

Island biogeography can help address habitat fragmentation

Safeguarding habitat for species and conserving communities and ecosystems require thinking and working at the landscape level. One key conceptual tool for doing so is the *equilibrium model of island biogeography*. This model, introduced by conservation biologist E. O. Wilson and ecologist Robert MacArthur in 1963, originally explained how species came to be distributed among oceanic islands. Since then, researchers have also applied it to "habitat islands"—patches of one habitat type isolated within "seas" of others.

The island biogeography model explains how the number of species on an island results from an equilibrium balance between the number added by immigration and the number lost through extirpation. It predicts an island's species richness based on its size and distance from the mainland:

- The farther an island is located from a continent, the fewer species tend to find and colonize it; this is called the *distance effect*. Thus, remote islands host fewer species because of lower immigration rates (**FIGURE 7.21A**).
- Large islands have higher immigration rates because they present fatter targets for wandering or dispersing organisms to encounter (**FIGURE 7.21B**).
- Large islands have lower extinction rates because more space allows for larger populations, which are less vulnerable to dropping to zero by chance (**FIGURE 7.21C**).

Together, these latter two trends give large islands more species at equilibrium than small islands—a phenomenon called the *area effect*. Large islands also tend to contain more species because they generally possess more habitats than smaller islands, providing suitable environments for a wider variety of arriving species. Very roughly, the number of species on an island is expected to double as island size increases tenfold. This effect can be illustrated through *species-area curves*, which quantify the number of species per area in a particular habitat (**FIGURE 7.22**).

The patterns established by island biogeography and the species-area relationship hold up for terrestrial habitat "islands," as well, such as forests cut into smaller areas by logging and road building (**FIGURE 7.23**), a process known as **habitat fragmentation**. Expanding agriculture, spreading cities, highways, logging, and many other impacts have chopped up large contiguous expanses of habitat into small, disconnected ones. Fragmentation of

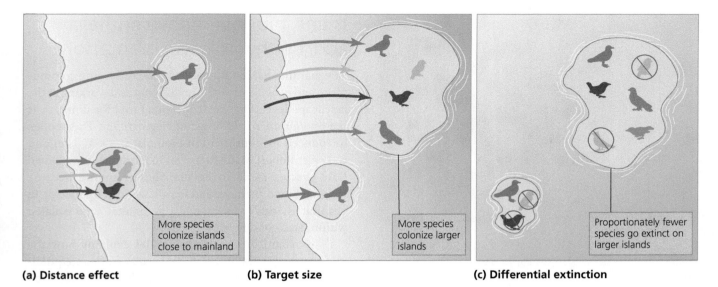

(a) Distance effect **(b) Target size** **(c) Differential extinction**

FIGURE 7.21 Islands located close to a continent receive more immigrants than islands that are distant **(a)**, so that near islands end up with more species. Large islands present fatter targets for dispersing organisms to encounter **(b)**, so that more species immigrate to large islands than to small islands. Large islands also experience lower extinction rates **(c)**, because their larger area can support larger populations.

forests and other habitats constitutes one of the prime threats to biodiversity. In response, conservation biologists have designed landscape-level strategies to try to optimize the arrangement of areas to be preserved.

Habitat fragmentation has the greatest impact on large species and, especially, migratory species. Bears, mountain lions, elephants, caribou, and other animals that need large ranges in which to roam may disappear. Bird species that thrive in the interior of forests may fail to reproduce when forced near the edge of a fragment of habitat. Their nests often are attacked by predators

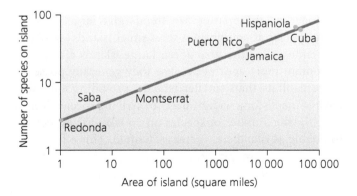

FIGURE 7.22

The larger the island, the greater the number of species—a prediction borne out by data from around the world. By plotting the number of amphibians and reptile species on Caribbean islands as a function of the areas of these islands, the species-area curve shows that species richness increases with area. The increase is not linear, but logarithmic; note the scales of the axes.
Source: Data from MacArthur, R. H., and E. O. Wilson (1967) The Theory of Island Biogeography. Princeton University Press.

and parasites that favour open habitats surrounding the fragment or that travel along habitat edges. Avian ecologists judge forest fragmentation to be a main reason why populations of many songbirds of eastern North America are declining; an additional significant impact is predation by feral (escaped) house cats.

Because habitat fragmentation is such a central issue in biodiversity conservation, and because there are limits on how much land can be set aside, conservation biologists have argued heatedly about whether it is better to make wildlife reserves large in size and few in number, or many in number but small in size. Nicknamed the **SLOSS dilemma**, for "**S**ingle **L**arge **o**r **S**everal **S**mall," this debate is ongoing and complex, but it seems clear that large species that roam great distances, such as the caribou, would benefit more from the "single large" approach to reserve design. In contrast, creatures such as insects that live as larvae in small areas may do just fine in a number of small isolated reserves, especially if they can disperse as adults by flying from one reserve to another.

A related issue is whether **corridors** of protected land are important for allowing animals to travel between islands of protected habitat. In theory, connections between fragments provide animals with access to more habitats, and help enable gene flow to maintain populations in the long term. Many land management agencies and environmental groups try, when possible, to join new reserves to existing reserves for these reasons. The establishment and maintenance of greenbelts and natural corridors is one of the guiding principles in environmental and natural resource management in Canada today.

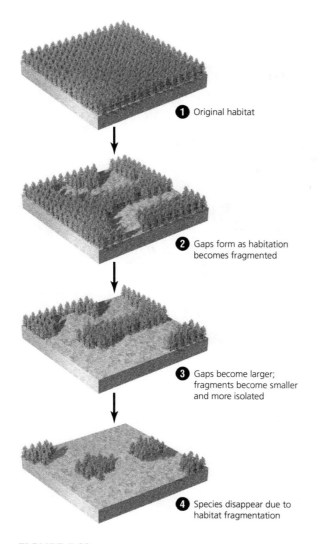

❶ Original habitat

❷ Gaps form as habitation becomes fragmented

❸ Gaps become larger; fragments become smaller and more isolated

❹ Species disappear due to habitat fragmentation

FIGURE 7.23
Forest clearing, farming, road building, and other types of human land use and development can fragment natural areas, leaving small "islands" of habitat. Habitat fragmentation usually begins when gaps are created within a natural habitat. As development proceeds, these gaps expand, join together, and eventually dominate the landscape, stranding islands of habitat in their midst. As habitat becomes fragmented, fewer populations can persist, and numbers of species in the fragments decrease with time.

Captive breeding and cloning are single-species approaches

Conservation efforts that aim to save species by maintaining their habitat are examples of *in situ* conservation; *in situ* is a Latin phrase that means "in its natural or original place." In conjunction with this, many conservation biologists are going to impressive lengths to save individual threatened and endangered species. Traditional *ex situ* (out-of-place) conservation efforts involve the preservation of species in zoos, aquaria, seed banks, arboretums, and the like. In the past few decades, many zoos and

botanical gardens have become centres for the **captive breeding** of endangered species, raising individuals for the purpose of reintroducing them into the wild.

One example of a captive breeding program is aimed at saving the California condor, North America's largest bird (**FIGURE 7.24**). Condors were persecuted in the early twentieth century, collided with electrical wires, and succumbed to lead poisoning from scavenging carcasses of animals killed with lead shot. By 1982, only 22 condors remained, and biologists decided to take all the birds into captivity, in hopes of boosting their numbers and then releasing them. The ongoing program is succeeding. So far, over 100 of the 250 birds raised in captivity have been released into the wild at sites in California and Arizona, where a few pairs have begun nesting.

Other reintroduction programs have been more controversial. Reintroducing wolves to Yellowstone National Park—an effort that involved imported wolves from across the border in Canada—has proven popular with the public. However, reintroducing wolves to sites in Arizona and New Mexico met stiff resistance from ranchers who fear the wolves will attack their livestock. The program is making slow headway, and several of the wolves have been shot. China is considering a reintroduction program for the Siberian tiger, which has been extirpated from China, part of its natural range. The Chinese government is preparing 600 captive Siberian tigers for release into the forests in the far northeastern part of the country. However, critics note that the forests are so fragmented that efforts would be better focused on improving habitat first.

Some reintroduction programs require international cooperation. For example, the only naturally occurring wild population of whooping cranes nests and breeds each spring in Wood Buffalo Park, straddling the border between Alberta and the Northwest Territories. The flock then migrates and winters over in the Aransas National Wildlife Refuge on the Gulf coast of Texas. The population of almost 2000 cranes in the late 1800s dipped to an all-time low of just 15 in 1941, after being decimated by hunting. In the past few years the population has slowly increased to

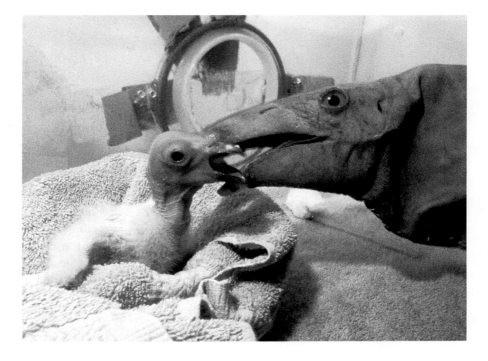

FIGURE 7.24
In efforts to save the California condor *(Gymnogyps californianus)* from extinction, biologists have raised hundreds of chicks in captivity with the help of hand puppets designed to look and feel like the heads of adult condors. Using these puppets, biologists feed the growing chicks in an enclosure and shield them from all contact with humans, so that when the chick is grown it does not feel an attachment to people.

about 180 birds as a result of careful reintroductions, led by the International Crane Recovery Team consisting of scientists from both Canada and the United States.[22]

Another example of (tentatively) successful captive breeding and reintroduction is that of the swift fox *(Vulpes velox)*, a small, slender, tan-coloured fox whose natural habitat is the prairies of Manitoba, Saskatchewan, and Alberta, as well as the western grasslands of the United States (FIGURE 7.25). It is mainly nocturnal and is named for its speed *(velox)*; it races through the prairie grasslands at up to 60 km per hour. In the first part of the twentieth century, the swift fox disappeared entirely from the wild in Canada, mostly as a result of the loss of habitat. The last swift fox was captured in Canada in 1928; it was considered extirpated by 1938 and officially declared as such by COSEWIC in 1978.[23]

In 1971 Miles and Beryl Smeeton of the Wildlife Reserve of Western Canada imported two pairs of swift foxes from the U.S., with the intention of starting a captive breeding and release program. Over the next decade or so the organization (later renamed the Cochrane Ecological Institute) developed partnerships, first with the University of Calgary, then with the Canadian Wildlife Service, and finally with the government of Saskatchewan and Fish and Wildlife Service of Alberta. In 1983 a reintroduction program was started to replace swift foxes back into parts of their native territory in Canada.[24] Many of the foxes that were reintroduced came from wild populations in the United States; some were bred in captivity in Canada.

In the mid- to late 1980s, 155 reintroduced foxes were radio-collared and tracked by program-related research-

FIGURE 7.25
The swift fox has been successfully reintroduced into parts of its natural range in Canada, where it had been declared extirpated.

ers, who determined that relocation was considerably more successful than captive breeding and relocation; the survival rate after the first year for the relocated foxes was 85%, as compared with 25% for the captive-bred foxes.[25] But with fewer and fewer foxes available for relocation, program scientists began to experiment with different release approaches for the captive-bred foxes. In a "soft" release, young foxes are kept in an outdoor pen over the winter to acclimatize, then released in the spring or winter. In a "hard" release, the young foxes are released straight into the wild. Researchers determined that the hard release is as successful as the soft release, in terms of the survival rates for the animals, and more cost-effective.[26]

According to Joel Nicholson, a biologist with Alberta Fish and Wildlife, "the swift fox reintroduction program has been one of the most successful *canid* reintroductions in the world."[27] A 2005–2006 count of the swift fox population in Alberta, Saskatchewan, and Montana counted 1162 foxes, mostly born in the wild. The swift fox is no longer considered extirpated, but it is still designated as an endangered species under SARA in Canada.

The newest idea for saving species from extinction is to create more individuals by cloning them. In this technique, DNA from an endangered species is inserted into a cultured egg without a nucleus, and the egg is implanted into a closely related species that can act as a surrogate mother. So far two Eurasian mammals have been cloned in this way. With future genetic technology, some scientists even talk of recreating extinct species from DNA recovered from preserved body parts. However, even if cloning can succeed from a technical standpoint, most biologists agree that such efforts are not an adequate response to biodiversity loss. Without ample habitat and protection in the wild, having cloned animals in a zoo does little good.

Some species act as "umbrellas" to protect communities

Sometimes individual species can be used as tools for the broader conservation of communities and ecosystems. Species-specific legislation can provide legal justification and resources for species conservation, but no such laws exist for communities, habitats, or ecosystems. Large species that roam great distances, such as tigers, bears, and elephants, require large areas of habitat. Meeting the habitat needs of these so-called *umbrella species* automatically helps meet those of thousands of less charismatic animals, plants, and fungi that would never elicit as much public interest.

Environmental advocacy organizations have found that using large, charismatic vertebrates as spearheads for biodiversity conservation has been an effective strategy.

This approach of promoting particularly visible *flagship species* is evident in the long-time symbol of the World Wide Fund for Nature (World Wildlife Fund in North America, or WWF), the giant panda. The panda is a large endangered animal requiring sizeable stands of undisturbed bamboo forest. Its lovable appearance has made it a favourite with the public—and an effective tool for soliciting funding for conservation efforts that protect far more than just the panda.

At the same time, many conservation organizations today are moving beyond the single-species approach. The Nature Conservancy, for instance, is a *land trust* that focuses on whole communities and landscapes by acquiring large tracts of land for conservation. The most ambitious effort may be the Wildlands Network, a group proposing to restore huge amounts of North America's land to its pre-settlement state in an interconnected network of habitats.

Conservation efforts are both international and national

Canada enacted its long-awaited endangered species law, the *Species at Risk Act (SARA)*, in 2002. The federal government was careful to stress cooperation with landowners and provincial governments, rather than presenting the law as a decree from the national government. Canada's environment minister at the time, David Anderson, wanted to avoid the hostility unleashed by the "command-and-control" approach of the U.S. *Endangered Species Act (ESA)* some 30 years before. That hostility against ESA continues to this day in the United States, although the legislation can point to some significant successes in protecting endangered species.

Environmentalists and many scientists in Canada have protested that SARA is too weak and fails to protect species and habitat adequately. One of the main objections is that the process of listing a species is not based strictly on scientific information but is heavily influenced by both politics and economics. The process for listing a species in the SARA Registry, which qualifies it for legal protection under the Act, begins with monitoring and an assessment of the status of the species by the *National General Status Working Group (NGSWG)*. The *Committee on the Status of Endangered Wildlife in Canada (COSEWIC)* may then propose designation (or a change in designation) for a particular species. The Minister of the Environment then responds to the assessment and the proposed designation. Between 2003 and 2006, for example, COSEWIC recommended 186 plants and animals for SARA listing, of which 30 were turned down.

Arne Mooers and colleagues from Simon Fraser University have studied the final decisions made by the federal government on SARA listings recommended by COSEWIC, and they have found that science often takes a back seat to economics and politics. A 2006 study by the researchers showed that animals that are of economic value (including fish) and animals from Canada's North have the least chance of being approved for legal protection under SARA. For example, none of the 10 species from Nunavut that were recommended for listing by COSEWIC was approved. The only marine fish that was approved for listing (of the 11 recommended) was the green sturgeon, which is considered inedible and is thus avoided by the commercial fishing industry.[28] At the beginning of this chapter, you learned about some of the complexities involved in designating the polar bear as a threatened species; to date, the polar bear has retained its SARA designation of "special concern."

Today many nations have laws protecting species, although they are not always well enforced. At the international level, the United Nations has facilitated several treaties to protect biodiversity. The 1973 *Convention on International Trade in Endangered Species of Wild Fauna and Flora (CITES)* protects endangered species by banning the international transport of their body parts. When nations enforce it, CITES can protect the tiger and other rare species whose body parts are traded internationally.

In 1992, leaders of many nations agreed to the *Convention on Biological Diversity*. This treaty embodies three goals: to conserve biodiversity, to use biodiversity in a sustainable manner, and to ensure the fair distribution of biodiversity's benefits. The Convention aims to help:

- Provide incentives for biodiversity conservation
- Manage access to and use of genetic resources
- Transfer technology, including biotechnology
- Promote scientific cooperation
- Assess the effects of human actions on biodiversity
- Promote biodiversity education and awareness
- Provide funding for critical activities
- Encourage every nation to report regularly on their biodiversity conservation efforts

The treaty's many accomplishments so far include ensuring that Ugandan people share in the economic benefits of wildlife preserves, increasing global markets for "shade-grown" coffee and other crops grown without removing forests, and replacing pesticide-intensive farming practices with sustainable ones in some rice-producing Asian nations. As of 2007, 188 nations had become parties to the Convention on Biological Diversity. Those choosing *not* to do so include Iraq, Somalia, the Vatican, and the United States. This decision is one example of why the U.S. government is no longer widely regarded as a leader in biodiversity conservation efforts.

Hot spots highlight areas of high biodiversity

One international approach oriented around geographic regions, rather than single species, has been the effort to map **biodiversity hot spots**. The concept of biodiversity hot spots was introduced in 1988 by British ecologist Norman Myers as a way to prioritize regions that are most important globally for biodiversity conservation. A hot spot is an area that supports an especially great number of species that are endemic, that is, found nowhere else in the world (**FIGURE 7.26**). To qualify as a hotspot, a location must harbour at least 1500 endemic plant species, or 0.5% of the world total. In addition, a hot spot must have already lost 70% of its habitat as a result of human impact and be in danger of losing more.

The nonprofit group Conservation International maintains a list of 34 biodiversity hot spots (**FIGURE 7.27**). The ecosystems of these areas together once covered 15.7% of the planet's land surface, but today, because of habitat loss, cover only 2.3%. This small amount of land is the exclusive home for 50% of the world's plant species and 42% of all terrestrial vertebrate species. The hot spot concept gives incentive to focus on these areas of endemism, where the greatest number of unique species can be protected with the least amount of effort.

FIGURE 7.26
The golden lion tamarin *(Leontopithecus rosalia)*, a species endemic to Brazil's Atlantic rainforest, is one of the world's most endangered primates. Captive breeding programs have produced roughly 500 individuals in zoos, but the tamarin's habitat is fast disappearing.

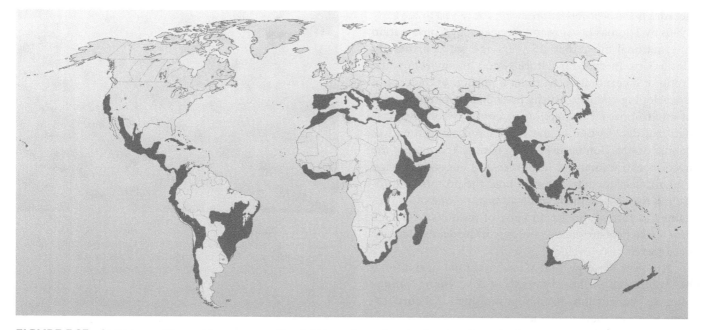

FIGURE 7.27   Some areas of the world possess exceptionally high numbers of species found nowhere else. Some conservation biologists have suggested prioritizing habitat preservation in these areas, dubbed *biodiversity hot spots*. Shown in red are the 34 biodiversity hot spots mapped by Conservation International.   *Source: Data from Conservation International, 2008.*

The World Wide Fund for Nature (WWF) has organized its conservation efforts around the concept of the **ecoregion**, a large area of land or water with a geographically distinct assemblage of natural communities that share similar environmental conditions and ecological dynamics, and interact ecologically in ways that are critical for their long-term persistence.[29] The organization has identified a "Global 200" list of ecoregions that are priorities for conservation, including ecoregions (there are actually 238 of them on the list) from both terrestrial and marine settings.

Community-based conservation is increasingly popular

Taking a global perspective and prioritizing optimal locations to set aside as parks and reserves makes good sense. However, setting aside land for preservation affects the people that live in and near these areas. In past decades, many conservationists from developed nations, in their zeal to preserve ecosystems in other nations, too often neglected the needs of people in the areas they wanted to protect. Many developing nations came to view this international environmentalism as a kind of neocolonialism.

Today this has largely changed, and many conservation biologists actively engage local people in efforts to protect land and wildlife in their own backyards, in an approach sometimes called *community-based conservation*. Setting aside land for preservation deprives local people of access to natural resources, but it can also guarantee that these resources will not be used up or sold to foreign corporations and can instead be sustainably managed. Moreover, parks and reserves draw ecotourism, which can support local economies.

In the small Central American country of Belize, conservation biologist Robert Horwich and his group Community Conservation have helped start a number of community-based conservation projects. The Community Baboon Sanctuary consists of tracts of riparian forest that farmers have agreed to leave intact, to serve as homes and traveling corridors for the black howler monkey, a centrepiece of ecotourism. The fact that the reserve uses the local nickname for the monkey signals respect for residents, and today a local women's cooperative is running the project. A museum was built, and residents receive income for guiding and housing visiting researchers and tourists. Community-based conservation has not always been so successful, but in a world of increasing human population, locally based management that meets people's needs sustainably will likely be essential.

Innovative economic strategies are being employed

As conservation moves from single-species approaches to the hotspot approach to community-based conservation, innovative economic strategies are also being attempted. One strategy that has increased over the past couple of decades is the *debt-for-nature swap*, conceived in the early 1980s by Thomas Lovejoy and pioneered by Conservation International more than 25 years ago with partners in Costa Rica. In debt-for-nature swaps, an environmental group or a corporation takes on a portion of the debt of a developing country, usually in exchange for some form of environmental protection or conservation. Because national debt is one of the principal driving forces of habitat destruction in developing nations (because of the need to extract natural resources and generate foreign capital), debt-for-nature swaps hold the promise of protecting the environment while addressing one of its fundamental threats. So far, in spite of millions of dollars devoted to debt-for-nature swaps worldwide, results have been mixed.

A newer strategy that Conservation International has pioneered is the *conservation concession*. Nations often sell concessions to foreign multinational corporations, allowing them to extract resources from the nation's land. A nation can, for instance, earn money by selling to an international logging company the right to log its forests. Conservation International has stepped in and paid nations for concessions for conservation rather than resource extraction. The nation gets the money *and* keeps its natural resources intact. The South American country of Surinam, which still has extensive areas of pristine rainforest, entered into such an agreement and has virtually halted logging while pulling in $15 million. It remains to be seen how large a role such strategies will play in the future protection of biodiversity.

Parks and Reserves

As resources dwindle, as forests, grasslands, and soils are degraded, as species disappear, and as the landscape fills with more people, the arguments for conservation of resources—for their conservation, as well as their sustainable use—have grown stronger. Also growing stronger is the argument for the preservation of land—setting aside tracts of relatively undisturbed land and habitat intended to remain forever undeveloped.

Why do we create parks and reserves?

Historian Alfred Runte cited four traditional reasons that parks and protected areas have been established:

1. Enormous, beautiful, or unusual features such as the Rocky Mountains and Clayoquot Sound inspire people to protect them—an impulse termed *monumentalism* (**FIGURE 7.28**).

FIGURE 7.28
The awe-inspiring beauty of some regions of Canada was one reason for the establishment of national parks. Scenic vistas such as this one in Banff National Park have inspired millions of people to visit them.

2. Protected areas offer recreational value to tourists, hikers, fishers, hunters, and others.
3. Protected areas offer *utilitarian* benefits and ecosystem services. For example, undeveloped watersheds provide cities with clean drinking water and a buffer against floods.
4. Parks make use of sites lacking economically valuable material resources or that are hard to develop; land that holds little monetary value is easy to set aside.

In Canada, the protection of exploitable resources and the benefits to human health have also been historical reasons for the establishment of parks. To these traditional reasons, another has been added in recent years: the preservation of biodiversity and ecosystems. A park or reserve is widely viewed as an island of habitat that can, scientists hope, maintain species that might otherwise disappear.

Today there are 43 national parks in the Parks Canada system, covering a total of 27 million ha, or 2.7% of the total land area of Canada.[30] Approximately 16 million people visit Canada's national parks each year. Yellowstone National Park in the United States was the very first national park, established in 1872, followed soon after by Yosemite National Park. Canada's first national park was established in Banff, Alberta, in 1885. Provincial parks in Canada number in the hundreds, and cover more area than national parks. Canada's parks system includes other types of protected areas as well, such as marine conservation areas and cultural, historic, and natural heritage sites.

The Canadian Wildlife Service, part of Environment Canada, contributes to the management and scientific understanding of wildlife and habitat management in Canada. Many sites in the parks system also serve as

wildlife refuges, which are havens for the conservation of wildlife and habitat, as well as, in some cases, being available for hunting, fishing, wildlife observation, photography, environmental education, and other public uses.

Some wildlife advocates find it objectionable that hunting is allowed in many parks and refuges. However, hunters have long been in the forefront of the conservation movement and have traditionally supplied the bulk of funding for land acquisition and habitat management for the refuges. Ducks Unlimited Canada is an example of a nonprofit, nongovernmental organization founded by hunters, but with the specific goal of conserving wetlands. Canada's Aboriginal peoples also retain some of their traditional hunting rights in federal and provincial parklands.

Not everyone supports land set-asides. The restriction of activities in some wilderness areas has generated opposition among those who seek to encourage resource extraction and development, as well as hunting and increased motor vehicle access, on protected Crown lands. The drive to extract more resources, secure local control of lands, and expand recreational access to public lands is epitomized by the *wise-use movement*, a loose confederation of individuals and groups that coalesced in the 1980s and 1990s in response to the increasing success of environmental advocacy. Wise-use advocates are dedicated to protecting private property rights; opposing government regulation; transferring federal lands to state, local, or private hands; and promoting motorized recreation on public lands. The wise-use movement, which has been described as "anti-conservation," includes many farmers, ranchers, trappers, and mineral prospectors, as well as groups representing the industries that extract timber, mineral, and fossil fuel resources.

Debate between mainstream environmental groups and wise-use spokespeople has been vitriolic. Each side claims to represent the will of the people and paints the other as the oppressive establishment. Wise-use advocates have played key roles in ongoing debates over policy issues such as whether recreational activities that disturb wildlife should be allowed.

Nongovernmental entities, including private nonprofit groups, also preserve land. **Land trusts** are local or regional organizations that purchase land with the aim of preserving it in its natural condition. The Nature Conservancy can be considered the world's largest land trust, but smaller ones are springing up throughout North America. Probably the earliest private land trust in Canada was the Hamilton Naturalists Club in Ontario, which began to acquire land for conservation purposes in 1919.[31] **FIGURE 7.29** shows the dramatic increase in land trusts operating in Canada, particularly since the 1970s.

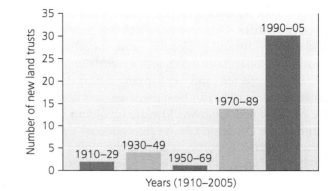

FIGURE 7.29
Land trusts that acquire land for the purpose of conservation and promote private land stewardship have increased dramatically in Canada since the first, the Hamilton Naturalists Club, in 1919.

Parks and reserves are increasing internationally

Many nations have established national park systems and are benefiting from ecotourism as a result—from Costa Rica to Ecuador to Thailand to Tanzania. The total worldwide area in protected parks and reserves increased more than fourfold from 1970 to 2000, and in 2003 the world's 38 536 protected areas covered 1.3 billion ha, or 9.6% of the planet's land area. However, parks in developing countries do not always receive the funding, legal support, or enforcement support they need to manage resources, provide for recreation, and protect wildlife from poaching and timber from logging. Thus many of the world's protected areas are merely *paper parks*—protected on paper but not in reality.

For example, the parks system in Costa Rica—now a significant source of national income and pride—initially received little real support from the government. According to Costa Rican conservationist Mario Boza, in their early years the parks were granted only five guards, one vehicle, and no funding. Today government support for protected areas in Costa Rica is much stronger. Fully 12% of the nation's area is contained in national parks, and a further 16% is devoted to other types of wildlife and conservation reserves. (In comparison, 6.3% of Canada's land area is protected as a nature reserve or wilderness area, with a total of all protected areas of any type only 10.4%.[32])

Some types of protected areas fall under national sovereignty but are designated or partly managed internationally by the United Nations. *World Heritage Sites* are an example; currently over 830 sites across 184 countries are listed for their natural or cultural value. Gros Morne National Park and Nahanni National Park are two Canadian examples of World Heritage Sites. Another example is the Mountain Gorilla Reserve shared by three African countries. This reserve, which integrates national parklands of Rwanda, Uganda, and the Democratic Republic of Congo, is an example of a *transboundary park*, an area of protected land overlapping national borders. Transboundary parks can be quite large, and account for 10% of protected areas worldwide, involving over 100 countries; the Waterton Glacier International Peace Park on the Canada–U.S. border is another example.

Biosphere reserves are tracts of land with exceptional biodiversity that couple preservation with sustainable development to benefit local people. They are designated by UNESCO (the United Nations Educational, Scientific, and Cultural Organization), following application by local stakeholders. Each biosphere reserve consists of (1) a *core* area that is isolated from the surroundings, and serves to preserve habitat and biodiversity, (2) a *buffer zone* that allows local activities and limited development that do not hinder the core area's function, and (3) an outer *transitional zone* in which agriculture, human settlement, and other land uses can be pursued in a sustainable way (FIGURE 7.30). Edge habitat can be quite different in character from habitat in the forest core, particularly in terms of properties such as light levels, density of vegetation, and moisture. The design of biosphere reserves seeks to address this concern and to reconcile human needs with the interests of wildlife and the goal of habitat preservation.

Clayoquot Sound was designated as Canada's 12th biosphere reserve in 2000 (FIGURE 7.31), in an attempt to build cooperation among environmentalists, timber companies, native people, and local residents and busi-

FIGURE 7.31
Clayoquot Sound was declared a UNESCO Biosphere Reserve in 2000.

nesses (see "Central Case: Battling Over the Last Big Trees at Clayoquot Sound"). The core area consists of provincial parks and Pacific Rim National Park Reserve. Environmentalists hoped the designation would help promote stronger land preservation efforts. Local residents supported it because outside money was being offered for local development efforts. The timber industry did not stand in the way once it was clear that harvesting operations would not be affected. The designation has brought Clayoquot Sound international attention, but it has not created new protected areas and has not altered land use policies.

Conclusion

The erosion of biological diversity on our planet is threatening to result in a modern mass extinction event equivalent to the mass extinctions of the geological past. Human-induced habitat alteration, invasive species, pollution, and overharvesting of biotic resources, now amplified by global climatic change, are the primary causes of biodiversity loss.

The loss of biodiversity matters. Human society could not function without biodiversity's pragmatic benefits. As a result, conservation biologists and environmental scientists are rising to the challenge of conducting science aimed at saving endangered species, preserving their habitats, restoring their populations, and keeping natural ecosystems intact. The innovative strategies of these scientists and of environmental and natural resource managers around the world hold promise to slow the degradation of habitat and loss of biodiversity that threatens life on Earth.

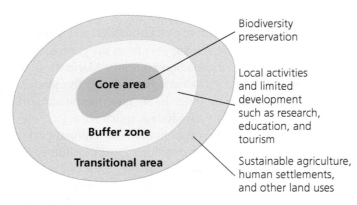

FIGURE 7.30
Biosphere reserves are international efforts that couple preservation with sustainable development to benefit local residents. Each reserve includes a core area that preserves biodiversity, a buffer zone that allows limited development, and a transition zone that permits various uses.

CANADIAN ENVIRONMENTAL PERSPECTIVES

Biruté Mary Galdikas

Canadian Biruté Mary Galdikas is an advocate for endangered orangutans in the rainforests of Indonesia.

- Biological **anthropologist**
- Field **primatologist**
- **Conservationist** and orangutan **advocate**

They are sometimes called the "trimates"—three women who made such groundbreaking expansions upon our understanding of primate behaviour that they practically carved out their own private niche in the world of science. All three—Jane Goodall, who studies chimpanzees and works to conserve their habitat; Dian Fossey, who worked with mountain gorillas; and Biruté Mary Galdikas, whose research provided the baseline for what we know today about orangutans—were hand-picked and funded originally by Louis Leakey, the famous palaeontologist whose work helped uncover the prehistory of our own species. Leakey was convinced that the women would make great strides in "field primatology," the observation of our closest genetic relatives in their own natural habitat, because of their comparative lack of scientific training (an "uncluttered mind") and what he felt was the greater patience and empathy of

female researchers. For whatever reason, Leakey was right.

Galdikas was born in Germany but grew up as a naturalized Canadian in Toronto. She met Leakey in California in 1969, several years after Goodall and Fossey had begun to establish their names and unconventional research techniques. She convinced him upon their first meeting that she deserved a place among them, and he set about gathering the funds needed to sponsor her first research outing to the rainforests of Indonesia. Once there, Galdikas had an even tougher time than her predecessors. The approach of all three was to allow the primates to gradually become accustomed to their presence, so that they could observe the animals' natural behaviour. It was a tall order for Goodall and Fossey, but even more so for Galdikas. Orangutans are more solitary than chimps or gorillas; not only did they not welcome Galdikas, but they actively tried to dissuade her from approaching by throwing things at her and even defecating on her. It took 12 long years for Galdikas to habituate one of the orangutans to her presence.

Her patience paid off in scientific results. In her doctoral thesis for UCLA in 1978, Galdikas documented a number of behaviours that had never before been witnessed in wild orangutans, including the observation that male and female orangutans form relationships that last for extended periods. She later made observations on tool use among orangutans that would come to be considered as classic research. For example, in the journal *Science* she documented her observation that wild orangutans spontaneously use tools for a number of different purposes. It had previously been thought that only captive orangutans—influenced by constant exposure to humans—were tool users.

This provided a basis for later research suggesting that some orangutan groups in the wild have developed basic "cultural" differences, such as having specific sounds for communicating with members of the group.

Today Galdikas has part-time affiliations with Simon Fraser University in British Columbia and Universitas Nasional in Jakarta, Indonesia. Like Goodall and Fossey (until the latter's death in 1985), she devotes most of her time to advocacy for the critically endangered orangutans and conservation of their rapidly disappearing habitat—the rainforests of Borneo and Sumatra. Her group, Orangutan Foundation International, runs a rescue and rehabilitation centre that saves young orangutans orphaned by fire, deforestation, or hunting; nurses them back to health; and returns them to the wild.

"To follow them, you would have had to just jump in the swamp, which was neck-deep there, and that's when I thought, 'Gee, this is going to be really hard.'"—**Biruté Mary Galdikas, on her first encounter with orangutans in the rainforest of Indonesia.**

Thinking About Environmental Perspectives

In June of 2008, Spain's parliament voted in favour of new legislation that would extend, for the first time ever, certain limited rights to great apes. The proposed laws make it illegal to kill, torture, or arbitrarily imprison apes, including their use in medical experimentation, circuses, and films. What do you think of this? Is it "about time" for a law of this type, to provide protection to our closest genetic relatives? Or is it an ill-conceived attempt to extend "human" rights to nonhumans?

REVIEWING OBJECTIVES

You should now be able to:

Characterize the scope and value of biodiversity on Earth

- Roughly 1.8 million species have been described so far, but scientists agree that the world holds millions more. Some taxonomic groups (such as insects) hold far more diversity than others.
- Diversity is unevenly spread across different habitats and areas of the world.
- Biodiversity is vital for functioning ecosystems and the services they provide us.
- Wild species are sources of food, medicine, and economic development. Many people also feel that humans have a psychological need to connect with the natural world.

Describe ways to measure biodiversity

- Biodiversity is important not only at the species level, but also at the genetic level and at the levels of ecosystems, communities, and habitats.
- Global estimates of biodiversity are based on extrapolations from scientific assessments in local areas and certain taxonomic groups.

Evaluate the primary causes of biodiversity loss

- Extinction occurs naturally. Species have gone extinct at a background rate of roughly one species per 1 to 10 million species each year. Earth's life has experienced five mass extinction events in the past 440 million years.
- Human impact is now causing the beginnings of a sixth mass extinction.
- Habitat alteration is the main cause of current biodiversity loss. Invasive species, pollution, and overharvesting are also important causes. Climate change threatens to become a major cause of environmental change and biodiversity loss.

Specify the benefits and challenges of conserving habitat and the role of habitat fragmentation

- Conservation biology is an applied science that studies biodiversity loss and seeks ways to protect and restore biodiversity at all its levels.

- The fragmentation of habitat is a growing problem. It affects organisms because edge habitat differs from core habitat, and because many species need to be able to migrate over large areas. The establishment of natural corridors can help to address the problem.
- The equilibrium model of island biogeography and the area-size relationship explain how size and distance influence the number of species occurring on islands. This model can be applied to "islands" of habitat in fragmented terrestrial landscapes.

Contrast *in situ* and *ex situ* conservation approaches

- *In situ* conservation efforts involve the preservation of habitat so that species can continue to exist in their natural state. Increasingly, landscape-level conservation is being pursued in its own right.
- *Ex situ* conservation efforts, in addition to the preservation of species in zoos, seed banks, and aquaria, include captive breeding and reintroduction programs.

Compare and contrast traditional and innovative conservation efforts

- Most conservation efforts and laws so far have focused on threatened and endangered species. Species that are charismatic and well known are often used as tools to conserve habitats and ecosystems.
- International conservation approaches include treaties, identification of biodiversity hotspots, community-based conservation, debt-for-nature swaps, and conservation concessions.

Outline reasons for setting aside parks, reserves, and other protected areas

- Public demand for preservation and recreation has led to the creation of parks, reserves, and wilderness areas in North America and across the world.
- Biosphere Reserves and World Heritage Sites are two types of internationally-designated protected lands.
- Because habitat fragmentation affects wildlife, conservation biologists are working on how best to design parks and reserves.

TESTING YOUR COMPREHENSION

1. What is biodiversity? List and describe three levels of biodiversity.
2. What are the five primary causes of biodiversity loss? Can you give a specific example of each?
3. List and describe five invasive species and the adverse effects they have had.
4. Define the term *ecosystem services*. Give five examples of ecosystem services that humans would have a hard time replacing if their natural sources were eliminated.
5. What is the relationship between biodiversity and food security? Between biodiversity and pharmaceuticals? Give three examples of potential benefits of biodiversity conservation for food security and medicine.
6. Describe four reasons why people suggest biodiversity conservation is important.
7. What is the difference between an umbrella species and a keystone species? Could one species be both an umbrella species and a keystone species?
8. Explain the island biogeography model. In what way is this model relevant to the management of habitat fragmentation?
9. What is a biodiversity hot spot?
10. Describe community-based conservation.

THINKING IT THROUGH

1. Biologist E. O. Wilson has said that, "Except in pockets of ignorance and malice, there is no longer an ideological war between conservationists and developers. Both share the perception that health and prosperity decline in a deteriorating environment." Do you agree or disagree? How do people in your community view biodiversity?
2. Many arguments have been advanced for the importance of preserving biodiversity. Which argument do you think is most compelling, and why? Which argument do you think is least compelling, and why?
3. Some people argue that we shouldn't worry about endangered species because extinction has always occurred. How would you respond to this view?
4. According to most scientists, the polar bear population in Canada's North is declining, but some Inuit hunters believe that the population is stable or even increasing. Please offer two reasons why it might be extremely difficult to settle this scientific question.
5. What would you say are some advantages of focusing on conserving single species, versus trying to conserve broader communities, ecosystems, or landscapes? What might be some of the disadvantages? Which do you think is the better approach, or should we use both?
6. You are attending a town meeting, called to discuss the proposed development of a shopping mall and condominium complex. The development would eliminate a 40-hectare stand of forest, the last sizeable forest stand in the town. The developers say the forest loss will not matter because plenty of small forest stands still exist scattered throughout town. One of the town's decision makers asks you to comment about the development's possible impacts on the community's biodiversity. What will you choose to tell your fellow citizens and the town's decision makers at this meeting?
7. You are an influential legislator in a country that has no endangered species act, and you want to introduce legislation to protect your country's vanishing biodiversity. Consider the Canadian Species at Risk Act, as well as international efforts such as CITES and the Convention on Biological Diversity. What strategies would you write into your legislation? How would your law be similar to and different from the existing Canadian and international efforts?

INTERPRETING GRAPHS AND DATA

Habitat alteration is the primary cause of present-day biodiversity loss. Of all human activities, the one that has resulted in the most habitat alteration is agriculture. Between 1850 and 2000, 95% of the native grasslands of the midwestern United States were converted to agricultural use. As a result, conventional farming practices replaced diverse natural communities with greatly simplified ones. The vast monocultures of industrialized agriculture produce bountiful harvests, but at substantial costs in lost ecosystem services.

Data from a recent study reviewing the scientific literature on the effects of organic farming practices on biodiversity are shown in the graph.

1. Overall, how many studies showed a positive effect of organic farming on biodiversity, relative to conventional farming? How many studies reported a negative effect? How many studies reported no effect?

2. For which group or groups of organisms is evidence of positive effects the strongest? Reference the numbers to support your choice(s).

3. Recall the ecosystem services provided by biodiversity. What services do the groups you chose in question 2 provide?

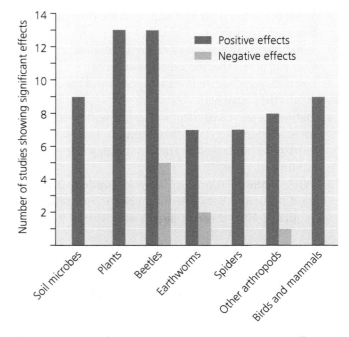

Numbers of scientific studies reporting negative or positive effects on biodiversity of organic agriculture versus conventional farming practices..
Source: Data from Hole, D., et al. (2005) Does organic farming benefit biodiversity? Biological Conservation 122: 113–130.

CHAPTER ENDNOTES

1. Derocher, A. E., N. J. Lunn, and I. Stirling (2004) Polar bears in a warming climate, *Integr. Comp. Biol,* 44: 163–176.

2. U.S. Fish and Wildlife Service (2009) *Spotlight Species Action Plan: Polar Bear.* http://ecos. fws.gov/speciesProfile/profile/speciesProfile. action?spcode=A0IJ#recovery

3. IUCN (2011) *IUCN Red List of Threatened Species.* Version 2011.1 *Ursus maritimus: Summary.* www.iucnredlist.org/apps/redlist/details/22823/0

4. *Encyclopedia of Food and Culture.* Arctic: Inuit food lists and categories. www.enotes.com/food-encyclopedia/arctic. Accessed 18 June 2011.

5. Derocher, A. E., N. J. Lunn, and I. Stirling (2004) Polar bears in a warming climate, *Integr. Comp. Biol,* 44:163–176.

6. IUCN (2011) *IUCN Red List of Threatened Species.* Version 2011.1 *Ursus maritimus: Summary.* www. iucnredlist.org/apps/redlist/details/22823/0

7. CBC News (January 5, 2011) Iqaluit polar bear hunting quota unclear. www.cbc.ca/news/canada/north/ story/2011/01/05/iqaluit-polar-bear-quota.html Accessed 18 June 2011.

8. Environment Canada Environmental Monitoring and Assessment Network (EMAN). *Status of Amphibian and Reptile Species in Canada.* www.eman-rese.ca/ eman/reports/publications/2004/amph_rept_status/.

9. Millennium Ecosystem Assessment (2005) *Ecosystems and Human Well-Being: Synthesis,* Island Press, Washington, DC.

10. IUCN (2011) *IUCN Red List of Threatened Species.* Version 2011.1. www.iucnredlist.org. Accessed 18 June 2011.

11. Bamosky, A. D., N. Matzke, et al. (2011) Has the Earth's sixth mass extinction already arrived? *Nature* 471: 51.

12. World Wide Fund for Nature and U.N. Environment Programme (2010) *The 2010 Living Planet Report,* Gland, Switzerland: WWF.

13. Wild Species 2005, National General Status Working Group (2005) www.wildspecies.ca/wildspecies2005/index.cfm?lang=e

14. The National General Status Working Group is composed of representatives from the provinces and territories and the three federal agencies whose mandate includes wildlife: Canadian Wildlife Service, Department of Fisheries and Oceans, and Parks Canada, with additional ex officio input from Natural Resources Canada and Agriculture and Agri-Food Canada. NGSWG advises COSEWIC, the Committee on the Status of Endangered Wildlife in Canada, which in turn recommends the listing of species on the SARA Registry.

15. Wild Species 2005, National General Status Working Group (2005) www.wildspecies.ca/wildspecies2005/index.cfm?lang=e. This report is updated every five years; the 2010 report has been completed but is not yet available as of June 2011.

16. Wild Species 2005, National General Status Working Group (2005) www.wildspecies.ca/wildspecies2005/index.cfm?lang=e

17. Millennium Ecosystem Assessment (2005) *Ecosystems and Human Well-Being: Synthesis*, Island Press, Washington, DC.

18. Leopold, A. (1953) *Round River*, Oxford University Press, New York, pp. 145–146.

19. Wilson, E. O. (1984) *Biophilia*, Havard University Press, Cambridge, MA.

20. Louv, R. *Last Child in the Woods: Saving Our Children from Nature-Deficit Disorder*, Algonquin Books of Chapel Hill, Chapel Hill, NC.

21. Wilson, E. O. (1994) *Naturalist*, Shearwater Books, Washington, DC.

22. Whooping Crane Eastern Partnership. www.bring-backthecranes.org/back/proj-facts.htm

23. Species at Risk Public Registry, Government of Canada. www.sararegistry.gc.ca/species/speciesDetails_e.cfm?sid=140

24. Weagle, K., and C. Smeeton. Captive breeding of swift fox for reintroduction: Final report to funding bodies 1994 to 1997. Cochrane Ecological Institute. www.ceinst.org/Final%20Report%20to%20Funders%2097.pdf

25. Cotterill, S. E. (1997) Status of the swift fox *(Vulpes velox)* in Alberta. Alberta Environmental Protection, Wildlife Management Division, Wildlife Status Report No. 7, Edmonton, AB. www.srd.gov.ab.ca/fishwildlife/status/swfox/cons.html

26. Cotterill, S. E. (1997) Status of the swift fox *(Vulpes velox)* in Alberta. Alberta Environmental Protection, Wildlife Management Division, Wildlife Status Report No. 7, Edmonton, AB. www.srd.gov.ab.ca/fishwildlife/status/swfox/cons.html

27. Nature Conservancy of Canada. The endangered swift fox. www.natureconservancy.ca/site/News2?abbr=ncc_work_&page=NewsArticle&id=5047

28. Mooers, A. Ø., L. R. Prugh, M. Festa-Bianchet, and J. A. Hutchings (2006) Biases in legal listing under Canadian endangered species legislation. *Conservation Biology*, 21(3): 572–575.

29. Worldwide Fund for Nature. Ecoregions, www.world-wildlife.org/science/ecoregions/item1847.html

30. Parks Canada, Canada's National Parks and National Reserves. http://www.pc.gc.ca/docs/v-g/nation/nation103_e.asp

31. Campbell, L., and C. D. A. Rubec (2006) *Land Trusts in Canada: Building Momentum for the Future.* Ottawa: Wildlife Habitat Canada and the Stewardship Section, Canadian Wildlife Service, Environment Canada.

32. Environment Canada. *State of the Environment Infobase.* www.ec.gc.ca/soer-ree/English/Indicator_series/techs.cfm?tech_id=1&issue_id=2

MyEnvironmentPlace

Go to **www.myenvironmentplace.ca** where you will find quizzes, animations, your Pearson eText, and more.

Forests and Forest Management

8

Old-growth trees like this one at Clayoquot Sound, BC, have long been the focus of conflicts between logging companies and environmentalists.

Upon completing this chapter, you will be able to

- Describe the basic functional processes of trees and their role in biogeochemical cycling
- Summarize the principal types of forest biomes, especially those indigenous to Canada
- Describe the ecological roles and economic contributions of forests
- Trace the history and scale of forest loss and identify the current drivers of deforestation

- Outline the major methods of harvesting timber
- Explain the fundamentals of forest management, including approaches to fire management, and identify forest management agencies in Canada and internationally

CLAYOQUOT PEACE CAMP

HOW MANY ARRESTS TILL THE REAL CRIMINALS GO TO JAIL?

CANADA

Hudson Bay

Clayoquot Sound

CENTRAL CASE:
BATTLING OVER THE LAST BIG TREES AT CLAYOQUOT SOUND

"Clear-cutting . . . may be either desirable or undesirable, acceptable or unacceptable, according to the type of forest and the management objectives."
—DR. HAMISH KIMMINS, UNIVERSITY OF BRITISH COLUMBIA, 1992

"What we have is nothing less than an ecological Holocaust occurring right now in British Columbia."
—MARK WAREING, WESTERN CANADA WILDERNESS COMMITTEE, 1990

It was the largest act of civil disobedience in Canadian history, and it played out along a seacoast of majestic beauty, at the foot of some of the world's biggest trees. At Clayoquot Sound on the western coast of Vancouver Island, British Columbia, protestors blocked logging trucks, preventing them from entering stands of ancient temperate rainforest. The activists chanted slogans, sang songs, and chained themselves to trees.

Loggers complained that the protestors were keeping them from doing their jobs and making a living. In the end, 850 of the 12 000 protestors were arrested, and this remote, mist-enshrouded land of cedars and hemlocks became ground zero in the debate over how we manage forests.

That was in 1993, and the activists were opposing **clear-cutting**, the logging practice that removes all trees from an area. Most of Canada's old-growth temperate rainforest had already been cut, and the forests of Clayoquot Sound were among the largest undisturbed stands of temperate rainforest left on the planet.

Timber from **old-growth forests**—complex, primary forests in which the trees are at least 150 years old—had long powered British Columbia's economy. Historically, one in five jobs in BC depended on its $13 billion timber industry, and many small towns would have gone under without it. By 1993, however, the timber industry was cutting thousands of jobs a year because of mechanization, and the looming depletion of old growth threatened to slow the industry. Meanwhile, Greenpeace was convincing overseas customers to boycott products made from trees clear-cut by multinational timber company MacMillan-Bloedel. Soon British Columbia's premier found himself trying to persuade European nations not to boycott his province's main export.

In 1995, the provincial government called for an end to clear-cutting at Clayoquot Sound, after its appointed scientific panel of experts submitted a new forestry plan for the region. The plan recommended reducing harvests, retaining 15–70% of old-growth trees in each stand, decreasing the logging road network, designating forest reserve areas, and managing *riparian* (water's-edge) zones. Two years later, the provincial government reversed many of these regulations, and a new premier pronounced forest activists "enemies of British Columbia."

The antagonists struck a deal; wilderness advocates and MacMillan-Bloedel agreed to log old growth in limited areas, using environmentally friendly practices. In 1998, First Nations people of the region formed a timber company, Iisaak Forest Resources, in agreement with MacMillan-Bloedel's successor, Weyerhaeuser, and began logging at Clayoquot Sound in a more environmentally sensitive manner (see photo).

In the Nuu-chah-nulth language of First Nations people from the Clayoquot Sound area, *iisaak* (pronounced *E-sock*) means "respect," which became a guiding principle for forestry in Clayoquot Sound. The *variable retention harvesting* they applied—logging selectively with the goal of retaining a certain percentage and particular characteristics of the forest ecosystem—is more expensive than normal clear-cutting. Iisaak Forest Resources hoped to recoup some of the extra cost by achieving a premium price for the cut timber and through ecotourism and the sustainable exploitation of other forest resources.

Logging continues at some parts of Clayoquot Sound.

Leaving most of the trees standing accomplished what forest advocates had predicted: People from all over the world—1 million each year—are now visiting Clayoquot Sound for its natural beauty and are kayaking and whale-watching in its waters. Ecotourism (along with fishing and aquaculture) has surpassed logging as a driver of local economies. The United Nations designated the site as a biosphere reserve in 2000, encouraging land protection and sustainable development. From the perspective of ecotourism, the trees appear to be worth more standing than cut down.

Tensions continue today, and logging has never completely stopped at Clayoquot Sound—even in areas near park and biosphere reserve boundaries—to the dismay of environmental activists.[1] Local forest advocates worry that the provincial government's new Working Forest Policy will increase logging, and the town of Tofino petitioned the province to exempt Clayoquot Sound's forests from the policy.

Ultimately, Iisaak Forest Resources found it difficult to make money doing sustainable forestry and entered into an agreement with the environmental organization Ecotrust Canada in 2006. Today logging is being done more sustainably, and at a profit, under this arrangement. The provincial government is considering new forestry plans that would shift logging out of old-growth forests and into younger forests that were already logged in the past. As long as our demand for lumber, paper, and forest products keeps increasing, pressures will keep building on the remaining forests on Vancouver Island and around the world.

The Forest and the Trees

Forest covers roughly 31% of Earth's land surface (FIGURE 8.1), about 4 billion hectares.[2] Forests provide habitat for countless organisms and help maintain soil, air, and water quality. They play key roles in our planet's biogeochemical cycles, serving as one of the most important reservoirs in the carbon cycle. Forests have also long provided humanity with wood for fuel, construction, paper production, and more.

Trees have several basic requirements

Trees are the fundamental biological component of forests, although, as you will learn, forests have many other crucial components, both biotic and abiotic, and not all forests are completely dominated by trees.

Trees, like all other plants, are autotrophs. They create their own food energy by photosynthesis, through which they extract carbon from atmospheric carbon dioxide and recombine it with water to make carbohydrates (sugars, such as glucose; FIGURE 8.2). For photosynthesis to occur and the tree to survive, there are several fundamental requirements:

- An amenable temperature (the specific temperature range varies by species)

- Air (with which the tree exchanges carbon, hydrogen, oxygen, and nitrogen)
- Light (the energy source for photosynthesis)
- Soil (the source for mineral nutrients)
- Water (needed for a variety of reasons)

The nutrients required for plant growth are supplied through the tree's roots from the soil, using soil water as the transfer medium. As we have discussed previously (in the context of soil and agriculture), nutrients that are required in relatively large amounts are called **macronutrients**; for trees, these include nitrogen (N), phosphorus

roots

FOREST

Forest is a late-thirteenth-century word from the Old French *forest* (modern *forêt*). It originally referred to an extensive tree-covered district set aside under the protection of the king for royal hunting. It probably came from the Latin term *forestem silvam*, "the outside woods," used during the time of Charlemagne to refer to a royal forest. It may also be related to the Latin root of the word *forum*, referring to a court or a judgment—in other words, "legally protected land."

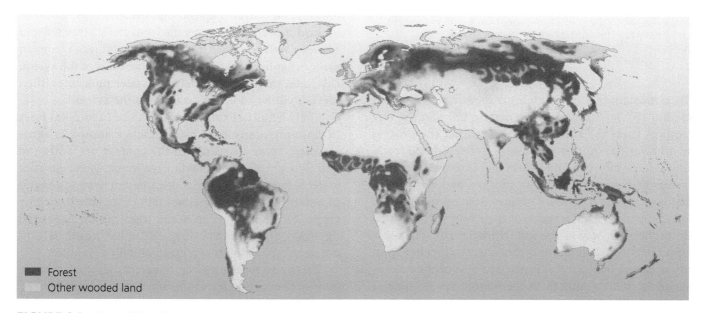

Forest
Other wooded land

FIGURE 8.1   About 31% of Earth's land surface is covered by forest. Most of this consists of the boreal forests of the north and the tropical forests of South America and Africa. Other lands (including tundra, shrubland, and savannah) can be classified as "wooded land," implying a more open forest type that supports trees, but at sparser densities.   *Source: Data from U.N. Food and Agriculture Organization (FAO) (2005)* Global Forest Resources Assessment 2005 *(with updated information from* Global Forest Resources Assessment 2010).

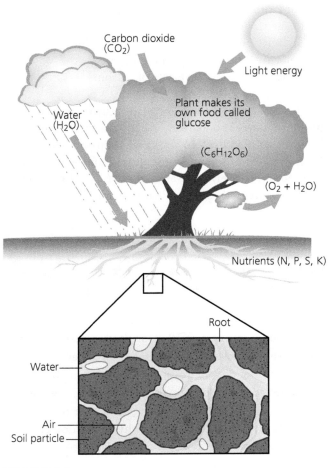

FIGURE 8.2
Trees acquire carbon from the air, via photosynthesis. They utilize
light energy to carry out photosynthesis for the production of
carbohydrates, such as glucose, from atmospheric carbon dioxide.
Macronutrients such as phosphorus, sulphur, and potassium are
provided by the mineral components of the soil, through the tree's
roots by way of soil water. Nitrogen comes from a variety of sources,
but primarily from the atmosphere via nitrogen fixation.

(P), potassium (K), magnesium (Mg), calcium (Ca), and
sulphur (S), in addition to the carbon (C) that the tree
acquires from the atmosphere. Recall that the process
of *nitrogen fixation* by soil-dwelling bacteria converts
atmospheric nitrogen into a form that is usable by plants,
including trees. Lightning is another natural process
that leads to the fixation of atmospheric nitrogen in the
soil. Thus trees acquire much of their nitrogen from the
atmosphere, by way of the soil. Nitrogen also can come
from the decomposition of organisms, fecal matter from
animals, and artificial fertilizers. The rest of the macronutrients come mainly from the dissolution of mineral
grains in soil water.

Nutrients that are required by living organisms only
in small amounts are called **micronutrients**; for trees,
these include iron (Fe), manganese (Mn), zinc (Zn),

copper (Cu), boron (B), chlorine (Cl), and molybde-
num (Mo).

Trees, like all plants, need water for several reasons.
First, water is used in photosynthesis, for which the
general simplified reaction is:

$$6CO_2 + 6H_2O = C_6H_{12}O_6 + 6O_2$$

Second, water acts as a solvent, dissolving mineral
constituents from particles in the soil. As shown in
FIGURE 8.2, these are taken up by the tree's roots, to
be used as nutrients. Third, in addition to transporting nutrients, water transports chemicals from one part
of the tree to wherever they are needed to carry out the
metabolic processes that keep the tree alive. Fourth, water
provides support for cells. All plant cells require internal
water pressure (called *turgidity*) in their cells, or they will
wilt and eventually die. (Turgidity is the main way that
nonwoody plants stay upright. Trees have additional
structural support in the form of woody trunks that help
them to remain upright.)

Trees (and other plants) require water to pass from
their roots through their trunks and branches and
evaporate from their leaf surfaces (**FIGURE 8.3**); this is
called **transpiration**. Transpiration cools the plant, as
well as assisting in the movement of nutrients. It also
helps small openings in the leaves, called *stomata*, to
open, allowing for the intake of carbon dioxide during
photosynthesis. Transpiration occurs when solar energy
causes water to evaporate from leaf surfaces, resulting
in negative internal water pressure. Water is drawn up
through the roots and trunk through narrow, strawlike
tubes called *xylem*. Soil water moves into the roots by
osmosis and is drawn up through the xylem by *adhesion*,
upward movement that results from the surface tension
between water (a polar molecule, you will recall from an
earlier chapter) and the capillary-like walls of the xylem.
Cohesion, the attraction between water molecules, then
serves to draw additional water into the xylem.

This helps to explain why it is useful to plant trees
in close proximity to crops, a practice known as **agroforestry**, as we discussed in the chapter on "Soils and
Soil Resources." Crop plants have much shallower root
systems than trees, in general; a tree can draw water and
minerals from depth, making them available to nearby
crops. At the same time, some trees can be harvested
for wood, fruits, nuts, honey, and other products, and
domesticated animals can graze on fallen leaf litter.

Trees also function as an important link between the
biogeochemical cycles of the atmosphere, hydrosphere,
biosphere, and geosphere. Transpiration is an important
step in the hydrologic cycle, moderating the movement
of water from the atmosphere to the ground and from the
ground back to the atmosphere.

How water moves through a tree

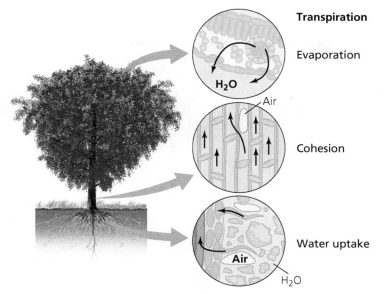

Transpiration

Evaporation

H_2O

Air

Cohesion

Water uptake

Air

H_2O

FIGURE 8.3   The driving force for transpiration is evaporation from leaf surfaces. Water is drawn into root hairs and upward through the xylem by adhesion and cohesion.

When trees draw mineral nutrients and water from depth through their root systems, they deliver them to near-surface soil layers, where they become available for other plants (**FIGURE 8.4**). This is sometimes referred to as *water and nutrient pumping*. Trees also deliver organic material back to the topsoil, in the form of **litter**, which consists of fallen branches and leaves.

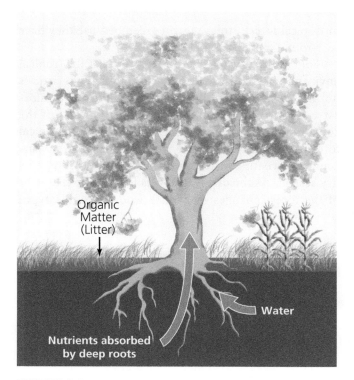

Organic Matter (Litter)

Water

Nutrients absorbed by deep roots

FIGURE 8.4

Trees act like pumps, drawing nutrients and water from depth through their root systems. In this way, they can provide nutrients and water to plants with shallower root systems. They also act as a link in biogeochemical cycles and the hydrologic cycle.

There are three major groups of forest biomes

A **forest**, strictly speaking, is a land area with significant tree cover, in which the **canopy** (the upper level of leaves and branches defined by the treetops) is largely **closed**. A **woodland** is a wooded (treed) area in which the canopy is more **open**; that is, there are some openings between the trees that allow light to penetrate to the ground, or **floor**, of the forest (**FIGURE 8.5**).

There are three major types of forest biomes, corresponding roughly to the high, middle, and equatorial latitudes. However, there are *many* local variations, as well as altitudinal variations; we will look more closely at the forests of Canada later in this chapter.

Boreal forest.   The **boreal forest** is a high-latitude forest type (mainly in the Northern Hemisphere) that is characterized by cold, relatively dry climates with short growing seasons. The boreal forest biome stretches across much of Canada, Russia, and Scandinavia. Further to the north, the boreal forest grades through the **taiga** into the more open northern **tundra** biome. Boreal forests are characterized by evergreen, **coniferous** trees—trees whose "leaves" take the form of needles and that produce seed pods in the form of cones. Evergreen, waxy-coated needles and cones are energy- and water-saving adapta-

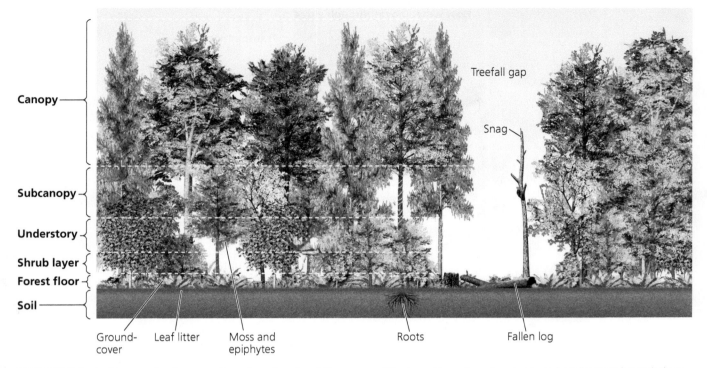

FIGURE 8.5   In this generalized cross-section of a mature forest, the crowns of the largest trees form the canopy, and smaller trees beneath them form the shaded subcanopy and understory. Shrubs and groundcover grow just above the forest floor, which may be covered in leaf litter rich with invertebrate animals. Vines, mosses, lichens, and epiphytes cover portions of trees and the forest floor. Snags (standing dead trees), whose wood can be easily hollowed out, provide food and nesting and roosting sites for woodpeckers and other animals. Fallen logs nourish the soil and young plants and provide habitat for countless invertebrates as the logs decompose. Gaps caused by fallen trees let light through the canopy and create small openings in the forest, allowing early successional plants to grow in patches within the mature forest.

tions that help trees cope with short growing seasons and low precipitation.

Temperate forest   The **temperate forest**, the second major forest biome type, occurs in midlatitude areas of seasonal climate, which typically experience a distinct winter season and summer growing season. Temperate forests occur throughout eastern North America, northeastern Asia, and western and central Europe. Temperate forests cover much less area globally than boreal forests, in part because people have already cleared so many of them. Trees in temperate forests must be adapted to a seasonal climate and wide ranges in temperature and precipitation. Temperate forests are often characterized by **deciduous** trees—trees whose leaves turn colour (*senesce*) and drop off in the fall, in preparation for a period of winter dormancy.

Tropical forest   The third major forest biome type is the **tropical forest**. Tropical rainforests, which host extremely diverse flora and fauna, occur in the wet, tropical climates of equatorial South and Central America, equatorial Africa, and Indonesia and Southeast Asia. Trees in rainforests are often evergreen, but not for the energy-saving reasons that boreal trees are evergreen;

in tropical forests, trees remain green because they have year-round growing conditions.

For **rainforests** we tend to think first of the tropical environment, but in fact their central characteristic is not high temperature, but high rainfall. Thus, rainforest variations include the evergreen rainforests of the cool, wet Pacific Northwest. Similarly, there are tropical forests in which the climate is warm but not wet year-round, alternating instead between a rainy season and a dry season. As the dry season gets longer, the character of the forest changes and other wooded biome types

roots

BOREAL AND TAIGA

Boreal is a late fifteenth-century word deriving from the Latin *boreas*, meaning "north wind." It originated from the Greek *Boreas*, "god of the north wind." **Taiga** is a Russian word of Mongolian origin, used in the late nineteenth century in reference to the coniferous forest of Siberia.

emerge, such as the more open tropical dry forest and savannah biomes.

An additional unique type of forest biome comprises coastal forests, such as *mangroves*. Trees in mangrove forests are adapted to conditions of constant standing water and fluctuating water salinity. They provide valuable habitat for shallow-water marine organisms and they protect shorelines from the battering of storm waves. Mangroves and other coastal forests are discussed in the chapter on marine and coastal systems and fisheries.

Forests grade into open wooded lands

These broad descriptions of the major types of forest biomes should make it obvious that not all "forests" are completely dominated by trees. At the drier end of the climatic spectrum (in cold, high-latitude regions as well as hot, low-latitude regions), the canopies of wooded areas tend to be even more open. **Shrublands** are wooded areas that are covered by smaller, bushier trees, or *shrubs*, often interspersed with occasional taller trees. Tundra is a high-latitude (and high-altitude), cold version of shrubland. **Savannah** is an open area dominated by grasses, with widely scattered trees. Finally, **grasslands** are lands that are dominated by grasses and other nonwoody vegetation. Again, all of these basic biome types have many local variations (**FIGURE 8.6**).

Grasslands, savannahs, and even shrublands are not forests, strictly speaking, although any of them can be partially "wooded." It is common to group these biome types together under the category of **drylands**, emphasizing their central defining characteristic of low precipitation. This is a broad category that includes some areas with a relatively long dry season alternating with a rainy season; some semi-arid regions that experience low precipitation year-round; and—at the extreme end of the dryland spectrum—the arid *desert* biome.

Because drylands are characterized by low overall precipitation, they tend to be extremely sensitive to environmental change and are easily damaged if land use practices become overly intensive. Therefore, *desertification* and *land degradation* are major environmental issues in dryland management. Much of the world's dry woodland and grassland has been converted for the purpose of agriculture or rangeland. We will discuss this in greater detail below.

Canada is a steward for much of the world's forest

Canada's current 402 million ha of forested and other wooded land (310 million ha of which is "true" forest)[3] represent over 10% of the world's forest cover, 40% of Canada's total land area, 25% of the world's natural (rather than planted) forest, 30% of the world's boreal forest, and 20% of the world's temperate rainforest. Canada's wooded lands include some of the world's largest intact forest ecosystems. Canada has the highest amount of forested land per capita in the world.[4] About one-third of the nation's forested land is in British Columbia, and 38% is in Québec and Ontario.[5]

According to the Food and Agriculture Organization of the United Nations, which monitors the status of the world's forests, more than 50% of Canada's primary forest remains more or less intact.[6] In comparison, of the original 4 million km^2 (400 million ha) of forested land in the United States, the vast majority was deforested by the late nineteenth century. (In the early 1900s, forest cover in the United States began to stabilize, however, and in the past few decades, the United States has seen an increase in forested land.)

Canada clearly has an obligation to the rest of the world to manage our forests as effectively and sustainably as possible. The Boreal Forest Conservation Framework puts Canada's stewardship responsibilities with regard to the boreal forest in perspective, stating, in part, that

> *Canada's boreal region contains one-quarter of the world's remaining original forests. The largest intact forest ecosystem left on Earth, Canada's boreal is home to a rich array of wildlife including migratory songbirds, waterfowl, bears, wolves and some of the world's largest woodland caribou herds. The boreal region's natural wealth sustains many of Canada's Aboriginal communities, who have lived in harmony with the boreal for thousands of years. It also sup-*

FIGURE 8.6
Savannah and grassland are characterized by a relatively dry climate and dispersed trees.

ports thousands of jobs and contributes billions to the Canadian economy.

The Boreal Forest Conservation Framework is based on a shared vision to sustain the ecological and cultural integrity of the Canadian boreal forest region, in perpetuity. The Framework's goal is to conserve the cultural, sustainable economic and natural values of the entire Canadian boreal region by employing the principles of conservation biology to protect at least 50% of the region in a network of large interconnected protected areas, and to support sustainable communities, world-leading ecosystem-based resource management practices, and state-of-the-art stewardship practices in the remaining landscape.[7]

The members of the Boreal Leadership Council are described as "historically unlikely partners" and include representatives from industry and finance; nongovernmental organizations, nonprofits, and environmental groups; and Aboriginal organizations and governing bodies. This type of collaborative, cross-disciplinary, cross-sectoral management process is typical of Canada's historical approach to the management of complex and sometimes thorny environmental issues, and it is one of the reasons that Canada has been considered a leader in environmental management.

Canada's forests are varied

Canada's forest biomes include many regional variations, some of which are described next.

Forests of the north   The boreal forest, the largest forested region of Canada, stretches through all of the provinces and territories except Nova Scotia and Prince Edward Island (**FIGURE 8.7A**). White spruces,

(a) Northern boreal forest

FIGURE 8.7
Canada's forest biomes include many regional variations, some of which are seen here.

(b) Western ponderosa pine forest

(c) Eastern deciduous forest

tamarack, and jack and lodgepole pines are the main coniferous species in the boreal forest, and white birch, aspen, and balsam poplars are the main deciduous trees. In the north the boreal forest merges with the tundra, an open woodland biome. The term *taiga* is sometimes used casually as a synonym for boreal forest, but technically the taiga is the transitional zone between the boreal forest and the northern tundra.

Forests of the west In the west is the *subalpine forest region* of the mountains of British Columbia and western Alberta, with characteristic Engelmann spruce, alpine fir, and lodgepole pines, and the *montane forest region* in British Columbia's central plateau, with Rocky Mountain Douglas fir, lodgepole pine, trembling aspen, and ponderosa pine (FIGURE 8.7B). The *coast forest region*, found at Clayoquot Sound and elsewhere on Vancouver Island, is the temperate rainforest, characterized by western red cedar, western hemlock, Sitka spruce, yellow cypress, and deciduous big-leaf maple, red alder, cottonwoods, Garry oak and arbutus. The *Columbia forest region* of the Kootenay, Thompson, and Fraser river valleys includes species like western white pine, Engelmann spruce, western larch, and grand fir.

Forests of the east In the east, the *deciduous forest region* north of Lake Erie and Lake Ontario is the smallest forest region in Canada, characterized by deciduous species such as sugar maple, beech, elms, and oaks and by conifers such as the eastern white pine and eastern hemlock (FIGURE 8.7C). In this region there are also pockets of "Carolinian" species such as the tulip tree and black gum, which are more common further to the south in the eastern United States. The *Great Lakes–St. Lawrence forest region* extends from northwestern New Brunswick, through the St. Lawrence, Lac St. Jean, and Saguenay river valleys, over southern and central Ontario, and into Manitoba. Typical conifers include the eastern white and red pine and eastern hemlock. The characteristic deciduous species is yellow birch. Finally, the *Acadian forest region* of Nova Scotia, New Brunswick, and Prince Edward Island is typified by spruce and balsam fir, with common deciduous sugar maple, yellow birch, and beech.[8]

Forests are ecologically valuable

Because of their structural complexity and their ability to provide many niches for organisms, forests comprise some of the richest ecosystems for biodiversity (FIGURE 8.8). Trees furnish food and shelter for an immense diversity of vertebrate and invertebrate animals. Countless

FIGURE 8.8
Forests are ecologically valuable. They are especially important as habitat because of their structural complexity, as shown here in the old-growth forest of Cathedral Grove on Vancouver Island.

insects, birds, mammals, and other organisms subsist on the leaves, fruits, and seeds that trees produce.

Some animals are adapted for living in the dense treetop canopy, where beetles, caterpillars, and other leaf-eating insects abound, providing food for birds such as tanagers and warblers, while arboreal mammals from squirrels to sloths to monkeys consume fruit and leaves. Other animals specialize on the *subcanopies* of trees, and still others utilize the bark, branches, and trunks. Cavities in trunks provide nest and shelter sites for a wide variety of vertebrates. Dead and dying trees are valuable for many species; these *snags* are decayed by insects that, in turn, are eaten by woodpeckers and other animals.

Meanwhile, the shrubs and groundcover plants of the **understory**, the forest floor and the lowest levels of growth, give a forest structural complexity and provide habitat for still more organisms. Moreover, the leaves, stems, and roots of forest plants are colonized by an extensive array of fungi and microbes, in both parasitic and mutualistic relationships. Much of a forest's diversity resides on the forest floor, where the soil is generally nourished by fallen leaves and branches, called *litter*. There, myriad soil organisms help decompose plant material and cycle nutrients.

An additional habitat consideration in forests is the difference between the forest **core**, in the middle of a large forested area, and the forest **edge**. Edge habitat—even if it is still forested—can be quite different in character from habitat in the forest core, particularly in light levels, density of vegetation, and moisture. Research has demonstrated that wildlife adapted to forest core habitats declines when forced to occupy edge habitats, in parts of the forest that are immediately adjacent to surrounding areas. Fragmentation of wooded areas greatly increases the ratio of edge to core habitat, even if the total wooded area is not greatly reduced.

In general, forests with a greater diversity of plants, such as tropical rainforests, host a greater diversity of organisms overall. And in general, fully mature forests, such as the undisturbed old-growth forests remaining at Clayoquot Sound, contain more biodiversity than younger forests. Older forests offer more structural diversity and thus more microhabitats and resources to support more species.

Trees provide ecosystem services of value to people

In addition to hosting a significant proportion of the world's biodiversity, forests provide all manner of vital ecosystem services that are of value to people. Forest vegetation stabilizes soil and prevents erosion. The principal direct cause of soil erosion and degradation is the removal of vegetation. This is especially true in tropical rainforests where, counterintuitively, soils are not particularly fertile because most of the biomass of the system resides in the trees and other forest plants. Once the trees have been removed, the soil is exposed to wind and water and can quickly erode.

As mentioned above, trees and other forest plants help regulate the hydrologic cycle, slowing runoff, lessening flooding, and purifying water as they take it in from the soil and release it to the atmosphere. Tree branches and leaves physically block and soften the fall of rain, which further protects the soil from degradation. Forests also store carbon, release oxygen, and act as a moderating influence on climate. By performing these and other ecological functions, forests are indispensable for human survival and well-being.

Harvesting Forest Products

In addition to the immense value of their ecological services, forests provide people with economically valuable harvestable products. It has been estimated that over 1.6 billion people worldwide depend on forests directly for their livelihood, but all of us use forest products in our daily lives.

Forest products are economically valued

For millennia, wood from forests has fuelled our fires, keeping people warm and well fed. It has housed people, keeping us sheltered. It built the ships that carried people and cultures from one continent to another. It allowed us to produce paper, the medium of the first information revolution.

In recent decades, industrial harvesting has allowed the extraction of more timber than ever before, supplying all these needs of a rapidly growing human population and its expanding economy. The exploitation of forest resources has been instrumental in helping our society achieve the standard of living we enjoy today. Indeed, without industrial timber harvesting, you would not be reading this book.

Most commercial logging today takes place in Canada, Russia, and other nations that hold large expanses of boreal forest and in tropical countries with large amounts of rainforest, such as Brazil and Indonesia. Timber harvested from coniferous trees (such as those that dominate the boreal forest) is called **softwood**, whereas timber that comes from deciduous trees is called **hardwood**. (The terms are not related to the actual hardness of the wood.) The softwood lumber industry is extremely important to Canada's economy.

Forests also supply non-wood products in abundance. Some of these *NTFPs* (for *non-timber forest products*) include medicinal and herbal products, such as ginseng, echinacea, and St. John's wort; decorative products, such as Christmas trees, wreaths, and other greenery; and many edible products, including fruits, honey, edible mushrooms including truffles, and a large variety of nuts. Many Aboriginal and indigenous peoples make their livelihoods by harvesting non-timber forest products. The *seringeiro* rubbertappers of the Brazilian Amazon come to mind as one example of a group of people whose lifestyle is adapted to the sustainable extraction of forest resources.

Nations maintain and use forests for all these economic and ecological reasons. An international survey in 2010 found that globally, about 30% of forests were designated primarily for timber production and harvesting of other forest products.[9] Others are designated for a variety of functions, including conservation of biodiversity, protection of soil and water quality, and social services such as recreation, tourism, education, and conservation of culturally important sites (FIGURE 8.9).

Timber is harvested by several methods

When they harvest trees, timber companies use any of several methods. From the 1950s through the 1970s, many timber harvests were conducted using the **clear-**

Designated functions of the world's forests 2010

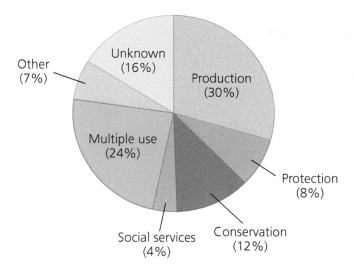

FIGURE 8.9
Worldwide, nations designate over one-third of forests primarily for production of timber and other forest products. Smaller areas are designated for conservation of biodiversity, protection of soil and water quality, and "social services" such as recreation, tourism, education, and conservation of culturally important sites. About one-third of forests are designated for combinations of these functions.
Source: Data from U.N. Food and Agriculture Organization (FAO) (2010) Global Forest Resources Assessment 2010, Key Findings, *p. 10.*

FIGURE 8.10
Clear-cutting is the most cost-efficient method for timber companies, but it can have severe ecological consequences, including soil erosion and species turnover. Although certain species do use clear-cut areas as they regrow, most people find these areas esthetically unappealing, and public reaction to clear-cutting has driven changes in forestry methods.

cutting method, in which all trees in an area are cut, leaving only stumps. Clear-cutting is generally the most cost-efficient method in the short term, but it has the greatest impacts on forest ecosystems (FIGURE 8.10). In the best-case scenario, clear-cutting may mimic natural disturbance events such as fires, tornadoes, or windstorms that knock down trees across large areas. In the worst-case scenario, entire communities of organisms are destroyed or displaced, soil erodes, and the penetration of sunlight to ground level changes microclimatic conditions such that new types of plants replace those that had comprised the native forest. Essentially, clear-cutting sets in motion an artificially driven process of succession in which the resulting climax community may turn out to be quite different from the original climax community.

Clear-cutting occurred widely across North America at a time when public awareness of environmental problems was blossoming. The combination produced public outrage toward the timber industry and public forest managers. Eventually the industry integrated other harvesting methods (FIGURE 8.11). A set of approaches dubbed **new forestry** called for timber cuts that came closer to mimicking natural disturbances. For instance, "sloppy clear-cuts" that leave a variety of trees standing were intended to mimic the changes a forest might experience if hit by a severe windstorm.

Clear-cutting (FIGURE 8.11A) is still widely practised, but other methods involve cutting some trees and leaving some standing. In the *seed-tree* approach (FIGURE 8.11B), small numbers of mature and vigorous seed-producing trees are left standing so that they can reseed the logged area. In the *shelterwood* approach (also FIGURE 8.11B), small numbers of mature trees are left in place to provide shelter for seedlings as they grow. These three methods all lead to even-aged stands of trees.

Selection systems, in contrast, allow uneven-aged stand management. In selection systems (FIGURE 8.11C), such as the variable retention harvest system practised on Clayoquot Sound, only some trees in a forest are cut at any one time. The stand's overall rotation time may be the same as in an even-aged approach because multiple harvests are made, but the stand remains mostly intact between harvests. Selection systems include single-tree selection, in which widely spaced trees are cut one at a time, and group selection, in which small patches of trees are cut.

It was a form of selection harvesting that Iisaak Forest Services and other logging organizations pursued at Clayoquot Sound after old-growth advocates applied pressure and the scientific panel published its guidelines. Not wanting to bring a complete end to logging when so many local people depended on the industry for work, these activists and scientists instead promoted what they considered a more environmentally friendly method of timber removal.

However, selection systems are by no means ecologically harmless. Moving trucks and machinery over an extensive network of roads and trails to access individual trees

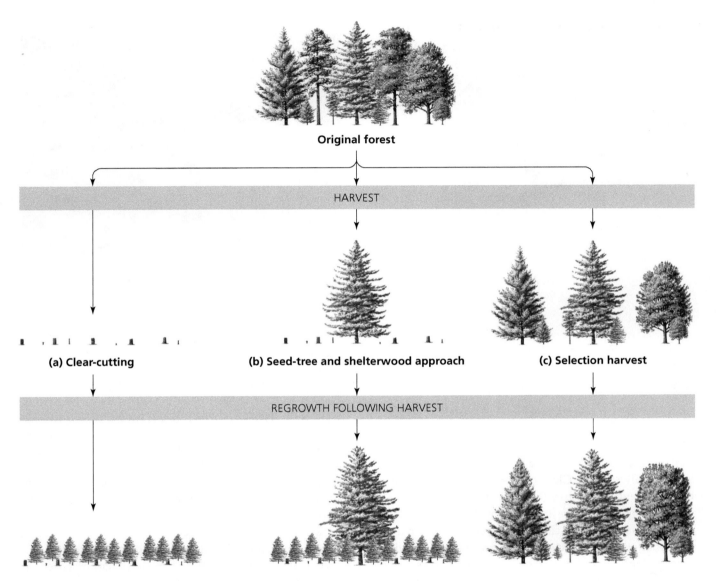

Original forest

HARVEST

(a) Clear-cutting   **(b) Seed-tree and shelterwood approach**   **(c) Selection harvest**

REGROWTH FOLLOWING HARVEST

FIGURE 8.11   Foresters and timber companies have devised various methods to harvest timber from forests. In clear-cutting **(a)**, all trees in an area are cut, extracting a great deal of timber inexpensively but leaving a vastly altered landscape. In seed-tree systems and shelterwood systems **(b)**, small numbers of large trees are left in clear-cuts to help reseed the area or provide shelter for growing seedlings. In selection systems **(c)**, a minority of trees is removed at any one time, while most are left standing. These last two methods involve less environmental impact than clear-cutting, but all methods can cause significant changes to the structure and function of natural forest communities.

compacts the soil and disturbs the forest floor. Selection methods are also unpopular with timber companies because they are expensive.

The bottom line, from an ecological perspective, is that all methods of logging result in habitat disturbance, which invariably affects the plants and animals inhabiting an area. All methods change forest structure and composition. Most methods increase soil erosion, leading to siltation of waterways, which can degrade habitat and affect drinking water quality. Most methods also speed runoff, sometimes causing flooding. In extreme cases, as when steep hillsides are clear-cut, landslides can result.

Plantation forestry has grown in North America

The North American timber industry is largely centred on production from plantations of fast-growing tree species that are single-species monocultures. Forest plantations now make up about 7% of forested land globally (**FIGURE 8.12A**).[10] Logging in Canada is largely offset by **reforestation**, the planting of trees after logging, and **afforestation**, the planting of trees where forested cover has not existed for some time (over 50 years). Because all trees in a given stand are planted at the same time, the stands are **even-aged**, with all trees the same age

0   100

Primary forests	Other naturally regenerated forests	Planted forests
36%	57%	7%0

(a) Primary and planted forests, % 2010

(b) Tree plantation

FIGURE 8.12
(a) Approximately 7% of global forested land today is forest plantation and this is increasing. **(b)** Even-aged tree stand management is practised on tree plantations where all trees are of equal age, as seen in the stand in the foreground that is regrowing after clear-cutting. In uneven-aged tree stand management, harvests are designed to maintain a mix of tree ages, as seen in the more mature forest in the background. The increased structural diversity of uneven-aged stands provides superior habitat for most wild species and makes these stands more akin to ecologically functional forests.

(**FIGURE 8.12B**). Stands are cut after a certain number of years (called the *rotation time*), and the land is replanted with seedlings.

It is important to acknowledge that planting new trees will not replace complex old-growth forests that may have taken hundreds of years to develop. Even when regrowth outpaces removal, the character of forests may still change. In North America and worldwide, primary forest continues to be lost and to be replaced by younger second-growth forest. Most ecologists and foresters view these plantations more as crop agriculture than as ecologically functional forests. Because there are few tree species and little variation in tree age, plantations do not offer many forest organisms the habitat they need.

The principle of **maximum sustainable yield**, a basic principle of renewable resource management, argues for cutting trees shortly after they have gone through their fastest stage of growth, and trees often grow most quickly at intermediate ages. Thus, trees may be cut long before they have grown as large as they would in the absence of harvesting. Although this practice may maximize timber production over time, it can cause drastic changes in the ecology of a forest by eliminating habitat for species that depend on mature trees. However, some harvesting methods aim to maintain **uneven-aged** stands, where a mix of ages (and often a mix of tree species) makes the stand more similar to a natural forest.

Land Conversion and Deforestation

The harvesting of timber and other forest products is not new; it has occurred throughout human history. We all depend in some way on wood, and people have cleared forests for millennia to exploit forest resources. Historically, as agriculture emerged and some cultures began to adopt a sedentary or settled lifestyle, the clearing of forested land for settlement and farming would have been one of the very first significant human-generated environmental impacts. Forest clearing has even been used as an approach in warfare (both modern and ancient) and to flush out game for hunting purposes. Land conversion, combined with some bad practices in agriculture, ranching, and forestry, has led to **deforestation**, the loss of forested area worldwide.

The growth of Canada and the U.S. were fuelled by land clearing and logging

Historically, logging for timber and the clearing of land for settlement and farming propelled the growth of both Canada and the United States throughout the phenomenal expansion westward across the North American continent over the past 400 years. The vast deciduous forests of the eastern United States were virtually stripped of their trees by the mid-nineteenth century, making way for countless small farms. Timber from these forests built the cities of eastern North America.

As the farming economy shifted to an industrial one, wood was used to stoke the furnaces of industry. Once most of the mature trees were removed from the eastern hardwood forests, timber companies moved to the south and west, eventually harvesting some of the continent's biggest trees in the Rocky Mountains, the Sierra Nevada, and the Pacific Coast ranges (FIGURE 8.13).

By the early twentieth century, very little **primary forest**—long-standing natural forest, uncut by people—

was left in the United States. Today, the largest oaks and maples found in eastern North America, and even most redwoods of the California coast, are **second-growth** trees: trees that have sprouted and grown to partial maturity after old-growth timber has been cut. The size of the gargantuan trees they replaced can be seen in the enormous stumps that remain in the more recently logged areas of the Pacific Coast. The scarcity of old-growth trees on the North American continent today explains the concern that scientists have for old-growth ecosystems and the passion with which environmental advocates have fought to preserve ancient forests in areas such as Clayoquot Sound.

In spite of vigorous historical logging, much of Canada remains forested (FIGURE 8.14A). The principal cause of deforestation in Canada today is not logging but land clearing for agriculture. Deforestation continues in Canada, but in 2008 it affected less than 0.02% (approximately 46 000 ha in net loss) of Canada's forests (FIGURE 8.14B,C). Fire, urban development, hydroelectric dams, and, increasingly, outbreaks of parasites and other invasive pest species such as the Asian longhorned beetle, mountain pine beetle, and spruce budworm are also significant causes of deforestation (see "The Science Behind the Story: Changing Climate and the Spruce Budworm on Vancouver Island"). Many scientists expect that climate change will be an important driver of deforestation in the near future.

FIGURE 8.13
Huge trees were harvested in many locations in Canada in the first part of the nineteenth century, including the pines shown here in Madawaska River Valley near Ottawa. Early timber harvesting practices in North America caused significant environmental impacts and removed virtually all the virgin timber from one region after another.

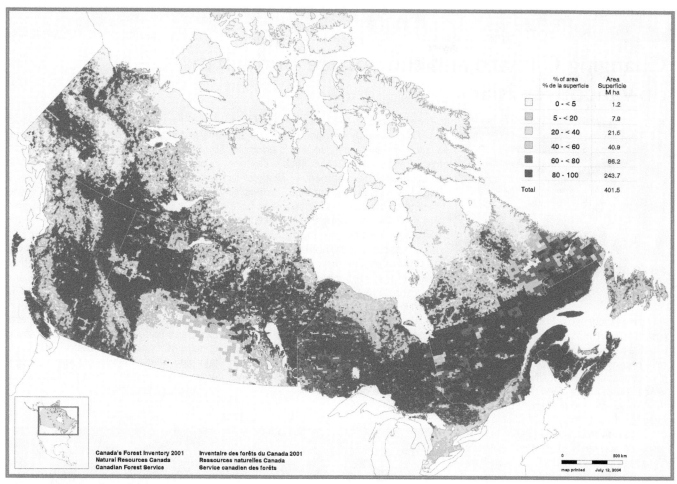

% of area % de la superficie	Area Superficie M ha
0 - < 5	1.2
5 - < 20	7.9
20 - < 40	21.6
40 - < 60	40.9
60 - < 80	86.2
80 - 100	243.7
Total	401.5

Canada's Forest Inventory 2001   Inventaire des forêts du Canada 2001
Natural Resources Canada   Ressources naturelles Canada
Canadian Forest Service   Service canadien des forêts

0   500 km
map printed   July 12, 2004

(a) Forested land in Canada

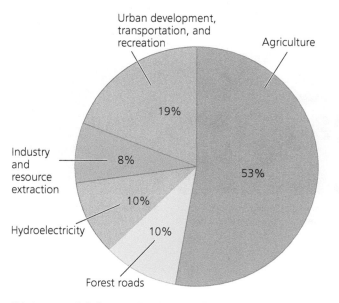

Urban development, transportation, and recreation — 19%

Agriculture — 53%

Industry and resource extraction — 8%

Hydroelectricity — 10%

Forest roads — 10%

(b) Causes of deforestation in Canada today

(c) Land-clearing for agriculture

FIGURE 8.14   In spite of vigorous logging and deforestation during the westward expansion from the 1600s to the early 1900s, much of Canada remains forested today **(a)**. This is in contrast to the United States, where the majority of primary forest had been removed by the late 1800s. Today in Canada the principal causes of deforestation **(b)** are urban development and land clearing for agriculture **(c)**, as seen here in a photo of Quyon, Québec.

THE SCIENCE BEHIND THE STORY

Changing Climate and the Spruce Budworm on Vancouver Island

Spruce budworm larva on a Douglas fir.

As climate changes, ecosystems change too. On southern Vancouver Island, the invasive parasitic western spruce budworm (see photo) is no longer the problem that it once was, as a result of a local increase in sea temperature over the past century that has limited the availability of the pest's food.[11]

Ross Benton and Dr. Alan Thomson, research scientists at Natural Resources Canada's Pacific Forestry Centre in Victoria, have investigated the effects of changing climate at a local level. Their research shows that a 90-year increase in overall winter temperature on southern Vancouver Island has nearly eliminated western spruce budworm outbreaks in the area. "This pest will always be there at a very low level, but its population can't expand," says Benton. "The opportunity for the bug to infest its host, the Douglas fir, is less and less."

Although spruce budworm outbreaks have been known in this area since 1909, it is unlikely to happen again, says Benton. During outbreaks in the first part of the twentieth century, the budworm defoliated a total area of 35 732 ha on southern Vancouver Island. However, the changing climate now means that food isn't available when the budworm larvae hatch. Budworm development is triggered by temperature,

whereas development of Douglas firs is triggered more by light and day length. As a result, the budworm larvae are emerging from their shelters earlier than a century ago, whereas development of Douglas fir buds has remained constant. "The pest is starting to develop earlier and can't bore into the outer sheathing that protects new buds," says Benton. "The food is there, but not accessible," adds Thomson.

Although this may sound like good news, it may not be, according to Dr. Thomson. "Previous problems with budworm outbreaks are gone, but new species that weren't a problem before may become one." He points out that although spruce budworm outbreaks are no longer a problem in this part of the Island, British Columbia's interior forests are experiencing large-scale outbreaks.

Meanwhile, another invasive insect, the mountain pine beetle (see photo), has been one of the highest-profile forestry problems in British Columbia in the past two decades. "Without the mountain pine beetle, the budworm would be big news," says Dr. Thomson. According to the government of British Columbia, by 2011 the pine beetle had affected more than 17.5 million ha of lodgepole pine forest in the province (see photo), killing more than 700 million cubic metres of timber, and the province has invested more than $756 million to fight the infestation.[12] However, the British Columbia Ministry of Forests, Land, and Natural Resources Operations concludes that the infestation of mountain pine beetles, which are killed by cold winters, peaked in 2005 and has declined considerably since then.[13]

Mountain pine beetles have killed millions of cubic metres of timber in British Columbia. Warmer summers and milder winters promote the activity of these invasive beetles.

Agriculture is the major cause of conversion of forests and grasslands

Agriculture now covers more of the planet's surface than does forest. Thirty-eight percent of Earth's terrestrial surface is devoted to agriculture—more than the area of North America and Africa combined. Of this land, 26% supports pasture, and 12% consists of crops and arable land. Agriculture is the most widespread type of human land use and the principal driver of land conversion today, causing tremendous impacts on land and ecosystems (see **FIGURE 8.14B** and **C**). Although agricultural methods such as organic farming and no-till farming can be sustainable, the majority of the world's cropland hosts either intensive traditional agriculture or monocultural industrial agriculture, involving heavy use of fertilizers, pesticides, and irrigation.

In many parts of the developing world, forests are cleared for traditional *swidden* agriculture, in which a small area of forest is cleared (often by *slash-and-burn*), and crops are planted. After one or two seasons of planting, when the soil has been depleted of nutrients, the farmer moves on to clear another patch of forest, leaving the first clearing in a *fallow* or resting state, giving it time to replenish itself. This can be a sustainable practice if the initial clearings are given sufficient time—often as much as 7 years is needed—in which to replenish the nutrient content of the soil. However, social and economic pressures in the developing world, including population pressure, have led to shorter and shorter fallow times, with the result that the cleared forest soils erode away, rather than regenerating. After that, the soil will no longer support either crops or forests.

In theory, the marketplace should discourage people from farming with intensive methods that degrade land they own if such practices are not profitable. But agriculture in many countries (including Canada) is supported by government subsidies, which amount to billions of dollars in some cases. For example, the Brazilian government provides financial incentives to farmers to clear areas of the Amazon rainforest for agriculture. Proponents of agricultural subsidies stress that the vagaries of weather make profits and losses from farming unpredictable from year to year. To persist, these proponents say, an agricultural system needs some way to compensate farmers for bad years. Opponents of subsidies argue that subsidization of environmentally destructive agricultural practices is unsustainable.

Livestock graze one-fourth of Earth's land surface

Most cattle in North America today are raised in feedlots, but they have traditionally been raised by grazing on open **rangelands**, grasslands or wooded areas converted for the purpose of supporting livestock (**FIGURE 8.15**). Grazing can be sustainable, but overgrazing damages soils, waterways, and vegetative communities. Range managers are responsible for regulating ranching on public lands, and they advise ranchers on sustainable grazing practices.

Cropland agriculture uses less than half the land taken up by livestock grazing, which covers a quarter of the world's land surface. Human use of rangeland, however, does not necessarily exclude its use by wildlife or its continued functioning as a grassland ecosystem. Grazing can be sustainable if done carefully and at low intensity. In the West, some ranching proponents claim that cattle are merely taking the place of the vast herds of bison that once roamed the plains. Indeed, most of the world's grasslands have historically been home to large herds of grass-eating mammals, and grasses have adapted to herbivory.

Poorly managed grazing can have adverse impacts on soil and grassland ecosystems. In Central and South America, the conversion of forested land and grasslands to rangelands occurred with phenomenal rapidity during the decades from the 1940s to the 1970s. The dramatic loss of forested land has led a few countries, notably Costa Rica, to institute some tough new environmental restrictions.

Ranchers and environmentalists have traditionally been at loggerheads. In the past several years, however, they have been finding some common ground, teaming up to preserve ranchland against what each of them views

FIGURE 8.15
Livestock grazing, shown here in Alberta, covers a quarter of Earth's land surface.

in common as a threat—the encroaching housing developments of suburban sprawl. Although developers often pay high prices for ranchland, many ranchers do not want to see the loss of the wide-open spaces and the ranching lifestyle that they cherish.

Bad practices and other pressures have led to deforestation

Deforestation has altered the landscapes and ecosystems of much of our planet. Forest resources can, in principle, be harvested sustainably, but unfortunately this hasn't always happened. Impacts are greatest in tropical areas because of the potentially massive loss of biodiversity, and in dryland regions because of the vulnerability of these lands to desertification. In addition, deforestation adds carbon dioxide (CO_2) to the atmosphere: CO_2 is released when plant matter is burned or decomposed, and thereafter less vegetation remains to soak up CO_2. Deforestation is thereby one contributor to global climate change. Deforestation can cause soil degradation and species extinctions, and, as we saw in the case of Easter Island, it has in some cases helped bring whole civilizations to ruin.

Globally, about 13 million ha of forest are deforested each year—equivalent to the area of Nova Scotia and New Brunswick combined. This has been the average yearly rate of deforestation from 2000 to 2011, down from an average of about 16 million ha per year in the 1990s.[14] In Canada, as in some other economically developed nations, reforestation and afforestation have more than offset losses to forested area in the past decade or so, leading to a (small) net increase in forested land.

Today forests are being felled at the fastest rates in the tropical rainforests of Latin America and Africa (FIGURE 8.16). Developing countries in these regions are striving to expand areas of settlement for their burgeoning populations and to boost their economies by extracting natural resources and selling them abroad. Moreover, many people in these societies cut trees for fuelwood for their daily cooking and heating needs. In contrast, areas of Europe and eastern North America are slowly gaining forest cover as they recover from severe deforestation of past decades and centuries. Overall, the world is losing its forests (see "The Science Behind the Story: Surveying Earth's Forests").

Land uses such as grazing, farming, and timber harvesting need not have strongly adverse impacts. It is not these activities themselves that inherently cause environmental problems, but rather the overexploitation of resources beyond what ecosystems can handle. Unfortunately, economic and social pressures, particularly in the developing world, often drive overexploitation and unsustainable practices.

Deforestation is proceeding rapidly in many developing nations

Uncut primary tropical forests still remain in many developing countries. These nations are in the position Canada faced a century or two ago: having a vast frontier that they can develop for human use. Today's advanced technology, however, has allowed these countries to exploit their resources and push back their frontiers even faster than occurred in North America. As a result, deforestation is

FIGURE 8.16
South America and Africa are experiencing rapid deforestation as they develop, extract resources, and clear new agricultural land for growing populations. In Europe, forested area is slowly increasing as some formerly farmed areas are allowed to grow back into forest. The data for North and Central America reflect a balance of forest regrowth in North America and forest loss in Central America. In Asia, natural forests are being lost, but the extensive planting of tree plantations (here counted as forests) in China has increased forest cover for Asia since 2000.
Source: Data from U.N. Food and Agriculture Organization, Global Forest Resources Assessment, 2010.

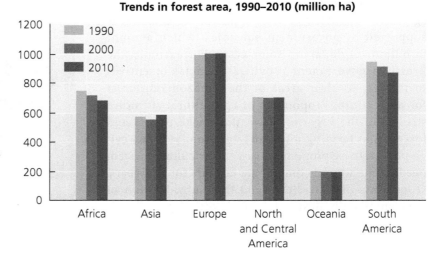

Trends in forest area, 1990–2010 (million ha)

■ 1990
■ 2000
■ 2010

(Africa, Asia, Europe, North and Central America, Oceania, South America)

(a) Logging in Borneo

(b) *Rafflesia arnoldii* in bloom

FIGURE 8.17
Logging, both illegal and legal **(a)**, and associated deforestation are rampant in Borneo, Malaysia. The central habitat of *Rafflesia arnoldii*, the world's largest flower **(b)**, and that of many other important and threatened species, is in Borneo.

extremely rapid in places such as Brazil, Indonesia, and parts of West Africa.

Developing nations are often desperate enough for economic development, and for foreign capital with which to maintain the interest payments on enormous national debt loads, that they impose few or no restrictions on logging. Often their timber is extracted by foreign multinational corporations, which have paid fees to the developing nation's government for a *concession*, or right to extract the resource. In such cases, the foreign corporation has little or no incentive to manage forest resources sustainably. Many of the short-term economic benefits are reaped not by local residents but by the corporations that log the timber and export it elsewhere. Local people may or may not receive temporary employment from the corporation, but once the timber is harvested they no longer have the forest and the ecosystem services it once provided.

In Sarawak, the Malaysian portion of the island of Borneo, foreign corporations that were granted logging concessions have deforested several million hectares of tropical rainforest since 1963 (**FIGURE 8.17A**). The clearing of this forest—one of the world's richest, hosting such organisms as orangutans and the world's largest flower, *Rafflesia arnoldii* (**FIGURE 8.17B**)—has had direct impacts on the 22 tribes of people who live as hunter-gatherers in Sarawak's rainforest. The Malaysian government did not consult the tribes about the logging, which decreased the wild game on which these people depended. Oil palm agriculture was established afterward, leading to pesticide and fertilizer runoff that killed fish in local streams. The tribes protested peacefully and finally began blockading logging roads. The government, which at first jailed them, now is negotiating, but it insists on converting the tribes to a farming way of life.

Forest Management Principles

Professionals who manage forests through the practice of **forestry** (or **silviculture**) must balance the central importance of forests as ecosystems with civilization's demand for wood products. Sustainable forest management, like the management of other renewable natural resources, is based on maintaining equilibrium between *stocks* and *flows*. In principle, the removal or **harvesting** of material from the resource by logging should not occur at a rate that exceeds the capability of the resource to replenish or regenerate itself.

Public forests in Canada are managed for many purposes

Nearly 94% of Canada's forest is publicly owned; the majority of this is under provincial jurisdiction. Only about 6–8% of forested land in Canada is privately owned,

THE SCIENCE BEHIND THE STORY

Surveying Earth's Forests

This old-growth forest is in British Columbia.

In the time it takes you to read this sentence, 2 hectares of tropical forest will have been cleared.

Where do such numbers come from? How do we know how much forest our planet is losing—or how much forest there was to begin with?

Every 5 to 10 years since 1948, the United Nations Food and Agriculture Organization (FAO) has conducted a global inventory of forest resources. FAO researchers ask the world's national governments to respond to provide data on forest area, types of forest, deforestation, regrowth, and other parameters. However, nations may not keep accurate data or may not care to share it.

In recent years, satellite technology has provided a way to confirm information from national surveys. With remote sensing data from satellites, we can measure and map forest cover from space.

Satellites that observe Earth's surface measure wavelengths of energy being emitted. This information is processed and used to infer what materials are on the surface. Plants absorb most wavelengths of light but reflect infrared radiation and green light (which is why plants appear green). When satellite data show green and infrared wavelengths reflected from the surface but an absence of other wavelengths such as red and blue, the presence of vegetation can be inferred.

Researchers use data from a number of satellites (for instance, the Land Remote Sensing Satellite [Landsat], the Advanced Very High Resolution Radiometer [AVHRR], and the Moderate Resolution Imaging Spectroradiometer [MODIS]) to infer vegetative cover. By quantifying plant cover, researchers can compare one site to another and can measure how sites change across seasons or years.

The 2001 study of global forest cover by the United Nations Environment Programme (UNEP) used AVHRR data and loaded this into a geographic information system, or GIS. Researchers then added data on human population distribution, political boundaries, and land protected against development. The study found that forests in densely populated nations such as India and Indonesia were under pressure from expanding human settlement and require urgent conservation efforts.

The global forest inventory is updated on a continuing basis. In 2011, the FAO released its latest global accounting of forests. In the *Global Forest Resources Assessment 2010*, researchers combined remote sensing data, questionnaire responses, analysis from forestry experts, and statistical modeling to form a comprehensive picture of the state of the world's forests, globally, by region, and by individual country.

Major findings of the most recent FAO assessment included the following:

- Forests cover 31% of the world's land area.
- Just 10 nations account for two-thirds of all forests.
- 30% of forests are designated primarily for wood production.
- Forests store 289 billion metric tonnes of carbon in living tissue, and more overall than the atmosphere.
- Some rare tree species valued for wood (such as teak and mahogany) are in danger of vanishing.
- 80% of forests are publicly owned, but private ownership is increasing.
- Forestry directly employs 10 million people.

By comparing the results with those of previous assessments, the FAO could

---

about 1.5% by logging companies, with the remainder under federal or territorial control.[15] An increasing amount of land in Canada, including forested land, is under Aboriginal jurisdiction as land claims are settled.[16]

In Canada, timber is extracted from both privately owned and publicly held forests by private timber companies. In fact, much of the resource extraction industry in Canada—both logging and mining—is carried out on Crown lands (mainly provincial). The provinces and territories and the federal government have different requirements governing the acquisition of rights to carry out resource extraction on Crown lands. Under the Constitution, provinces and territories own and regulate the natural resources within their boundaries.

The federal role in forestry is based on its responsibility for the national economy, trade, science and technology, the environment, and federal Crown lands and parks, as well as Aboriginal and treaty rights, which are constitutionally protected by the federal Constitution Act of 1982.

The Canadian Forest Service, part of Natural Resources Canada, was established in 1899, and given the responsibility to preserve timber on Crown lands and to develop policies to encourage tree culture.[17] Since then, the Canadian Forest Service has been involved in the scientific study and monitoring of Canada's forests and in managing the extraction of timber and non-timber forest products from national forests. The National Forest Strategies began to be offi-

also reveal trends through time. Major findings included the following:

- Globally, we deforest 13 million hectares per year (the annual average from 2000 to 2010). This is down from about 16 million hectares per year in the 1990s.
- Regions vary in rates of forest loss or gain.
- Primary forests are being lost more quickly than second-growth forests.
- Forest plantations make up only 7% of forested land, but are increasing in area.

- Carbon storage by the world's forests decreased by approximately 0.5 Gt per year from 2000 to 2010, primarily because of a decrease in world forested area.

The study examined how our society was progressing toward sustainable management of forests. Researchers examined a number of indicators (see the figure). Among other trends, they found that more forests are being managed for multiple uses and that the use of forests for recreation and education is increasing rapidly. About 12% of forests

are designated for biodiversity conservation, and only 8% for soil and water conservation.[18]

These trends are occurring against a backdrop of continued net loss of forests, especially primary forests. Overall, the report concludes that the outlook is mixed: "There are many good signs and positive trends, but many negative trends remain. While intensive forest plantation and conservation efforts are on the rise, primary forests continue to become degraded or converted to agriculture at alarming rates in some regions."

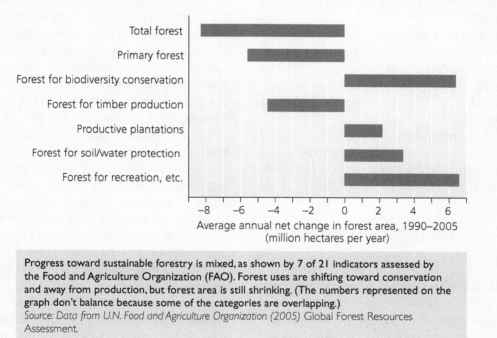

Progress toward sustainable forestry is mixed, as shown by 7 of 21 indicators assessed by the Food and Agriculture Organization (FAO). Forest uses are shifting toward conservation and away from production, but forest area is still shrinking. (The numbers represented on the graph don't balance because some of the categories are overlapping.)
Source: Data from U.N. Food and Agriculture Organization (2005) Global Forest Resources Assessment.

cially developed in 1980. The current National Forest Strategy makes reference to Canada's obligation to the world to maintain and preserve the vast forests of which we are the stewards. The vision statement of this document reads, in part:

The health of the forest is directly linked to environmental processes on local, regional and international scales as well as to the social, cultural, spiritual and economic well-being of us all. As a result, we want to improve our understanding of how we are a part of and how we affect the forest—in short, to act on our increasingly informed understanding to become even better stewards of our forest resource.[19]

For the past half century, forest management throughout North America has nominally been guided by the policy of **multiple use**, meaning that forests were to be managed for recreation, wildlife habitat, mineral extraction, and various other uses. In reality, however, timber production was most often the primary use. In recent decades, increased awareness of the problems associated with logging has prompted many citizens to protest the way public forests are managed in Canada. These citizens have urged that provincial forests be managed for recreation, wildlife, and ecosystem integrity, rather than for timber. They want forests managed as ecologically functional entities, not as cropland for trees.

The National Forest Strategy for 2003–2008 includes the following objectives:

- Implementing ecosystem-based management (as described above)
- Improving the environmental, social, and economic sustainability of forest communities, through legislation and policies
- Recognizing the historical and legal rights of Aboriginal peoples and their fundamental connection to the forest ecosystem
- Stimulating the diversification of markets for forest products, benefits, and services
- Enhancing the skills and knowledge of forest practitioners, to promote innovation for competitiveness and sustainability
- Actively engaging Canadians in sustainability through the planning, maintenance, and management of urban forests
- Strengthening policies and services that support the contribution of private woodlots to forest sustainability
- Creating a comprehensive national forest reporting system that consolidates data, information, and knowledge for all valued features of the forest, both urban and rural.[20]

Today many managers practise ecosystem-based management

Increasing numbers of renewable resource managers today espouse ecosystem-based management. **Ecosystem-based management** attempts to manage the harvesting of resources in ways that minimize impact on the ecosystems and ecological processes of the forest. In Canada, ecosystem-based management aims to preserve forest health, structure, functions, composition, and biodiversity. This has been partly achieved by the establishment, over time, of a system of provincially, federally, and internationally protected areas (discussed below). An additional goal of ecosystem-based forest management is to maintain Canada's forests as viable reservoirs, or *sinks*, for atmospheric carbon.[21] This is crucial for managing carbon emissions in the global effort to control climate change.

As an example, the plan proposed in 1995 by the Scientific Panel for Sustainable Forest Practices on Clayoquot Sound and approved by British Columbia's government was essentially a plan for ecosystem-based management. By carefully managing ecologically important areas such as riparian corridors, by considering patterns at the landscape level, and by affording protection to some forested areas, the plan aimed to allow continued

timber harvesting at reduced levels while preserving the functional integrity of the ecosystem.

Although ecosystem-based management has gained a great deal of support in recent years, it is challenging for managers to determine how best to implement this type of management. Ecosystems are complex, and our understanding of how they operate is limited. Thus, ecosystem-based management has often come to mean different things to different people.

Adaptive management evolves and improves

Some management actions will succeed, and some will fail. A wise manager will try new approaches if old ones are not effective. **Adaptive management** involves systematically testing different management approaches and aiming to improve methods as time goes on. It entails monitoring the results of one's practices and continually adjusting them as needed, based on what is learned. This approach is intended as a fusion and partnership of science and management because hypotheses about how best to manage resources are explicitly tested and the results of the testing used to modify management approaches. Adaptive management can be time-consuming and complicated, however. It has posed a challenge for many managers because those who adopt new approaches must often overcome inertia and resistance to change from proponents of established practices.

Adaptive management has become a guiding principle for forest management in Canada. In British Columbia the Ministry of Forests and Range has embraced adaptive management, promoting the approach through collaborative projects that range from testing alternative forestry practices, to monitoring whole watersheds, to evaluating the effectiveness of various land and resource management strategies.[22] The following are some examples of adaptive management projects that have been undertaken in British Columbia forests:

- The West Arm Demonstration Forest Experiments, which were designed to study a broad range of forest values and to evaluate the effectiveness and impacts of several new forest management approaches
- The Donna Creek Biodiversity Project, which tested whether maintenance of tall stumps and small residual tree islands benefits cavity-using animals within clear-cuts
- The Grizzly Bear Habitat Project, which was designed to assist in the development of forestry management systems to maintain grizzly habitat, while at the same time producing timber[23]

Fire is a natural phenomenon in forests

Ecological research shows that many ecosystems depend on fire, particularly in the boreal forest. Certain plants such as jack pines have seeds that germinate only in response to fire. This makes evolutionary sense; when a seedling grows after a fire, there are no big trees to take the light from it, and it can benefit from nutrients contained in the ash of the burnt forest. Researchers studying tree rings have documented that many ecosystems historically experienced frequent fires. Burn marks in tree rings reveal past fires, giving scientists an accurate history of fire events extending back hundreds or even thousands of years. Many wooded dryland ecosystems also depend on fire. For example, researchers have found that North America's grasslands and open pine woodlands burn regularly in the natural system.

Ecosystems dependent on fire are adversely affected by its suppression; pine woodlands become cluttered with hardwood understory that ordinarily would be cleared away by fire, for instance, and animal diversity and abundance decline.

Fires depend on the triad of oxygen, heat, and fuel to progress. In the forest context, branches, fallen logs, sticks, and leaf litter accumulate on the forest floor, producing kindling and fuel for future fires. Climate and weather are crucial components. An overall dry climate or unusually dry weather can contribute to dry litter and upper soil layers in which organic matter can be easily ignited. This leads to *ground fires* (FIGURE 8.18A), in which the litter layer itself burns, as opposed to *crown fires*, in which the upper tree canopy is ignited (FIGURE 8.18B). Storms also bring winds that can fan fires. Topography is another important component of forest fires. A fire burning up the slope of a canyon (FIGURE 8.18C) can be particularly challenging to contain. Winds blowing up the hillslope can fan the fire, whereas the heat from below ignites dry fuel on upslope areas. Lightning is responsible for igniting the majority of naturally induced forest fires. (Other causes of forest fires are volcanic eruptions and, of course, human carelessness.)

Fire policy has stirred controversy

The management of fires is one of the most controversial aspects of forest management today. For over a century, land management agencies throughout North America have suppressed fire whenever and wherever it breaks out (as per the warnings of "Smokey the Bear": "Only *you* can prevent forest fires!").

In the long term, fire suppression can lead to a buildup of dead wood; this can fuel catastrophic fires that truly damage forests, destroy human property, and threaten human lives. Fuel buildup helped cause the 1988 fires

(a) Ground fire

(b) Crown fire

(c) Slope fire

FIGURE 8.18
Fires need fuel, oxygen, and a heat source. The buildup of dry litter and organic matter in soil layers can lead to ground fires **(a)**, in which the litter layer itself burns. Fires that move into the top part of the canopy **(b)** are called crown fires. Fires can move very quickly up slopes **(c)**, fanned by wind and fuelled by heat from below.

FIGURE 8.19
Forest fires are natural phenomena to which many plants are adapted and which maintain many ecosystems. However, climate change combined with the suppression of fire over the past century has led to a buildup of dry litter and woody debris, which serve as fuel to increase the severity and frequency of fires. As a result, catastrophic wildfires have become more common in recent years. Shown here, a devastating forest fire ripped through Slave Lake, Alberta, in May 2011, destroying much of the town.

in Yellowstone National Park, the 2003 fires in southern California, the 2003 fires in British Columbia, and thousands of other wildfires across the continent each year (FIGURE 8.19). Fire suppression and fuel buildup have made catastrophic fires significantly greater problems than they were in the past. Now, global climate change is bringing drier weather to much of the Canadian Prairies, further worsening the wildfire risk. At the same time, increasing residential development on the edges of forested land is placing more homes in fire-prone situations.

To reduce fuel load and improve the health and safety of forests, forest management agencies have in recent years been burning areas of forest under carefully controlled conditions. These **prescribed burns**, or **controlled burns**, have worked effectively, but they have been implemented on only a relatively small amount of land.

weighing the issues

HOW TO HANDLE FIRE?

A century of fire suppression has left vast swaths of forested lands in North America in danger of catastrophic wildfires. Yet we will probably never have adequate resources to conduct careful prescribed burning over all these lands. Can you suggest any solutions to help protect people's homes near forests while improving the ecological condition of some forested lands? Do you think people should be allowed to develop homes in fire-prone areas?

Another significant and controversial aspect of fire management concerns what happens after a fire, which may include the physical removal of small trees, underbrush, and dead trees by timber companies. The removal of dead trees, or snags, following a natural disturbance is called **salvage logging**. From an economic standpoint, salvage logging may seem to make good sense. Proponents of salvage logging argue that forests regenerate best after a fire if they are logged and replanted with seedlings. Moreover, they maintain, salvage logging reduces future fire risk by removing woody debris that could serve as fuel for the next fire. However, snags have immense ecological value; the insects that decay them provide food for wildlife, and many birds, mammals, and reptiles depend on holes in snags for nesting and roosting sites. Removing timber from recently burned land can also cause severe erosion, collapse of streambanks, and soil damage.

Sustainable forestry is gaining ground

Any company can claim that its timber harvesting practices are sustainable, but how is the purchaser of wood products to know whether they really are? In the last several years, a consumer movement has grown that is making informed consumer choice possible. Several organizations now examine the practices of timber companies and offer **sustainable forestry certification** to products produced using methods they consider sustainable (FIGURE 8.20).

FIGURE 8.20
A Brazilian woodcutter taking inventory marks timber harvested from a forest certified for sustainable management in Amazonian Brazil. A consumer movement centred on independent certification of sustainable wood products is allowing consumer choice to promote sustainable forestry practices.

CANADIAN ENVIRONMENTAL PERSPECTIVES

Tzeporah Berman

Thinking About Environmental Perspectives

- **Co-founder** of the environmental nonprofit organization **ForestEthics**
- **Anti-logging activist**
- **Market campaigner** and **"corporate re-educator"**

In the spring of 1992, 22-year-old Tzeporah Berman returned to Vancouver Island to continue her university field-work studying marbled murrelet nests. But she could not find the nesting area. The approach to the site had been logged, and with the landmarks obliterated, she could not get her bearings. Gradually, the reality dawned: this *was* the nesting site. She found a ring of stumps that had been the 70-metre-high Sitka spruce trees under which she had camped. She found a trickle of water that had been a waterfall and pool where she had swum. Eagles wheeled overhead, surveying their fallen nests.

Sitting on a stump, in tears, Berman reconsidered her summer and her future.

She had planned to finish environmental studies and then go into law. But by the time she did that, she decided, there would be no marbled murrelets left. The next day, a van stopped on its way to a blockade in Clayoquot Sound. Berman climbed in.[24]

The rest, as they say, is history. Berman was right in the midst of the historic protests at Clayoquot Sound, described in the Central Case. Eventually she was arrested and dragged into court for "aiding and abetting" the commission of hundreds of criminal acts by the thousands of other Clayoquot protestors (the charges were dropped). She became a figurehead for the cause—sometimes hugged and sometimes attacked in public, she experienced death threats and even had her apartment burned by an unknown arsonist. The reference to "enemies of the state" made by the premier of British Columbia was aimed at Berman and her associates.

Working for Greenpeace, Berman began her transformation into "corporate re-educator" while helping to organize a huge (and very successful) public boycott against logging company MacMillan-Bloedel. The boycott, or "market campaign," focused specifically on MacMillan-Bloedel's customers. Did Pacific Bell know, they would ask, that their phone books were made from the ancient rainforest of Clayoquot Sound? Surely the company would be alarmed at this, and if they weren't, certainly Pacific Bell's customers would be. Alarmed, Pacific Bell called MacMillan-Bloedel; so did Scott Paper and the *New York Times*.[25] As the tide began to turn, Berman realized that money and the wishes of customers could be leveraged to convince large corpora-

tions that having environmentally responsible policies is not only the *right* thing to do, but also the most *financially sound* thing to do.

Today ForestEthics, the nonprofit group that Berman and others founded in 1994, collaborates with some of the same corporations they previously boycotted. Through its Corporate Action Program, ForestEthics has turned "corporate adversaries into allies."[26] It works with companies such as The Home Depot, Dell, Victoria's Secret, Estée Lauder, and Staples (the largest paper retailer in the world) to develop strong, financially sound, cutting-edge corporate environmental policies. By some accounts, Berman's actions and her work through ForestEthics have saved as many as 5 million hectares of forest from destruction in Canada and elsewhere in the world.

"The influence of the marketplace is integral to protecting the key areas of the natural forest that are left. Economic prosperity in the long term is tied to ecological prosperity now."[27]—**Tzeporah Berman**

Thinking About Environmental Perspectives

Tzeporah Berman and her colleagues used the threat of public dissatisfaction and boycotts to convince large corporations to adopt responsible policies regarding logging and product sources. Can you think of other cases where large, multinational corporations have been convinced to change their policies because of environmental or social justice concerns and campaigns on the part of their customers?

Organizations such as the International Organization for Standardization (ISO), the Sustainable Forestry Initiative (SFI) program, and the Forest Stewardship Council (FSC) have varying standards for certification. Consumers can look for the logos of these organizations on forest products they purchase. The FSC is widely perceived to have the strictest certification standards. In 2001, Iisaak, the Native-run timber company at Clayoquot

Sound, became the first tree farm license holder in British Columbia to receive FSC certification.

Consumer demand for sustainable wood has been great enough that The Home Depot and other major retail businesses have begun selling sustainable wood. The decisions of such retailers are influencing the logging practices of many timber companies. In British Columbia, 70% of the province's annual harvest now is certified or meets ISO requirements. Sustainable forestry is more costly for the timber industry, but if certification standards can be kept adequately strong, then consumer choice in the marketplace can be a powerful driver for good forestry practices for the future.

Conclusion

Forests and other terrestrial biomes provide crucial ecosystem services, supporting a vast diversity of species and providing goods that have economic value to humans as well. Managing natural resources sustainably is particularly important for resources such as timber and soil, which otherwise can be carelessly exploited, degraded, or overharvested. Canada and many other nations have established various federal and regional agencies to oversee and manage publicly held land and the natural resources that are extracted from public land. Historically, forest management in North America has reflected general trends in land and resource management. Early emphasis on resource extraction evolved into policies on sustained yield and multiple use, a shift that occurred as land and resource availability declined and as the public became more aware of environmental degradation.

Public forests today are managed not only for timber production, but also for recreation, wildlife habitat, and ecosystem integrity. Meanwhile, support for the preservation of natural lands has resulted in parks, wilderness areas, and other reserves, both in North America and abroad. These trends are positive ones because the preservation and conservation of land and resources are essential if we wish our society to be sustainable and to thrive in the future.

REVIEWING OBJECTIVES

You should now be able to:

Describe the basic functional processes of trees and their role in biogeochemical cycling

- Trees have the same basic requirements as other plants: sunlight, water, nutrients, air, and an amenable temperature.
- Trees function as a link between the biogeochemical cycles of the atmosphere, hydrosphere, biosphere, and geosphere.

Summarize the principal types of forest biomes, especially those indigenous to Canada

- About 30% of Earth's land surface is covered by forest—land with significant tree cover. Canada is a steward for much of this.
- There are three main sets of forest biomes: northern or boreal forests; temperate forests; and tropical forests.
- Canada's north is dominated by coniferous boreal forest. The west is characterized by subalpine, montane, and coastal forest types, and the east by temperate deciduous forests. The central Prairies are characterized by more-open woodland and grassland ecosystems.

Describe the ecological roles and economic contributions of forests

- Forests provide habitat and support biodiversity.
- Forests contribute ecosystem services that are of great value to people, including protection of soils, moderation of the climate system and the hydrologic cycle, carbon storage, and oxygen cycling.

- Forests provide us economically important timber, as well as a wide variety of nontimber forest products such as fruit, nuts, honey, rubber, and many others.

Trace the history and scale of forest loss and identify the current drivers of deforestation

- Forests have been cleared since the beginnings of human civilization, for a wide variety of reasons.
- Developed nations deforested much of their land during the process of settlement, farming, and industrialization.
- Agriculture has contributed greatly to deforestation and has had enormous impacts on landscapes and ecosystems worldwide.
- Today deforestation is taking place most rapidly in developing nations, driven by proximate factors such as logging and pest infestations and by root factors that are largely economic or political.

Outline the major methods of harvesting timber

- Harvesting methods for timber include clear-cutting and other even-aged techniques, as well as selection strategies that maintain uneven-aged stands that more closely resemble natural forest.
- Harvesting timber and other forest products can be sustainable as long as the principle of maximum sustainable harvest is maintained, so the stock does not become depleted.
- Certification of sustainable forest products allows consumer choice in the marketplace to influence forestry techniques.

Explain the fundamentals of forest management, including approaches to fire management, and identify forest management agencies in Canada and internationally

- Forest managers increasingly focus not only on extraction of forest products, but also on sustaining the ecological systems that make resources available.
- Forest managers are beginning to implement ecosystem-based management and adaptive management.

- Fire policy has been politically controversial, but scientists agree that we need to address the impacts of a century of fire suppression.
- The Canadian Forest Service, Parks Canada, Canadian Wildlife Service, and Environment Canada each play a role in managing Canada's forests at the federal level. Agriculture and Agri-Foods Canada oversees the management of rangelands. The United Nations Food and Agriculture Organization monitors the status of the world's forests.

TESTING YOUR COMPREHENSION

1. Where do trees acquire the nitrogen that they need? What about the carbon?
2. How does water move through trees, and why is water important for tree survival?
3. What is a forest, and how does a forest differ from a woodland or savannah?
4. How do minerals differ from timber when it comes to resource management?
5. Compare and contrast maximum sustainable yield, adaptive management, and ecosystem-based management. Why would pursuing maximum sustainable yield sometimes conflict with what is ecologically desirable?

6. Name several major causes of deforestation. Where is deforestation most severe today?
7. Compare and contrast the major methods of timber harvesting.
8. Describe several ecological effects of logging. How has the Canadian Forest Service responded to public concern over the ecological effects of logging?
9. Are forest fires a bad thing? Explain your answer.
10. What are some of the organizations—both governmental and non-governmental—that are important in forest management today, both in Canada and internationally? Name three and briefly describe their roles.

THINKING IT THROUGH

1. Do you think maximum sustainable yield represents an appropriate policy for resource managers to follow? Why or why not?
2. People in developed countries are fond of warning people in developing countries to stop destroying the rainforest. People in developing countries often respond that this is hypocritical because the developed nations became wealthy by deforesting their land and exploiting its resources in the past. What would you say to the president of a developing nation, such as Brazil, that is seeking to clear much of its forest?
3. Can you think of a land use conflict, similar to what occurred at Clayoquot Sound, but closer to your home? How was it resolved? If it is unresolved, then how could it be resolved?
4. Your town is proposing a development that would cut through a large forested area. The size of the forested

area would not be substantially reduced, but it would be cut into several smaller pieces by road. Explain to the town council the difference between core and edge habitat and why they should reconsider the development.
5. You have just become the supervisor of a national forest. Timber companies are requesting to cut as many trees as you will let them, and environmentalists want no logging at all. Ten percent of your forest is old-growth primary forest, and the remaining 90% is secondary forest. Your forest managers are split among preferring maximum sustainable yield, ecosystem-based management, and adaptive management. What management approach(es) will you take? Will you allow logging of all, none, or some old-growth trees? Will you allow logging of secondary forest? If so, what harvesting strategies will you encourage? What would you ask your scientists

before deciding on policies on fire management and salvage logging?

6. You have just been elected mayor of a town on Clayoquot Sound. A timber company that employs 20% of your town's residents wants to log a hillside above the town, and the provincial government is supportive of the harvest. But owners of ecotourism businesses that run whale-watching excursions and rent kayaks to out-of-town visitors are complaining that the logging would destroy the area's esthetic appeal and devastate their businesses—and these businesses provide 40% of the tax base for your town. Greenpeace is organizing a demonstration in your town soon, and news reporters are beginning to call your office, asking what you will do. How will you proceed?

INTERPRETING GRAPHS AND DATA

The invention of the movable-type printing press by Johannes Gutenberg in 1450 stimulated a demand for paper that has only increased as the world population has grown.

The twentieth-century invention of the xerographic printing process used in photocopiers and laser printers has accelerated our demand for paper, with most raw fibre for paper production coming from wood pulp from forest trees.

1. How many millions of tonnes of paper and paperboard were consumed worldwide in 1970? 1980? 1990? 2000?

2. By what percentage did worldwide consumption of paper and paperboard increase from 1970 to 1980? From 1980 to 1990? From 1990 to 2000?

3. Name three steps that your campus could take to reduce its paper consumption.

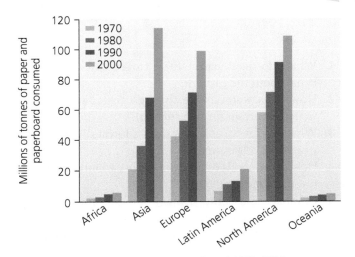

Global consumption of paper and paperboard, 1970–2000.
Source: Data from the Food and Agriculture Organization of the United Nations.

CHAPTER ENDNOTES

1. *Friends of Clayoquot Sound Newsletter* (Fall 2007–Winter 2008).

2. Food and Agriculture Organization of the United Nations (2011) *Global Forest Resources Assessment 2010*. www.fao.org/docrep/013/i1757e/i1757e.pdf

3. Food and Agriculture Organization of the United Nations (2011) *Global Forest Resources Assessment 2010: Canada Country Report (2009)*. www.fao.org/docrep/013/al472E/al472e.pdf

4. Canadian Council of Forest Ministers (2008) *A Vision for Canada's Forests: 2008 and Beyond*. www.ccfm.org/pdf/Vision_EN.pdf

5. National Forest Strategy 2003–2008: *A Sustainable Forest: The Canadian Commitment*. National Forest Strategy Steering Committee. http://nfsc.forest.ca/strategies/strategy5.html

6. Food and Agriculture Organization of the United Nations. (2010). *Global Forest Resources Assessment 2010: Canada Country Report (2009)*. www.fao.org/docrep/013/al472E/al472e.pdf (Primary forests are defined by the FAO as forests of native species in which there are no clearly visible indications of human activity and ecological processes are not significantly disturbed.)

7. Canadian Boreal Institute, Boreal Leadership Council, www.borealcanada.ca

8. Armson, K., Knowledge of the Environment for Youth (KEY) Environmental Literacy Series, The KEY Foundation (1999) *Canadian Forests: A Primer*.

9. Food and Agriculture Organization of the United Nations (2010) *Global Forest Resources Assessment 2010*. www.fao.org/docrep/013/i1757e/i1757e.pdf

10. Food and Agriculture Organization of the United Nations (2010) *Global Forest Resources Assessment 2010*. www.fao.org/docrep/013/i1757e/i1757e.pdf

11. Turner, J. (2008) Changing climate stops pest outbreaks on Vancouver Island. Forest NewsTips. http://cfs.nrcan.gc.ca/news/585

12. Government of British Columbia (April 15, 2011) News release. www2.news.gov.bc.ca/news_releases_2009-2013/2011JTI0056-000378.htm

13. Government of British Columbia (2011) Mountain pine beetle facts. www.for.gov.bc.ca/hfp/mountain_pine_beetle/facts.htm

14. Food and Agriculture Organization of the United Nations (2010) *Global Forest Resources Assessment 2010*. www.fao.org/docrep/013/i1757e/i1757e.pdf

15. Canada's National Forest Inventory, 2001; Canadian Forest Service, http://nfi.cfs.nrcan.gc.ca/canfi/facts_e.html

16. National Forest Strategy 2003–2008: *A Sustainable Forest: The Canadian Commitment*. National Forest Strategy Steering Committee. http://nfsc.forest.ca/strategies/strategy5.html

17. NRCAN, Canadian Forest Service. *About the Canadian Forest Service: Our History*. http://cfs.nrcan.gc.ca/aboutus/organization/3

18. Food and Agriculture Organization of the United Nations (2010) *Global Forest Resources Assessment 2010*. www.fao.org/docrep/013/i1757e/i1757e.pdf

19. National Forest Strategy 2003–2008: *A Sustainable Forest: The Canadian Commitment*. National Forest Strategy Steering Committee. http://nfsc.forest.ca/strategies/strategy5.html

20. National Forest Strategy 2003–2008: *A Sustainable Forest: The Canadian Commitment*. National Forest Strategy Steering Committee. http://nfsc.forest.ca/strategies/strategy5.html

21. National Forest Strategy 2003–2008: *A Sustainable Forest: The Canadian Commitment*. National Forest Strategy Steering Committee. http://nfsc.forest.ca/strategies/strategy5.html

22. British Columbia, Ministry of Forestry and Range, Forest Practices Branch. Adaptive Management Initiatives in the BC Forest Service. www.for.gov.bc.ca/hfp/amhome/amhome.htm

23. British Columbia, Forest Services Branch, Ministry of Forestry and Range. www.for.gov.bc.ca/hfp/amhome/canadaprojects.htm

24. These two paragraphs are directly quoted from *The Clayoquot Women* by Bob Bossin. www3.telus.net/oldfolk/women.htm

25. The preceding three sentences are quoted directly from *The Clayoquot Women* by Bob Bossin. www3.telus.net/oldfolk/women.htm

26. ForestEthics. *About ForestEthics*. http://forestethics.org/article.php?list=type&type=9

27. As quoted by Julia Dault, *Enviro Heroes: Tzeporah Berman*. Green Living Online. www.greenlivingonline.com/EnviroHeroes/enviro-heroes-tzeporah-berman

MyEnvironmentPlace

Go to **www.myenvironmentplace.ca** where you will find quizzes, animations, your Pearson eText, and more.

Freshwater Systems and Water Resources

9

Canada has abundant fresh water, but much of it is at risk. This waterfall is in La Mauricie National Park, Québec.

Upon successfully completing this chapter, you will be able to

- Explain the importance of water and the hydrologic cycle to ecosystems, human health, and economic pursuits
- Delineate the distribution of fresh water on Earth
- Describe major types of freshwater ecosystems
- Discuss how we use water and alter freshwater systems

- Assess problems of water supply and propose solutions to address depletion of fresh water
- Assess problems of water quality and propose solutions to address water pollution
- Explain how waste water is treated

Hudson Bay

CANADA

Great Lakes

UNITED STATES

CENTRAL CASE:
TURNING THE TAP: THE PROSPECT OF CANADIAN BULK WATER EXPORTS

"Water promises to be to the twenty-first century what oil was to the twentieth century: the precious commodity that determines the wealth of nations."
—*FORTUNE MAGAZINE*, MAY 2000

"The wars of the twenty-first century will be fought over water."
—WORLD WATER COMMISSION CHAIRMAN ISMAIL SERAGELDIN

"I predict that the United States will be coming after our fresh water aggressively within three to five years. I hope that when the day comes, Canada will be ready."
—PETER LOUGHEED, FORMER PREMIER OF ALBERTA

There are few topics more emotional or more controversial for Canadians than the subject of fresh water. Some argue that water is our legacy, our natural capital, and that its abundance defines us as Canadians. They fear that we will place our sovereignty at risk if we allow large-scale diversions of fresh water, or bulk water exports, from Canadian water bodies. Once bulk water exports are allowed to begin flowing to the thirsty southwestern United States, they maintain, they will be impossible to stop.

For others, access to fresh water is a fundamental human right. They argue that those who possess it in abundance have the moral duty to provide water to those who lack it. As the stewards of 25% of the world's wetlands, 7% of the world's renewable flowing water, and 18% of the world's surface fresh water (mainly in the Great Lakes),[1] Canada truly has abundant resources to manage.

For some, water is a valuable, marketable commodity, which Canadians possess in surplus, and for which prices will continue to increase in the coming decades. Canada could be in an enviable position of economic and strategic strength in a world water market.

Others maintain that we should not even consider exporting our water to serve those who have mistreated, mismanaged, and depleted their own water supplies. Transporting large quantities of water from Canadian water bodies would cause massive changes, perhaps even permanent damage, to our natural ecosystems. And to what end, if those who would import our water have such a poor track record in appropriately managing this precious resource?

For example, desert areas of the southwestern United States are home to the enormous and rapidly increasing populations of cities like Los Angeles, Phoenix, and Las Vegas. The Imperial Valley of California—a natural desert (the sand dune scenes from *Star Wars: Return of the Jedi* were filmed there)—is one of the most fertile agricultural areas in the world, turning out water-intensive fruits like strawberries all winter. This is possible only because vast quantities of water are transported to the area from the Colorado River, via the 132-km All-American Canal. These deserts could never, under natural circumstances, sustainably support such large populations and water-dependent human activities.

Finally, there are those who reason that the very thirsty states of the American Southwest will be coming for our water before long anyway and that perhaps we would be wise to sell it to them before they contemplate taking it by force.

As an environmental issue and a political issue it is confusing, complicated, and controversial, but it is crucially important for us as humans, as Canadians, and as citizens of North America and the world. Canada possesses some of the most enviable water resources in the world, but we also are some of the most wasteful users of water; per capita daily use of water in Canada (about 343 L/day) is surpassed only by the United States.

Water is already exported to the United States from Canada. The 66 bottlers of water in Canada produced more than 2.3 billion litres of bottled water in 2006; more than a third of it was exported, mostly to the United States.[2] Significant *interbasin transfers*—the transportation of water from one drainage basin to another—already occur between Canada and the United States. Most of this—about 97% of the volume—is for electrical power production.[3]

However, Canada has not yet approved the wholesale bulk export or massive diversion of water to the United States. The North American Free Trade Agreement (NAFTA) identifies water as a marketable and tradable commodity, which effectively means that Canada is prohibited from restricting water for use exclusively within its national boundaries. Interestingly, Simon Reisman, Canada's chief trade negotiator for NAFTA, was a director of the GRAND Canal Company, a private-sector proponent of bulk water diversion.[4] The "GRAND" (Great Recycling and Northern Development) Canal scheme would involve damming James Bay and diverting the 20 rivers that flow into it toward the south. Another large-scale bulk water export plan, NAWAPA (North American Water and Power Alliance), would divert the Yukon, Peace, and Liard rivers through an 800-km-long canal running along the Rocky Mountain Trench and into the United States.

For the moment, Canada's fresh water is protected against bulk exports by a watershed-based approach in which each province and territory individually prohibits bulk water exports under the *International Boundary Waters Treaty Act*. Because Canada's position on bulk water exports has been relatively firm, some American companies are eyeing the significant water resources in Alaska as an alternative source.

This discussion is ongoing, and it will continue in the coming decades. What is **your** position on bulk water exports? You may be called upon, before too long, to decide.

Freshwater Systems

"Water, water, everywhere, nor any drop to drink." The well-known line from Coleridge's poem *The Rime of the Ancient Mariner* describes the situation on our planet quite well. Water may seem abundant to us, but water that we can drink is actually quite rare and limited (FIGURE 9.1). Roughly 97.5% of Earth's water resides in the oceans and is too salty to drink or use to water crops. Only 2.5% is considered **fresh water**, water that is relatively pure, with few dissolved salts. Because most fresh water is tied up in glaciers, icecaps, and underground aquifers, just over 1 part in 10 000 of Earth's water is easily accessible for human use.

Water is constantly moving among the reservoirs specified in FIGURE 9.1 via the hydrologic cycle. As water moves, it redistributes heat, erodes mountain ranges, builds river deltas, maintains organisms and ecosystems, shapes civilizations, and gives rise to political conflicts. Let us first examine the portions of the hydrologic cycle that are most conspicuous to us—surface water bodies—and take stock of the ecological systems they support.

Rivers and streams wind through landscapes

Water from rain, snowmelt, or springs runs downhill and converges where the land dips lowest, forming streams,

roots

WATER

The word *water* was used in its present-day spelling by English poet Geoffrey Chaucer in the 1300s. Prior to that, it was spelled *wæter* in Old English. The origin was probably the Proto-Indo-European word *wodōr*. Among the many relatives of this word are the Greek *húdōr* (from which is derived the English prefix *hydro-*), the Latin *unda* (meaning "wave"), and the Gaelic *uisge* (from which is derived the English word *whiskey*).

creeks, or brooks. These watercourses merge into rivers, whose water eventually reaches the ocean (or sometimes ends in a landlocked water body). A smaller river flowing into a larger one is a **tributary**, and the area of land drained by a river and all its tributaries is that river's **drainage basin** or **watershed**.

Rivers shape the landscape through which they run. The force of water rounding a river's bend gradually eats away at the outer shore, eroding soil from the bank. Meanwhile, sediment is deposited along the inside of the bend, where water currents are weaker. In this way, over time, river bends become exaggerated in shape (FIGURE 9.2). Eventually, a bend may become such an extreme

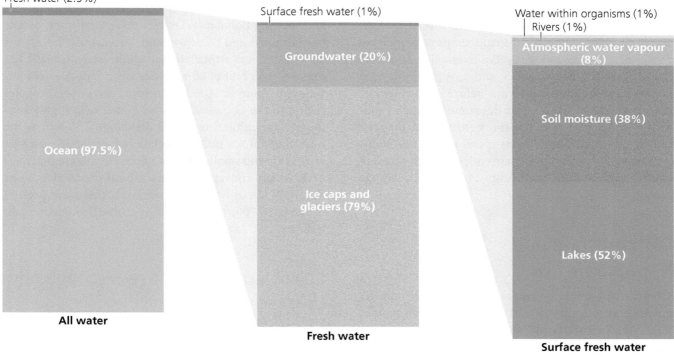

FIGURE 9.1   The world ocean is by far the largest reservoir in the hydrosphere, and it is a saltwater reservoir. Only 2.5% of Earth's water is fresh water. Of that 2.5%, most is tied up in glaciers and ice caps. Of the 1% that is surface water, most is in lakes and soil moisture. Data from United Nations Environment Programme (UNEP) and World Resources Institute.

FIGURE 9.2
Rivers and streams flow downhill, shaping landscapes, as shown by an oxbow of this meandering river in Alberta.

FIGURE 9.3
Shallow, ephemeral or seasonal water bodies with ample vegetation are called wetlands and include swamps, bogs, and marshes, such as this one in Botswana, Africa.

loop (called an *oxbow*) that water erodes a shortcut from one end of the loop to the other, pursuing a direct course. The bend is cut off and remains as an isolated U-shaped water body called an *oxbow lake*.

Over thousands or millions of years, a river may shift from one course to another, back and forth over a large area, carving out a flat valley. Areas nearest a river's course that are flooded periodically are said to be within the river's **floodplain**. Frequent deposition of silt from flooding makes floodplain soils especially fertile. As a result, agriculture thrives in floodplains, and **riparian** (riverside) forests are productive and species-rich.

The water of rivers and streams hosts diverse ecological communities. Algae and detritus support many types of invertebrates, from water beetles to crayfish. Insects as diverse as dragonflies, mayflies, and mosquitoes develop as larvae in streams and rivers before maturing into adults that take to the air. Fish consume aquatic insects, and birds, such as kingfishers, herons, and ospreys, dine on fish. Many amphibians spend their larval stages in streams, and some live their entire lives in streams. Salmon migrate from oceans up rivers and streams to spawn.

Wetlands include marshes, swamps, and bogs

Systems that combine elements of fresh water and dry land are enormously rich and productive. Often lumped under the term **wetlands**, such areas include different types of systems. In freshwater **marshes** (**FIGURE 9.3**), shallow water allows plants to grow above the water's surface. Cattails and bulrushes are plants typical of North American marshes. **Swamps** also consist of shallow water

rich in vegetation, but they occur in forested areas. The cypress swamps of the southeastern United States, where cypress trees grow in standing water, are an example. Swamps are also created when beavers build dams across streams with limbs from trees they have cut, flooding wooded areas upstream. **Bogs** are ponds thoroughly covered with thick floating mats of vegetation and can represent a stage in aquatic succession; an example is the Mer Bleue Bog in Ontario.

Wetlands are extremely valuable as habitat for wildlife. They also provide important ecosystem services by slowing runoff, reducing flooding, recharging aquifers, and filtering pollutants. Despite these vital roles, people have drained and filled wetlands extensively, largely for agriculture. It is estimated that southeastern Canada has lost well over half of all wetlands since European colonization, with up to 90% loss in some areas. The Potholes region of the Canadian Prairies is the most highly productive agricultural region of the country, as well as the host of about 4.5 million hectares of wetlands. The vast grasslands and small wetlands of the Potholes region have been widely converted to agricultural production, such that only about half of the wetlands that were present in the late 1700s (prior to European settlement) remain today.[5]

Lakes and ponds are ecologically diverse systems

Lakes and ponds are bodies of open standing water. Their physical conditions and the types of life within them vary with depth and the distance from shore. As a result, scientists have described several zones typical of lakes and ponds (**FIGURE 9.4**).

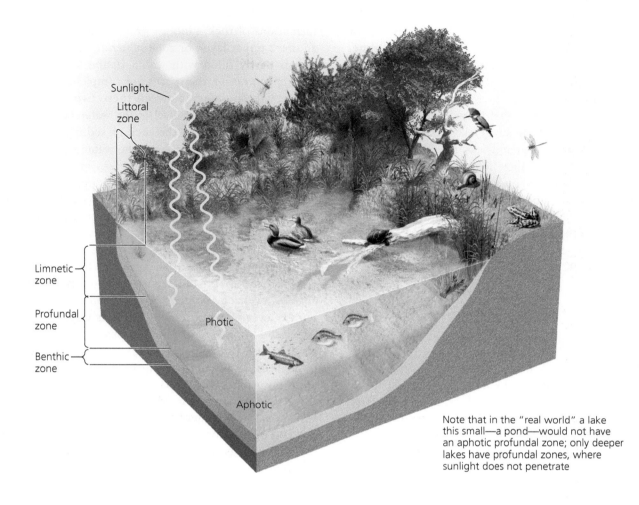

Sunlight

Littoral zone

Limnetic zone

Profundal zone

Benthic zone

Photic

Aphotic

Note that in the "real world" a lake this small—a pond—would not have an aphotic profundal zone; only deeper lakes have profundal zones, where sunlight does not penetrate

FIGURE 9.4   In lakes and ponds, emergent plants grow around the shoreline in the littoral zone. The limnetic zone is the layer of open, sunlit water, where photosynthesis takes place. Sunlight does not reach the deeper profundal (aphotic) zone. The benthic zone, which is the bottom of the water body, often is muddy, rich in detritus and nutrients, and low in oxygen.

The region ringing the edge of a water body is named the **littoral zone**. Here the water is shallow enough that aquatic plants grow from the mud and reach above the water's surface. The nutrients and productive plant growth of the littoral zone make it rich in invertebrates—such as insect larvae, snails, and crayfish—on which fish, birds, turtles, and amphibians feed. The **benthic zone** extends along the bottom of the entire water body, from shore to the deepest point. Many invertebrates live in the mud on the bottom, feeding on detritus or preying on one another.

In the open portion of a lake or pond, away from shore, sunlight penetrates the shallow waters of the **limnetic zone**. Because light in the *photic* zone enables photosynthesis and plant growth, the limnetic zone supports phytoplankton, which in turn support zooplankton, both of which are eaten by fish. Within the limnetic zone, sunlight intensity (and therefore water temperature) decreases with depth. The water's turbidity affects

the depth of this zone; water that is clear allows sunlight to penetrate deeply, whereas turbid water does not. Below the limnetic zone is the **profundal zone**, the volume of open water that is in the *aphotic zone*, that is, the depth below which sunlight does not reach. This zone lacks plant life and thus is lower in dissolved oxygen and supports fewer animals. Aquatic animals rely on dissolved oxygen, and its concentration depends on the amount released by photosynthesis and the amount removed by animal and microbial respiration, among other factors. Note that the profundal zone is, by definition, aphotic, whereas the benthic zone may be photic or aphotic; "benthic" simply refers to "the bottom" of the water body, which may or may not be shallow enough for light to penetrate.

Ponds and lakes change over time naturally as streams and runoff bring them sediment and nutrients. **Oligotrophic** lakes and ponds, which have low-nutrient and high-oxygen conditions, may slowly give way to the high-nutrient, low-oxygen conditions of **eutrophic** water bodies (jump ahead to see FIGURE 9.20). Eventually, water bodies may fill in completely by the process of aquatic succession. As lakes or ponds change over time, species of fish, plants, and invertebrates adapted to oligotrophic conditions may give way to those that thrive under eutrophic conditions.

Some lakes are so large that they differ substantially in their characteristics from small lakes. These large lakes are sometimes known as inland seas; the Great Lakes are prime examples. Because they hold so much water, most of their biota is adapted to open water. Major fish species of the Great Lakes include lake sturgeon, lake whitefish, northern pike, alewife, bass, walleye, and perch. Lake Baikal in Asia is the world's deepest lake, at 1637 m deep, and the Caspian Sea is the world's largest enclosed body of water, at 371 000 km².

Groundwater plays key roles in the hydrologic cycle

Any precipitation reaching Earth's land surface that does not evaporate, flow into waterways, or get taken up by organisms infiltrates the surface. Most percolates downward through the soil to become **groundwater** (FIGURE 9.5). Groundwater makes up one-fifth of Earth's freshwater supply and plays a key role in meeting human water needs.

Groundwater is contained within **aquifers**: porous formations of rock, sand, or gravel that hold water. An aquifer's upper layer, or *zone of aeration*, contains pore spaces partly filled with water. In the lower layer, or *zone of saturation*, the spaces are completely filled with water. The boundary between these two zones is the **water table**. Below the level of the water table, all pore spaces and fractures in the rock or sediment are completely filled with water; above the water table, typically some water is present in the pore spaces, but the ground is not completely saturated. Picture a sponge resting partly submerged in a tray of water; the lower part of the sponge is completely saturated, whereas the upper portion may be moist but contains plenty of air in its pores. Any area where water infiltrates Earth's surface and reaches an aquifer below is known as an aquifer **recharge zone**.

There are two broad categories of aquifers. A **confined aquifer**, or *artesian aquifer*, exists when a water-bearing porous layer of rock, sand, or gravel is trapped between upper and lower layers of less permeable substrate (often clay). In such a situation, the water is under great pressure. In contrast, an **unconfined aquifer** has no impermeable upper layer to confine it, so its water is under less pressure and can be readily recharged by surface water.

Just as surface water becomes groundwater by infiltration and percolation, groundwater becomes surface water through springs (and human-drilled wells), sometimes keeping streams flowing when surface conditions are

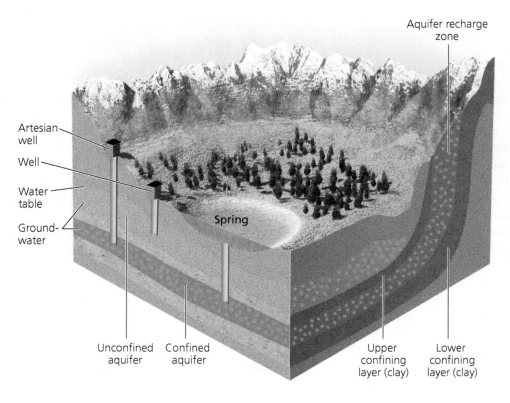

FIGURE 9.5
Groundwater may occur in unconfined aquifers above impermeable layers or in confined aquifers under pressure between impermeable layers. Water may rise naturally to the surface at springs and through the wells we dig. Artesian wells tap into confined aquifers to mine water under pressure.

otherwise dry. Groundwater flows downhill and from areas of high pressure to areas of low pressure, emerging to join surface water bodies at **discharge zones**. A typical rate of groundwater flow might be only about 1 m per day, so groundwater may remain in an aquifer for a long time. In fact, groundwater can be ancient. The average age of groundwater has been estimated at 1400 years, and some is many tens of thousands or even millions of years old.

The world's largest known aquifer is the Ogallala Aquifer, which underlies the Great Plains of the United States. Water from this massive aquifer has enabled American farmers to create a bountiful grain-producing region. The volumes, the specific characteristics, and even the exact areal extents of the major aquifers in Canada are not yet thoroughly known; they are being studied under the Natural Resources Canada (NRCAN) Groundwater Mapping Program (**FIGURE 9.6**).[6]

Among the most significant aquifers in Canada—both in terms of extent or volume of water and in terms of the areas and populations they service—are the Paskapoo Formation, which covers more than 10 000 km² of southwestern Alberta; the Oak Ridges Moraine, a series of glacial deposits that cover 1900 km² and provide much of the Greater Toronto area with water; and the Annapolis–Cornwallis Valley Aquifers in Nova Scotia, covering a surface area of 2400 km² in a valley running parallel to the Bay of Fundy.[7] Groundwater is of particular impor-

tance on Prince Edward Island, which draws nearly all of its water from aquifers that underlie most of the island.

Water is unequally distributed across Earth's surface

Different regions, even different areas within the same country, can possess vastly different amounts of groundwater, surface water, and precipitation. For example, even though the region of the southwestern United States is very dry, the country as a whole actually has water resources roughly equivalent to those of Canada; however, the main concentration of water resources in the United States is in Alaska. In terms of global extremes, precipitation ranges from a high of about 1200 cm per year at Mount Waialeale on the Hawaiian island of Kauai to virtually zero in Chile's Atacama Desert. Some polar areas also receive very little precipitation; thus, they qualify as deserts, even though they are cold rather than hot.

People are not distributed across the globe in accordance with water availability. Many areas with high population density are water poor, leading to inequalities in per capita water resources among and within nations (**FIGURE 9.7**). For example, Canada has 20 times as much water for each of its citizens as China does. The Amazon River carries 15% of the world's runoff, but its watershed

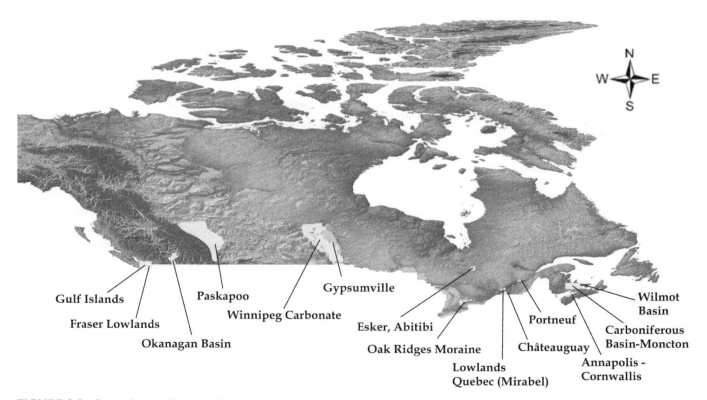

FIGURE 9.6   Some of the significant aquifers that are being studied in the Groundwater Mapping Program include the Paskapoo Formation, Oak Ridges Moraine, and Annapolis–Cornwallis Valley aquifers.

Available fresh water
(cubic metres per capita
per year)

- Less than 1000
- 1000–2000
- 2000–5000
- 5000–10 000
- 10 000–20 000
- 20 000–10 0000
- More than 100 000
- Insufficient data
- Major inland water body

FIGURE 9.7   Nations vary tremendously in the amount of fresh water per capita available to their citizens. For example, Iceland, Papua New Guinea, Gabon, and Guyana (dark blue in this map) each have more than 100 times as much water per person as do many Middle Eastern and North African countries. *Source:* Data from U.N. Environment Programme and World Resources Institute, as presented by Harrison, P., and F. Pearce. (2000). *AAAS Atlas of Population and the Environment.* Berkeley, CA: University of California Press.

holds less than half a percent of the world's human population. Asia possesses the most water of any continent but has the least water available per person, whereas Australia, with the least amount of water, boasts the most water available per person. Because of this mismatched distribution of water and population, one challenge has always been to transport fresh water from its source to where people need it.

Fresh water is distributed unevenly in time as well as space. India's monsoon season brings concentrated storms in which half of a region's annual rain may fall in a few hours. Northwest China receives three-fifths of its annual precipitation during three months when crops do not need it. The uneven distribution of water across time is one reason people have erected dams to store water, so that it can be distributed when needed.

Climate change will cause water problems and shortages

As if the existing mismatches between water availability and human need were not enough, global climate change will worsen conditions in many regions by altering precipitation patterns, melting glaciers, causing early-season runoff, and intensifying droughts and flooding.

Environment Canada reports that climate change is expected to affect fresh water and the hydrologic cycle in Canada in four main ways:[8]

1. The present midlatitude rain belt will shift northward.
2. Snowmelt and spring runoff will occur earlier than at present.
3. There will be more evapotranspiration, which will start earlier and continue longer.
4. The interior continental region will experience drier summers.

The last major drought in the Prairies occurred in 2001–2002, but if climate model predictions of warmer temperatures and decreasing precipitation in interior continental regions come to pass, it may mean that droughts will become more common, more severe, and more extended.

Additional impacts of global climatic warming in Canada could include warmer river temperatures, which would damage aquatic ecosystems and freshwater fish. Water temperatures in the Great Lakes are expected to increase and water levels to decrease.[9]

There also are several potential secondary problems. For example, if water levels drop, it may be necessary to dredge channels to accommodate shipping. This would stir up and re-suspend sediments, increasing the turbidity of the water and potentially reactivating toxic chemicals that had settled into bottom sediments. An anticipated problem in Atlantic Canada, because of rising sea levels, is saltwater intrusion into coastal groundwater aquifers, as well as saltwater disturbance of coastal estuaries.

How We Use Water

In our attempts to harness freshwater sources for countless purposes and pursuits, we have achieved impressive engineering accomplishments. In so doing, we also have altered many environmental systems. It is estimated that 60% of the world's largest 227 rivers (and 77% of those in North America and Europe) have been strongly or moderately affected by artificial dams, canals, and **diversions**; that is, the rerouting of water from its natural river channel by means of built structures. Artificial channel modifications, including straightening and concrete-lining of channels, are collectively referred to as **channelization**.

We are also using too much water. Data indicate that at present our consumption of fresh water in much of the world is unsustainable, and we are depleting many sources of surface water and groundwater. One-third of the world's people are already (in 2011) affected by water scarcity (with less than 1000 m^3 of water per person per year), according to the World Health Organization.

Water supplies our households, agriculture, and industry

We all use water at home for drinking, cooking, and cleaning (**FIGURE 9.8**). Farmers and ranchers use water to irrigate crops and water livestock. Most manufacturing and industrial processes require water. The proportions of each of these three types of use—residential/municipal, agricultural, and industrial—vary dramatically among nations (**FIGURE 9.9**). Nations with arid climates tend to use more fresh water for agriculture, and heavily industrialized nations use a great deal for industry. Globally, we

Water use in the home

FIGURE 9.8
According to Environment Canada, this is how Canadians apportion their use of water in the home.
Source: Data from Environment Canada, Water Use: Withdrawal Uses (as of 2006).

spend about 70% of our annual freshwater allotment on agriculture. Industry accounts for roughly 20%, and residential and municipal uses for only 10%.

When we remove water from an aquifer or surface water body and do not return it, this is called *consumptive use*. A large portion of agricultural irrigation and of many industrial and residential uses is consumptive. *Nonconsumptive use* of water does not remove, or only temporarily removes, water from an aquifer or surface water body. Using water to generate electricity at hydroelectric dams is an example of nonconsumptive use; water is taken in, passed through dam machinery to turn turbines, and released downstream.

We have erected thousands of dams

A **dam** is any obstruction placed in a river or stream to block the flow of water so that water can be stored in a

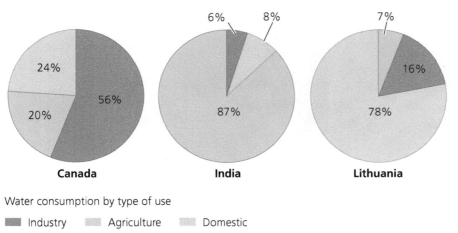

Water consumption by type of use

■ Industry ■ Agriculture ■ Domestic

FIGURE 9.9
Nations apportion their freshwater consumption differently. Industry consumes most water used in Canada, agriculture uses the most in India, and most water in Lithuania goes toward domestic use. The largest category of water withdrawal in Canada (more than 60% of the total) is that for water used in the production of electricity. This category includes only withdrawals, not in-stream use. Withdrawals for power production are not included in the data shown in this diagram.
Source: Data are based on information from U.N. Food and Agriculture Organization (FAO, 2000) and from Environment Canada, (2005), The Management of Water: Water Use.

reservoir. We build dams to prevent floods, provide drinking water, facilitate irrigation, and generate electricity (FIGURE 9.10; TABLE 9.1). Power generation with hydroelectric dams is discussed in greater detail in the chapter on Energy Alternatives.

Worldwide, we have erected more than 45 000 large dams (greater than 15 m high) across rivers in more than 140 nations, and tens of thousands of smaller dams. In the Prairie provinces alone there are almost 800 dams.[10] Only a few major rivers in the world remain undammed and free-flowing; these run through the tundra and taiga of Canada, Alaska, and Russia and in remote regions of Latin America and Africa.

Our largest dams are some of humanity's greatest engineering feats. The Gardiner Dam in Saskatchewan is the largest in Canada in terms of water-holding capacity; the Mica Dam in British Columbia is the tallest. The two behemoths in the United States are the Hoover and Glen Canyon dams. The Hoover Dam, probably the most

recognizable icon of the great dam-building period in the United States, holds 35.2 km³ of water in a reservoir that is 177 km long and 152 m deep. The Glen Canyon's reservoir is almost as large; together they store four times as much water as flows in the river in an entire year.

China's Three Gorges Dam is the world's largest

The complex mix of benefits and costs that dams produce is exemplified by the world's largest dam project, the Three Gorges Dam on China's Yangtze River. (It is worth noting that the second-largest dam in the world is not a water dam but the Syncrude tar sand tailings dam in Alberta.) The Three Gorges Dam, 186 m high and 2 km wide, was completed in 2006 (FIGURE 9.11A). When completely filled in 2010, its reservoir reached 616 km in length (as long as Lake Superior), holding more than

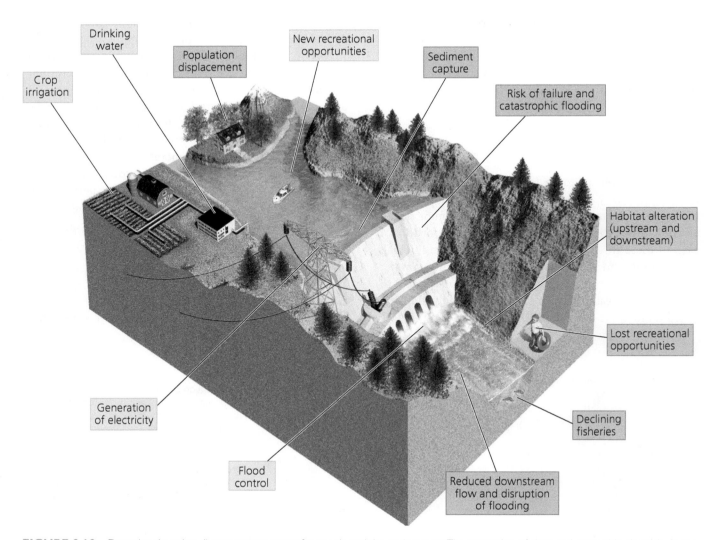

FIGURE 9.10 Damming rivers has diverse consequences for people and the environment. The generation of clean and renewable electricity is one of several major benefits (green boxes) of hydroelectric dams. Habitat alteration is one of several negative impacts (red boxes).

Table 9.1 Major Benefits and Costs of Dams	
Benefits	**Costs**
■ Power generation. Hydroelectric dams (pp. 595–598) provide inexpensive electricity.	■ Habitat alteration. Reservoirs flood riparian habitats and displace or kill riparian species. Dams modify rivers downstream. Shallow warm water downstream from a dam is periodically flushed with cold reservoir water, stressing or killing many fish.
■ Emissions reduction. Hydroelectric power produces no greenhouse gases in its operation (although some are produced during construction and maintenance of infrastructure). By replacing fossil fuel combustion as an electricity source, hydropower reduces air pollution and climate change, and their health and environmental consequences.	■ Fisheries declines. Salmon and other fish that migrate up rivers to spawn encounter dams as a barrier. Although "fish ladders" at many dams allow passage, most fish do not make it.
■ Crop irrigation. Reservoirs can release irrigation water when farmers most need it and can buffer regions against drought.	■ Population displacement. Reservoirs generally flood fertile farmland and have flooded many human settlements. An estimated 40–80 million people globally have been displaced by dam projects over the past half century.
■ Drinking water. Many reservoirs store plentiful, reliable, and clean water for municipal drinking water supplies, provided that watershed lands draining into the reservoir are not developed or polluted.	■ Sediment capture. Sediment settles behind dams. Downstream floodplains and estuaries are no longer nourished, and reservoirs fill with silt.
■ Flood control. Dams can prevent floods by storing seasonal surges, such as those following snowmelt or heavy rain.	■ Disruption of flooding. Floods create productive farmland by depositing rich sediment. Without flooding, topsoil is lost, and farmland deteriorates.
■ Shipping. By replacing rocky river beds with deep placid pools, dams enable ships to transport goods over longer distances.	■ Risk of failure. There is always risk that a dam could fail, causing massive property damage, ecological damage, and loss of life.
■ New recreational opportunities. People can fish from boats and use personal watercraft on reservoirs in regions where such recreation was not possible before.	■ Lost recreational opportunities. Tubing, whitewater rafting, fly-fishing, and kayaking opportunities are lost.

38 trillion litres of water. This project will enable boats and barges to travel farther upstream, provide flood control, and generate enough hydroelectric power to replace dozens of large coal or nuclear plants.

However, the Three Gorges Dam has cost $25 billion to build, and its reservoir flooded 22 cities and the homes of 1.24 million people, requiring the largest resettlement project in China's history (FIGURE 9.11B). The major earthquake in southern China in 2008 raised fears of potential damage to the great structure; the consequences of a collapse of a dam this large would be devastating.

The filling of the reservoir behind the dam also submerged 10 000-year-old archaeological sites, productive farmlands, and wildlife habitat. Moreover, the reservoir slows the river's flow so that suspended sediment is settling behind the dam. Indeed, the reservoir began accumulating sediment as soon as the dam was completed, and because the river downstream is deprived of sediment, the tidal marshes at the Yangtze's mouth are eroding away, leaving the city of Shanghai with a degraded coastal environment and less coastal land to develop. Many scientists worry that the Yangtze's many pollutants will also be trapped in the reservoir, making the water undrinkable. In fact, high levels of bacteria were found in the water as it began building up behind the dam. The Chinese government plans to sink $5 billion into building hundreds of sewage treatment and waste disposal facilities.

Lest you have the impression that large structures with extensive social and environmental impacts are constructed only in developing countries, consider the case of the St. Lawrence Seaway (FIGURE 9.11C). Although it took more than 50 years of discussion, once under way the St. Lawrence Seaway took only 5 years to complete; it opened in 1959. The seaway is a series of canals that connects the Great Lakes to the Atlantic Ocean, following the route of the St. Lawrence River. Its construction required the displacement of 6500 people from farms and homes along the canal route; whole villages were flooded, as well as historically important battlefields from the War of 1812. The Lost Villages Historical Society website (http://lostvillages.ca/) documents the construction of the St. Lawrence Seaway and the farms and villages that were affected.

Some dams are now being removed

People who feel that the costs of some dams have outweighed their benefits are pushing for such dams to be dismantled. By removing dams and letting rivers flow freely, these people say, we can restore riparian ecosystems, reestablish economically valuable fisheries, and revive river recreation, such as fly-fishing and rafting. Another common reason for the decommissioning of

(a) The Three Gorges Dam in Yichang, China

(c) **Archival photo of the construction of the St. Lawrence Seaway**

FIGURE 9.11
China's Three Gorges Dam, completed in 2003, is the world's largest dam **(a)**. Well over a million people were displaced, archaeological treasures were lost forever, and whole cities were levelled for its construction, as shown here in Sichuan Province **(b)**. The filling of the reservoir began in 2003 and was completed in 2010. The construction of the St. Lawrence Seaway **(c)** from 1954 to 1959 required the displacement of 6500 people and caused the flooding of 14 000 hectares of land, 7 villages, and 225 farms.

study of the response of the river and aquatic communities to changes in flow rate, water temperature, sedimentation, and other factors that accompany decommissioning.

Dikes and levees are meant to control floods

Flood prevention ranks high among reasons we control the movement of fresh water. People have always been attracted to riverbanks for their water supply and for the flat topography and fertile soil of floodplains. Flooding is a normal, natural process caused by snowmelt or heavy rain, and floodwaters spread nutrient-rich sediments over large areas, benefiting both natural systems and human agriculture.

In the short term, however, floods can do tremendous damage to the farms, homes, and property of people who choose to live in floodplains. To protect against floods, individuals and governments have built **dikes** and levees (long raised mounds of earth) along the banks of rivers to hold rising water in main channels. Many dikes are small and locally built, but some are massive. In Canada, the flood diversion wall that protects the city of Winnipeg from the Red River is a major example of a flood protection structure (**FIGURE 9.12**). In the United States the

(b) Displaced people in Sichuan Province, China

dams is that many aging dams are in need of costly repairs or have outlived their economic usefulness.

Roughly 500 dams have been removed in the United States in recent years, and more will soon follow. In Canada only a handful of dams have been decommissioned so far, but the concept of dam removal for river restoration and ecological recovery is beginning to take hold. Dam removals also provide opportunities for scientific

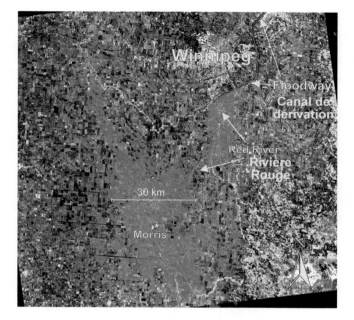

FIGURE 9.12
A flood diversion wall protected the city of Winnipeg during the 1997 Red River flood but may have exposed other villages to flooding. In this satellite image, the water appears blue, and the diversion wall can be seen in the upper righthand corner of the photograph, keeping the water from entering the core of the city of Winnipeg. A similar situation, necessitating controlled flooding of a small area to save a large area, occurred in 2011 when the Assiniboine River flooded.

Army Corps of Engineers has constructed thousands of kilometres of massive levees along the banks of major waterways (those that failed in New Orleans after Hurricane Katrina are examples). Although these structures prevent flooding at most times and places, they can sometimes worsen flooding because they force water to stay in channels and accumulate, building up enormous energy and leading to occasional catastrophic overflow events.

We divert—and deplete—surface water to suit our needs

People have long diverted water from rivers, streams, lakes, and ponds to farm fields, homes, and cities. *Diversion* refers to the process of removing water from its channel or modifying its flow for the purpose of using it elsewhere.

The Colorado River in the southwestern United States is one of the world's classic examples of diversion and overallocation of water from a major river. Early in its course, some Colorado River water is piped through a mountain tunnel and down the Rockies' eastern slope to supply the city of Denver. More is removed for Las

Vegas and other cities and for farmland as the water proceeds downriver. When it reaches Parker Dam on the California–Arizona state line, large amounts are diverted into the Colorado River Aqueduct, which brings water to millions of people in the Los Angeles and San Diego areas via a long open-air canal. From Parker Dam, Arizona also draws water, transporting it in the large canals of the Central Arizona Project. Farther south at Imperial Dam, water is diverted into the Coachella and All-American Canals, destined for agriculture, mostly in California's Imperial Valley. To make this desert bloom, Imperial Valley farmers soak the soil with subsidized water for which they pay one penny per 795 L.

What water is left in the Colorado River after all the diversions is just a trickle making its way to the Gulf of California and Mexico. On some days, water does not reach the gulf at all. This reduction in flow (**FIGURE 9.13**) has drastically altered the ecology of the lower river and the once-rich delta, changing plant communities, wiping out populations of fish and invertebrates, and devastating fisheries. It also led to a tense international incident between the United States and Mexico in the 1970s, necessitating high-level international talks and agreements concerning water reallocation, which improved the situation somewhat.

Nowhere are the effects of surface water depletion so evident as at the Aral Sea. Once the fourth-largest lake on Earth, just larger than Lake Huron, it has lost more than four-fifths of its volume in just 45 years (**FIGURE 9.14**). This dying inland sea, on the border of present-day Uzbekistan and Kazakhstan, is the victim of irrigation

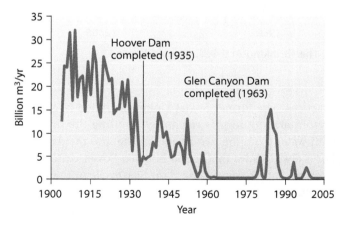

FIGURE 9.13
Flow at the mouth of the Colorado River has greatly decreased over the past century as a result of withdrawals, mostly for agriculture. The river now often runs dry at its mouth.
Source: Data from Postel, S. 2005. Liquid assets: The critical need to safeguard freshwater ecosystems. Worldwatch Paper 170. Washington, DC: Worldwatch Institute.

(a) Ships stranded by the Aral Sea's fast-receding waters

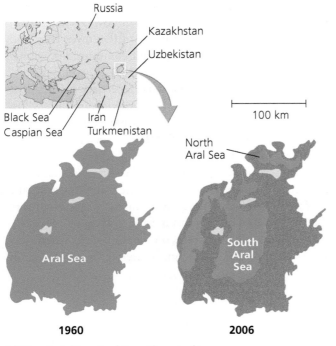

(c) The shrinking Aral Sea, then and now

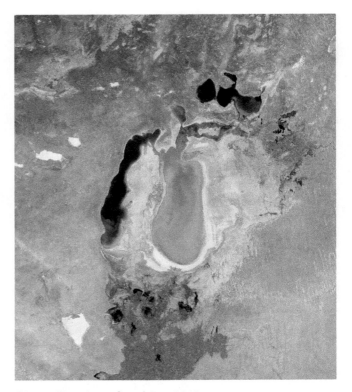

(b) Satellite view of Aral Sea, 2002

FIGURE 9.14
Ships lie stranded in the sand **(a)** because the waters of Central Asia's Aral Sea have receded so far and so quickly **(b)**. The Aral Sea was once the world's fourth-largest lake. However, it has been shrinking for the past four decades **(c)** because of overwithdrawal of water to irrigate cotton crops. Today restoration efforts are beginning to reverse the decline in the northern portion of the sea, and waters there are slowly rising.

practices. The former Soviet Union instituted large-scale cotton farming in this region by flooding the dry land with water from the two rivers leading into the Aral Sea. For a few decades this action boosted Soviet cotton production, but it caused the Aral Sea to shrink, and the irrigated soil became waterlogged and salinized.

Today 60 000 fishing jobs are gone, winds blow pesticide-laden dust up from the dry lake bed, and what cotton grows on the blighted soil cannot bring the regional economy back. However, all may not be lost: Scientists, engineers, and local people struggling to save the northern portion of the Aral Sea and its damaged ecosystems may now have finally begun reversing its decline.

Inefficient irrigation wastes water

The Green Revolution required significant increases in irrigation, and 70% more water is withdrawn for irrigation today than in 1960. During this period, the amount of land under irrigation has doubled. Expansion of irrigated agriculture has kept pace with population growth; irrigated area per capita has remained stable for at least four decades at around 460 m^2.

Irrigation can more than double crop yields by allowing farmers to apply water when and where it is needed. The world's 274 million hectares of irrigated

weighing the issues

FLOOD PROTECTION AT WHAT COST?

In May 2011, during record high-water levels on the Assiniboine River, the government of Manitoba deliberately breached a dike near Portage-la-Prairie, with the goal of releasing pressure in the Portage Reservoir and averting a much larger, uncontrolled flood. The controlled release put 150 homes and a considerable area of farmland at risk. In the end, the controlled breach worked, and no homes in the threatened area were significantly harmed.

A similar situation occurred during the Red River flood of 1997, during which the Red River Floodway diverted floodwater to protect the city of Winnipeg, but perhaps at the cost of flooding in smaller communities such as St. Agathe. Both events caused significant stress for those in the path of diverted floodwaters.

If you were a decision maker in Manitoba, would you have reached the same decision? Is it worthwhile to protect certain areas, even if it means risking others? What might you do to compensate those who were at risk?

cropland make up only 18% of world farmland but yield fully 40% of world agricultural produce, including 60% of the global grain crop. Still, most irrigation remains highly inefficient. Only about 45% of the fresh water we use for irrigation actually is taken up by crops. Inefficient "flood and furrow" irrigation, in which fields are liberally flooded with water that may evaporate from standing pools, accounts for 90% of irrigation worldwide. Overirrigation leads to waterlogging and salinization, which affect one-fifth of farmland today and reduce world farming income by $11 billion.

Many national governments have subsidized irrigation to promote agricultural self-sufficiency. Unfortunately, inefficient irrigation methods in arid regions, such as the Middle East, are using up huge amounts of groundwater for little gain. Worldwide, roughly 15–35% of water withdrawals for irrigation are thought to be unsustainable. In areas where agriculture is demanding more fresh water than can be sustainably supplied, *water mining*—withdrawing water faster than it can be replenished—is taking place (**FIGURE 9.15**). In these areas, aquifers are being depleted or surface water is being piped in from other regions.

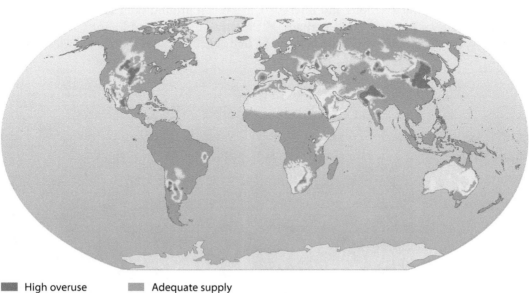

■ High overuse   ■ Adequate supply
■ Moderate overuse ■ Little or no use
■ Low overuse

FIGURE 9.15   Irrigation for agriculture is the main contributor to unsustainable water use. Mapped are regions where overall use of fresh water (for agriculture, industry, and domestic use) exceeds the available supply, requiring groundwater depletion or diversion of water from other regions. The map understates the problem because it does not reflect seasonal shortages.   Source: *Data from UNESCO. 2006. Water: A Shared Responsibility. World Water Development Report 2. Paris and New York: UNESCO and Berghahn Books.*

Wetlands have been drained for a variety of reasons

Throughout recent history, governments have encouraged laborious efforts to drain wetlands in order to promote settlement and farming. Many of today's crops grow on the sites of former wetlands—swamps, wooded marshes, bogs, and river floodplains—that people have drained and filled in (**FIGURE 9.16**). Wetlands also have historically been seen as "swamps"—insect-infested, smelly, and useless for any kind of industrial or agricultural development. In the 1930s the governor of Florida announced his intention to drain the entire Everglades, a unique cypress, mangrove, and tropical hardwood wetland that occupies much of the southern portion of the state. This attitude began to change dramatically in North America with the rise of the modern environmental movement in the 1970s and has continued to change as a result of research efforts to determine the economic value of services provided by wetlands.

In 1971, an international agreement was reached in Ramsar, Iran, concerning the documentation and protection of wetlands around the world. It is known as the *Ramsar Convention*, or more accurately, the *Convention on Wetlands of International Importance, Especially as Waterfowl Habitat*. The Ramsar Convention, to which Canada is a signatory, demonstrates the global concern regarding wetland loss and degradation. The mission of the treaty is the "conservation and wise use of all wetlands through local, regional, and national actions and international cooperation."[11] Today a large portion—perhaps 90%—of the original wetlands in southern Canada has been lost, but Canada as a whole still has the largest area of wetlands of any country in the world, according to Ramsar Convention data (**FIGURE 9.17**).[12]

Many people now have a different view of wetlands. Rather than seeing them as worthless swamps, science has made it clear that wetlands are valuable ecosystems. This scientific knowledge, along with a preservation ethic, has induced policy makers to develop regulations to safeguard remaining wetlands. Yet, because of loopholes, differing laws, development pressures—and even debate over the legal definition of wetlands—many of these vital ecosystems are still being lost.

We are depleting groundwater

Groundwater is more easily depleted than surface water because most aquifers recharge very slowly. If we compare an aquifer to a bank account, we are making more withdrawals than deposits, and the balance is shrinking. Today we are extracting 160 km^3 more water each year than is finding its way back into the ground. This is a major problem because one-third of Earth's human population—including 26% of the population of Canada—relies on groundwater for its needs. As aquifers are depleted, water tables drop. Groundwater becomes more difficult and expensive to extract, and eventually it may run out. In parts of Mexico, India, China, and other Asian and Middle Eastern nations, water tables are falling 1–3 m per year.

When groundwater is overpumped in coastal areas, saltwater can intrude into aquifers, making water undrinkable. This has occurred widely in the Middle East

FIGURE 9.16
Most of North America's wetlands have been drained and filled, and the land converted to agricultural use. The northern Great Plains region of Canada was pockmarked with thousands of "prairie potholes," water-filled depressions that served as nesting sites for most of the continent's waterfowl. Today many of these wetlands have been lost; shown are farmlands encroaching on prairie potholes.

FIGURE 9.17
The Columbia Wetlands, seen here, is Ramsar site number 1463—a wetland of international significance and the largest of its kind in British Columbia.

and in localities as varied as Florida, Turkey, and Bangkok. Moreover, as aquifers lose water, their substrate can become weaker and less capable of supporting overlying strata, and the land surface above may subside. For this reason, cities from Venice to Bangkok to Shanghai are slowly sinking. Mexico City's downtown has sunk over 10 m since the time of Spanish arrival; streets are buckled, old buildings lean at angles, and underground pipes break so often that 30% of the system's water is lost to leaks.

Sometimes land subsides suddenly in the form of **sinkholes**, areas where the ground gives way with little warning, occasionally swallowing people's homes (**FIGURE 9.18**). Once the ground subsides, soil can undergo *compaction*, becoming compressed and losing the porosity that enabled it to hold water. Recharging a depleted aquifer may thereafter become much more difficult.

Falling water tables also do vast ecological harm. Permanent wetlands exist where water tables are high

FIGURE 9.18
When too much groundwater is withdrawn too quickly, especially in areas underlain by soluble rocks such as limestone, the land above it may collapse in sinkholes.

enough to reach the surface, so when water tables drop, wetland ecosystems dry up. In Jordan, the Azraq Oasis covered 7500 ha and enabled migratory birds and other animals to find water in the desert. The water table beneath this oasis dropped 2.5–7 m during the 1980s because of increased well use by the city of Amman. As a result, the oasis dried up altogether during the 1990s. Today international donors are collaborating with the Jordanian government to try to find alternative sources of water and restore this oasis.

Our thirst for bottled water seems unquenchable

It seems to fit our busy lifestyle. Canadians' use of bottled water is surpassed only by that of Americans. Statistics Canada reports that almost 3 in 10 households in Canada today utilize bottled water as their main source for domestic drinking water. The proportion of households dependent on bottled water increases with household income, although the relationship between income and bottled water consumption is complex. Interestingly, in a 2008 study by Statistics Canada, university-educated households were shown to be *less* likely to consume bottled water.[13]

For the nation as a whole, some 820 million litres of water were bottled for Canadian consumption in 2000; by 2003 the amount had increased to almost 1.5 billion litres. This means that the average per capita consumption of 17.9 L of bottled water per year in 1995 had risen to 27.6 L by 2000, and then jumped to almost 50 L by 2003![14]

An interesting thing about bottled water is that much of it is just ordinary tap water—in fact, it has been estimated that as much as a quarter of all bottled water comes straight from a municipal water tap, sometimes with additional filtering or other treatment. Advertising and labelling legislation prohibits bottling companies from misrepresenting what is in the bottle, of course, so if you read the label carefully you should be able to determine whether the water has come from a "natural" source, such as groundwater or a spring, or from a municipal supply.

But is bottled water from a natural source necessarily more healthful or safer for you? Although most people think so, in fact there are fewer checks on bottled water and the bottling process than on municipal water supplies, which are rigorously monitored and regulated. Canada's *Food and Drugs Act* does not require a manufacturer to obtain a licence in order to bottle water (although the water itself is expected to meet the requirements established for food products). From an environmental perspective, it also takes a considerable amount of energy to produce bottled water, and there are some concerns about

weighing the issues

THE PRICE OF A LITRE

Do you drink bottled water? Why? (Do you think it is safer than municipal water? Do you prefer the taste? Is it more convenient?) What do you pay for a litre of bottled water? What do you pay for a litre of gas at the pump? What do you think *should* be reflected in these prices? What price do you think was paid for the water by the company that bottled it? What about the source of the water you consume—is it groundwater, and if so, is its source adequately protected? And what about the plastic waste that it generates?

the sustainability of groundwater withdrawal and lack of protection of the source water. Finally, concerns have been raised, even by Health Canada, about chemicals that might leach into water from plastic bottles under some circumstances.

So the next time you reach for a bottle of water, consider what's in the bottle, where it came from, how it was extracted and monitored, and exactly what you are paying for. *Then* decide whether you think it is worth generating an empty plastic bottle.

Will we see a future of water wars?

Depletion of fresh water leads to shortages, and resource scarcity can lead to conflict, as shown by the research of Thomas Homer-Dixon and others. Many predict that water's role in regional conflicts will increase as human population continues to grow in water-poor areas and as climate change alters regional patterns of precipitation. A total of 261 major rivers, whose watersheds cover 45% of the world's land area, are *transboundary* waterways—that is, they cross or flow along national borders, and disagreements are common. Water is already a key element in the hostilities among Israel, the Palestinian people, and neighbouring nations.

On the positive side, many nations have cooperated with neighbours to resolve water disputes. India has struck cooperative agreements over management of transboundary rivers with Pakistan, Bangladesh, Bhutan, and Nepal. In Europe, international conventions have been signed by multiple nations along the Rhine and the Danube rivers. The international agreements between Canada and the United States, governing the Great Lakes and other water bodies that straddle the boundary between our two nations, have been examples of largely successful water management agreements. Such progress gives reason to hope that future water wars will be few and far between.

Solutions to Depletion of Fresh Water

Human population growth, expansion of irrigated agriculture, and industrial development doubled our annual freshwater use between 1960 and 2000. We now use an amount equal to 10% of total global runoff. The hydrologic cycle makes fresh water a renewable resource, but if our usage exceeds what a lake, a river, or an aquifer can provide, we must reduce our use, find another water source, or be prepared to run out of water.

Solutions can address supply or demand

To address depletion of fresh water, we can aim either to increase supply or to reduce demand. Strategies for reducing demand include conservation and efficiency measures. Lowering demand is more difficult politically in the short term but may be necessary in the long term. In the developing world, international aid agencies are increasingly funding demand-based solutions over supply-based solutions because demand-based solutions offer better economic returns and cause less ecological and social damage.

To increase supply in a given area, people have transported water through pipes and aqueducts from areas where it is more plentiful or accessible. In many instances, water-poor regions have forcibly appropriated water from communities too weak to keep it for themselves. For instance, Los Angeles grew by using water it appropriated from other, less-inhabited regions of California. In so doing, it desertified the environments of those areas, creating dust bowls and destroying rural economies. In 1941, Los Angeles needed water and decided to divert streams feeding into Mono Lake, more than 565 km away in northern California. As the lake level fell 14 m over 40 years, salt concentrations doubled and aquatic communities suffered. Other desert cities in the American Southwest—such as Las Vegas, Phoenix, and Denver—are expected to double in population in the coming decades. Today Las Vegas is trying to win approval for a 450-km pipeline to import groundwater from sparsely populated eastern Nevada, where local residents and wildlife advocates oppose the diversion plan.

Desalination "makes" more water

Another supply-side strategy is to develop technologies to find or "make" more water. The best known technological approach to generate fresh water is **desalination**, or *desalinization*, the removal of salt from seawater or other water of marginal quality. One method of desalination mimics the hydrologic cycle by hastening evaporation from allotments of ocean water with heat and then condensing the vapour—essentially *distilling* fresh water. Another method involves forcing water through membranes to filter out salts; the most common process of this type is called *reverse osmosis*.

More than 7500 desalination facilities are operating worldwide, most in the arid Middle East and some in small island nations that lack groundwater. The largest plant, in Saudi Arabia, produces 485 million litres of fresh water every day (FIGURE 9.19). However, desalination is expensive, requires large inputs of fossil fuel energy, and generates concentrated salty waste.

Agricultural demand can be reduced

Because most water is used for agriculture, it makes sense to look first to agriculture for ways to decrease demand. Farmers can improve efficiency by lining irrigation canals to prevent leaks, levelling fields to minimize runoff, and adopting efficient irrigation methods. Low-pressure spray irrigation directs water downward toward plants, and drip irrigation systems target individual plants and introduce water directly onto the soil. Both methods reduce water lost to evaporation and surface runoff. Low-pressure precision sprinklers in use in a number of arid localities have efficiencies of 80–95% and have resulted in water savings of 25–37%. Experts have estimated that drip irrigation, which has efficiencies as high as 90%, could cut water use in half while raising yields by 20–90% and giving developing-world farmers $3 billion in extra annual income.

Choosing crops to match the land and climate in which they are being farmed can save huge amounts of water. Currently, crops that require a great deal of water, such as cotton, rice, and alfalfa, are often planted in arid areas with government-subsidized irrigation. As a result of the subsidies, the true cost of water is not part of the costs of growing the crop. Eliminating subsidies and growing crops in climates with adequate rainfall could greatly reduce water use. Finally, selective breeding and genetic modification can result in crop varieties that require less water.

FIGURE 9.19
The Jubail Desalinization Plant in Saudi Arabia is the largest facility in the world that turns saltwater into fresh water.

We can lessen residential and industrial water use in many ways

We can each help reduce agricultural water use by decreasing the amount of meat we eat because producing meat requires far greater water inputs than producing grain or vegetables. In households, we can reduce water use by installing low-flow faucets, showerheads, washing machines, and toilets. Automatic dishwashers, a European study showed, can use less water than does washing dishes by hand.[15] If your home has a lawn, it is best to water it at night, when water loss from evaporation is minimal. Better yet, you can replace a water-intensive lawn with native plants adapted to the region's natural precipitation patterns. An example is *xeriscaping*—landscaping with plants that are well adapted to a dry environment.

Industry and municipalities can take water-saving steps as well. Manufacturers are shifting to processes that use less water and in doing so are reducing their costs. Some cities are recycling municipal waste water for irrigation and industrial uses, or capturing excess surface runoff during their rainy seasons and pumping it into aquifers. Finding and patching leaks in pipes has saved some cities and companies large amounts of water—and money. A program of retrofitting enabled Massachusetts to reduce water demand by 31% and avoid an unpopular $500 million river diversion scheme.

Economic approaches to water conservation are being debated

Economists who want to use market-based strategies to achieve sustainable water use have suggested ending government subsidies of inefficient practices and letting water become a commodity whose price reflects the true costs of its extraction. Others worry that making water a fully priced commodity would make it less available to the world's poor and increase the gap between rich and poor. Because industrial use of water can be 70 times as profitable as agricultural use, market forces alone might favour uses that would benefit wealthy and industrialized people, companies, and nations at the expense of the poor and less industrialized.

Similar concerns surround another potential solution, the privatization of water supplies. In the past two decades, many public water systems were partially or wholly privatized, with their construction, maintenance, management, or ownership being transferred to private companies. This was done in the hope of increasing the systems' efficiency, but many firms have little incentive to allow equitable access to water for rich and poor alike. Already in some developing countries, rural residents without access to public water supplies, who are forced to buy water from private vendors, end up paying on average 12 times more than those connected to public supplies.

Other experiences indicate that decentralization of control over water, from the national level to the local level, may help conserve water. In Mexico, the effectiveness of irrigation systems improved dramatically once they were transferred from public ownership to the control of 386 local water user associations.

Regardless of how demand is addressed, the ongoing shift from supply-side to demand-side solutions is beginning to pay dividends. A new focus on demand (through government mandates and public education) has decreased public water consumption, and industries are becoming more water-efficient.

Freshwater Pollution and Its Control

The quantity and distribution of fresh water poses one set of environmental and social challenges. Safeguarding the *quality* of water involves another collection of environmental and human health dilemmas. To be safe for consumption by human beings and other organisms, water must be relatively free of disease-causing organisms and toxic substances.

Although developed nations have made admirable advances in cleaning up water pollution over the past few decades, the World Commission on Water concluded that more than half the world's major rivers are "seriously depleted and polluted, degrading and poisoning the surrounding ecosystems, threatening the health and livelihood of people who depend on them." The largely invisible pollution of groundwater, meanwhile, has been termed a "covert crisis."

Water pollution takes many forms

The term **pollution** describes the release into the environment of matter or energy that causes undesirable impacts on the health and well-being of humans or other organisms. Pollution can be physical, chemical, or biological and can affect water, air, or soil.

Water pollution comes in many forms and can cause diverse impacts on aquatic ecosystems and human health. We can categorize pollution into several types, including nutrient pollution, biological pollution by disease-causing organisms, toxic chemical pollution, physical pollution by sediment, and thermal pollution.

Nutrient pollution   You learned in previous chapters how nutrient pollution from fertilizers and other sources can lead to eutrophication and hypoxia in coastal

roots

POLLUTION

The word *pollution* comes from the Latin verb *polluere*, which means, "to soil, defile, or contaminate" and, in earlier Latin, "to desecrate or defile." It was used in its present sense, referring to contamination of the environment, as early as 1860, but it was not commonly used in this way until the middle 1950s.

marine areas. Eutrophication proceeds in a similar fashion in freshwater systems, where phosphorus is usually the nutrient that spurs growth. When excess phosphorus enters surface waters, it fertilizes algae and aquatic plants, boosting their growth rates and populations. Although such growth provides oxygen and food for other organisms, algae can cover the water's surface, depriving deeper-water plants of sunlight. As algae die off, they provide food for decomposing bacteria. Decomposition requires oxygen, so the increased bacterial activity drives down levels of dissolved oxygen. These levels can drop too low to support fish and shellfish, leading to dramatic changes in aquatic ecosystems.

Eutrophication (FIGURE 9.20) is a natural process, but excess nutrient input from runoff from farms, golf courses, lawns, and sewage can dramatically increase the rate at which it occurs. We can reduce nutrient pollution by treating waste water, reducing fertilizer application, planting vegetation to increase nutrient uptake, and purchasing phosphate-free detergents.

Pathogens and waterborne diseases   Disease-causing organisms (pathogenic viruses, protists, and bacteria) can enter drinking water supplies when these are contaminated with human waste from inadequately treated sewage or with animal waste from feedlots. Specialists monitoring water quality can tell when water has been contaminated by waste when they detect fecal coliform bacteria, which live in the intestinal tracts of people and other vertebrates. These bacteria are usually not pathogenic themselves, but they serve as indicators of fecal contamination, which may mean that the water holds other pathogens that can cause ailments, such as giardiasis, typhoid, or hepatitis A.

Biological pollution by pathogens causes more human health problems than any other type of water pollution. According to the World Health Organization in 2010, despite advances in many parts of the world, major problems still exist. On the positive side, 5.9 billion people (87% of the population) have access to safe water as a result of some form of improvement in their water supply—an increase from 4.1 billion (79% of the population) in 1990. However, more than 1.1 billion people are still without safe water supplies. In addition, 2.6 billion people have no sewer or sanitation facilities. Most of these are Asians and Africans, and four-fifths of the people without sanitation live in rural areas. These conditions contribute to widespread health impacts and 5 million deaths per year.

Treating sewage constitutes one approach to reducing the risks that waterborne pathogens pose. Another is using chemical or other means to disinfect drinking water. Others include hygienic measures, such as public

(a) Oligotrophic water body

(b) Eutrophic water body

FIGURE 9.20
An oligotrophic water body **(a)** with clear water and low nutrient content may eventually become a eutrophic water body **(b)** with abundant algae and high nutrient content. Pollution of freshwater bodies by excess nutrients accelerates the process of eutrophication.

education to encourage personal hygiene and government enforcement of regulations to ensure the cleanliness of food production, processing, and distribution.

Toxic chemicals   Our waterways have become polluted with toxic organic substances of our own making, including pesticides, petroleum products, and other synthetic chemicals. Many of these can poison animals and plants, alter aquatic ecosystems, and cause a wide array of human health problems, including cancer. In addition, toxic metals (such as arsenic, lead, and mercury) and acids (from acid precipitation and acid drainage from mine sites) also cause negative impacts on human health and the environment.

Legislating and enforcing more stringent regulations of industry can help reduce releases of these toxic inorganic chemicals. Better yet, we can modify our industrial processes and our purchasing decisions to rely less on these substances.

Suspended matter   Although floods build fertile farmland, sediment and other suspended matter that is transported by rivers can also impair aquatic ecosystems. Mining, clear-cutting, land clearing for housing development, and careless cultivation of farm fields all expose soil to wind and water erosion. Some water bodies, such as China's Yellow River, are naturally sediment-rich, but many others are not. When a clear-water river receives a heavy influx of eroded sediment, aquatic habitat can change dramatically, and fish adapted to clear-water environments may not be able to adjust. We can reduce sediment pollution by better managing farms and forests and avoiding large-scale disturbance of vegetation.

Thermal pollution   Water's ability to hold dissolved oxygen decreases as temperature rises, so some aquatic organisms may not survive when human activities raise water temperatures. When we withdraw water from a river and use it to cool an industrial facility, we transfer heat energy from the facility back into the river where the water is returned. People also raise surface water temperatures by removing streamside vegetation that shades water.

Too little heat can also cause problems. On many dammed rivers, water at the bottoms of reservoirs is colder than water at the surface. When dam operators release water from the depths of a reservoir, downstream water temperatures drop suddenly. These low water temperatures may favour cold-loving invasive species over endangered native species.

Water pollution comes from point and non-point sources

Some water pollution is emitted from **point sources**—discrete locations, such as a factory or sewer pipe. In contrast, **non-point-source** pollution arises from multiple cumulative inputs over larger areas, such as farms, city streets, and residential neighbourhoods (**FIGURE 9.21**).

Many common activities give rise to non-point-source water pollution, such as applying fertilizers and pesticides to lawns, applying salt to roads in winter, and changing automobile oil. To minimize non-point-source pollution of drinking water, governments can limit development on watershed land surrounding reservoirs.

Scientists use several indicators of water quality

Most forms of water pollution are not very visible to the human eye, so scientists and technicians measure certain

physical, chemical, and biological properties of water to characterize **water quality**. Biological properties include the presence of fecal coliform bacteria and other disease-causing organisms, as discussed above. Algae and aquatic invertebrates are also commonly used as biological indicators of water quality.

Chemical properties include nutrient concentrations, pH, taste and odour, and hardness. "Hard" water contains naturally high concentrations of calcium and magnesium ions, which prevent soap from lathering and leave chalky deposits behind when heated or boiled. An important chemical characteristic is dissolved oxygen content. Dissolved oxygen is an indicator of aquatic ecosystem health because surface waters low in dissolved oxygen are less capable of supporting aquatic life.

Among physical characteristics, *turbidity* measures the density of suspended particles in a water sample. If scientists can measure only one parameter, they will often choose turbidity because it tends to correlate with many others and is thereby a good indicator of overall water quality. Fast-moving rivers that cut through arid or eroded landscapes, like the Yellow River, carry a great deal of sediment and are turbid and muddy looking as a result. The colour of the water can reveal particular substances present in a sample. Some forest streams run the colour of iced tea because of chemicals called tannins that occur naturally in decomposing leaf litter. Finally, temperature can be used to assess water quality. High temperatures can interfere with some biological processes, and warmer water holds less dissolved oxygen.

Groundwater pollution is a serious problem

Most efforts at pollution control have focused on surface water. Yet increasingly, groundwater sources once assumed to be pristine have been contaminated by pollution from industrial and agricultural practices. Groundwater pollution is largely hidden from view and is extremely difficult to monitor (**FIGURE 9.22**); it can be out-of-sight, out-of-mind for decades until widespread contamination of drinking supplies is discovered.

Groundwater pollution is also more difficult to manage than surface water pollution. Rivers flush their pollutants fairly quickly, but groundwater retains its contaminants until they decompose, which in the case of persistent pollutants can be many years or decades. The long-lived pesticide DDT, for instance, is still found widely in aquifers in North America, even though it was banned 40 years ago. Moreover, chemicals break down much more slowly in aquifers than in surface water or soils. Groundwater generally contains less dissolved

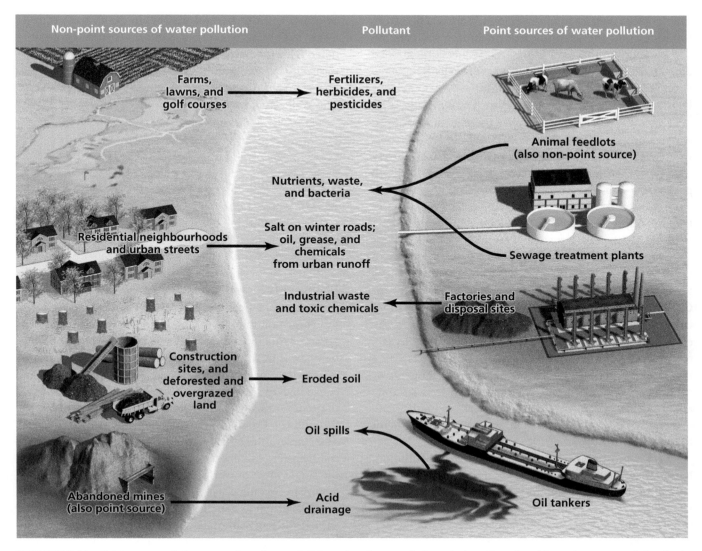

| Non-point sources of water pollution | Pollutant | Point sources of water pollution |

Farms, lawns, and golf courses → Fertilizers, herbicides, and pesticides

Animal feedlots (also non-point source)

Nutrients, waste, and bacteria

Sewage treatment plants

Residential neighbourhoods and urban streets → Salt on winter roads; oil, grease, and chemicals from urban runoff

Industrial waste and toxic chemicals ← Factories and disposal sites

Construction sites, and deforested and overgrazed land → Eroded soil

Oil spills

Abandoned mines (also point source) → Acid drainage

Oil tankers

FIGURE 9.21 Point-source pollution comes from discrete facilities or locations, usually from single outflow pipes. Non-point-source pollution (such as runoff from streets, residential neighbourhoods, lawns, and farms) originates from numerous sources spread over large areas.

FIGURE 9.22
Groundwater supplies must be closely monitored, especially in areas where the potential for contamination is high. It is much easier to prevent contamination of groundwater than to remediate after contamination has occurred.

oxygen, microbes, minerals, and organic matter, so decomposition is slower. For instance, concentrations of the herbicide alachlor decline by half after 20 days in soil, but in groundwater this takes almost 4 years.

There are many sources of groundwater pollution, including some natural sources

Some chemicals that are toxic at high concentrations, including aluminum, fluoride, nitrates, and sulphates, occur naturally in groundwater. After all, water that resides in aquifers is surrounded by rocks—the natural sources for many chemical compounds, both benign and toxic— for hundreds to tens of thousands of years. During that time of close contact many compounds are leached from the rocks into the groundwater (including the calcium and magnesium that lead to water "hardness," mentioned above). The poisoning of Bangladesh's wells by arsenic is one case of natural contamination (see "The Science Behind the Story: Arsenic in the Waters of Bangladesh").

However, there is no escaping the fact that groundwater pollution from human activity is widespread. Industrial, agricultural, and urban wastes—from heavy metals to petroleum products to industrial solvents to pesticides—can leach through soil and seep into aquifers. Pathogens and other pollutants can enter groundwater through improperly designed wells and from the pumping of liquid hazardous waste below ground.

Leakage from underground septic tanks, tanks of industrial chemicals, and tanks of oil and gas also pollutes groundwater (FIGURE 9.23). According to Environment Canada, without adequate corrosion protection, more than half of underground gasoline storage tanks can be expected to begin leaking by the time they are 15 years old, and just 1 L of gasoline can contaminate up to 1 million L of groundwater.[16] Intercepting carcinogenic or otherwise toxic pollutants, such as chlorinated solvents and gasoline, before they reach aquifers is vital because once an aquifer is contaminated, it is extremely difficult to remediate.

Agriculture also contributes to groundwater pollution. Nitrate from fertilizers has leached into groundwater in agricultural areas throughout Canada and in 49 of the 50 U.S. states. Nitrate in drinking water has been linked to cancers, miscarriages, and "blue baby syndrome," which reduces the oxygen-carrying capacity of infants' blood. Agriculture can also contribute pathogens, primarily

FIGURE 9.23
Leaky underground gasoline storage tanks have been a major source of groundwater pollution. They are particularly problematic in the Atlantic provinces, where reliance on groundwater is very high.

originating from animal wastes. In 2000, the groundwater supply of Walkerton, Ontario, became contaminated with the bacterium *Escherichia coli*, or *E. coli*. Two thousand people became ill, and seven died (see "The Science Behind the Story: When Water Turns Deadly: The Walkerton Tragedy").

Legislative and regulatory efforts have helped reduce pollution

As numerous as our freshwater pollution problems may seem, it is important to remember that many of them were worse a few decades ago, when Lake Erie was declared officially "dead."

Citizen activism and government response during the 1960s and 1970s resulted in fundamental changes in environmental practices and legislation that made it illegal to discharge pollution from a point source without a permit, set standards for industrial waste water and for contaminant levels in surface waters, and funded construction of sewage treatment plants. In Canada most such legislation is enacted and enforced at the provincial level, although the federal government sets environmental guidelines through the *Canadian Environmental Protection Act* and other federal legislation, and regulates any interprovincial transfers of hazardous materials. However, probably the single most powerful act that serves to protect water quality in Canada is a federal law, the *Fisheries Act*, which makes it illegal to damage any water body that serves as a habitat for fish (although mining companies are exempt from this Act under some circumstances). Thanks to such legislation, point-source pollution has been reduced, and rivers and lakes in most parts of North America are cleaner than they have been in decades.

The Great Lakes represent a success story in fighting water pollution. Much of this work has been carried out through the International Joint Commission (IJC), the *Great Lakes Water Quality Agreement*, and the *International Boundary Waters Treaty Act*. In the 1970s the Great Lakes, which hold 18% of the world's surface fresh water, were badly polluted with waste water, fertilizers, and toxic chemicals. Today, coordinated efforts of the Canadian and U.S. governments have paid off. Releases of toxic chemicals are down, and phosphorus runoff has decreased. Bird populations are rebounding, and Lake Erie is now home to the world's largest walleye fishery.

The Great Lakes' troubles are by no means over—sediment pollution is still heavy, PCBs and mercury still settle on the lakes from the air, and fish are not always safe to eat. However, the progress so far shows how conditions can improve when citizens push their governments to take action.

THE SCIENCE BEHIND THE STORY

Arsenic in the Waters of Bangladesh

These skin lesions were caused by arsenic poisoning in Bangladesh.

In the 1970s, UNICEF, with the help of environmental scientists at the British Geological Survey, launched a campaign to improve access to fresh water in Bangladesh. By digging thousands of small artesian wells, the designers of the program hoped to reduce Bangladeshis' dependence on disease-ridden surface waters. In the mid-1990s, however, scientists began to suspect that the wells dug to improve Bangladeshis' health were contaminated with arsenic, a poison that, if ingested frequently, can cause serious skin disorders and other illnesses, including cancer.

A medical doctor sounded the first alarm. In 1983, dermatologist K. C. Saha of the School of Tropical Medicine in Calcutta, India, saw the first of many patients from West Bengal, an area of India just west of Bangladesh, who showed signs of arsenic poisoning. Through a process of elimination, contaminated well water was identified as the likely cause of the poisoning. The hypothesis was confirmed by groundwater testing and by the work of epidemiologists, among them Dipankar Chakraborti of Calcutta's Jadavpur University.

However, it was not until the late 1990s that large-scale testing of Bangladesh's wells began. By 2001, when the British Geological Survey and the government of Bangladesh published their final report, 3524 wells had been tested. Of the shallow wells—those less than 150 m deep—46% exceeded the World Health Organization's maximum recommended level of 10 µg/L of arsenic. Extrapolating across all of Bangladesh, the scientists estimated that as many as 2.5 million wells serving 57 million people were contami-

nated. As the figure shows, arsenic contamination is most prevalent in southern Bangladesh, but localized hot spots are found in northern regions of the country.

Scientists have not yet reached consensus on the chemical processes by which Bangladesh's shallow aquifers became contaminated. All agree that the arsenic is of natural origin; what remains unclear is how the low levels of arsenic naturally present in soils were dissolved in the aquifers in elemental and highly toxic form. One initial explanation, suggested by Chakraborti and his colleagues, placed most of the blame on agricultural irrigation. By drawing large amounts of water out of aquifers during Bangladesh's dry season, they argued, irrigation had permitted oxygen to enter the aquifers and prompted the release of arsenic from pyrite, a common mineral.

Other scientists contend that pyrite oxidation cannot explain most cases of arsenic contamination. In a 1998 paper in the journal *Nature*, Ross Nickson of the University College London and his colleagues suggested that arsenic was being released from iron oxides carried into Bangladesh by the Ganges River. They pointed to results of a hydrochemical survey that measured the chemical composition of aquifers throughout Bangladesh. Contrary to the predictions of the pyrite oxidation hypothesis, the survey found that arsenic concentrations tended to increase with aquifer depth and to be inversely correlated with concentrations of sulphur, a component of pyrite. Nickson and his colleagues concluded that highly reducing chemical conditions created by buried organic matter, such as peat, had probably leached arsenic from iron oxides over thousands of years.

Massachusetts Institute of Technology hydrologist Charles Harvey and colleagues have suggested that irrigation may contribute to the arsenic problem after all but not because of pyrite oxidation. In a 2002 paper in the journal *Science*, they described an experiment in which more than a dozen wells were dug near the capital city of Dhaka. Contrary to the pyrite oxidation hypothesis, and in agreement with Nickson and his colleagues, they found little evidence of a connection between sulphur or oxygen and arsenic.

However, they also found that they could increase arsenic concentrations by injecting organic matter, such as molasses, into their experimental wells. In the process of being metabolized by microbes, the molasses appeared to be freeing arsenic from iron oxides. A similar process might take place naturally, Harvey's team argued, when runoff from rice paddies, ponds, and rivers recharges aquifers that have been depleted by heavy pumping for irrigation. In support of this hypothesis, they found that much of the carbon in the shallow wells was of recent origin. Other scientists, however, have found arsenic in much older waters. This finding suggests that Bangladesh's arsenic problem may be caused by multiple hydrological and geological factors.

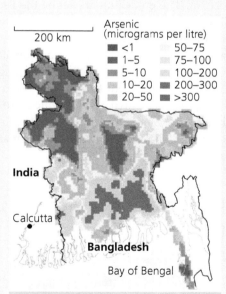

Arsenic (micrograms per litre)
- <1
- 1–5
- 5–10
- 10–20
- 20–50
- 50–75
- 75–100
- 100–200
- 200–300
- >300

200 km

India

Calcutta

Bangladesh

Bay of Bengal

In a modern tragedy, thousands of wells dug for drinking water in Bangladesh at the urging of international aid workers turned out to be contaminated with arsenic. This map shows that arsenic concentrations are highest in the southern portion of the country.
Source: Kinniburgh, D. G., and P. L. Smedley, eds. (2001). Arsenic Contamination of Groundwater in Bangladesh. Department of Public Health Engineering Bangladesh, British Geological Survey Report.

Other developed nations have also reduced water pollution. In Japan, Singapore, China, and South Korea, legislation, regulation, enforcement, and investment in wastewater treatment have brought striking water quality improvements. However, non-point-source pollution, eutrophication, and acid precipitation remain major challenges.

We treat our drinking water

Technological advances have also improved our ability to control pollution. The treatment of drinking water and the treatment of waste water are mainstream practices in developed nations today. Health Canada publishes standards for drinking water contaminants, which local governments and water suppliers are obligated to meet. Categories for standards include microbiological parameters (viruses, bacteria, protozoa, turbidity); chemical and physical parameters (including both health and esthetic guidelines); and radiological parameters. More than 80 characteristics are considered in these guidelines; some have numerical standards associated with them, while others do not. The guidelines are set by the Federal–Provincial–Territorial Committee on Drinking Water, which includes members from Health Canada, Environment Canada, and the Council of Environment Ministers, as well as the Canadian Advisory Council on Plumbing.

Before being sent to your tap, water from a reservoir or aquifer is treated with chemicals to remove particulate matter; passed through filters of sand, gravel, and charcoal; and/or disinfected with small amounts of an agent, such as chlorine.

It is better to prevent pollution than to mitigate the impacts after it occurs

In many cases, solutions to pollution will need to involve prevention, not simply **"end-of-pipe"** treatment and cleanup. With groundwater contamination, preventing pollution in the first place is by far the best strategy when one considers the other options for dealing with the problem: Filtering groundwater before distributing it can be extremely expensive; pumping water out of an aquifer, treating it, and then injecting it back in, repeatedly, takes an impracticably long time; and restricting pollutants on lands above selected aquifers would simply shift pollution elsewhere.

There are many things ordinary people can do to help minimize freshwater pollution. One is to exercise the power of consumer choice in the marketplace by purchasing phosphorus-free detergents and other "environmentally friendly" products. Another is to become involved in protecting local waterways. Locally based "riverwatch" groups or watershed associations enlist volunteers to collect data and help provincial and federal agencies safeguard the health of rivers and other water bodies. Such programs are proliferating as citizens and policy makers increasingly demand clean water.

Waste Water and Its Treatment

Waste water refers to water that has been used by people in some way. It includes water carrying sewage; water from showers, sinks, washing machines, and dishwashers; water used in manufacturing or cleaning processes by businesses and industries; and stormwater runoff.

Although natural systems can process moderate amounts of waste water, the large and concentrated amounts generated by our densely populated areas can harm ecosystems and pose threats to human health. Thus, attempts are now widely made to treat wastewater before releasing it into the environment.

Municipal wastewater treatment involves several steps

In rural areas, **septic systems** are the most popular method of waste water disposal. In a septic system, waste water runs from the house to an underground septic tank, inside which solids and oils separate from water. The clarified water proceeds downhill to a drain field of perforated pipes laid horizontally in gravel-filled trenches underground. Microbes decompose the waste water these pipes emit. Periodically, solid waste needs to be pumped from the septic tank and taken to a landfill.

In more densely populated areas, municipal sewer systems carry waste water from homes and businesses to centralized treatment locations. There, pollutants in waste water are removed by physical, chemical, and biological means (**FIGURE 9.24**).

At a treatment facility, *primary treatment*, the physical removal of contaminants in settling tanks or clarifiers, generally removes about 60% of suspended solids from waste water. Waste water then proceeds to *secondary treatment*, in which water is stirred and aerated so that aerobic bacteria degrade organic pollutants. Roughly 90% of suspended solids may be removed after secondary treatment. Finally, the clarified water is treated with chlorine, and sometimes ultraviolet light, to kill bacteria.

(*text continued on page 272*)

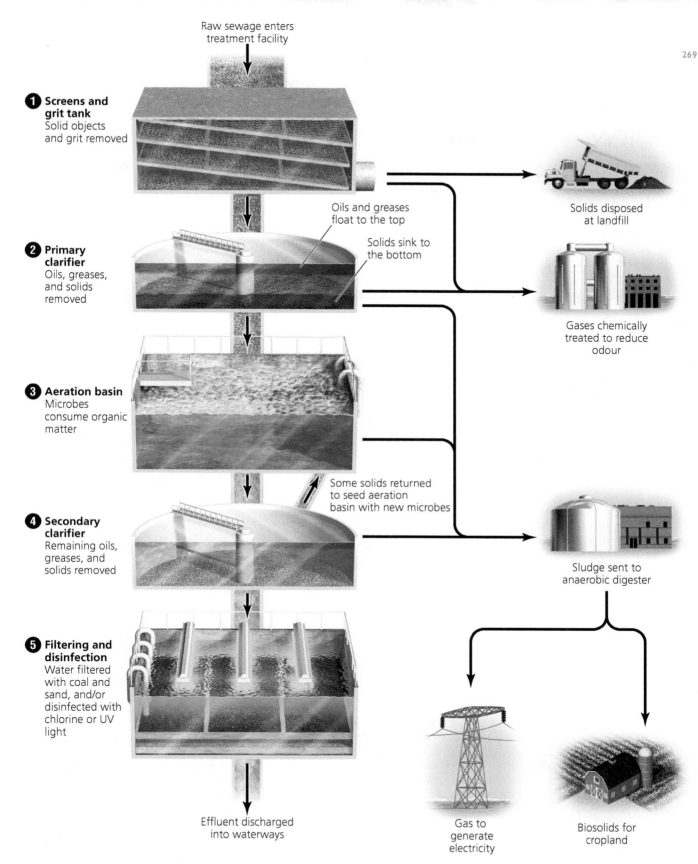

1 **Screens and grit tank**
Solid objects and grit removed

Raw sewage enters treatment facility

2 **Primary clarifier**
Oils, greases, and solids removed

Oils and greases float to the top

Solids sink to the bottom

Solids disposed at landfill

Gases chemically treated to reduce odour

3 **Aeration basin**
Microbes consume organic matter

4 **Secondary clarifier**
Remaining oils, greases, and solids removed

Some solids returned to seed aeration basin with new microbes

Sludge sent to anaerobic digester

5 **Filtering and disinfection**
Water filtered with coal and sand, and/or disinfected with chlorine or UV light

Effluent discharged into waterways

Gas to generate electricity

Biosolids for cropland

FIGURE 9.24   Shown here is a generalized process from a modern, environmentally sensitive wastewater treatment facility. Waste water initially passes through screens to remove large debris and into grit tanks to let grit settle **(1)**. It then enters tanks called primary clarifiers **(2)**, in which solids settle to the bottom and oils and greases float to the top for removal. Clarified water then proceeds to aeration basins **(3)** that oxygenate the water to encourage decomposition by aerobic bacteria. Water then passes into secondary clarifier tanks **(4)** for removal of further solids and oils. Next, the water may be purified by chemical treatment with chlorine, passage through carbon filters, and/or exposure to ultraviolet light **(5)**. The treated water (called *effluent*) may then be piped into natural water bodies, used for urban irrigation, flowed through an artificial wetland, or used to recharge groundwater. In addition, most treatment facilities control odour in the early steps and use anaerobic bacteria to digest sludge removed from the waste water. Sludge from digesters may be sent to farm fields as fertilizer, and gas from digestion may be used to generate electric power.

THE SCIENCE BEHIND THE STORY

When Water Turns Deadly: The Walkerton Tragedy[17]

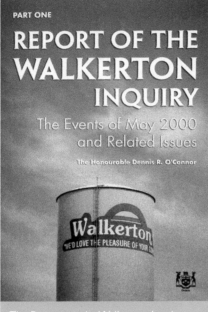

PART ONE

REPORT OF THE WALKERTON INQUIRY

The Events of May 2000 and Related Issues

The Honourable Dennis R. O'Connor

The Report on the Walkerton Inquiry, 2002, by Justice Dennis O'Connor, investigated both the events surrounding the Walkerton tragedy and the broader issues in Ontario's approach to water quality management.

Until May 2000, there was little to distinguish Walkerton from dozens of small towns in southern Ontario.[18]

That's how Justice Dennis O'Connor started his 2002 report entitled *Report of the Walkerton Inquiry: The Events of May 2000 and Related Issues.* He continued with a matter-of-fact summary of events:

In May 2000, Walkerton's drinking water system became contaminated with deadly bacteria, primarily Escherichia coli O157:H7. Seven people died, and more than 2,300 became ill. The community was devastated. The losses were enormous. There were widespread feelings of frustration, anger, and insecurity.[19]

In response to these events the Ontario government ordered the public inquiry, which found that contaminants entered Walkerton's municipal water wells around May 12, via any of a number of pathways. The transport of contaminants and their eventual entry into three wells were probably facilitated by heavy rains. The main source for the contaminants was animal wastes from livestock on a nearby farm. The farmer had followed appropriate procedures, the inquiry concluded, and was not at fault.

The contaminants were *Escherichia coli* and, less importantly, *Campylobacter jejuni.* Both are short, curved, rod-shaped bacteria (see photo) that occur commonly in the feces of birds, bats, and other warm-blooded animals. Symptoms of infection in humans include bloody diarrhea and stomach pain.

Some strains of *E. coli,* including the O157:H7 strain found at Walkerton, can be deadly. *C. jejuni* also has been linked to the development of a debilitating and sometimes fatal condition, Guillain-Barré syndrome. These are seriously pathogenic organisms.

Events began to unfold in Walkerton about six days after the initial contamination. Twenty children missed school on May 18; two were admitted to hospital. Multiple cases of intestinal illness prompted the medical officer of health, Dr. Murray McQuigge, to inquire about the safety of the water supply. Three times he was assured of its safety by Stan Koebel, manager of the Walkerton Public Utilities Commission (PUC). On May 21, Dr. McQuigge issued a boil-water advisory, in spite of the PUC's assurances.

The inquiry later concluded that Ontario's procedures for water safety testing were faulty and inadequate, and that PUC operators were insufficiently trained, had not done the daily testing they were supposed to do, and falsified data entries to give the impression that testing had taken place.

The inquiry concluded that chlorine residual testing and turbidity monitoring would have allowed for the detection and resolution of the problem. Chlorine residual testing is a simple approach that indicates whether sufficient chlorine has been added to the water to inactivate all the bacteria. If no "leftover" or residual chlorine remains in the water, then all of the added chlorine was used up and it is possible that some bacteria remain active. *Turbidity* refers to lack of clarity in the water; sometimes this is caused by suspended sediment, but a concentration of microorganisms can also cause turbidity. If chlorine residual testing and turbidity monitoring had been done on a daily basis, the problems would have been detected earlier and the outbreak could have been contained.

If a problem had been detected, further testing would have been triggered to identify the cause. This would have included technologies that detect an enzyme called beta-glucuronidase, which is produced by almost all forms of *E. coli* and very few other bacteria.

The sample is placed in a medium that changes colour or fluoresces if it is exposed to the enzyme. Sometimes it is necessary to culture the bacteria for a few days to have a sufficient concentration in the sample.

Most tests reveal the presence of *E. coli* but neither the exact amount nor the strain. Professor Ulrich Krull and colleagues at the University of Toronto Mississauga have developed a detection technology based on DNA. These *biosensors* contain short sequences of single-stranded DNA or *ssDNA,* which link or *hybridize* with complementary sequences of ssDNA in the sample, if they are present. An indicator, such as a fluorescing gel, shows that hybridization has occurred. Biosensors are useful because they instantly reveal not only the presence of the bacteria, but also the specific strain.

In his report, Justice O'Connor brought forward some pressing concerns about Ontario's approach to drinking water. Health Canada sets guidelines for drinking water quality; the provinces and territories have the responsibility to meet these guidelines and ensure drinking water safety. In some provinces this responsibility falls to the health ministry, in others the environment ministry. In 2002 Ontario passed the *Safe Drinking Water Act* to address the concerns raised by Justice O'Connor through the Walkerton Inquiry.

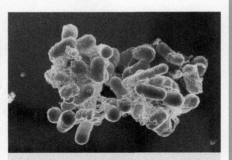

The contaminants found in the municipal water supply in Walkerton in 2000 included the bacteria *C. jejuni* and the deadly O157:H7 strain of *E. coli,* shown here.

CANADIAN ENVIRONMENTAL PERSPECTIVES

David Schindler

University of Alberta ecologist David Schindler warns that Canadian freshwater resources are under stress.

- **Ecosystem ecologist** and Killam Memorial **Professor** of Biological Sciences at the University of Alberta
- **Limnologist** and **biogeochemist**
- **Freshwater advocate**

Although his is not a "household name," it is probable that no other environmental scientist in Canada today is better known or more highly regarded for his commitment to freshwater resources and ecosystems than the University of Alberta's David Schindler.

Schindler is an ecologist and a *limnologist*—a scientist who studies ponds, lakes, wetlands, and freshwater ecology. He received a D. Phil. in ecology from Oxford University, where he attended as a Rhodes Scholar in the late 1960s. After serving two years as an Assistant Professor at Trent University, Schindler joined the Fisheries Research Board of Canada, which later became the Department of Fisheries and Oceans, as the founding director of the Experimental Lakes Area (ELA), one of the most successful and productive long-term research programs on freshwater

systems. (You will learn more about the ELA in "Central Case: The Rain and the Big Nickel," which looks at the impacts of acid rain on northern lakes.)

Through his work at ELA, Schindler contributed significantly to the scientific understanding of the effects of phosphorus and acid rain on lake ecosystems. This understanding helped lead to restrictions on the phosphorus content of detergents and sewage, as well as changes in air quality legislation in Canada, the United States, and the European Union. In recognition of his contributions to the scientific understanding of freshwater ecosystems, Schindler has received many prizes, awards, medals, and honorary degrees, including the first Stockholm Water Prize, the Volvo International Environment Prize (he is the only Canadian to win either prize), the Tyler Environmental Prize, and the Gerhard Herzberg Canada Gold Medal for Science and Engineering, which came with a research grant of $1 million.

Professor Schindler has most recently turned his attention to the Alberta tar sand developments and their intensive use of water. In an article entitled *The Myth of Abundant Canadian Water* he wrote, "It is perhaps ironic that Alberta, the province most vociferously opposed to controlling greenhouse gases in order to protect its pampered petrochemical industries, will almost certainly be the first to suffer from freshwater shortages."[20] In the same article he continued, "To a water expert, looking ahead is like the view from a locomotive, 10 seconds before the train wreck. Sometime in the coming century, the increasing human demand for water, the increasing scarcity of water due to climate warming, and one of the long droughts of past centuries will collide, and Albertans will learn first-hand what water scarcity is all about."[21] Schindler is also now making important contributions to the scientific understanding of the effects of global warming and of stratospheric ozone depletion on northern lakes.

Dr. Schindler's instruction at the University of Alberta is somewhat out of the ordinary for a typical science professor. He co-teaches a graduate course entitled Limnology: The Philosophy, Sociology, and Politics of Science and Public Policy in Canada; Environmental Decision Making.[22] The course is consistent with what is perhaps his most important achievement, which goes beyond the science. It lies instead in his success at communicating the scientific message about freshwater vulnerability to those who most need to hear it. In a profile of Schindler's achievements, the Natural Sciences and Engineering Research Council of Canada noted that he has "succeeded in conveying his knowledge and its importance to legislators in Canada and around the world and to the general public,"[23] and that through his work and teaching he has inspired many students to become involved with research and careers in environmental science. This contribution will have a lasting impact on Canada and Canadians.

"The time to make these decisions is now, not after our water is gone."[24]—**David Schindler**

Thinking About Environmental Perspectives

David Schindler is widely recognized as a model for active, engaged science, and it is often noted that he has inspired many students to enter the field of environmental science. Is there a professor in your college or university who has inspired you to continue in your studies? How do you think Professor Schindler manages to balance his scientific research with his political activism on behalf of freshwater resources? Compare Schindler's story to the Environmental Profile on David Suzuki in the first chapter of the book, recalling that Suzuki chose to give up doing science on a daily basis in order to focus more exclusively on environmental activism.

Most often, the treated water, called **effluent**, is piped into rivers or the ocean following primary and secondary treatment. Sometimes, however, "reclaimed" water is used for lawns and golf courses, for irrigation, or for industrial purposes, such as cooling water in power plants.

As water is purified throughout the treatment process, solid material called *sludge* is removed. Sludge is sent to digesting vats, where microorganisms decompose much of the matter. The result, a wet solution of "biosolids," is then dried and disposed of in a landfill, incinerated, or used as fertilizer on cropland. Methane-rich gas created by the decomposition process is sometimes burned to generate electricity, helping to offset the cost of the treatment facility.

Artificial wetlands can aid treatment

Natural wetlands already perform the ecosystem service of water purification, and wastewater treatment engineers are now manipulating wetlands and even constructing wetlands *de novo* to employ them as tools to cleanse waste water. The practice of treating waste water and other types of polluted runoff with so-called **constructed** (or **artificial**) **wetlands** is growing quickly. For example, the government of Nova Scotia and the Nova Scotia Agricultural College are constructing a test series of three artificial wetlands that will be used to filter agricultural runoff from livestock operations. Generally in this approach, waste water that has gone through primary treatment

at a conventional facility is pumped into the wetland, where microbes living amid the algae and aquatic plants decompose the remaining pollutants. Water cleansed in the wetland can then be released into waterways or allowed to percolate underground.

Constructed wetlands also serve as havens for wildlife and areas for human recreation. Restored and artificial wetlands in Ontario, Alberta, Nova Scotia, and many other locations in Canada are serving as wetland habitats for birds and wildlife, while helping to recharge depleted aquifers.

Conclusion

Citizen action, government legislation and regulation, new technologies, economic incentives, and public education are all enabling us to confront what will surely be one of the great environmental challenges of the new century: ensuring adequate quantity and quality of fresh water for ourselves and for the planet's ecosystems.

Accessible fresh water is only a minuscule percentage of the hydrosphere, but we generally take it for granted. With our expanding population and increasing water usage, we are approaching conditions of widespread scarcity. Water depletion and water pollution are already taking a toll on the health, economies, and societies of the developing world, and they are beginning to do so in arid areas of the developed world. There is reason to hope that we may yet attain sustainability in our water usage, however. Potential solutions are numerous, and the issue is too important to ignore.

REVIEWING OBJECTIVES

You should now be able to:

Explain the importance of water and the hydrologic cycle to ecosystems, human health, and economic pursuits

- We depend utterly on drinkable water, and a functioning hydrologic cycle is vital to maintaining ecosystems and our civilization.

Delineate the distribution of fresh water on Earth

- Of all the water on Earth, only about 1% is readily available for our use.
- Water availability varies in space and time, and regions vary greatly in the amounts they possess.

Describe major types of freshwater ecosystems

- The main types of freshwater ecosystems include rivers and streams, wetlands, and lakes and ponds.

Discuss how we use water and alter freshwater systems

- We use water for agriculture, industry, and residential use. The ratio of these uses varies among societies, but globally 70% is used for agriculture.
- Most of the world's rivers are dammed. Dams bring a diverse set of benefits and costs. Increasingly, people are proposing dam removal.
- We divert water with canals and irrigation ditches and attempt to control floods with dikes and levees.
- We pump water from aquifers and surface water bodies, sometimes at unsustainable rates.

Assess problems of water supply and propose solutions to address depletion of fresh water

- Water tables are dropping worldwide from unsustainable groundwater extraction. Surface water extraction has caused rivers to run dry and water bodies to shrink.
- Unequal water distribution amid shrinking supplies may heighten political tensions over water in the future.
- Solutions to expand supply, such as desalination, are worth pursuing, but not to the exclusion of finding ways to decrease demand.
- Solutions to reduce demand include technology, approaches, and consumer products that increase efficiency in agriculture, industry, and the home.

Assess problems of water quality and propose solutions to address water pollution

- Water pollutants include excessive nutrients, microbial pathogens, toxic chemicals, sediment, and thermal pollution.

- Water pollution stems from point sources and non-point sources.
- Scientists who monitor water quality use biological, chemical, and physical indicators.
- Groundwater pollution can be more persistent than surface water pollution.
- Legislation and regulation have improved water quality in developed nations in recent decades.
- Preventing water pollution is better than mitigation.

Explain how waste water is treated

- Septic systems are used to treat waste water in rural areas.
- Waste water is treated physically, biologically, and chemically in a series of steps at municipal wastewater treatment facilities.
- Artificial wetlands enhance wastewater treatment while restoring habitat for wildlife.

TESTING YOUR COMPREHENSION

1. Define *groundwater*. What role does groundwater play in the hydrologic cycle?
2. Why are sources of fresh water unreliable for some people and plentiful for others?
3. Describe three benefits of damming rivers and three costs. What particular environmental, health, and social concerns has China's Three Gorges Dam and its reservoir raised?
4. Why do the Colorado, Rio Grande, Nile, and Yellow rivers now slow to a trickle or run dry before reaching their deltas?
5. Why are water tables dropping around the world? What are some environmental costs of falling water tables?

6. Name three major types of water pollutants, and provide an example of each. List three properties of water that scientists use to determine water quality.
7. Why do many scientists consider groundwater pollution a greater problem than surface water pollution?
8. What are some anthropogenic (human) sources of groundwater pollution?
9. Describe how drinking water is treated. How does a septic system work?
10. Describe and explain the major steps in the process of wastewater treatment. How can artificial wetlands aid such treatment?

THINKING IT THROUGH

1. Discuss possible strategies for equalizing distribution of water throughout the world. Consider supply and transport issues. Have our methods of drawing, distributing, and storing water changed very much throughout history? How is the scale of our efforts affecting the availability of water supplies?

2. How can we lessen agricultural demand for water? Describe some ways in which we can reduce household water use. How can industrial uses of water be reduced?
3. Discuss some of the methods we can adopt, in addition to "end-of-pipe" solutions, to prevent contamination and ensure "water security."

4. How might desalination technology help "make" more water? Describe two methods of desalination. Where is this technology being used?

5. Let's say that you have been put in charge of water policy for your region. The aquifer beneath your region has been overpumped, and many wells have already run dry. Agricultural production last year decreased for the first time in a generation, and farmers are clamouring for you to do something. Meanwhile, the region's largest city is growing so fast that more water is needed for its burgeoning urban population. What policies would you consider to restore your region's water supply? Would you try to take steps to increase supply, to decrease demand, or both? Explain why you would choose such policies.

6. Having solved the water depletion problem in your region, your next task is to deal with pollution of the groundwater that provides the region's drinking water supply. Recent studies have shown that one-third of the province's groundwater has levels of pollutants that violate international standards for human health. Citizens are fearful for their safety, and the provincial government is threatening enforcement. What steps would you consider taking to safeguard the quality of your region's groundwater supply, and why?

INTERPRETING GRAPHS AND DATA

Close to 75% of the fresh water used by people is used in agriculture, and about 1 of every 14 people lives where water is scarce. By the year 2050, scientists project that two-thirds of the world's population will live in water-scarce areas, including most of Africa, the Middle East, India, and China. How much water is required to feed 7 billion people a basic dietary requirement of 2700 calories (11.3 kJ) per day? The answer depends on the efficiency with which we use water in agricultural production and on the type of diet we consume.

1. How many litres of water are needed to produce 2300 calories (9.6 kJ) of vegetable food? How many litres of water are needed to produce 400 calories (1.7 kJ) of animal food? How many litres of water are needed daily to provide this diet? Annually?

2. How many litres of water would be saved daily, compared to the diet in the graph, if the 2700 calories were provided entirely by vegetables? Annually?

3. Reflect on one of the quotes at the beginning of this chapter: "Water promises to be to the twenty-first century what oil was to the twentieth century: the precious commodity that determines the wealth of nations." How do you think the demographic

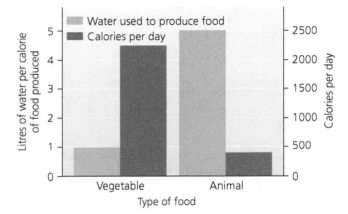

Amount of water needed to produce vegetable and animal food (orange), and global average calories per day consumed of vegetable and animal food (red) (1000 calories = 0.004184 kJ).
Source: Data from Wallace, J. S. (2000). Increasing agricultural water use efficiency to meet future food production. Agriculture, Ecosystems and Environment 82:105–119.

pressure on the water supply could affect world trade, particularly trade of agricultural products? Do you think it could affect prospects for peace and stability in and among nations? How so?

CHAPTER ENDNOTES

1. Environment Canada, *Fresh Water: Quick Facts,* www.ec.gc.ca/water/en/e_quickfacts.htm
2. Agriculture and Agri-Foods Canada, *The Canadian Bottled Water Industry,* www4.agr.gc.ca/AAFC-AAC/display-afficher.do?id=1171644581795&lang=e#sig
3. Quinn, F. (2007) *Water Diversion, Export, and Canada–U.S. Relations: A Brief History* (August). Program on Water Issues (POWI), Munk Centre for International Studies at the University of Toronto, www.powi.ca

4. Quinn, F. (2007) *Water Diversion, Export, and Canada–U.S. Relations: A Brief History* (August). Program on Water Issues (POWI), Munk Centre for International Studies at the University of Toronto, www.powi.ca

5. Prairie Pothole Joint Venture, *Introduction to the Prairie Pothole Region, 2005 Implementation Plan Section I*, www.ppjv.org

6. Natural Resources Canada, *Groundwater Mapping Program: Overview*, http://ess.nrcan.gc.ca/gm-ces/overview_e.php

7. Coté, François (2006) *Freshwater Management in Canada IV: Groundwater.* Library of Parliament, Parliamentary Information and Research Service, Science and Technology Division, February 2006, www.parl.gc.ca/information/library/PRBpubs/prb0554-e.html#aquifiers

8. Environment Canada, *Water—Vulnerable to Climate Change*, www.ec.gc.ca/water/en/info/pubs/FS/e_FSA9.htm

9. Environment Canada, Informational and Resources Services, *Water—Vulnerable to Climate Change*, www.ec.gc.ca/water/en/info/pubs/FS/e_FSA9

10. Environment Canada, *Fresh Water, Bulk Removal of Water*, www.ec.gc.ca/water/en/manage/removal/e_remove.htm

11. Ramsar Convention, www.ramsar.org

12. Ramsar Convention, www.ramsar.org

13. Statistics Canada (2008) Against the flow: Which households drink bottled water? *EnviroStats*, Summer, Vol. 2, No. 2, www.statcan.ca/Daily/English/080625/d080625c.htm

14. Statistics Canada (2008) Against the flow: Which households drink bottled water? *EnviroStats*, Summer, Vol. 2, No. 2, www.statcan.ca/Daily/English/080625/d080625c.htm

15. Stamminger, R. (May/June 2006). "Is a machine more efficient than the hand?". Home energy, http://www.homeenergy.org/show/article/nav/kitchen/id/180

16. Environment Canada, *The Management of Water: Leaking Underground Storage Tanks and Pipelines*, www.ec.gc.ca/water/en/manage/poll/e_tanks.htm

17. Based partly on information from O'Connor, Dennis R. (2002) *Report of the Walkerton Inquiry: The Events of May 2000 and Related Issues.* Toronto: Government of Ontario.

18. O'Connor, Dennis R. (2002) *Report of the Walkerton Inquiry: The Events of May 2000 and Related Issues.* Toronto: Government of Ontario.

19. O'Connor, D. R. (2002) *Report of the Walkerton Inquiry: The Events of May 2000 and Related Issues.* Toronto: Government of Ontario.

20. Schindler, D. (2006) *The Myth of Abundant Canadian Water*, March, www.innovationcanada.ca/en/articles/the-myth-of-abundant-canadian-water

21. Schindler, D. (2006) *The Myth of Abundant Canadian Water*, March, www.innovationcanada.ca/en/articles/the-myth-of-abundant-canadian-water

22. University of Alberta, Faculty of Science, Department of Biological Sciences, www.biology.ualberta.ca/faculty/david_schindler/?Page=1023

23. NSERC News Releases, *David Schindler*, www.nserc.gc.ca/news/2000/aoe_schindler_e.htm

24. Schindler, D. (2006) *The Myth of Abundant Water*, Canada Foundation for Innovation, March 1, 2006; www.innovationcanada.ca/en/articles/the-myth-of-abundant-canadian-water

MyEnvironmentPlace

Go to **www.myenvironmentplace.ca** where you will find quizzes, animations, your Pearson eText, and more.

Marine and Coastal Systems and Fisheries

10

Cod fishers haul in a dwindling catch.

Upon successfully completing this chapter, you will be able to

- Identify physical, geographical, chemical, and biological aspects of the marine environment
- Describe major types of marine ecosystems
- Outline historic and current human uses of marine resources

- Assess human impacts on marine environments
- Review the current state of ocean fisheries and reasons for their decline
- Evaluate marine protected areas and reserves as innovative solutions

Cod fishing has been a way of life for generations in Newfoundland and Labrador. Monster cod like these are no longer there to be harvested.

CENTRAL CASE:
LESSONS LEARNED: THE COLLAPSE OF THE COD FISHERIES

"All of a sudden they just crashed."
—DONALD PAUL, NEWFOUNDLAND FISHER, IN 1997

"Either we have sustainable fisheries, or we have no fishery."
—CANADIAN FISHERIES MINISTER DAVID ANDERSON, IN 1998

No fish has had more impact on human civilization than the Atlantic cod. Europeans exploring the coasts of North America 500 years ago discovered that they could catch these abundant fish by dipping baskets over the railings of their ships, and the race to harvest this resource helped lead to the colonization of the New World. Starting in the early 1500s, schooners captured countless millions of cod, and the fish became a dietary staple on both sides of the Atlantic.

Since then, cod fishing has been the economic engine for hundreds of coastal communities in eastern Canada and New England. In many Canadian coastal villages, cod fishing has been a way of life for generations (see photo). So it came as a shock when the cod all but disappeared, and governments had to step in and close the fisheries.

The Atlantic cod (*Gadus morhua*) is a type of *groundfish*, a fish that lives or feeds along the bottom. People have long coveted groundfish, such as halibut, pollock, haddock, and flounder. Adult cod eat smaller fish and invertebrates, commonly grow to 60–70 cm long, and can live 20 years. A mature female cod can produce several million eggs.

Atlantic cod inhabit cool ocean waters on both sides of the North Atlantic and occur in 24 discrete populations, called *stocks*. One stock inhabits the Grand

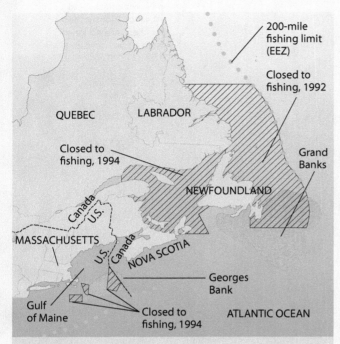

FIGURE 10.1
Ten stocks of Atlantic cod inhabit areas of the northwestern Atlantic Ocean, including the Grand Banks and Georges Bank, regions of shallow water that are especially productive for groundfish. Portions of these areas have been closed to fishing because cod populations have collapsed after being overfished.

Banks off the Newfoundland coast, and another lives on Georges Bank off Massachusetts (**FIGURE 10.1**).

The Grand Banks provided ample fish for centuries. With advancing technology, however, ships became larger and more effective at finding fish. By the 1960s, massive industrial trawlers from Europe were vacuuming up unprecedented numbers of groundfish. In 1977, Canada exercised its legal right to the waters 200 nautical miles from shore, the **Exclusive Economic Zone** established by the U.N. Convention on the Law of the Sea. Foreign fleets were expelled from most of the Grand Banks, and Canada's fishing industry was revved up like never before.

Catches began to dwindle in the 1980s. Too many fish had been taken, and trawling had destroyed much underwater habitat. Environmental factors also played a role. By 1992 the situation was dire: Scientists reported that mature cod were at just 10% of their long-term abundance. On July 2, Fisheries Minister John Crosbie announced a two-year ban on commercial cod fishing off of Newfoundland and Labrador, where the $700 million fishery supplied income to 16% of the province's

workforce. To compensate fishers, the government offered 10 weekly payments of $225, along with training for new job skills and incentives for early retirement. Over the next two years, 40 000 fishers and processing plant workers lost their jobs. Some coastal communities faced economic ruin; for generations, fishing had been their reason for being.

Cod stocks did not rebound by 1994, so the government extended the moratorium, enacted bans on all other major cod fisheries, and scrambled to offer more compensation, eventually spending more than $4 billion. In 1997–1998, Canada partially reopened some fisheries, but data soon confirmed that the stocks were not recovering. In April 2003, the cod fisheries were closed indefinitely, to recreational as well as commercial fishing. Today it remains illegal, for the most part, to fish for cod in these areas, and the Committee on the Status of Endangered Wildlife in Canada has placed Newfoundland cod populations on its endangered list. Fishers challenging the ban have been arrested, fined, and jailed.

Across the border in U.S. waters, cod stocks were collapsing in the Gulf of Maine and Georges Bank. In 1994, the National Marine Fisheries Service (NMFS) closed three prime fishing areas. Over the next several years, NMFS designed a number of regulations, but these steps were too little, too late. A 2005 report revealed that the cod were not recovering as hoped, and scientists are struggling to explain why. Research suggests that once the mature cod were eliminated, the species they preyed upon proliferated. Now those species compete with and prey on young cod, preventing the population from rebuilding.

The closures have allowed some other species to rebound. Seafloor invertebrates have begun to recover in the absence of trawling; spawning stocks of haddock and yellowtail flounder have risen; and sea scallops have increased in biomass fourteenfold in the Georges Bank fishery. Such recoveries in no-fishing areas show scientists, fishers, and policy makers that protecting areas of ocean can help save dwindling marine populations. In the Grand Banks, however, research has shown that the fundamental nature of the ecosystem has shifted from a bottom-oriented fauna to a shallow-water fauna. There are no signs that a complete recovery will ever be achievable.

The Ocean

It has been said that our planet Earth should more properly be named "Ocean." After all, ocean water covers the vast majority of our planet's surface. Moreover, the oceans strongly influence how our planet's systems work. They influence global climate, teem with biodiversity, facilitate transportation and commerce, and provide us with resources. Even landlocked areas far from the coasts are affected. The oceans provide fish for people to eat in Saskatchewan, supply oil to power cars in Ontario, and influence the weather in Manitoba. In this chapter you will learn about **oceanography**, the scientific study of the physics, chemistry, biology, and geology of the oceans.

Ocean covers most of Earth's surface

Although we generally speak of oceans (**FIGURE 10.2**) in the plural, giving each major basin a name—Pacific, Atlantic, Indian, Arctic, and Southern—all these oceans are connected, composing a single vast body of water. This one "world ocean" covers 71% of Earth's surface and contains about 97.5% of its surface water. The ocean takes up most of the hydrosphere, influences the atmosphere and lithosphere, and encompasses much of the biosphere, including at least 250 000 species. The world ocean touches and is touched by virtually every environmental system and every human endeavour.

The ocean contains more than water

Ocean water contains approximately 96.5% H_2O by mass; most of the remainder consists of ions from dissolved salts (**FIGURE 10.3**). Ocean water is salty primarily because ocean basins are the final repositories for water that runs off the land. Rivers carry sediment and dissolved salts from the continents into the ocean, as do winds. Evaporation from the ocean surface then removes pure water, leaving a higher concentration of salts. If we were able to evaporate all the water from the oceans, the empty basins would be covered with a layer of dried salt 63 m thick.

The **salinity**—basically, the saltiness—of ocean water generally ranges from 33 to 37 parts per thousand (ppt, also denoted ‰ or "per mil"), varying from place to place because of differences in evaporation, precipitation, and freshwater runoff from land and glaciers. Salinity near the

roots

SALINITY

The term **salinity** likely derives from the Latin words *salinum* ("salt cellar") or *salinae* ("salt pit"), both of which have the Latin root *sal*, meaning "salt." The suffix *-ity* derives from the Latin *-itatem*, which is used to denote a state or condition of being.

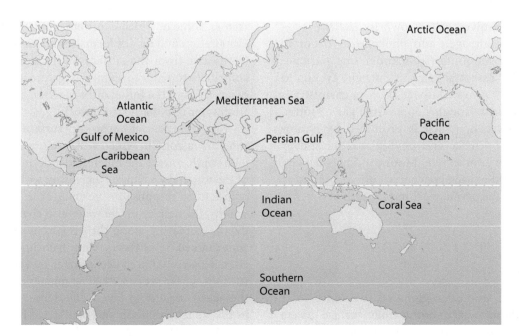

FIGURE 10.2   The world ocean is connected in a single vast body of water, with different names. The Pacific Ocean is the largest and, like the Atlantic and Indian Oceans, includes both tropical and temperate waters. The smaller Arctic and Southern Oceans include the waters in the north and south polar regions, respectively. Many smaller bodies of water are named as seas or gulfs; a selected few are shown here.

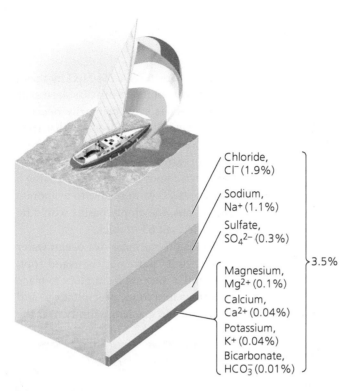

FIGURE 10.3
Ocean water consists of 3.5% salt, by mass, as shown by the proportionally thin coloured slices of the cube in this diagram. Most of this salt is NaCl in solution, so sodium and chloride ions are abundant. A number of other ions and trace elements are also present.

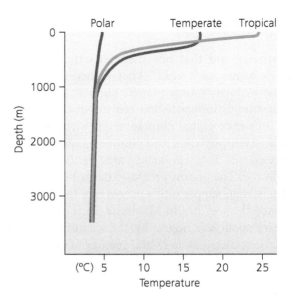

FIGURE 10.4
Ocean water varies in temperature with depth. Water temperatures near the surface are warmer because of daily heating by the Sun, and within the top 1000 m they become rapidly colder with depth. This temperature differential is greatest in the tropics because of intense solar heating and is least in the polar regions. Deep water at all latitudes is equivalent in temperature.
Source: Garrison, T. (2005). Oceanography, 5th ed. Belmont, CA: Brooks/Cole.

equator is low because this region has a great deal of precipitation, which is relatively salt free. In contrast, surface salinity is high at latitudes roughly 30–35 degrees north and south, where evaporation exceeds precipitation.

Besides the dissolved salts shown in FIGURE 10.3, nutrients such as nitrogen and phosphorus occur in seawater in trace amounts (well under one part per million) and play essential roles in nutrient cycling in marine ecosystems. Another aspect of ocean chemistry is dissolved gas content. Roughly 36% of the gas dissolved in seawater is oxygen, which is produced by photosynthetic plants, bacteria, and phytoplankton, and by diffusion from the atmosphere. Marine animals depend on this oxygen, and oxygen concentrations are highest in the upper layer of the ocean, reaching 13 ml/L of water.

Ocean water is vertically structured

Surface waters in tropical regions receive more solar radiation and therefore are warmer than surface waters in temperate or polar regions. In all regions, however, temperature declines with depth (FIGURE 10.4). Water density increases as salinity rises and as temperature

falls. These relationships give rise to different layers of water; heavier (colder and saltier) water sinks, and lighter (warmer and less salty) water remains nearer the surface. Waters of the surface zone are heated by sunlight each day and are stirred by wind such that the properties are fairly uniform throughout the zone. The salinity of surface water is influenced by a variety of interacting factors, some of which contribute to greater salinity (e.g., evaporation and sea ice formation, both of which remove freshwater from the surface layer) and some of which contribute to reduced salinity (e.g., precipitation, melting of sea ice, and the influx of river water, all of which bring freshwater into the surface layer).

Below the zone of warm, salty surface water is the **thermocline**, a zone in which temperature decreases rapidly with depth, toward the much colder deep layer. The salinity of the water also changes, increasing with depth along the *halocline*. In response to the changes in temperature and salinity, the density of the water also changes rapidly with depth, increasing along the *pycnocline*. The transitional zone marked by the thermocline, halocline, and pycnocline contains about 18% of ocean water by volume, compared with the surface zone's 2%. The remaining 80% resides in the ocean's vast deep layer. The dense, dark, cold water in this zone is sluggish and unaffected by winds, storms, sunlight, or daily temperature fluctuations.

Despite the daily heating and cooling of surface waters, ocean temperatures are much more stable than temperatures on land. Midlatitude oceans experience yearly temperature variation of only around 10°C, and tropical and polar oceans are still more stable. The reason for this stability is that it takes a lot of energy to break the hydrogen bonds between water molecules; the result is that water has a very high *heat capacity*, a measure of the heat required to increase temperature by a given amount. High heat capacity enables the ocean to absorb a tremendous amount of heat from the atmosphere. In fact, the heat content of the entire atmosphere is equal to that of just the top 2.6 m of the ocean. By absorbing heat and releasing it to the atmosphere, the ocean helps regulate Earth's climate.

Ocean water flows vertically and horizontally, influencing climate

Surface winds and heating in seawater create huge vertical flows of water, or **currents. Upwelling,** the vertical flow of cold, deep water toward the surface, occurs where horizontal currents diverge, or flow away from one another. Because upwelled water is rich in nutrients from the bottom, upwellings are often sites of high primary productivity and lucrative fisheries. Upwellings also occur where strong winds blow away from or parallel to coastlines (**FIGURE 10.5**). An example is the western coast of Vancouver Island, where north winds and the Coriolis effect move surface waters away from the shore, raising nutrient-rich water from below and creating a biologically rich region. The cold water also chills the air along the coast, giving Vancouver Island its famous cool, rainy summers.

In areas where surface currents converge, or come together, surface water sinks and **downwelling** occurs. Downwelling transports water rich in dissolved gases,

providing an influx of oxygen for deep-water life. Vertical currents also occur in the deep zone, where differences in water density can lead to rising and falling convection currents, similar to those seen in molten rock and in air.

The **thermohaline circulation** is the global oceanic circulation system of upwelling and downwelling currents. It connects surface water flows to deeper water flows, with far-reaching effects on global climate. The term *thermohaline* comes from root words that mean "heat" and "salinity." In this worldwide circulatory system, warmer, fresher water moves along the surface and water in the deep zones, which is colder, saltier, and denser, circulates far beneath the surface.

In the Atlantic Ocean, warm surface water flows northward from the equator in the Gulf Stream, carrying heat to high latitudes and keeping Europe warmer than it would otherwise be. As the surface water of this conveyor belt system releases heat energy and cools, it becomes denser and sinks, creating **North Atlantic Deep Water (NADW).** The sinking of this cold, dense water keeps the northern part of the Atlantic basin connected to the global thermohaline circulation system; without it, the climate in areas bordering the North Atlantic would be very different (see "The Science Behind the Story: Tip Jets and NADW off the Coast of Greenland"). A similar phenomenon happens in the Southern Ocean, where extremely cold, salty water sinks to form **Antarctic Bottom Water (AABW).** Without or with weaker thermohaline circulation, Earth would be a very different place: The climate of France would be similar to that of Newfoundland; tropical regions would become even hotter, as their heat would not be moved north by the Gulf Stream; the deep ocean could become lifeless, lacking the oxygen-rich waters provided by the thermohaline circulation; biological productivity in the Pacific and Indian Oceans would suffer, as

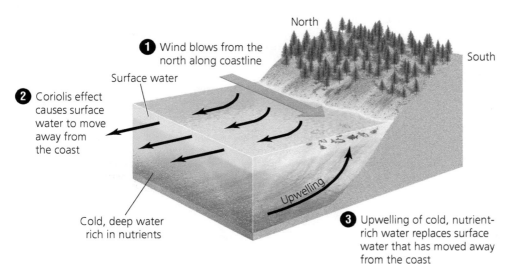

North

① Wind blows from the north along coastline

Surface water

South

② Coriolis effect causes surface water to move away from the coast

Cold, deep water rich in nutrients

Upwelling

③ Upwelling of cold, nutrient-rich water replaces surface water that has moved away from the coast

FIGURE 10.5
Upwelling is the movement of bottom waters upward. This type of vertical current often brings nutrients up to the surface, creating rich areas for marine life. For example, north winds blow along the western coast of Vancouver Island (1), while the Coriolis effect draws wind and water away from the coast (2). Water is then pulled up from the bottom (3) to replace the water that moves away from shore.

THE SCIENCE BEHIND THE STORY

Tip Jets and NADW off the coast of Greenland

Dr. Kent Moore of the University of Toronto in a research plane over the North Atlantic.

The formation of North Atlantic Deep Water (NADW), in which extremely cold water sinks in the northern part of the Atlantic to join the deep oceanic circulation, is an integral part of the global thermohaline circulation. It is also crucial for keeping the northern Atlantic basin connected to the rest of the global circulation system. If NADW formation were suppressed, the warm Gulf Stream current—responsible for the relatively mild climate of northeastern North America and Western Europe—could be cut off from entering the North Atlantic, with devastating climatic consequences for this region and globally.

Given its importance, it is surprising to learn that ocean water sinks to form NADW only under extremely specific conditions, and these conditions occur in just a handful of geographic locations in the North Atlantic. What's more, as Professor Kent Moore from the University of Toronto and his colleagues have discovered, the sinking of cold ocean water is also dependent upon highly specialized conditions in the atmosphere off the coast of Greenland.

To investigate the conditions under which NADW forms, Dr. Moore deploys scientific buoys in the North Atlantic, which measure the temperature and other characteristics of ocean water (yes, pretty much like the buoys in the first part of the movie *The Day After Tomorrow*). With data from these buoys, he is able to pinpoint the exact locations where ocean water

becomes cold and dense enough to sink, becoming NADW.

Dr. Moore, an atmospheric physicist, and colleagues have also investigated the role of the atmosphere in oceanic circulation in this part of the Atlantic. They do this by comparing satellite imagery and buoy data to information they collect by flying aboard a research plane equipped with scientific instruments for measuring a wide variety of atmospheric conditions. The aircraft, a modified four-engine passenger jet, is nicknamed FAAM (Facility for Airborne Atmospheric Measurements).

The scientists have discovered that the topography of Greenland plays a fundamental role in oceanic circulation in the North Atlantic, and specifically determines the locations where NADW circulation can be triggered. High-speed wind events, with wind speeds greater than 25 m/sec, are common near the southern end of Greenland, which acts as a massive topographic barrier. The topographic barrier funnels and directs the winds in one direction or another, forming very narrow

high-speed wind streams over the adjacent ocean. These events are called *tip jets* (or *reverse tip jets*, depending on the direction of flow) and Dr. Moore describes the experience of flying through one of these high-speed wind streams as "rough."

What Dr. Moore and his colleagues have discovered, in particular, is that tip jets and related wind events are intimately associated with the formation of NADW. The high-speed winds have the effect of drawing warmth away from surface ocean water, cooling it sufficiently to increase its density and trigger sinking. The locations where this occurs are extremely localized because of the narrow channeling of winds that must pass either around or over the topographic barriers formed by the coast of Greenland.

Given the importance of NADW and the thermohaline circulation system in regulating climate, particularly around the North Atlantic, Professor Moore agrees that there is much fundamental research that needs to be carried out to improve our understanding of these atmospheric and oceanic processes and connections.

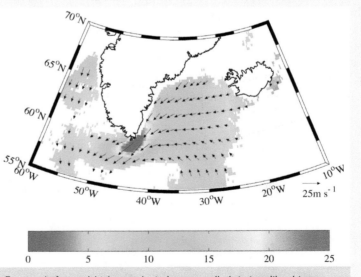

Extremely focused, high-speed wind events called tip jets, like this one off Cape Farewell on the southern coast of Greenland, are crucial in the formation of North Atlantic Deep Water because they draw heat away from surface water. In this figure, based on satellite imagery from February 2007, wind speeds are shown in metres per second.

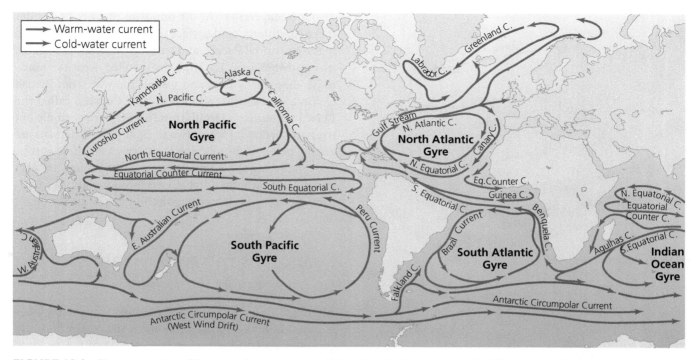

FIGURE 10.6   The upper waters of the oceans flow in currents, which are long-lasting and predictable global patterns of water movement. Warm- and cold-water currents interact with the planet's climate system, and people have used them for centuries to navigate the ocean.   *Source: Garrison, T. (2005). Oceanography, 5th ed. Belmont, CA: Brooks/Cole.*

fewer nutrients from depth would make it to the surface layer where photosynthesis happens; and the removal of greenhouse gases from the atmosphere to the deep ocean would cease, thus accelerating global climate change.

Ocean water also flows horizontally, in vast riverlike flows (**FIGURE 10.6**), driven mainly by wind systems and differences in air pressure. These surface currents flow within the upper 400 m of water, horizontally and for great distances. Long-lasting patterns in surface currents influence global climate, and play key roles in the phenomena known as El Niño and La Niña. They have also been crucial in navigation and human history; currents helped carry Polynesians to Easter Island, Darwin to the Galápagos, and Europeans to the New World. Currents transport heat, nutrients, pollution, and the larvae of many marine species from place to place.

Some horizontal surface currents are very slow; others, like the Gulf Stream, are rapid and powerful. From the Gulf of Mexico, the Gulf Stream moves up the U.S. Atlantic coast and flows past the eastern edges of Georges Bank and the Grand Banks at a rate of 160 km per day (nearly 2 m/s). Averaging 70 km across, the Gulf Stream continues across the North Atlantic, bringing warm water to Europe and moderating that continent's climate, which otherwise would be much colder.

Some of the ocean's surface currents take the form of enormous gyres. A **gyre** is an oceanic current that flows in a circular motion as a result of the *Coriolis force* (an artifact of Earth's rotation, which we will discuss in

greater detail in the chapter on atmospheric science and air pollution). There are five great gyres in the world ocean: the North Atlantic, South Atlantic, North Pacific, South Pacific, and Indian Ocean gyres (see **FIGURE 10.6**).

La Niña and El Niño demonstrate the atmosphere–ocean connection

Horizontal ocean currents can have far-reaching impacts on climate. An example is the La Niña–El Niño cycle, which demonstrates the linkages between the oceanic and atmospheric systems. Under normal conditions, prevailing winds blow from east to west along the equator, from a region of high pressure in the eastern Pacific to one of low pressure in the western Pacific, forming a large-scale convective loop, or atmospheric circulation pattern (**FIGURE 10.7A**). The winds push surface waters westward, causing water to "pile up" in the western Pacific. As a result, water near Indonesia can be 50 cm higher and 8°C warmer than water near South America. The westward-moving surface waters allow cold water to rise up from the deep in a nutrient-rich upwelling along the coast of Peru and Ecuador.

El Niño conditions are triggered when air pressure increases in the western Pacific and decreases in the eastern Pacific, causing the equatorial winds to weaken. Without these winds, the warm water that collects in the

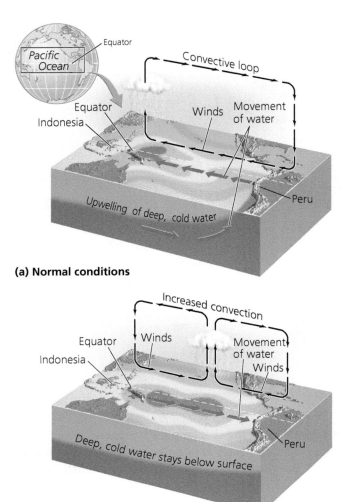

(a) Normal conditions

(b) El Niño conditions

FIGURE 10.7
In these diagrams, red and orange colours denote warmer water, and blue and green colours denote colder water. Under normal conditions **(a)**, prevailing winds push warm surface waters toward the western Pacific. Under El Niño conditions **(b)**, the winds weaken and the warm water flows back across the Pacific toward South America, like water sloshing in a bathtub. This shuts down upwelling along the American coast and alters precipitation patterns regionally and globally.
Source: Adapted from National Oceanic and Atmospheric Administration, Tropical Atmospheric Ocean Project.

western Pacific flows eastward (**FIGURE 10.7B**), suppressing upwellings along the Pacific coast of South, Central, and North America, and shutting down the delivery of nutrients that support marine life and fisheries. Coastal industries, such as Peru's anchovy fisheries, are devastated by each El Niño event; the 1982–1983 event caused more than $8 billion in economic losses worldwide. El Niños alter weather patterns around the world, creating rainstorms and floods in areas that are generally dry (such as southern California), and causing drought and fire in regions that are typically moist (such as Indonesia). In Canada, El Niño tends to produce weather that is drier and warmer than normal, with more frequent droughts.

La Niña events are the opposite of El Niño; under these conditions, cold surface waters extend far westward in the equatorial Pacific, and weather patterns are affected in opposite ways. La Niña–influenced weather tends to be abnormally cool and wet all the way from British Columbia to southern Québec. These cycles, called the **El Niño–Southern Oscillation (ENSO)**, are periodic but irregular, occurring every two to eight years. Scientists are getting better at deciphering the triggers for these events, and predicting their impacts on weather. They are also investigating whether globally warming air and sea temperatures may be increasing the frequency and strength of these cycles.

Seafloor topography can be rugged and complex

Although oceans are depicted on most maps and globes as smooth, blue swaths, portions of the ocean floor are complex. As you learned in the context of the tectonic and rock cycles, underwater volcanoes shoot forth enough magma to build islands above sea level, such as the Hawaiian Islands. Steep canyons similar in scale to the Grand Canyon lie just offshore of some continents. The lowest spot in the oceans—the Mariana Trench in the South Pacific—is deeper than Mount Everest is high, by more than 2.1 km. Our planet's longest mountain range also is under water—the Mid-Atlantic Ridge, which runs the length of the Atlantic Ocean, is just part of it (**FIGURE 10.8**).

Georges Bank and the Grand Banks are essentially huge underwater mounds formed from the debris

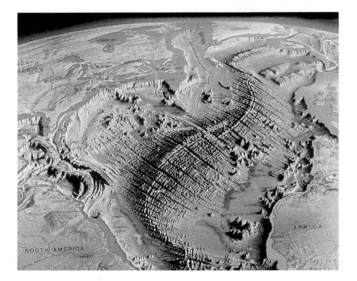

FIGURE 10.8
The seafloor can be rugged. The spreading margin between tectonic plates at the Mid-Atlantic Ridge gives rise to a vast underwater volcanic mountain chain.

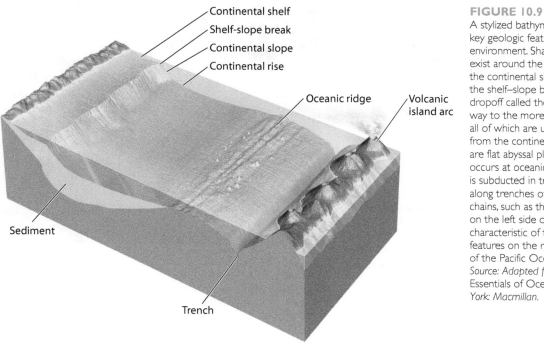

Continental shelf
Shelf-slope break
Continental slope
Continental rise
Oceanic ridge
Volcanic island arc
Sediment
Trench

FIGURE 10.9
A stylized bathymetric profile shows key geologic features of the submarine environment. Shallow regions of water exist around the edges of continents over the continental shelf, which drops off at the shelf–slope break. The relatively steep dropoff called the continental slope gives way to the more gradual continental rise, all of which are underlain by sediments from the continents. Vast areas of seafloor are flat abyssal plain. Seafloor spreading occurs at oceanic ridges, and oceanic crust is subducted in trenches. Volcanic activity along trenches often gives rise to island chains, such as the Aleutian Islands. Features on the left side of this diagram are more characteristic of the Atlantic Ocean, and features on the right are more characteristic of the Pacific Ocean.
Source: Adapted from Thurman, H. V. (1990). Essentials of Oceanography, 4th ed. New York: Macmillan.

dumped by glaciers at their southernmost extent. As climate warmed and the glaciers retreated, sea level rose and this hilly terrain became submerged. The 200-nautical-mile fishing limit established by the Convention on the Law of the Sea is particularly problematic here because of the underwater topography—about 10% of the Grand Banks lies outside of Canada's Exclusive Economic Zone, which makes it very difficult to regulate the entire fishery as a system.

We can gain an understanding of underwater geographic features by examining a stylized map (**FIGURE 10.9**) that reflects *bathymetry* (the measurement of ocean depths) as well as topography. In bathymetric profile, gently sloping **continental shelves** underlie the shallow waters bordering the continents. Continental shelves vary in width from 100 m to 1300 km, averaging 70 km wide, with an average slope of 1.9 m/km. These shelves drop off with relative suddenness at the *shelf–slope break*. From there, the **continental slope** angles more steeply downward to the *continental rise*, the gentling slope that connects the continental shelf to the **abyssal plain**, the flat bottom of the deep ocean.

Most of the abyssal plain is flat, but volcanic peaks that rise above the ocean floor provide physical structure for marine animals and are often the site of productive fishing grounds. Some island chains, such as the Florida Keys, are formed by the development of reefs and lie atop the continental shelf. Others, such as the Aleutian Islands, which curve across the North Pacific from Alaska toward Russia, are volcanic in origin. The Aleutians are also the site of a deep trench that, like the Mariana Trench, formed at a convergent tectonic plate boundary, where one slab of crust dives beneath another in the process of subduction. These trenches are the deepest places on Earth.

Marine and Coastal Ecosystems

With their variation in topography, temperature, salinity, nutrients, and sunlight, marine and coastal environments feature a variety of ecosystems. Most marine and coastal ecosystems are powered by solar energy, with sunlight driving photosynthesis by phytoplankton in the photic zone. Yet even the darkest ocean depths host life.

Regions of ocean water differ greatly, and some zones support more life than others. The uppermost 10 m of water absorb 80% of the solar energy that reaches the water's surface. For this reason, nearly all of the oceans' primary productivity occurs in the well-lit top layer, or **photic zone**. Generally, the warm, shallow waters of continental shelves are most biologically productive and support the greatest species diversity. Habitats and ecosystems occurring between the ocean's surface and floor are termed **pelagic**, whereas those that occur on the ocean floor are called **benthic**.

Open-ocean ecosystems vary in their biological diversity

Biological diversity in pelagic regions of the open ocean is highly variable in its distribution. Primary productiv-

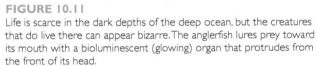

roots

NEKTON AND PLANKTON

Nekton, referring to marine animals that actually swim, was coined by German biologist Ernst Haeckel in 1890 and was derived from the Greek *nektos*, meaning "swimming." **Plankton**, referring to microscopic organisms that float rather than swim, was coined by German physiologist Viktor Hensen in 1891 and is derived from the Greek *planktos*, meaning "wandering, drifting, roaming."

FIGURE 10.11
Life is scarce in the dark depths of the deep ocean, but the creatures that do live there can appear bizarre. The anglerfish lures prey toward its mouth with a bioluminescent (glowing) organ that protrudes from the front of its head.

ity and animal life near the surface are concentrated in regions of nutrient-rich upwelling. Marine animals that actively swim are referred to as **nekton**. They are contrasted with **plankton**, microscopic organisms that float rather than swim, including *phytoplankton* (typically algae and other protists, rather than plants, even though the prefix *phyto-* means "plant") and *zooplankton* (animals).

Phytoplankton are particularly important, because they constitute the base of the marine food chain in the pelagic zone. These photosynthetic algae, protists, and cyanobacteria feed zooplankton, which in turn become food for nektonic fish, jellyfish, whales, and other free-swimming animals (**FIGURE 10.10**). Predators at higher trophic levels include larger fish, sea turtles, and sharks. Many fish-eating birds, such as puffins, petrels, and shearwaters, feed at the surface of the open ocean, returning periodically to nesting sites on islands and coastlines.

In recent years biologists have been learning more about animals of the very deep ocean, although tantalizing questions remain. In deep-water ecosystems, animals have adapted to deal with extreme water pressures and to live in the dark without food from photosynthetic organisms. Some of these often bizarre-looking creatures scavenge carcasses or organic detritus that falls from above. Others are predators, and still others attain food from symbiotic mutualistic bacteria. Some species carry bacteria that produce light chemically by *bioluminescence* (**FIGURE 10.11**).

Some ecosystems form around hydrothermal vents, where heated water spurts from the seafloor, often carrying minerals that precipitate to form large rocky structures. Tubeworms, shrimp, and other creatures in these recently discovered systems use symbiotic bacteria to derive their energy by chemosynthesis from chemicals in the heated water, rather than from sunlight. They manage to thrive within amazingly narrow zones between scalding-hot and icy cold water.

Shallow-water systems are highly productive

Large brown algae, or **kelp**, grow from the floor of continental shelves, reaching upward toward the sunlit surface. Some kelp reaches 60 m in height and can grow 45 cm in a single day. Dense stands of kelp form underwater "forests" along many temperate coasts (**FIGURE 10.12**). Kelp forests supply shelter and food for invertebrates and fish, which in turn provide food for higher trophic level predators, such

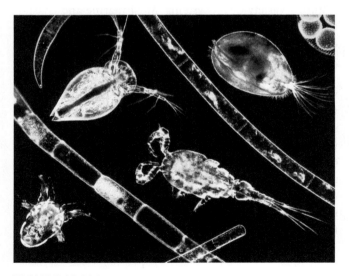

FIGURE 10.10
The uppermost reaches of ocean water contain billions upon billions of phytoplankton—tiny photosynthetic algae, protists, and bacteria that form the base of the marine food chain—as well as zooplankton, small animals and protists that dine on phytoplankton and comprise the next trophic level.

through photosynthesis. Most corals are colonial, and the colourful surface of a coral reef consists of millions of densely packed individuals. As the corals die, their skeletons remain part of the reef while new corals grow atop them, increasing the reef's size.

Like kelp forests, coral reefs protect shorelines by absorbing wave energy. They also host tremendous biodiversity (**FIGURE 10.13A**). Reefs provide complex physical structure (and thus many varied habitats) in shallow nearshore waters, which are regions of high primary productivity. Besides the staggering diversity of anemones, sponges, hydroids, tubeworms, and other sessile (stationary) invertebrates, innumerable molluscs, flatworms, sea stars, and urchins patrol the reefs, while thousands of fish species find food and shelter in reef nooks and crannies.

Coral reefs are experiencing worldwide declines, however. Many have undergone **coral bleaching**, a process

FIGURE 10.12
"Forests" of tall brown algae known as *kelp* grow from the floor of the continental shelf. Numerous fish and other creatures eat kelp or find refuge among its fronds.

as seals and sharks. Sea otters, a keystone species, control sea urchin populations; when otters disappear, urchins overgraze the kelp, destroying the forests and creating "urchin barrens." Kelp forests also absorb wave energy and protect shorelines from erosion. People eat some types of kelp, and kelp provides compounds known as alginates, which serve as thickeners in a wide range of consumer products, including cosmetics, paints, paper, and soaps. In shallow subtropical and tropical waters, coral reefs occur. A **coral reef** is a mass of calcium carbonate composed of the skeletons of tiny colonial marine organisms. A coral reef may occur as an extension of a shoreline, along a barrier island paralleling a shoreline, or as an *atoll*, a ring around a submerged island.

Corals themselves are tiny invertebrate animals related to sea anemones and jellyfish. They remain attached to rock or existing reef and capture passing food with stinging tentacles. Corals also derive nourishment from microscopic symbiotic algae, known as *zooxanthellae*, which inhabit their bodies and produce food

(a) Coral reef community

(b) Bleached coral

FIGURE 10.13
Corals reefs provide food and shelter for a tremendous diversity **(a)** of fish and other creatures. However, these reefs face multiple environmental stresses from human impacts, and many corals have died as a result of coral bleaching **(b)**, in which corals lose their zooxanthellae. Such bleaching is evident in the whitened portion of this coral.

that occurs when the coloured symbiotic zooxanthellae leave the coral, depriving it of nutrition. Corals lacking zooxanthellae lose colour and frequently die, leaving behind ghostly white patches in the reef (**FIGURE 10.13B**). Coral bleaching is not entirely understood. For example, it is not known exactly why the zooxanthellae leave during coral bleaching—or even *if* they leave; it has been hypothesized, alternatively, that they may lose their pigmentation (hence the "bleaching"), possibly as a result of *photodamage* caused by exposure to ultraviolet radiation.[1]

Coral bleaching may result from stress caused by increased sea surface temperatures associated with global climate change, from changes in light levels in some shallow-water areas, from an influx of pollutants, or from some combination of these and other unknown factors, both natural and anthropogenic. In addition, coral reefs sustain significant damage when divers stun fish with cyanide or by throwing explosives over the side of the boat, a common fishing and fish collection practice (for the pet trade) in the waters of Indonesia and the Philippines. Tourism also has been a significant burden on coral reefs globally; each scuba diver who breaks off a small piece of a reef contributes to its demise. Even with the advent of ecotourism, which of course advocates taking only photographs, the traffic of

divers' feet and hands on the reefs continues to take a toll. Finally, as global climate change proceeds, the oceans are becoming more acidic, as excess carbon dioxide from the atmosphere reacts with seawater to form carbonic acid. Acidification threatens to deprive corals of the carbonate ions they need to produce their structural parts.

A few coral species without symbiotic algae thrive in waters outside the tropics and build reefs on the ocean floor at depths of 200–500 m. These little-known reefs, which occur in cold-water areas off the coasts of Norway, Spain, the British Isles, and elsewhere, are only now beginning to be studied by scientists. Already, however, many have been badly damaged by trawling—the same practice that has so degraded the benthic habitats of groundfish, such as the Atlantic cod. Norway and other countries are now beginning to protect some of these deep-water reefs.

Intertidal zones undergo constant change

Where the ocean meets the land, **intertidal** or **littoral** ecosystems (**FIGURE 10.14**) spread between the uppermost

Tidal zones

FIGURE 10.14   The rocky intertidal zone is the swath of a rocky shoreline between the lowest and highest reaches of the tides. This is an ecosystem rich in biodiversity, typically containing large invertebrates, such as sea stars (starfish), barnacles, crabs, sea anemones, corals, bryozoans, snails, limpets, chitons, mussels, nudibranchs (sea slugs), and sea urchins. Fish swim in tidal pools, and many types of algae cover the rocks. Areas higher on the shoreline are exposed to the air more frequently and for longer periods, so organisms that can best tolerate exposure specialize in the upper intertidal zone. The lower intertidal zone is exposed less frequently and for shorter periods, so organisms less able to tolerate exposure thrive in this zone.

reach of the high tide and the lowest limit of the low tide. **Tides** are the periodic rising and falling of the ocean's height at a given location, caused by the gravitational pull of the Moon and Sun. High and low tides occur roughly six hours apart, so intertidal organisms spend part of each day submerged in water, part of the day exposed to the air and sunlight, and part of the day being lashed by waves. Subject to tremendous extremes in temperature, moisture, light exposure, and salinity, these creatures must also protect themselves from marine predators at high tide and terrestrial predators—even opportunistic predators like crows, seagulls, and raccoons—at low tide.

The intertidal environment is a tough place to make a living, but it is home to a remarkable diversity of organisms. Rocky shorelines can be full of life among the crevices, which provide shelter and pools of water (*tidepools*) during low tides. Sessile animals, such as anemones, mussels, and barnacles, live attached to rocks, filter-feeding on plankton in the water that washes over them. Urchins, sea slugs, chitons, and limpets eat intertidal algae or scrape food from the rocks. Sea stars (starfish) creep slowly along, preying on the filter-feeders and herbivores at high tide. Crabs clamber around the rocks, scavenging detritus.

The rocky intertidal zone is so diverse because environmental conditions, such as temperature, salinity, and moisture, change dramatically from the high to the low reaches. This environmental variation gives rise to horizontal bands formed by dominant organisms as they array themselves according to their habitat needs. Sandy intertidal areas, such as those of Cape Cod, host less biodiversity, yet plenty of organisms burrow into the sand at low tide to await the return of high tide, when they emerge to feed.

Coastal ecosystems protect shorelines

Along many of the world's coasts at temperate latitudes, **salt marshes** occur where the tides wash over gently sloping sandy or silty substrates. Rising and falling tides flow into and out of channels called *tidal creeks* and at highest tide spill over onto elevated marsh flats (**FIGURE 10.15**).

Salt marshes boast very high primary productivity and provide critical habitat for shorebirds, waterfowl, and the adults and young of many commercially important fish and shellfish species. Salt marshes also filter out pollution (hence the use of constructed or artificial wetlands for wastewater management). Coastal marshes stabilize shorelines against **storm surges**, temporary increases in sea level that accompany the low atmospheric pressures of intense storms, and storm waves, the very wind-driven large waves that crash onto the shore during a major

FIGURE 10.15

Salt marshes, like the Malbay salt marsh in the Gaspé Peninsula, shown here, occur in temperate intertidal zones where the substrate is muddy, allowing salt-adapted grasses to grow. Tidal waters generally flow through marshes in channels called *tidal creeks*, amid flat areas called *benches*, sometimes partially submerging the grasses.

storm. However, people like to live along coasts, and coastal sites are desirable for commerce. As a result, vast expanses of salt marshes have been altered to make way for coastal development. When salt marshes are destroyed, we lose the ecosystem services they provide. When Hurricane Katrina struck the Gulf Coast of Louisiana, for instance, the flooding was made worse because vast areas of salt marshes had vanished because of development, subsidence from oil and gas drilling, and dams that had held back marsh-building sediment. In tropical and subtropical latitudes, mangrove forests replace salt marshes along gently sloping sandy and silty coasts. The **mangrove** is a tree with a unique type of root system that curves upward (like a snorkel) to obtain oxygen lacking in the mud in which the tree grows, and curves downward like stilts to support the tree in changing water levels (**FIGURE 10.16**). Fish, shellfish, crabs, snakes, and other organisms thrive among the root networks, and birds feed and nest in the dense foliage of these coastal forests. Besides serving as nurseries for fish and shellfish that people harvest, mangroves also provide materials that people use for food, medicine, tools, and construction.

Mangrove forests in tropical areas have been destroyed as people have developed coastal areas for residential, commercial, and recreational uses. Shrimp farming in particular has driven the conversion of large areas of mangroves. We have eliminated half the world's mangrove forests, and their area continues to decline by 2%–8% per year. When mangroves are removed, coastal areas lose the ability to slow runoff, filter pollutants, and retain soil. As a result, offshore systems, such as coral reefs, are more readily degraded.

Moreover, mangrove forests protect coastal communities against storm surges and tsunamis (tidal waves), as

FIGURE 10.16
Mangrove forests are important ecosystems along tropical and subtropical coastlines throughout the world. Mangrove trees, such as these at Lizard Island, Australia, show specialized adaptations for growing in saltwater and provide habitat for many types of fish, birds, crabs, and other animals.

was shown when the 2004 Indian Ocean tsunami devastated areas where mangroves had been removed but caused less damage where mangroves were intact. The loss of coastal mangroves may also have played a role in the scale of devastation from Hurricane Nargus in Burma (Myanmar), a disaster that was greatly exacerbated by political stubbornness after the fact. Despite these important ecosystem services provided by mangroves, we have granted only about 1% of the world's remaining mangroves protection against development.

Freshwater meets saltwater in estuaries

Many salt marshes and mangrove forests occur in or near **estuaries**, water bodies where rivers flow into the ocean, mixing freshwater with saltwater. Estuaries are biologically productive ecosystems that experience fluctuations in salinity as tides and freshwater runoff vary daily and seasonally. For shorebirds and for many commercially important shellfish species, estuaries provide critical habitat. For *anadromous* fishes (fishes, such as salmon, that spawn in freshwater and mature in saltwater), estuaries provide a transitional zone where young fish make the passage from freshwater to saltwater.

Estuaries around the world have been affected by urban and coastal development, water pollution, habitat alteration, and overfishing. The Gaspé Peninsula of Québec—where the St. Lawrence River flows into the Gulf of St. Lawrence and from there into the Atlantic Ocean—is one area in Canada where estuaries and salt marshes are important ecosystems. Florida Bay, where freshwater from the Everglades system mixes with saltwater, provides another example. This estuary has suffered pollution and a reduction in freshwater flow caused by irrigation and fertilizer use by sugarcane farmers, housing development, septic tank leakage, and other human impacts. Coastal ecosystems have borne the brunt of human impact because two-thirds of Earth's people choose to live within about 150 km of the ocean.

Human Use and Impact

Our species has a long history of interacting with the ocean. We have long travelled across ocean waters, clustered our settlements along coastlines, and been fascinated by the beauty, power, and vastness of the seas. We have also left our mark upon them by exploiting the ocean for resources and polluting the waters with our waste.

The ocean provides transportation routes

We have used the ocean for transportation for thousands of years, and the ocean continues to provide affordable

---

weighing the issues

COASTAL DEVELOPMENT

A developer wants to build a large marina on an estuary in your coastal town. The marina would boost the town's economy but eliminate its salt marshes. As a homeowner living adjacent to the marshes, how would you respond?

means of moving people and products over vast distances. Ocean shipping has accelerated the global reach of some cultures and has promoted interaction among long-isolated peoples. It has had substantial impacts on the environment as well. The thousands of ships plying the world's oceans today carry everything from cod to cargo containers to crude oil. Ships transport ballast water, which, when discharged at ports of destination, may transplant aquatic organisms picked up at ports of departure. Some of these species, such as the zebra mussel, establish themselves and become invasive.

We extract energy and minerals

We mine the ocean for commercially valuable energy. Worldwide, about 30% of our crude oil and nearly half of our natural gas come from seafloor deposits. Most offshore oil and gas is concentrated in petroleum-rich regions, such as the North Sea and the Gulf of Mexico, but energy companies extract smaller amounts of oil and gas from diverse locations, among them the Grand Banks and adjacent Canadian waters. Proposals to drill for oil and gas in Georges Bank, however, have been stalled until recently by the Canadian government, in large part because of fears that spilled oil could damage the region's valuable fisheries.

Ocean sediments also contain a novel potential source of fossil fuel energy. **Methane hydrate** is an icelike solid consisting of molecules of methane (CH_4, the main component of natural gas) embedded in a crystal lattice of water molecules. Methane hydrates are stable at temperature and pressure conditions found in many sediments on the Arctic seafloor and the continental shelves. It is estimated that the world's deposits of methane hydrates may hold twice as much carbon as all known deposits of oil, coal, and natural gas combined.

Could methane hydrates be developed as an energy source to power our civilization through the twenty-first century and beyond? Perhaps, but a great deal of research remains before scientists and engineers can be sure how to extract these energy sources safely. Destabilizing a methane hydrate deposit could lead to a catastrophic release of gas. This could cause a massive landslide and tsunami, and would release huge amounts of methane, a potent greenhouse gas, into the atmosphere, exacerbating global climate change.

Fortunately, the ocean also holds potential for providing renewable energy sources that do not emit greenhouse gases. Engineers have developed ways of harnessing energy from waves, tides, and the heat of ocean water. These promising energy sources await further research, development, and investment.

We can extract minerals from the ocean floor, as well. By using large vacuum cleaner–like hydraulic dredges, miners collect sand and gravel from beneath the sea. Also extracted are sulphur from salt deposits in the Gulf of Mexico and phosphorite from offshore areas near the California coast and elsewhere. Other valuable minerals found on or beneath the seafloor include calcium carbonate (used in making cement) and silica (used as fire-resistant insulation and in manufacturing glass), as well as rich deposits of manganese, copper, zinc, silver, and gold ore. Many minerals are concentrated in manganese nodules, small ball-shaped accretions that are scattered across parts of the ocean floor. More than 1.5 trillion tonnes of manganese nodules may exist in the Pacific Ocean alone, and their reserves of metal may exceed all terrestrial reserves.

The logistical difficulty of mining the ocean floor has kept it only marginally economical or uneconomical so far, but that is changing very rapidly. A Canadian company called Nautilus Minerals has developed approaches that make use of existing offshore oil exploration technologies to mine the seafloor. In 2010 it opened the world's first underwater gold, silver, copper, and zinc mine, offshore from Papua New Guinea.

Seafloor mineral development has been one of the most controversial factors in the very long history of attempts to convene a comprehensive, binding Law of the Sea, an international legal discussion that actually began as early as the 1600s. To this day, the United States abstains from participating in some aspects of the Law of the Sea, primarily because of proposed restrictions on seafloor mining. The existing Law of the Sea, or **United Nations Convention on the Law of the Sea (UNCLOS)**, is based on a series of international conferences that took place between 1973 and 1982. This version of UNCLOS established the 200-nautical-mile Exclusive Economic Zones of nations (replacing the previous 12-mile zone), which greatly enhanced the ability of nations to control and manage their own coastal zones.

Marine pollution threatens resources and marine life

People have long used the ocean as a sink for waste and pollution. Even into the mid-twentieth century, it was common for coastal cities to dump trash and untreated sewage along their shores. Halifax only began to treat municipal sewage outflow into Halifax Harbour—approximately 181 million litres per day[2]—in the early 2000s. A surprising number of Canadian towns continue to discharge raw sewage into coastal and inland waters, even today. Fort Bragg, a bustling town on the northern

Californian coast, boasts of its Glass Beach, an area where beachcombers collect sea glass, the colourful surf-polished glass sometimes found on beaches after storms. But Glass Beach is in fact the site of the former town dump, and besides well-polished glass, the perceptive visitor may also spot old batteries, rusting car frames, and other trash protruding from the bluffs above the beach.

Oil, plastic, industrial chemicals, and excess nutrients all eventually make their way from land into the oceans. Raw sewage and trash from cruise ships and abandoned fishing gear from fishing boats add to the input. The scope of trash in the sea can be gauged by the amount picked up each September by volunteers who trek beaches in the Ocean Conservancy's International Coastal Cleanup. In this nonprofit organization's 25th annual cleanup, almost 500 000 people from more than 100 nations picked up 16 million kilograms of trash.

Plastic bags and bottles, cigarette butts, discarded fishing nets, gloves, fishing line, buckets, floats, abandoned cargo, and much else that people transport on the sea or deposit into it can harm marine organisms. Because most plastic is not biodegradable, it can drift for decades before washing up on beaches. Marine mammals, seabirds, fish, and sea turtles may mistake floating plastic debris for food and can die as a result of ingesting material they cannot digest or expel. Fishing nets and crab and lobster traps that are lost or intentionally discarded can continue snaring animals for decades (**FIGURE 10.17**). The "Great Pacific Garbage Patch" is a large mass of plastics and other anthropogenic debris (roughly 20 million km^2) that is floating in the pelagic zone, trapped in the circular currents of the North Pacific gyre. Its existence and extent were documented in 1988 by the U.S. National Oceanic and Atmospheric Administration.

FIGURE 10.17
This northern fur seal became entangled in a discarded fishing net. Each year, many thousands of marine mammals, birds, and turtles are killed by plastic debris, abandoned nets, and other trash that people have dumped in the ocean.

Of 115 marine mammal species, 49 are known to have eaten or become entangled in marine debris, and 111 of 312 species of seabirds are known to ingest plastic. All five species of sea turtle in the Gulf of Mexico have died from consuming or contacting marine debris. Marine debris affects people, as well. Surveys of fishers have shown that more than half have encountered equipment damage and other problems from plastic debris.

Corals and other marine organisms that build their shells out of calcium carbonate ($CaCO_3$) also are susceptible to negative effects from **ocean acidification**. This refers to a decrease in the acidity (pH) of ocean water caused by the uptake of atmospheric carbon dioxide by surface water. Carbon dioxide mixed with water can react to form carbonic acid, which can cause calcium carbonate shells to dissolve. The carbon dioxide content of the atmosphere is increasing, and this increase appears to be causing ocean acidification. Surface ocean water, acting as a "sink" for carbon dioxide, may therefore mitigate some changes in the chemistry of the atmosphere that are associated with global climate change, but with potentially serious negative consequences for corals and other marine organisms.

Oil pollution comes from many sources

Major oil spills, such as the *Exxon Valdez* spill in Prince William Sound, Alaska, and the massive BP *Deepwater Horizon* spill of 2010 in the Gulf of Mexico, make headlines and cause serious environmental problems. However, the majority of oil pollution in the oceans comes not from large spills in a few particular locations but from the accumulation of innumerable, widely spread small sources (non-point sources), including leakage from small boats and runoff from human activities on land. Moreover, the amount of petroleum spilled into the oceans in a typical year is equalled by the amount that seeps into the water from naturally occurring seafloor deposits (**FIGURE 10.18**). (This was not the case in 2010, when the massive spill from the BP *Deepwater Horizon* rig exceeded all other human sources of oil spilled that year.)

Minimizing the amount of oil we release into coastal waters is important, because petroleum pollution is detrimental to marine life and to our economies. Petroleum can physically coat and kill marine organisms and can poison them when ingested. In response to headline-grabbing oil spills, governments worldwide have begun to implement more stringent safety standards for tankers, such as requiring industry to pay for tugboat escorts in sensitive and hazardous coastal waters, double hulls to preclude punctures, and the development of prevention

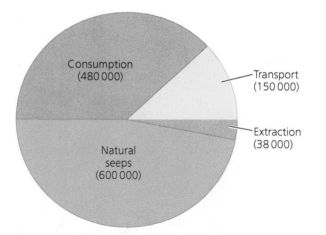

Sources of petroleum input into oceans (metric tonnes)

FIGURE 10.18
Of the 1.3 million metric tonnes of petroleum entering the world's oceans in a typical year, nearly half is from natural seeps. Petroleum consumption by people accounts for 38% of total input, and this includes numerous diffuse non-point sources, especially runoff from rivers and coastal communities and leakage from two-stroke engines. Spills during petroleum transport account for 12%, and leakage during petroleum extraction accounts for 3%. For comparison, in 2010 the BP *Deepwater Horizon* spill released about 800 000 metric tonnes of oil into the Gulf of Mexico.
Source: Data from National Research Council. (2003). Oil in the Sea III. Inputs, Fates, and Effects. Washington, DC: National Academies Press.

and response plans for major spills. The oil industry has resisted many such safeguards. Today, the ship that oiled Prince William Sound is still plying the world's oceans, renamed the *Sea River Mediterranean* and still featuring only a single hull.

Pollutants can contaminate seafood

Marine pollution can make some fish and shellfish unsafe for people to eat. One prime concern today is mercury contamination. Mercury is a toxic heavy metal that is emitted in coal combustion and from other sources. After settling onto land and water, mercury bioaccumulates in animals' tissues and biomagnifies as it makes its way up the food chain. As a result, fish and shellfish at high trophic levels can contain substantial levels of mercury. Eating seafood high in mercury is particularly dangerous for young children and for pregnant or nursing mothers, because the fetus, baby, or child can suffer neurological damage as a result.

Pollution from fertilizer runoff or other nutrient inputs can spur unusually rapid growth of phytoplankton, causing eutrophication and hypoxia. Excessive nutrient concentrations sometimes give rise to popula-

tion explosions among several species of marine algae that produce powerful toxins that attack the nervous systems of vertebrates. Blooms of these algae occur periodically on both the east and west coasts of Canada. Some algal species produce reddish pigments that discolour surface waters, and blooms of these species are nicknamed **red tides** (**FIGURE 10.19**). Harmful algal blooms can cause illness and death among zooplankton, birds, fish, marine mammals, and people as their toxins are passed up the food chain. They also cause economic loss for communities dependent on fishing or beach tourism. Reducing nutrient runoff into coastal waters can lessen the frequency of these outbreaks. When they occur, we can minimize their health impacts by monitoring to prevent human consumption of affected organisms.

As severe as the impacts of marine pollution can be, however, most marine scientists concur that the more worrisome dilemma is overharvesting. Unfortunately, the old cliché that "there are always more fish in the sea" is not true; the ocean today has been overfished, and like the groundfish of the Northwest Atlantic, many stocks have been largely depleted.

Emptying the Ocean

The ocean and its biological resources have provided for human needs for thousands of years, but today we are placing unprecedented pressure on marine resources. Half the world's marine fish populations are fully exploited, meaning that we cannot harvest them more intensively without depleting them, according to the U.N. Food and Agriculture Organization (FAO). An additional one-quarter of marine fish populations are overexploited and already being driven toward extinction. Thus only one-quarter of the world's marine fish populations can yield more than they are already yielding without being driven into decline.

The total global fisheries catch, after decades of increases, levelled off after about 1988 (**FIGURE 10.20**), despite increased fishing effort. Fishery collapses, such as those off Newfoundland and Labrador and New England, are ecologically devastating and also take a severe economic toll on human communities that depend on fishing. If current trends continue, predicted a comprehensive 2006 study in the journal *Science*, populations of *all* ocean species that we fish for today will collapse by the year 2048.

As our population grows, we will become even more dependent on the oceans' bounty. This makes it vital, say many scientists and fisheries managers, that we turn immediately to more sustainable fishing practices.

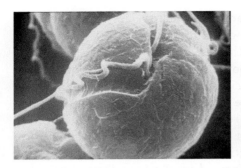

(a) Dinoflagellate (*Gymnodinium*)

FIGURE 10.19
In a harmful algal bloom, certain types of algae multiply to great densities in surface waters, producing toxins that can bioaccumulate and harm organisms. Red tides are a type of harmful algal bloom in which the algae, such as dinoflagellates of the genus *Gymnodinium* **(a)**, produce pigment that turns the water red **(b)**.

(b) Red tide, Gulf of Carpentaria, Australia

We have long overfished

People have always harvested fish, shellfish, turtles, seals, and other animals from the oceans. Although much of this harvesting was sustainable, scientists are learning that people began depleting some marine species centuries or millennia ago. Overfishing then accelerated during the colonial period of European expansion and intensified further in the twentieth century.

A recent synthesis of historical evidence reveals that ancient overharvesting likely affected ecosystems in ways we only partially understand today. Several large animals, including the Caribbean monk seal, Steller's sea cow, and Atlantic grey whale, were hunted to extinction prior to the twentieth century—before scientists were able to study them or the ecological roles they played. Overharvesting of the vast oyster beds of the Chesapeake Bay led to the collapse of its oyster fishery in the late nineteenth century.

FIGURE 10.20
The total global fisheries catch has increased over the past half-century, but in recent years growth has stalled, and many fear that a global catch decline is imminent if conservation measures are not taken soon. The figure shows trends with and without data on China's substantial fishing industry, which had been withheld from international scrutiny for many years.
Source: Data from U.N. Food and Agricultural Organization (FAO), 2009.

World capture and aquaculture production

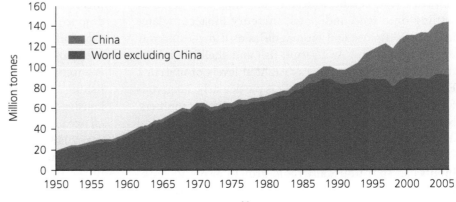

Eutrophication and hypoxia resulted, because there are no longer oysters to filter algae and bacteria from the water. In the Caribbean, green sea turtles ate sea grass and likely kept it cropped low, like a lawn. But with today's turtle population a fraction of what it was, sea grass grows thickly, dies, and rots, giving rise to disease, such as sea grass wasting disease, which ravaged sea grass in the 1980s. The best-known case of historical overharvesting is the near-extinction of many species of whales. This resulted from commercial whaling that began centuries ago and was curtailed only in 1986. Since then, some species have been recovering, but others have not.

Groundfish in the Northwest Atlantic historically were so abundant that the people who harvested them never imagined they could be depleted. Yet careful historical analysis of fishing records has revealed that even in the nineteenth century, fishers repeatedly experienced locally dwindling catches and each time needed to introduce some new approach or technology to extend their reach and restore their catch rate.

Fishing has become industrialized

Today's commercial fishing fleets are highly industrialized, employing fossil fuels, huge vessels, and powerful new technologies to capture fish in volumes never dreamed of by nineteenth-century mariners. So-called *factory fishing* vessels even process and freeze their catches while at sea. The global reach of today's fleets makes our impacts much more rapid and intensive than in past centuries.

The modern fishing industry uses a number of methods to capture fish at sea. Some vessels set out long *driftnets* that span large expanses of water (**FIGURE 10.21A**). These strings of nets are arrayed strategically to drift with currents so as to capture passing fish, and are held vertical by floats at the top and weights at the bottom. Driftnetting usually targets species that traverse the open water in immense schools (flocks), such as herring, sardines, and mackerel. Specialized forms of driftnetting are used for sharks, shrimp, and other animals.

Longline fishing (**FIGURE 10.21B**) involves setting out extremely long lines with up to several thousand baited hooks spaced along their lengths. Tuna and swordfish are among the species targeted by longline fishing.

Trawling entails dragging immense cone-shaped nets through the water, with weights at the bottom and floats at the top to keep the nets open. Trawling in open water captures pelagic fish, whereas *bottom-trawling* (**FIGURE 10.21C**) involves dragging weighted nets across the floor of the continental shelf to catch groundfish and other benthic organisms, such as scallops.

(a) Driftnetting

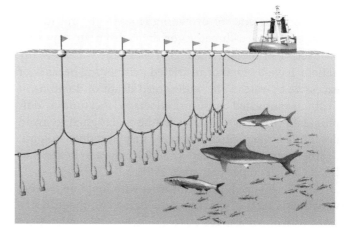

(b) Longlining

(c) Bottom-trawling

FIGURE 10.21
Commercial fishing fleets use several main methods of capture. In driftnetting **(a)**, huge nets are set out to drift through the open water to capture schools of fish. In longlining **(b)**, lines with numerous baited hooks are set out in open water. In bottom-trawling **(c)**, weighted nets are dragged along the floor of the continental shelf. All methods result in the capture of nontarget animals. The illustrations above are schematic for clarity and do not capture the immense scale that these technologies can attain; for instance, industrial trawling nets can be large enough to engulf multiple jumbo jets.

Some fishing practices kill nontarget animals and damage ecosystems

Unfortunately, some fishing practices catch more than just the species they target. **By-catch** refers to the accidental capture of animals, and it accounts for the deaths of many thousands of fish, sharks, marine mammals, and birds each year. For example, the FAO reports that in South and Central American shrimp fisheries in the 1990s, for each 1 kg of shrimp caught, 10–33 kg of other animals were caught; 30% of the by-catch was used, while the rest was discarded as trash.[3]

Driftnetting captures substantial numbers of dolphins, seals, and sea turtles, as well as countless nontarget fish. Most of these end up drowning (mammals and turtles need to surface to breathe) or dying from air exposure on deck (fish breathe through gills in the water). Many nations have banned or restricted driftnetting because of excessive by-catch. The widespread death of dolphins in driftnets motivated consumer efforts to label tuna as "dolphin-safe" if its capture uses methods designed to avoid dolphin by-catch. Such measures helped reduce dolphin deaths from an estimated 133 000 per year in 1986 to fewer than 2000 per year since 1998.

Similar by-catch problems exist with longline fishing, which kills turtles, sharks, and albatrosses, magnificent seabirds with wingspans up to 3.6 m. Several methods are being developed to limit by-catch from longline fishing, but an estimated 300 000 seabirds of various species die each year when they become caught on hooks while trying to ingest bait.

Bottom-trawling can destroy entire communities and ecosystems. The weighted nets crush organisms in their path and leave long swaths of damaged sea bottom. Trawling is especially destructive to structurally complex areas, such as reefs, that provide shelter and habitat for many animals. In recent years, underwater photography has begun to reveal the extent of structural and ecological disturbance done by trawling (**FIGURE 10.22**). Trawling is often likened to clear-cutting and strip-mining, and in heavily fished areas, the bottom may be damaged more than once. At Georges Bank, it is estimated that the average expanse of bottom has been trawled three times.

We can see the effects of large-scale industrialized fishing in the catch records of groundfish from the Northwest Atlantic. Although cod had been harvested since the 1500s on the Grand Banks, catches more than doubled once immense industrial trawlers from Europe, Japan, and the United States appeared in the 1960s (**FIGURE 10.23A**). These record-high catches lasted only a decade; the industrialized approach removed so many fish that the stock has not recovered. Likewise, on Georges Bank, cod catches rose greatly in the 1960s, remained high for 30 years, and then collapsed (**FIGURE 10.23B**).

Throughout the world's oceans, today's industrialized fishing fleets are depleting marine populations quickly. In a 2003 study, Canadian fisheries biologists Ransom Myers and Boris Worm analyzed fisheries data from FAO archives, looking for changes in the catch rates of fish in various regions of ocean since they were first exploited by industrialized fishing. For one region after another, they found the same pattern: Catch rates dropped precipitously, with 90% of large-bodied fish and sharks eliminated within only a decade (**FIGURE 10.24**). Following that, populations stabilized at 10% of their former levels. This means, Myers and Worm concluded, that the oceans today contain only one-tenth of the large-bodied animals they once did.

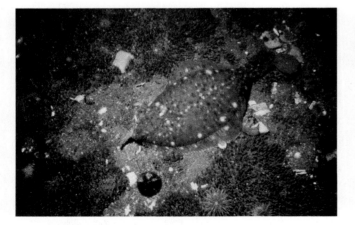

(a) Before trawling

(b) After trawling

FIGURE 10.22   Bottom-trawling causes severe structural damage to reefs and benthic habitats, and it can decimate underwater communities and ecosystems. A photo of an untrawled location **(a)** on the seafloor of Indonesia shows bottom-dwelling fish and a vibrant and diverse coral reef community. A photo of a trawled location **(b)** nearby shows a flattened and lifeless expanse of broken coral.

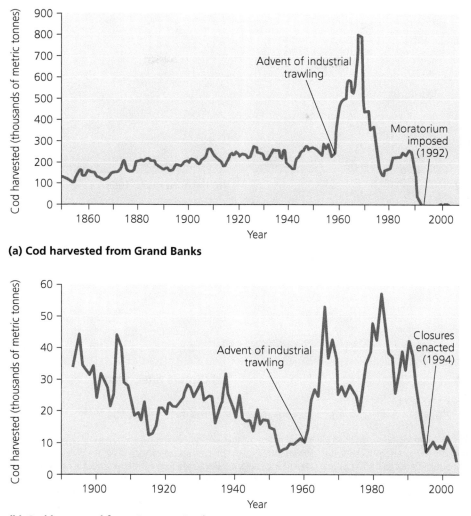

(a) Cod harvested from Grand Banks

(b) Cod harvested from Georges Bank

FIGURE 10.23   In the North Atlantic off the coast of Newfoundland and Labrador, commercial catches of Atlantic cod **(a)** increased with intensified fishing by industrial trawlers in the 1960s and 1970s. The fishery subsequently crashed, and moratoria imposed in 1992 and 2003 have not brought it back. A similar pattern is seen in the cod catches at Georges Bank **(b)**; industrial fishing produced 30 years of high catches, followed by a collapse and the closure of some areas to fishing. Note also that in each case, there is one peak before 1977 and one after 1977. The first peak and decline resulted from foreign fishing fleets, whereas the second peak and decline resulted from Canadian and U.S. fleets, respectively, after they laid claim to their 200-nautical-mile Exclusive Economic Zones.   *Source: Data in (a) from Millennium Ecosystem Assessment, 2005. Data in (b) from O'Brien, et al. 2005. Georges Bank Atlantic Cod. In Mayo, R. K. and M. Terceiro, eds. Assessment of 19 Northeast Groundfish Stocks Through 2004. Woods Hole, MA: Northeast Fisheries Science Center.*

As we have seen, when animals at high trophic levels are removed from a food web, the proliferation of their prey can alter the nature of the entire community. Many scientists now conclude that most marine communities may have been very different prior to industrial fishing.

Several factors mask declines

Although industrialized fishing has depleted fish stocks in region after region, the overall global catch has remained roughly stable for two decades (see **FIGURE 10.20**). The seeming stability of the total global catch can be explained by several factors that mask population declines. One is that fishing fleets have been travelling longer distances to reach less-fished portions of the ocean. They also have been fishing in deeper waters; average depth of catches was 150 m in 1970 and 250 m in 2000. Moreover, fishing fleets have been spending more time fishing and have been setting out more nets and lines—expending increasing effort just to catch the same number of fish.

Improved technology also helps explain large catches despite declining stocks. Today's Japanese, European, Canadian, and U.S. fleets can reach almost any spot on the globe with vessels that attain speeds of 80 km/h. They have access to an array of technologies that militaries have developed for spying and for chasing enemy submarines, including advanced sonar mapping equipment, satellite navigation, and thermal sensing systems. Some fleets

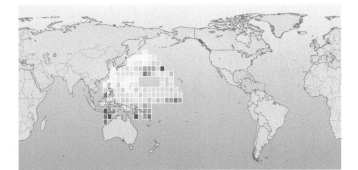

(a) Capture rates, 1952

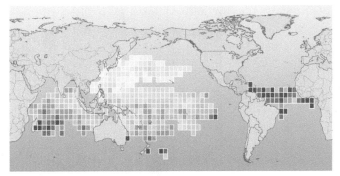

(b) Capture rates, 1958

(c) Capture rates, 1964

(d) Capture rates, 1980

Number of fish caught per 100 hooks

<1   1-2   2-3   3-4   4-5   5-6   6-8   8-10   10+

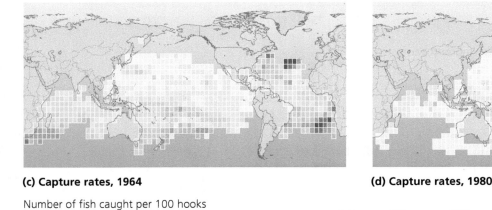

FIGURE 10.24   As industrial fishing fleets reached each new region of the world's oceans, capture rates of large predatory fishes were initially high and then within a decade declined markedly. In the figure, darker colours signify high capture rates, and lighter colours signify low capture rates. High capture rates in the southwestern Pacific in 1952 **(a)** gave way to low ones in later years. Excellent fishing success in the tropical Atlantic and Indian Oceans in 1958 **(b)** had turned mediocre by 1964 **(c)** and poor by 1980 **(d)**. High capture rates in the north and south Atlantic in 1964 (c) gave way to low capture rates there in 1980 (d).   *Source: Adapted from Myers, R. A. and B. Worm. 2003. Rapid worldwide depletion of predatory fish communities. Nature 423:280–283.*

rely on aerial spotters to find schools of commercially valuable fish, such as bluefin tuna. One final cause of misleading stability in global catch numbers is that not all data supplied to international monitoring agencies may be accurate, for a variety of reasons, including economic pressure to falsify data.

We are "fishing down the food chain"

Overall figures on total global catch tell only part of the story, because they do not relate the species, age, and size of fish harvested. Careful analyses of fisheries data have revealed in case after case that as fishing increases, the size and age of fish caught decline. Cod caught in the Northwest Atlantic today are on average *much* smaller than they were decades ago, and it is now rare to find a cod more than 10 years of age, although cod of this age formerly were common. The reproductive potential of today's smaller cod is much less—an

order of magnitude less—than that of the giant cod of previous decades.

In addition, as particular species become too rare to fish profitably, fleets begin targeting other species that are in greater abundance. Generally this means shifting from large, desirable species to smaller, less desirable ones. Fleets have time and again depleted popular food fish (such as cod) and shifted to species of lower value (such as capelin, smaller fish that cod eat). Because this often entails catching species at lower trophic levels, this phenomenon has been termed "fishing down the food chain," a concept proposed by UBC fisheries scientist Daniel Pauly and colleagues in 1998.

Aquaculture has benefits and drawbacks

There has been a dramatic increase in farm fisheries, or **aquaculture**, over the past few decades. From a small percentage of the total fish harvest only 20 years ago, aquaculture now accounts for more than 30% of world production. Freshwater fish species—including rainbow trout, brook trout, arctic char, and tilapia, as well as Atlantic, coho, and chinook salmon—are currently farmed in Canada. Canada is the fourth-largest producer of farmed salmon in the world[4] and the economic value of the aquaculture industry is now well over a half-billion dollars annually. Shellfish—including clams, oysters, scallops, and mussels, as well as some types of marine plants, algae, and oysters for pearl production—are also raised in controlled environments.

Aquaculture can help improve a region's or nation's food security by increasing overall amounts of fish available. It also reduces pressure on overharvested and declining wild stocks, as well as reducing by-catch and providing employment for fishers who can no longer fish from depleted natural stocks. Aquaculture also relies far less on fossil fuels than do fishing vessels, and provides a safer work environment. Fish farming can be remarkably energy-efficient, producing as much as 10 times as much fish per unit area as is harvested from oceanic waters on the continental shelf, and up to 1000 times as much as is harvested from the open ocean.

Along with its benefits, aquaculture has some disadvantages. Dense concentrations of farmed animals can increase the incidence of disease, which necessitates antibiotic treatment and results in additional expense. If farmed aquatic organisms escape into ecosystems where they are not native, they may spread disease to native stocks or may outcompete native organisms for food or habitat. The opposite has also occurred—recent research suggests that wild Pacific salmon swimming near aquaculture pens may pass parasites, which then spread rapidly as a result of the high population densities in the pens.

The high-density fish populations involved in aquaculture also produce a significant amount of waste, both from the farmed organisms and from the feed that goes uneaten and decomposes in the water column. Farmed fish often are fed grain, and growing grain to feed animals that we then eat can reduce the energy efficiency of food production and consumption. In other cases, farmed fish are fed fishmeal made from wild ocean fish, such as herring and anchovies, whose harvest may place additional stress on wild fish populations.

Aquaculture has also led to damaging landscape changes in some coastal ecosystems, including the removal of protective mangrove forests. Coastlines evolve geologically as natural barriers to the battering of storm waves and winds. When these barriers are removed or disrupted, shorelines are left defenceless. The world saw the effects of shoreline modification graphically illustrated during the devastating Sumatra-

Andaman tsunami of December 24, 2004, a seismic sea wave generated by a major submarine earthquake off the coast of Indonesia. Many of the coastlines in this part of South Asia and the Pacific had been significantly altered for aquaculture pen construction. The tsunami met with little natural resistance as it rushed onshore.

Consumer choice can influence marine harvest practices

To most of us, marine fishing practices may seem a distant phenomenon over which we have no control. Yet by exercising careful choice when we buy seafood, consumers can influence the ways in which fisheries function. Purchasing ecolabelled seafood, such as dolphin-safe tuna, is one way to exercise choice, but in most cases consumers have no readily available information about how their seafood was caught.

Several nonprofit organizations have recently devised concise guides to help consumers make informed choices. These guides differentiate fish and shellfish that are overfished or whose capture is ecologically damaging from those that are harvested more sustainably. TABLE 10.1 has some examples from such a consumer guide, prepared by SeaChoice, a consortium of Canadian conservation organizations, which also provides a wealth of information about sustainable fisheries for the public on its website.

Modern whaling provides an interesting example of consumer influences on marine harvesting practices. Whaling has been carried out for centuries (possibly millennia) by traditional societies from Scandinavia to northern Canada to Japan. Modern whaling began in the nineteenth century off the eastern coast of North America, in response to the demand for whale oil and, later, for meat. By the middle of the twentieth century, the catch was so large that it exceeded sustainable limits, and some species were close to extinction. In 1986 the International Whaling Commission banned whaling in an effort to allow stocks to replenish; this moratorium probably averted the extinction of several species, at least temporar-

weighing the issues
EATING SEAFOOD

After reading this chapter, do you plan to alter your decisions about eating seafood in any way? If so, how? If not, why not? Do you think consumer buying choices can exert an influence on fishing practices? On mercury contamination in seafood?

Table 10.1   Seafood Choices for Consumers

Best Choices

- Abalone (U.S. Farmed)
- Arctic Char (Farmed in Recirculating Systems)
- Barramundi (U.S. Farmed in Fully Recirculating Systems)
- Capelin (Iceland)
- Catfish (U.S. Farmed)
- Clams (Farmed)
- Clams, Softshell/Steamers (Wild-caught)
- Cobia (U.S. Farmed)
- Cod, Atlantic (Hook-and-line from Iceland and Northeast Arctic)
- Cod, Pacific (U.S. Bottom Longline, Jig and Trap)
- Crab, Dungeness (California, Oregon and Washington)
- Crab, Kona (Australia)
- Crab, Stone
- Crawfish/Crayfish (U.S. Farmed)
- Croaker, Atlantic (U.S. Non-trawl)
- Giant Clam/Geoduck (Wild-caught)
- Haddock (Hook-and-line from U.S. Atlantic)
- Halibut, Pacific (U.S.)
- Lobster, California Spiny (California)
- Lobster, Caribbean Spiny (Florida)
- Lobster, Spiny (Baja California, Mexico)
- Mackerel, Atlantic (Canada)
- Mackerel, King (U.S. Atlantic and U.S. Gulf of Mexico)

- Mackerel, Spanish (U.S. Atlantic and U.S. Gulf of Mexico)
- Mahi Mahi (Troll/Pole from U.S. Atlantic)
- Mullet, Striped
- Mussels (Farmed)
- Oysters (Farmed)
- Perch, Yellow (Lake Erie)
- Pollock, Atlantic (Gillnet and Purse Seine from Norway)
- Prawn, Freshwater (U.S. Farmed)
- Prawn, Spot (Canadian Pacific)
- Rockfish, Black (Hook-and-line from California, Oregon and Washington)
- Sablefish/Black Cod (Alaska and Canadian Pacific)
- Salmon (Drift Gillnet, Purse Seine and Troll, from Alaska)
- Salmon Roe (Drift Gillnet, Purse Seine and Troll, from Alaska)
- Salmon, Freshwater Coho (U.S. Farmed in Tank Systems)
- Sardines, Pacific (U.S.)
- Scad, Big-eye (Hawaii)
- Scad, Mackerel (Hawaii)
- Scallops (Farmed)
- Scallops, Sea (Diver-caught in Laguna Ojo de Liebre and Guerrero Negro, Baja California Sur, Mexico)
- Sea Urchin Roe (Canada)
- Seatrout, Spotted (Wild-caught from Florida and Louisiana)

- Shrimp (U.S. Farmed in Fully Recirculating Systems or Inland Ponds)
- Shrimp, Pink (Oregon)
- Squid, Longfin (U.S. Atlantic)
- Striped Bass (U.S. Wild-caught)
- Striped Bass (U.S. Farmed or Wild-caught)
- Swordfish (Hawaii Harpoon, Handline)
- Swordfish (Harpoon & Handline-caught from Canada, the U.S., North Atlantic & East Pacific)
- Tilapia (U.S. Farmed)
- Trout, Rainbow/Steelhead (U.S. Farmed)
- Tuna, Albacore (Troll/Pole from the Canadian and U.S. Pacific)
- Tuna, Albacore ("White" Canned) (Troll/pole from the Canadian and U.S. Pacific)
- Tuna, Bigeye (Troll/Pole from the U.S. Atlantic)
- Tuna, Skipjack (Worldwide Troll, Pole-and-line)
- Tuna, Skipjack ("Light" Canned) (Troll/Pole)
- Tuna, Yellowfin (Troll/Pole from the Pacific and U.S. Atlantic)
- White Seabass (Hook-and-line from California)
- Whitefish, Lake (Lake Huron and Lake Superior)
- Whitefish, Lake (Trap-net from Lake Michigan)
- Wreckfish

Source: Monterey Bay Aquarium Seafood Watch (2012). Buyer's Guide: All Regions Guide. "Best Choices," www. montereybayaquarium.org/cr/SeafoodWatch/web/sfw_regional.aspx

---

ily. There is a large market for whale meat in Japan, with the result that Japan officially objected to the moratorium. Japan continues whaling today, ostensibly for scientific research purposes, although it is quite widely believed that this is a front for commercial whaling. Whaling is carried out legally by Inuit communities in Canada's North, where whale meat is part of the traditional diet.

Marine biodiversity loss erodes ecosystem services

Overfishing, pollution, habitat change, and other factors that deplete biodiversity can threaten the ecosystem services we derive from the oceans. In the 2006 study in

Science that predicted global fisheries' collapse by 2048, the study's 14 authors analyzed all existing scientific literature to summarize the effects of biodiversity loss on ecosystem function and ecosystem services. They found that across 32 different controlled experiments conducted by various researchers, systems with less species diversity or genetic diversity showed less primary and secondary production and were less able to withstand disturbance.

The team also found that when biodiversity was reduced, so were habitats that serve as nurseries for fish and shellfish. Moreover, biodiversity loss was correlated with reduced filtering and detoxification (as from wetland vegetation and oyster beds), which can lead to harmful algal blooms, dead zones, fish kills, and beach closures.

Marine Conservation

Because we bear responsibility and stand to lose a great deal if valuable ecological systems collapse, marine scientists have been working to develop solutions to the problems that threaten the oceans. Many have begun by taking a hard look at the strategies used traditionally in fisheries management.

Fisheries management has been based on maximum sustainable yield

Fisheries managers conduct surveys, study fish population biology, and monitor catches. They then use that knowledge to regulate the timing of harvests, the techniques used to catch fish, and the scale of harvests. The goal is to allow for maximal harvests of particular populations while keeping fish available for the future—the concept of **maximum sustainable yield**. If data indicate that current yields are unsustainable, managers might limit the number or total biomass of that species that can be harvested, or they might restrict the type of gear fishers can use.

Despite such efforts, several fish and shellfish stocks have plummeted, and many scientists and managers now feel it is time to rethink fisheries management. One key change these reformers suggest is to shift the focus away from individual species and toward viewing marine resources as elements of larger ecological systems. This means considering the impacts of fishing practices on habitat quality, on species interactions, and on other factors that may have indirect or long-term effects on populations. One key aspect of such an *ecosystem-based management* approach is to set aside areas of ocean where systems can function without human interference.

We can protect areas in the ocean

Hundreds of **marine protected areas (MPAs)** have been established, most of them along the coastlines of developed countries[5] (**FIGURE 10.25**). However, despite their name, marine protected areas do not necessarily protect all their natural resources, because nearly all MPAs allow fishing and other extractive activities. As a recent report from an environmental advocacy group put it, even national marine sanctuaries "are dredged, trawled, mowed for kelp, crisscrossed with oil pipelines and fibre-optic cables, and swept through with fishing nets."

Because of the lack of true refuges from fishing pressure, many scientists—and some fishers—want to establish areas where fishing is prohibited. Such "no-take" areas have come

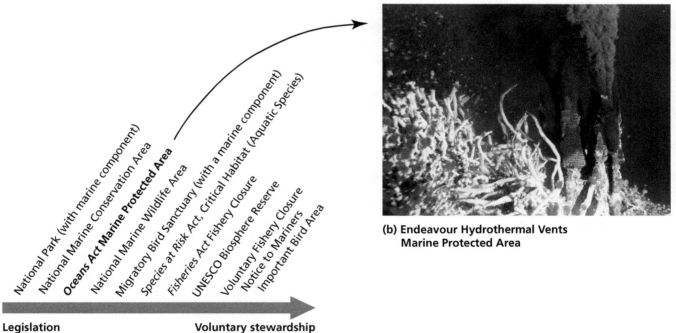

(b) Endeavour Hydrothermal Vents Marine Protected Area

National Park (with marine component)
National Marine Conservation Area
Oceans Act Marine Protected Area
National Marine Wildlife Area
Migratory Bird Sanctuary (with a marine component)
Species at Risk Act, Critical Habitat (Aquatic Species)
Fisheries Act Fishery Closure
UNESCO Biosphere Reserve
Voluntary Fishery Closure
Notice to Mariners
Important Bird Area

Legislation   **Voluntary stewardship**

(a)

FIGURE 10.25   There are numerous tools that can be used to protect marine areas in Canada, which range from legislated to voluntary measures **(a)**. Canada's first official marine protected area, designated in 2003, was the Endeavour Hydrothermal Vents area on the Juan da Fuca Ridge off the west coast of Vancouver Island **(b)**.

to be called **marine reserves**. Designed to preserve entire ecosystems intact without human interference, marine reserves are also intended to improve fisheries. Scientists argue that marine reserves can act as production factories for fish for surrounding areas, because fish larvae produced inside reserves will disperse outside and stock other parts of the ocean. Proponents maintain that by serving both purposes, marine reserves are a win–win proposition for environmentalists and fishers alike.

Many fishers dislike the idea of no-take reserves, however, just as most were opposed to the Canadian groundfish moratoria and the Georges Bank closures. Nearly every marine reserve that has been established or proposed has met with pockets of intense opposition from people and businesses that use the area for fishing or recreation. Opposition comes from commercial fishing fleets as well as from individuals who fish recreationally. Both types of fishers are concerned that marine reserves will simply put more areas off-limits to fishing. In some parts of the world, protests have become violent. For instance, to protest fishing restrictions, fishers in the Galápagos Islands destroyed offices at Galápagos National Park and threatened researchers and park managers with death.

Reserves can work for both fish and fishers

In the past decade, data synthesized from marine reserves around the world have been indicating that reserves *do* work as win–win solutions that benefit ecosystems, fish populations, and fishing economies. In 2001, 161 prominent marine scientists signed a "consensus statement" summarizing the effects of marine reserves. Besides boosting fish biomass, total catch, and record-sized fish, the report stated, marine reserves yield several benefits. Within reserve boundaries, they

- Produce rapid and long-term increases in abundance, diversity, and productivity of marine organisms
- Decrease mortality and habitat destruction
- Lessen the likelihood of extirpation of species

Outside the reserve boundaries, marine reserves

- Can create a "spillover effect" when individuals of protected species spread outside reserves
- Allow larvae of species protected within reserves to "seed the seas" outside reserves

The consensus statement was backed up by research into reserves worldwide. At Apo Island in the Philippines,

biomass of large predators increased eightfold inside a marine reserve, and fishing improved outside the reserve. At two coral reef sites in Kenya, commercially fished and keystone species were up to 10 times as abundant in the protected area as in the fished area. At Leigh Marine Reserve in New Zealand, snapper increased fortyfold, and spiny lobsters were increasing by 5%–11% yearly. Spillover from this reserve improved fishing and ecotourism, and local residents who once opposed the reserve now support it.

The review of data from existing marine reserves as of 2001 revealed that just one to two years after their establishment, marine reserves

- Increased densities of organisms on average by 91%
- Increased biomass of organisms on average by 192%
- Increased average size of organisms by 31%
- Increased species diversity by 23%

Since that time, further research has shown that reserves create a fourfold increase in catch per unit of effort in fished areas surrounding reserves and that they can greatly increase ecotourism by divers and snorkelers.

On Georges Bank, once commercial trawling was halted in 1994, populations of many organisms began to recover. As benthic invertebrates began to come back, numbers of groundfish, such as haddock and yellowtail flounder, rose inside the closed areas, and scallops increased by 14 times. Moreover, fish from the closure areas appear to be spilling over into adjacent waters, because fishers have been catching more and more groundfish from Georges Bank as a whole since the late 1990s. From these and other data sets, increasing numbers of scientists, fishers, and policy makers are advocating the establishment of fully protected marine reserves as a central management tool.

How should reserves be designed?

If marine reserves work in principle, the question becomes how best to design reserves and arrange them into networks. Scientists today are asking how large reserves need to be, how many there need to be, and where they need to be placed. Involving fishers directly in the planning process is crucial for coming up with answers to such questions. In Canada, marine reserves are managed by Parks Canada through the National Marine Conservation Areas Program, and their management plans are designed as partnerships among coastal communities; Aboriginal people; provincial, territorial, and federal government agencies; and other stakeholders.

CANADIAN ENVIRONMENTAL PERSPECTIVES

Farley Mowat

Canadian author Farley Mowat has written extensively about his experiences in the Arctic. Books like *A Whale for the Killing* and *Sea of Slaughter* led the Sea Shepherd Conservation Society to name one of its fleet of "eco-piracy" boats after him.

- ■ **Author**
- ■ **Conservationist** and **naturalist**
- ■ **Animal welfare activist**

He is a "natural storyteller," a gifted writer, and a Canadian icon. His books—more than 18 million of them sold, in many languages—have helped familiarize readers with wildlife and life in wild places. They have raised awareness and changed attitudes, and have even influenced Canadian government policies. Books like *Never Cry Wolf* (1963) are fixtures in Canadian classrooms. Some of his books have brought controversy and criticism, and one, *Sea of Slaughter* (1984), apparently contributed to his being barred from entering the United States.[6]

Farley Mowat was born in Ontario but grew up in Saskatoon during the Great Depression. As a child he was fascinated with nature and kept numerous wild animals and even insects as household pets. Mowat's first formal writing as a young teenager was an article on birds. Several of his later books, such as *Owls in the Family* (1961), were based on reminiscences of animals and nature experiences from his childhood. Mowat served in active combat duty during the Second World War. His

intense battlefield experiences eventually provided material and inspiration for some of his later writings, such as *My Father's Son: Memories of War and Peace* (1992).

After returning from the war he studied biology at the University of Toronto, which eventually led him to a two-year sojourn in the Arctic. His first book, *People of the Deer* (1952), was based on his frustration upon becoming aware of the destitute situation of the Ihalmiut, an Inuit band who, he felt, had been misunderstood and exploited by white people.

A number of Mowat's subsequent books also were based on his experiences in the Arctic. He won the Governor General's Award for *Lost in the Barrens* (1956), which tells the story of two young people—one white, the other Cree—who are lost in the Arctic wilderness. They manage to survive for part of the winter, but ultimately are rescued by an Inuit boy whose extensive knowledge of the Arctic environment saves them.

Mowat's relationship with the people of Newfoundland and Labrador, where he lived for eight years, is complex. His 1968 book *This Rock Within the Sea: A Heritage Lost* tells of a noble people with a calling to the sea. By 1972, however, *A Whale for the Killing* dramatically illustrated his disillusionment after an unfortunate beached whale was inhumanely shot to death. The book is also a plea for action to save whales from extinction.

In 1984, *Sea of Slaughter* was published, providing an overview of animal life in the North Atlantic since the early days of European fishing and whaling. Roger Tory Peterson compared the environmental significance of *Sea of Slaughter* to that of Rachel Carson's *Silent Spring*, saying, "In this masterpiece, Canada's most beloved naturalist-author is as angry about the assault on the living sea as Rachel Carson was about the land in *Silent Spring*."[7] On a promotional tour for *Sea of Slaughter*, Mowat attempted to enter the United States but was barred. He explored the possible reasons for this in his next book, *My Discovery of America* (1985).

Mowat has the distinction—perhaps dubious—of having a ship named after him. The *R/V Farley Mowat* is one of a small fleet

of vessels that belong to the Sea Shepherd Conservation Society, of which Mowat is the international chair. Sea Shepherd, founded by Paul Watson (a co-founder of Greenpeace), is an eco-activist organization that has pledged to sink or sabotage any vessels it believes to have violated international whaling laws. Greenpeace, also an activist environmental group, has repeatedly distanced itself from Sea Shepherd because of the extreme nature of its approach.

On April 12, 2008, the Department of Fisheries and Oceans, Transport Canada, Canadian Coast Guard, and RCMP took possession of the *Farley Mowat* for alleged violations of the *Marine Mammal Regulations*.[8] The Sea Shepherd Conservation Society, which claims the charges to be false, says of the *Farley Mowat*, "She is a protector, and a symbol of hope for a better, more humane, and more ecologically conscious future."[9] The vessel has since been sold and will be used for scientific research expeditions.

"So ends the story of how the Sea of Whales became a Sea of Slaughter as, one by one, from the greatest to the least, each in turn according to its monetary worth, the several cetacean nations perished in a roaring holocaust fuelled by human avarice." —**Farley Mowat, Sea of Slaughter (1984)**

Thinking About Environmental Perspectives

The Sea Shepherd Conservation Society, of which Farley Mowat is the international chair, has been criticized for extremism. Its anti-whaling actions have included ramming, disabling, and otherwise confronting whaling vessels from the Faeroe Islands (in the North Atlantic) to Antarctica. Sea Shepherd maintains the position that standing by and observing illegal activities that endanger ocean life is not an acceptable pathway, and it pledges to take whatever actions are necessary to protect sea life and habitats. What do you think? Are extreme and potentially dangerous actions, like ramming a vessel, acceptable, or perhaps even necessary, in some circumstances?

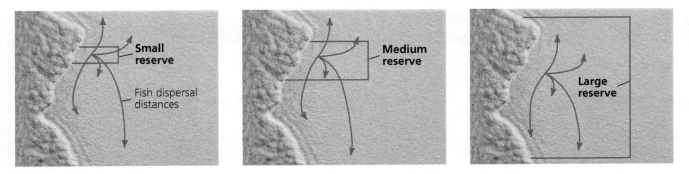

FIGURE 10.26 Marine reserves of different sizes may have varying effects on ecological communities and fisheries. Young and adult fish and shellfish of different species can disperse different distances, as indicated by the red arrows in the figure. A small reserve (left panel) may fail to protect animals because too many disperse out of the reserve. A large reserve (right panel) may protect fish and shellfish very well but will provide relatively less "spillover" into areas where people can legally fish. Thus medium-sized reserves (middle panel) may offer the best hope of preserving species and ecological communities while also providing adequate fish to fishers and human communities.   *Source: Halpern, B. S., and R. R. Warner. 2003. Matching marine reserve design to reserve objectives. Proceedings of the Royal Society of London B 270:1871–1878.*

Of several dozen studies that have estimated how much area of the ocean should be protected in no-take reserves, estimates range from 10% to 65%, with most falling between 20% and 50%. Other studies are modelling how to optimize the size and spacing of individual reserves so that ecosystems are protected, fisheries are sustained, and people are not overly excluded from marine areas (**FIGURE 10.26**). If marine reserves are designed strategically to take advantage of ocean currents, many scientists say, then they may well seed the seas and help lead us toward solutions to one of our most pressing environmental problems.

Conclusion

The ocean covers most of our planet and contains diverse topography and ecosystems, some of which we are only now beginning to explore and understand. We are learning more about the ocean and coastal environments while intensifying our use of their resources and causing these areas more severe impacts. In so doing, we are coming to understand better how to use these resources without depleting them or causing undue ecological harm to the marine and coastal systems on which we depend.

Today, scientists are demonstrating that setting aside protected areas of the ocean can serve to maintain natural systems and also to enhance fisheries. This is vital at a time when we are depleting many of the world's marine fish stocks. As historical studies reveal more information on how much biodiversity the ocean formerly contained and has now lost, we may increasingly look beyond simply making fisheries stable and instead consider restoring the ecological systems that once flourished in our waters.

REVIEWING OBJECTIVES

You should now be able to:

Identify physical, geographical, chemical, and biological aspects of the marine environment

- The ocean covers 71% of Earth's surface and contains more than 97% of its surface water.
- Ocean water contains 96.5% H_2O by mass and various dissolved salts.
- Colder, saltier water is denser and sinks. Water temperatures vary with latitude, and temperature variation is greater in surface layers.
- Persistent currents move horizontally through the oceans, driven by density differences, sunlight, and wind.

- Vertical water movement includes upwelling and downwelling, which affect the distribution of nutrients and life.
- Seafloor topography can be complex.

Describe major types of marine ecosystems

- Major types of marine and coastal ecosystems include pelagic and deep-water open ocean systems, kelp forests, coral reefs, intertidal zones, salt marshes, mangrove forests, and estuaries.
- Many of these systems are highly productive and rich in biodiversity. Many also suffer heavy impacts from human influence.

Outline historic and current human uses of marine resources

- For millennia, people have fished the ocean and used ocean waters for transportation.
- Today we extract energy and minerals from the ocean.

Assess human impacts on marine environments

- People pollute ocean waters with trash, including plastic and nets that harm marine life.
- Marine oil pollution results from non-point sources on land, as well as from tanker spills at sea.
- Heavy metal contaminants in seafood affect human health, and nutrient pollution can lead to harmful algal blooms.
- Overharvesting is perhaps the major human impact on marine systems.

Review the current state of ocean fisheries and reasons for their decline

- Half the world's marine fish populations are fully exploited, 25% are already overexploited, and only 25% can yield more without declining.
- Global fish catches have stopped growing since the late 1980s, despite increased fishing effort and improved technologies.

- People began depleting marine resources long ago, but impacts have intensified in recent decades.
- Commercial fishing practices include driftnetting, longline fishing, and trawling, all of which capture nontarget organisms, called by-catch.
- Today's ocean holds only one-tenth the number of large animals that it did before the advent of industrialized commercial fishing.
- As fishing intensity increases, the fish available become smaller.
- Marine biodiversity loss affects ecosystem services.
- Consumers can encourage good fishery practices by shopping for sustainable seafood.
- Traditional fisheries management has not stopped declines, so many scientists feel that ecosystem-based management is needed.

Evaluate marine protected areas and reserves as innovative solutions

- We have established far fewer protected areas in the ocean than we have on land, and most marine protected areas allow many extractive activities.
- Marine reserves can protect ecosystems while also boosting fish populations and making fisheries sustainable.

TESTING YOUR COMPREHENSION

1. What proportion of Earth's surface does the ocean cover? What is the average salinity of ocean water? How are density, salinity, and temperature related in each layer of ocean water?
2. What factors drive the system of ocean currents? In what ways do these movements affect conditions for life in the oceans?
3. Where in the ocean are the most productive areas of biological activity located?
4. Describe three kinds of ecosystems found near coastal areas and the kinds of life they support.
5. Why are coral reefs biologically valuable? How are they being degraded by human impact?

6. What is causing the disappearance of mangrove forests and salt marshes?
7. Discuss three ways in which people are combating pollution in the oceans and on our coasts.
8. Describe an example of how overfishing can lead to ecological damage and fishery collapse.
9. Name three industrial fishing practices, and explain how they create by-catch and harm marine life.
10. How does a marine reserve differ from a marine protected area? Why do many fishers oppose marine reserves? Explain why many scientists say no-take reserves will be good for fishers.

THINKING IT THROUGH

1. What benefits do you derive from the ocean? How does your behaviour affect the ocean, both directly and indirectly? Give specific examples.
2. We have been able to reduce the amount of oil we spill into the ocean, but petroleum-based products, such as plastic, continue to litter the ocean and shorelines. Discuss some ways that we can reduce this threat to the marine environment.
3. Describe the trends in global fish capture over the past 50 years, and explain several factors that account for these trends.
4. Consider what you know about biological productivity in the ocean, about the scientific data on marine reserves, and about the social and political issues surrounding the establishment of marine reserves. What ocean regions do you think it would be particularly appropriate to establish as marine reserves? Why?
5. Image that you make your living fishing on the ocean, just as your father and grandfather did, and as most of your neighbours do in your small coastal village. Your region's fishery has just collapsed, however, and everyone is blaming it on overfishing. The govern-

ment has closed the fishery for three years, and scientists are pushing for a permanent marine reserve to be established on your former fishing grounds. You have no desire to move away from your village, so what steps will you take now? Will you protest the closure? What compensation will you ask of the government if it prevents you from fishing? Will you work with scientists to establish a reserve that improves fishing in the future, or will you oppose their attempts to create a reserve? What data and what assurances will you ask of them?

6. Let's say that you are mayor of a coastal town where some residents are employed as commercial fishers and others make a living serving ecotourists who come to snorkel and scuba dive at the nearby coral reef. In recent years, several fish stocks have crashed, and ecotourism is dropping off as fish disappear from the increasingly degraded reef. Scientists are urging you to help establish a marine reserve around portions of the reef, but most commercial and recreational fishers are opposed to this idea. What steps would you take to restore your community's economy and environment?

INTERPRETING GRAPHS AND DATA

The accompanying graph presents trends in the status of North Atlantic swordfish, a highly migratory species managed directly by the U.S. National Marine Fishery Service. The solid red line shows the mortality rate from fishing. The solid blue line indicates the biomass of the stock. The graph also indicates the date when an international recovery plan was implemented.

1. Describe the trends in swordfish stocks (1) before the adoption of an international management plan and (2) since the plan was adopted. Describe the interactions between fishing mortality and biomass as illustrated by the graph.
2. Based on the data in the graph, predict the likely trend in swordfish production over the next 10 years, assuming no change to the status quo.
3. This graph illustrates an effort that is succeeding, but not all rebuilding plans lead to stock recovery. Beyond the existence of a plan, what actions might play a role in supporting stock recovery efforts?

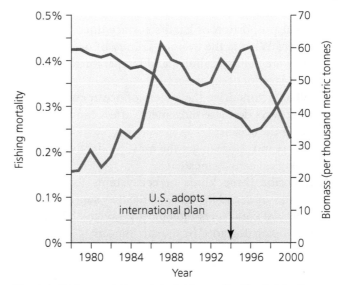

Trends in fishing mortality and stock biomass for North Atlantic swordfish, 1978–2000.

Source: Adapted from Rosenberg, A., et al. (2006). Rebuilding U.S. fisheries: Progress and problems. Frontiers in Ecology and the Environment 4(6).

CHAPTER ENDNOTES

1. NOAA Coral Health and Monitoring Program, *Coral Bleaching*, www.coral.noaa.gov/cleo/coral_bleaching.shtml

2. Halifax Regional Municipality, Halifax Harbour Project, www.halifax.ca/harboursol/WhatistheHarbourSolutionsProject.html

3. Clucas, I. (1997) *A Study of the Options for Utilization of Bycatch and Discards from Marine and Capture Fisheries,* Fishery Industries Division, FAO Fisheries Department, http://www.fao.org/docrep/W6602E/w6602E10.htm#10

4. Fisheries and Oceans Canada, Aquaculture Fact Sheets, *Fin Fish*, www.dfo-mpo.gc.ca/aquaculture/finfish_e.htm

5. Parks Canada, Fisheries and Oceans Canada, and Environment Canada (2005) *Canada's Marine Protected Areas Strategy,* www.dfo-mpo.gc.ca/oceans-habitat/oceans/mpa-zpm/fedmpa-zpmfed/pdf/mpa_e.pdf

6. The Canadian Encyclopedia *Historica*, Farley Mowat, www.thecanadianencyclopedia.com/index.cfm?PgNm=TCE&ArticleId=A0005502

7. Amazon.com, *Sea of Slaughter* by Farley Mowat (Reviews), www.amazon.com/Sea-Slaughter-Farley-Mowat/dp/1576300196

8. Department of Fisheries and Oceans, News Releases 2008, *Enforcement Actions Taken Against Farley Mowat—Update,* www.dfo-mpo.gc.ca/media/npress-communique/2008/20080414-eng.htm; the vessel remains in custody as of late 2008

9. Sea Shepherd Conservation Society, *Neptune's Navy*, www.seashepherd.org/fleet/fleet.html

MyEnvironmentPlace

Go to **www.myenvironmentplace.ca** where you will find quizzes, animations, your Pearson eText, and more.

Atmospheric Science and Air Pollution

11

This is Earth's atmosphere, from space.

Upon successfully completing this chapter, you will be able to

- Describe the composition, structure, and function of Earth's atmosphere
- Outline the scope of outdoor air pollution and assess potential solutions
- Explain stratospheric ozone depletion and identify steps taken to address it

- Define *acidic deposition* and illustrate its consequences
- Characterize the scope of indoor air pollution and assess potential solutions

The Inco Superstack, at 380 m tall, is the tallest smokestack in the Western Hemisphere.

CANADA

Hudson Bay

Ontario *Sudbury*

UNITED STATES

CENTRAL CASE:
THE RAIN AND THE BIG NICKEL

"Despite Canada's success at reducing acid-causing emissions, acid deposition is still affecting our environment."
—ENVIRONMENT CANADA, *2004 CANADIAN ACID DEPOSITION SCIENCE ASSESSMENT*

"The problem [of acid rain] has not gone away."
—GENE LIKENS, DIRECTOR OF THE INSTITUTE OF ECOSYSTEM STUDIES IN MILLBROOK, NEW YORK

Sudbury, Ontario, is home to some of the world's largest nickel and copper deposits. These are not ordinary mineral deposits—they were formed by rock melting that resulted from the impact of a meteorite 15 km in diameter more than 2 billion years ago. The impact left a crater almost 600 km in diameter and 40 km deep, in which the massive ore deposits were localized. A "sister" meteorite impact left a smaller crater, now filled by the deep, clear waters of Lake Wanapitei.

Sudbury also claims to be the "blueberry capital of the world," but here a downside becomes apparent. Blueberries thrive in highly acidic soils, but the soils of the Sudbury area are not naturally so acidic. What happened to create this blueberry-friendly environment?

Nickel mining and refining happened. Mining started in the Sudbury area in the late 1800s and continues today. The mining and, particularly, refining of ores (through *smelting*, in which the ore is crushed and heated to a very high temperature to segregate the metals of interest) generate emissions high in sulphur dioxide (SO_2). These sulphur-rich emissions, if released to the atmosphere, combine with water vapour to form sulphuric acid, which ultimately falls as *acidic deposition*. The rocks and soils of the Sudbury area are naturally susceptible to acidification because of their chemical composition.

As early as the 1920s, the degradation of the natural environment around Sudbury was recognized as a problem. Acid rain devastated the area's forests and water bodies. Pollution stained the treeless soil black. In 1969—quite early in the modern environmental movement (recall that the first Earth Day was in 1970)— the government of Ontario informed Inco, the principal mining company and main polluter in the area at the time, that it would be required to substantially decrease emissions from its facilities. Inco's response, cutting-edge in its day, was to build a "Superstack," 380 m tall, to carry emissions from the smelter far away from the immediate Sudbury area (see photo). The Superstack was completed in 1972, and to this day it remains the tallest smokestack in the Western Hemisphere.

Today we know that the Superstack was only a partial solution. It did disperse the sulphurous emissions, but rather than ending the acidic deposition it just spread the problem farther afield. Environment Canada estimates that 7000 lakes in northern Ontario and Québec were damaged by acid-causing emissions from smelters in Sudbury.[1] The sensitivity of the underlying granitic rocks contributed to the acidification problem, which affected not only forests and soils, but also fish and the sport fishing industry in an area of approximately 17 000 km[2].[2] Sulphur emissions from the Superstack were dispersed over a much broader area than they would have been, had the stack height been less.

Beginning in the early 1980s, Inco and Falconbridge (the other major producer of smelter emissions in the area) undertook vigorous efforts to clean their emissions prior to releasing them to the atmosphere. The result is that SO_2 emissions today have been reduced by as much as 90%. Lakes, forests, and soils in the region have shown significant biological and chemical improvements in the more than 30 years since the Superstack was constructed. However, many of the damaged lakes are still acidic and contaminated with metals.[3]

The Experimental Lakes Area in northwestern Ontario, set up in 1968 and maintained by Fisheries and Oceans Canada, is one facility where scientific research on lake acidification and recovery takes place. The area consists of 58 small lakes and their watersheds, with a permanent field research station. Here scientists carry out research on the impacts of acidification, investigate the process of recovery, and test a variety of remediation approaches. For example, many of the fish in a sulphur-acidified lake died of starvation as a result of the impacts of acidification on their food sources (see photo). When the lake was remediated, the fish population was able to recover. This kind of research gives scientists a better idea of the recovery process and the robustness of aquatic systems undergoing chemical and biological changes.[4]

The most important legacy of the Superstack is that it ushered in an era of ecological awareness, recovery, and restoration in Ontario, and of pride in the natural environment in the Sudbury area. Partners in the Regional Land Reclamation Program, launched in 1978, continue to carry out environmental research on acidification and the recovery process, which may prove useful in other parts of the world where acidification has caused ecological damage.

In the Experimental Lakes Area of northwestern Ontario, many of the trout in an experimentally acidified lake died of starvation as a result of the loss of their food sources (top). When the lake was remediated, the fish population was able to recover (bottom).

The Atmosphere and Weather

Every breath we take reaffirms our connection to the **atmosphere**, the thin layer of gases that surrounds Earth. We live at the bottom of this layer, which provides us with oxygen, absorbs hazardous solar radiation, burns up incoming meteors, transports and recycles water and nutrients, and moderates climate.

The atmosphere consists of roughly 78% nitrogen gas (N_2) and 21% oxygen gas (O_2). The remaining 1% is composed of argon gas (Ar) and minute concentrations of several other gases (**FIGURE 11.1**). These include *permanent gases* that remain at stable concentrations and *variable gases* that vary in concentration from time to time or place to place as a result of natural processes or human activities.

Over Earth's long history, the atmosphere's chemical composition has changed. Oxygen gas began to build up in an atmosphere dominated by carbon dioxide (CO_2), nitrogen, carbon monoxide (CO), and hydrogen (H_2) about 2.7 billion years ago, with the emergence of autotrophic microbes that emitted oxygen as a by-product of photosynthesis. Today, human activity is altering the quantities of some atmospheric gases, such as carbon dioxide, methane (CH_4), and ozone (O_3). In this chapter we will explore some of the atmospheric changes brought about by artificial pollutants, but we must first begin with an overview of Earth's atmosphere.

The atmosphere is layered

The atmosphere that stretches so high above us and seems so vast is actually just a thin coating about 1/100 of Earth's diameter, like the fuzzy skin of a peach. This coating consists of four layers that atmospheric scientists recognize by measuring differences in temperature, density, and composition (**FIGURE 11.2**).

The bottommost layer, the **troposphere**, blankets Earth's surface and provides us with the air we need to live. The movement of air within the troposphere is also largely responsible for the planet's weather. Although it is thin (averaging 11 km high) relative to the atmosphere's other layers, the troposphere contains three-quarters of the atmosphere's mass because air is denser near Earth's surface. On average, tropospheric air temperature declines by about 6°C for each kilometre in altitude, dropping to roughly –52°C at its highest point. At the top of the troposphere, however, temperatures cease to decline with altitude, marking a boundary called the *tropopause*. The tropopause acts like a cap, limiting mixing

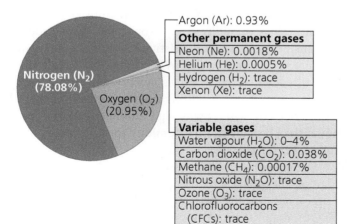

FIGURE 11.1

Earth's atmosphere consists mostly of nitrogen, secondarily of oxygen, and lastly of a mix of gases at dilute concentrations. Permanent gases are fixed in concentration. Variable gases vary in concentration as a result of either natural processes or human activities.
Source: Data from Ahrens, C. D. (2007). Meteorology Today, 8th ed. Belmont, CA: Brooks/Cole.

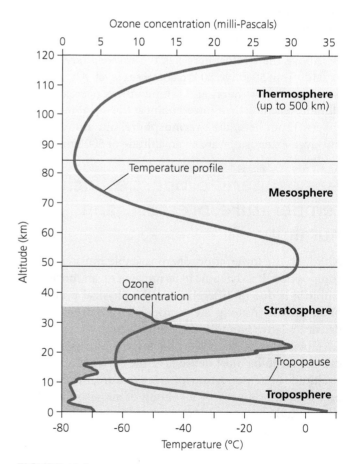

FIGURE 11.2

Temperature drops with altitude in the troposphere, rises with altitude in the stratosphere, drops in the mesosphere, and then rises again in the thermosphere. The tropopause separates the troposphere from the stratosphere. Ozone reaches a peak in a portion of the stratosphere, giving rise to the term *ozone layer*.
Source: Adapted from Jacobson, M. Z. (2002). Atmospheric Pollution: History, Science, and Regulation. Cambridge: Cambridge University Press; and Parson, E. A. (2003). Protecting the Ozone Layer: Science and Strategy. Oxford: Oxford University Press.

between the troposphere and the atmospheric layer above it, the stratosphere.

The **stratosphere** extends from 11 km to 50 km above sea level. Although similar in composition to the troposphere, the stratosphere is 1000 times as dry and less dense. Its gases experience little vertical mixing, so once substances (including pollutants) enter it, they tend to remain for a long time. The stratosphere attains a maximum temperature of –3°C at its highest altitude but is colder in its lower reaches. The reason is that ozone and oxygen absorb and scatter the Sun's ultraviolet (UV) radiation, so that much of the UV radiation penetrating the upper stratosphere fails to reach the lower stratosphere. Most of the atmosphere's minute amount of ozone concentrates in a portion of the stratosphere roughly from 17 km to 30 km above sea level, a region that has come to be called Earth's **ozone layer**. The ozone layer greatly reduces the amount of UV radiation that reaches Earth's surface. Because UV light can damage living tissue and induce mutations in DNA, the ozone layer's protective effects are vital for life on Earth.

Above the stratosphere lies the **mesosphere**, which extends from 50 km to 80 km above sea level. Air pressure is extremely low here, and temperatures decrease with altitude, reaching their lowest point at the top of the mesosphere. From here, the **thermosphere**, our atmosphere's top layer, extends upward to an altitude of 500 km.

Atmospheric properties include temperature, pressure, and humidity

Although the lower atmosphere is stable in its chemical composition, it is dynamic in its movement; air movement within it is due to differences in the physical properties of air masses. Among these properties are pressure and density, relative humidity, and temperature.

Gravity pulls gas molecules toward Earth's surface, causing air to be most dense near the surface and less so as altitude increases. **Atmospheric pressure**, the force per unit of area produced by a column of air, also decreases with altitude because at higher altitudes fewer molecules are pulled down by gravity (**FIGURE 11.3**). At sea level, atmospheric pressure is 1013 millibars (mb). Mountain climbers trekking to Mount Everest, the world's highest mountain, can look up and view their destination from Kala Patthar, a nearby peak, at roughly 5.5 km in altitude. At this altitude, pressure is 500 mb—half the atmosphere's air molecules are above the climber, and half are below. A climber who reaches Everest's peak (8.85 km), where the "thin air" is just more than 300 mb, stands above two-thirds of the molecules in the atmosphere. When we fly on

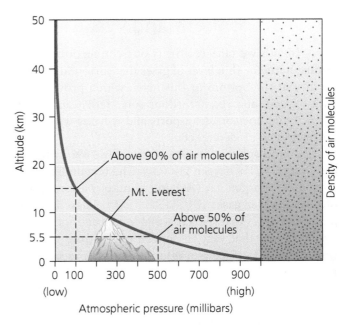

FIGURE 11.3
As one climbs higher through the atmosphere, gas molecules become less densely packed. As density decreases, so does atmospheric pressure. Because most air molecules lie low in the atmosphere, one needs to be only 5.5 km high to be above half the planet's air molecules. *Adapted from Ahrens, C. D. (2007). Meteorology Today, 8th ed. Belmont, CA: Brooks/Cole.*

a commercial jet airliner at a cruising altitude of 11 km, we are above roughly 80% of the atmosphere's molecules.

Another property of air is **relative humidity**, the ratio of water vapour a given volume of air contains to the maximum amount it *could* contain at a given temperature. Average daytime relative humidity in June in the desert at Phoenix, Arizona, is only 31% (meaning that the air contains less than a third of the water vapour it possibly can at its temperature), whereas on the tropical island of Guam, relative humidity rarely drops below 88%. People are sensitive to changes in relative humidity because we perspire to cool our bodies. When humidity is high, the air is already holding nearly as much water vapour as it can, so sweat evaporates slowly and the body cannot cool itself efficiently. This is why high humidity makes it feel hotter than it really is. Low humidity speeds evaporation and makes it feel cooler.

The temperature of air also varies with location and time. At the global scale, temperature varies over Earth's surface because the Sun's rays strike some areas more directly than others. At more local scales, temperature varies because of topography, plant cover, proximity of land to water, and many other factors. Sometimes these local variations are striking—the side of a hill that is sheltered from wind or direct sunlight can have a totally different weather pattern, or **microclimate**, from the side facing into the wind or sunlight.

Solar energy heats the atmosphere, helps create seasons, and causes air to circulate

Energy from the Sun heats air in the atmosphere, drives air movement, helps create seasons, and influences weather and climate. An enormous amount of solar energy continuously bombards the upper atmosphere—more than 1000 watts/m^2 where it hits directly, at a right angle, many thousands of times greater than the total output of electricity generated by human society. Of that solar energy, about 70% is absorbed by the atmosphere and planetary surface, while the rest is reflected back into space.

The spatial relationship between Earth and the Sun determines how much solar radiation strikes each point on Earth's surface. Sunlight is most intense when it shines directly overhead and meets the planet's surface at a perpendicular angle. At this angle, sunlight passes through a minimum of energy-absorbing atmosphere, and Earth's surface receives a maximum of solar energy per unit of surface area. Conversely, solar energy that approaches Earth's surface at an oblique angle loses intensity as it traverses a longer distance through the atmosphere, and it is less intense when it reaches the surface, where the oblique angle of the incoming solar energy also is spread over a larger surface area. This is why, on average, solar radiation intensity is highest near the equator and weakest near the poles (**FIGURE 11.4**).

Because Earth is tilted on its *axis* (an imaginary line connecting the poles) by about 23.5°, the Northern and Southern Hemispheres each tilt toward the Sun for half the year, resulting in the change in seasons (**FIGURE 11.5**). Regions near the equator are largely unaffected by this tilt; they experience about 12 hours each of sunlight and darkness every day throughout the year. Near the poles, however, the effect is strong, and seasonality is pronounced.

Land and surface water absorb solar energy, re-radiating heat and causing water to evaporate. Air near Earth's surface therefore tends to be warmer and moister than air at higher altitudes. These differences set into motion a process of convective circulation (**FIGURE 11.6**). Warm air, being less dense, rises and creates vertical currents. As air rises into regions of lower atmospheric pressure, it expands and cools. Once the air cools, it descends and becomes denser, replacing warm air that is rising. The air picks up heat and moisture near ground level and prepares to rise again, continuing the process. Similar convective circulation patterns occur in ocean waters and in magma beneath Earth's surface.

The atmosphere drives weather and climate

Weather and climate involve the physical properties of the troposphere, including temperature, pressure, humidity, cloudiness, and wind. **Weather** specifies atmospheric conditions over short time periods, typically hours or days, and within relatively small geographic areas. **Climate** describes the pattern of atmospheric conditions found across large geographic regions over long periods—seasons, years, or millennia. Writer Mark Twain once noted the distinction

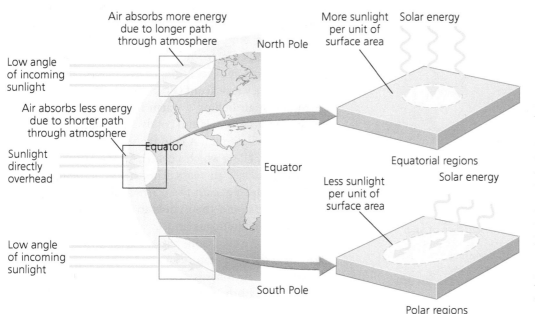

FIGURE 11.4
Because of Earth's curvature, polar regions receive, on average, less solar energy than equatorial regions. One reason is that sunlight gets spread over a larger area when striking the surface at an angle. Another reason is that sunlight approaching at a lower angle near the poles must traverse a longer distance through the atmosphere, during which more energy is absorbed or reflected. These patterns represent year-round averages; the latitude at which radiation approaches the surface perpendicularly varies with the seasons (see **FIGURE 11.5**).

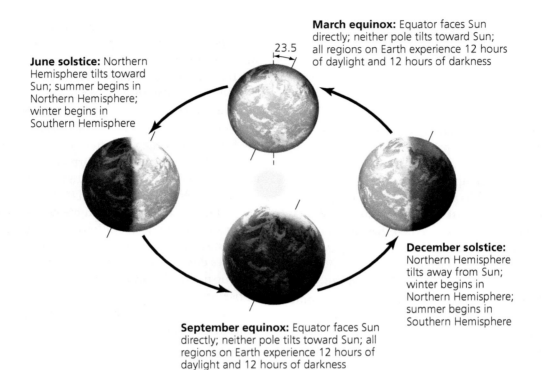

June solstice: Northern Hemisphere tilts toward Sun; summer begins in Northern Hemisphere; winter begins in Southern Hemisphere

March equinox: Equator faces Sun directly; neither pole tilts toward Sun; all regions on Earth experience 12 hours of daylight and 12 hours of darkness

23.5

December solstice: Northern Hemisphere tilts away from Sun; winter begins in Northern Hemisphere; summer begins in Southern Hemisphere

September equinox: Equator faces Sun directly; neither pole tilts toward Sun; all regions on Earth experience 12 hours of daylight and 12 hours of darkness

FIGURE 11.5   The seasons occur because Earth is tilted on its axis by 23.5 degrees. As Earth revolves around the Sun, the Northern Hemisphere tilts toward the Sun for one half of the year, and the Southern Hemisphere tilts toward the Sun for the other half of the year. In each hemisphere, summer occurs during the period in which the hemisphere is tilted toward the Sun.

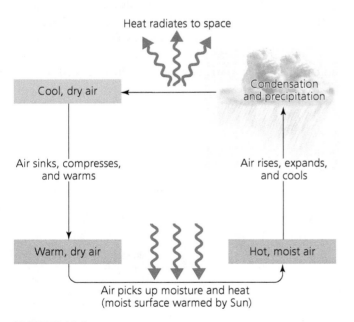

Heat radiates to space

Cool, dry air

Condensation and precipitation

Air sinks, compresses, and warms

Air rises, expands, and cools

Warm, dry air

Hot, moist air

Air picks up moisture and heat (moist surface warmed by Sun)

FIGURE 11.6
Weather is driven in part by the convective circulation of air in the atmosphere. Air being heated near Earth's surface picks up moisture and rises. Once aloft, this air cools, and moisture condenses, forming clouds and precipitation. Cool, drying air begins to descend, compressing and warming in the process. Warm, dry air near the surface begins the cycle anew.

between climate and weather by saying, "Climate is what we expect; weather is what we get."

Air masses interact to produce weather

Weather can change quickly when air masses with different physical properties meet. The boundary between air masses that differ in temperature and moisture (and therefore density) is called a **front**. The boundary along which a mass of warmer, moister air replaces a mass of colder, drier air is termed a **warm front** (**FIGURE 11.7A**). Some of the warm, moist air behind a warm front rises over the cold air mass and then cools and condenses to form clouds that may produce light rain. A **cold front** (**FIGURE 11.7B**) is the boundary along which a colder, drier air mass displaces a warmer, moister air mass. The colder air, being denser, tends to wedge beneath the warmer air. The warmer air rises, expands, and then cools to form clouds that can produce thunderstorms and even tornadoes (**FIGURE 11.7C**). Once a cold front passes through, the sky usually clears, and the temperature and humidity drop.

Adjacent air masses may also differ in atmospheric pressure. A **high-pressure system** contains air that

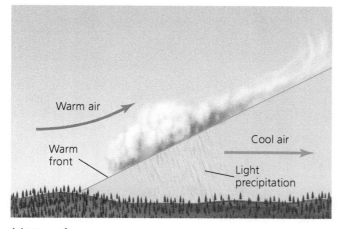

(a) Warm front

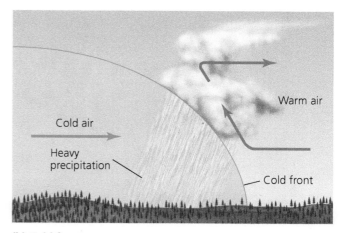

(b) Cold front

FIGURE 11.7

When a warm front approaches **(a)**, warmer air rises over cooler air, causing light or moderate precipitation as moisture in the warmer air condenses. When a cold front approaches **(b)**, colder air pushes beneath warmer air, and the warmer air rises, resulting in condensation and heavy precipitation. **(c)** Cold fronts often spawn thunderstorms and even tornadoes, like this one in the U.S. Midwest's "Tornado Alley," 2011.

(c) Active weather

moves outward away from a centre of high pressure as it descends. High-pressure systems typically bring fair weather. In a **low-pressure system**, air moves toward the low atmospheric pressure at the centre of the system and spirals upward. The air expands and cools, and clouds and precipitation often result.

Under most conditions, air in the troposphere decreases in temperature as altitude increases. Because warm air rises, vertical mixing results. Occasionally, however, a layer of cool air occurs beneath a layer of warmer air. This departure from the normal temperature profile is known as a temperature inversion, or **thermal inversion** (FIGURE 11.8) because the normal direction of temperature change is inverted. The cooler air at the bottom of the inversion layer is denser than the warmer air at the top, so it resists vertical mixing and remains stable. Thermal inversions can occur in different ways, sometimes involving cool air at ground level and sometimes producing an inversion layer higher above the ground (as shown in FIGURE 11.8B). One common type of inversion occurs in mountain valleys where slopes block morning sunlight, keeping ground-level air within the valley shaded and cool.

Vertical mixing normally allows air pollution to be diluted upward, but thermal inversions trap pollutants near the ground. A thermal inversion sparked a "killer smog" crisis in London, England, in 1952. A high-pressure system settled over the city, acting like a cap on the pollution; at least 4000 people—possibly as many as 12 000—died as a result of this event. Inversions regularly cause smog buildups in large metropolitan areas in valleys ringed by mountains, such as Los Angeles, Mexico City, Seoul, and Rio de Janeiro.

Large-scale circulation systems produce global climate patterns

At larger geographic scales, convective air currents contribute to broad climatic patterns (FIGURE 11.9A). Near the equator, solar radiation sets in motion a pair of convective cells known as **Hadley cells**. Here, where sunlight is most intense, surface air warms, rises, and expands. As it does so, it releases moisture, producing the heavy rainfall that gives rise to tropical rainforests near the equator.

After releasing much of its moisture, this air diverges and moves in currents heading northward and southward. The air in these currents cools and descends back to Earth at about 30° latitude north and south. Because the descending air has low relative humidity, the regions

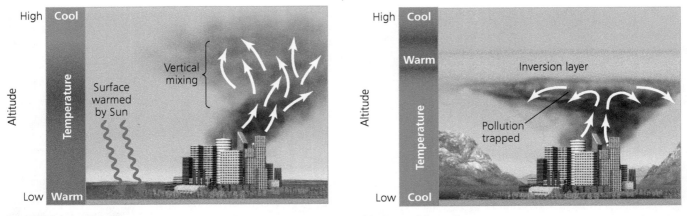

(a) Normal conditions

(b) Thermal inversion

FIGURE 11.8   A thermal inversion is a natural atmospheric occurrence that can worsen air pollution locally. Under normal conditions **(a)**, tropospheric temperature decreases with altitude. Air of different altitudes mixes, dispersing pollutants upward and outward from their sources. During a thermal inversion **(b)**, cool air remains near the ground underneath a layer of air that warms with altitude. Little mixing occurs, and pollutants are trapped near the surface.

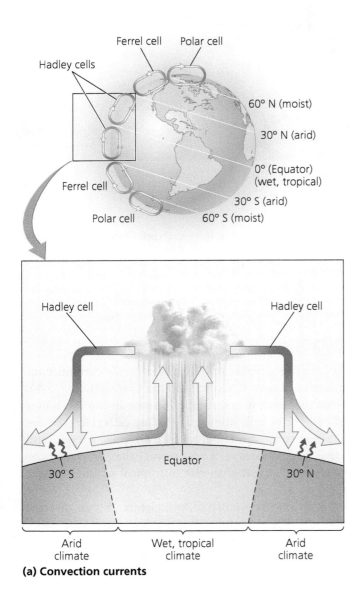

(a) Convection currents

FIGURE 11.9

A series of large-scale convective cells **(a)** helps determine global patterns of humidity and aridity. Warm air near the equator rises, expands, and cools, and moisture condenses, giving rise to a wet climate in tropical regions. Air travels toward the poles and descends around 30° latitude. This air, which loses its moisture in the tropics, causes regions around 30° latitude to be arid. This convective circulation, a Hadley cell, occurs on both sides of the equator. Between roughly 30° and 60° latitude north and south, Ferrel cells occur; and between 60° and 90° latitude, polar cells occur. Air rises around 60° latitude, creating a moist climate, and falls around 90°, creating a dry climate. Global wind currents **(b)** show latitudinal patterns as well. Trade winds between the equator and 30° latitude blow westward, whereas westerlies between 30° and 60° latitude blow eastward. Global air circulation patterns are further modified by the influence of continental land masses and by the Coriolis force, which causes freely moving objects to be deflected to the right in the Northern Hemisphere and to the left in the Southern Hemisphere.

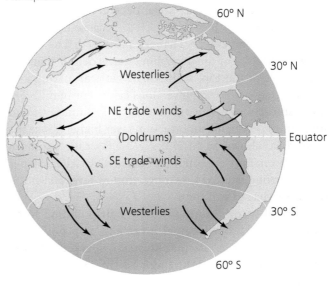

(b) Global wind patterns

Most people think that the term *trade winds*, the prevailing easterly surface winds in the tropics, originated because sailing ships used them to traverse the Atlantic for the purpose of trade in the fifteenth and sixteenth centuries. Sailing ships did make use of the trade winds, both for trade and for exploration, but the word itself originated in the early 1600s from the Old English word *tredan*, which meant "one's traditional business." In this sense, the term *trade* is not specifically related to commerce, but rather to the idea of something "habitual" or "regular," which certainly applies to the trade winds.

around 30° latitude are quite arid, giving rise to deserts. Two pairs of similar but less intense convective cells, called **Ferrel cells** and **polar cells**, lift air and create precipitation around 60° latitude north and south and cause air to descend at around 30° latitude and in the polar regions.

These three pairs of cells account for the latitudinal distribution of moisture across Earth's surface: warm, wet climates near the equator; arid climates and major deserts near 30° latitude; moist, temperate regions near 60° latitude; and dry, cold conditions near the poles. These patterns, combined with temperature variation, also help explain why biomes tend to be arrayed in latitudinal bands.

The Hadley, Ferrel, and polar cells interact with Earth's rotation to produce the global wind patterns shown in FIGURE 11.9B. As Earth rotates on its axis, locations on the equator spin faster than locations near the poles. As a result, the north–south air currents of the convective cells are deflected from a straight path as some portions of the globe move beneath them more quickly than others. This deflection is called the **Coriolis effect**, and it results in the curving global wind patterns evident in FIGURE 11.9B. The Coriolis effect influences the circulation of any freely moving fluid on Earth's surface, including ocean water, but its influence is not noticeable unless the scale of the circulation is quite large.

Between the equator and 30° latitude, the **trade winds** blow from east to west. Where the trade winds meet and are deflected toward the west, just north and south of the equator, lies a region with few winds known as the *doldrums*. Farther from the equator, between 30° and 60°

north and south latitude, the *westerlies* originate from the west and blow east. People used these global circulation patterns for centuries to facilitate ocean travel by wind-powered sailing ships.

The atmosphere interacts with the oceans to affect weather, climate, and the distribution of biomes. For instance, winds and convective circulation in ocean water together maintain ocean currents. Trade winds weaken periodically, leading to El Niño conditions. The atmosphere's interactions with other systems of the planet are complex, but even a basic understanding of how the atmosphere functions can help us comprehend how our pollution of the atmosphere can affect ecological systems, economies, and human health.

Outdoor Air Pollution

Throughout human history, we have made the atmosphere a dumping ground for airborne wastes. Whether from primitive wood fires or modern coal-burning power plants, people have generated air pollutants, gases and particulate material added to the atmosphere that can affect climate or harm people or other organisms. **Air pollution** refers to the release of air pollutants. In recent decades, government policy and improved technologies have helped us to substantially diminish outdoor air pollution, usually called *ambient air pollution*, in countries of the developed world. However, outdoor air pollution remains a problem, particularly in developing nations and in urban areas.

Natural sources can pollute

When we think of outdoor air pollution, we tend to envision smokestacks belching black smoke from industrial plants. However, natural processes produce a great deal of the world's air pollution. Some of these natural impacts can be exacerbated by human activity and land use policies.

Winds sweeping over arid terrain can send huge amounts of dust aloft. In 2001, strong westerlies lifted soil from deserts in Mongolia and China. The dust blanketed Chinese towns, spread to Japan and Korea, travelled eastward across the Pacific Ocean to the United States, then crossed the Atlantic, and left evidence atop the French Alps. Every year, hundreds of millions of tons of dust are blown westward by trade winds across the Atlantic Ocean from northern Africa to the Americas (FIGURE 11.10A). These dust storms bring nutrients to the Amazon basin, causing algal blooms off the west coast of Africa, as well as fungal and bacterial spores that have been linked to die-offs in Caribbean coral reef systems.

(a) Dust storm off west coast of Africa

(b) Grimsvötn volcano eruption, 2011

(c) Forest fire in Alberta

FIGURE 11.10
Massive dust storms, such as this one blowing across the Atlantic Ocean from Africa to the Americas **(a)**, are one type of natural air pollution. Volcanic eruptions are another source, as shown by Grimsvötn volcano in Iceland **(b)**, which erupted in 2011, causing air travel delays. A third natural cause of air pollution is fires in forests and grasslands **(c)**. Often, pollution from natural sources is made worse by human influence, such as when poor agricultural practices lead to soil erosion by wind or when fire suppression leads to more devastating fires.

Although dust storms are natural, the immense scale of these events is exacerbated by unsustainable farming and grazing practices that strip vegetation from the soil, promote wind erosion, and lead to desertification.

Volcanic eruptions release large quantities of particulate matter, as well as sulphur dioxide and other gases, into the troposphere. In 2010 and again in 2011, Icelandic volcanoes erupted voluminous clouds of ash, which shut down airports and delayed air travel in many parts of Britain and Europe. (**FIGURE 11.10B**). Major eruptions may blow matter into the stratosphere, where it can circle the globe and remain aloft for months or years.

Sulphur dioxide reacts with water and oxygen, and then condenses into fine droplets called **aerosols**, which reflect sunlight back into space and thereby cool the atmosphere and surface. The 1991 eruption of Mount Pinatubo in the Philippines ejected nearly 20 million tonnes of ash and aerosols and cooled global temperatures by roughly 0.5°C.

Burning vegetation also pollutes the atmosphere with soot and gases. More than 60 million hectares of forest and grassland burn in a typical year (**FIGURE 11.10C**). Fires occur naturally, but many are made more severe by human action. In North America, fuel buildup from decades of fire suppression has caused damaging forest fires in recent years. In the tropics, many fires result from the clearing of forests for farming and grazing by "slash-and-burn." In 1997, a severe drought brought on by the twentieth century's strongest El Niño event caused forest fires in Indonesia to rage out of control. Their smoke sickened 20 million Indonesians and caused a plane to crash and ships to collide. Combined with tens of thousands of fires in drought-plagued Mexico, Central America, and Africa, these fires released more carbon monoxide into the atmosphere during 1997–1998 than did our worldwide combustion of fossil fuels.

We create various types of outdoor air pollution

Since the onset of industrialization, human activity has introduced a variety of sources of air pollution. As with water pollution, air pollution can emanate from mobile or stationary sources, and from *point sources* or *non-point sources*. A point source describes a specific spot where large quantities of pollutants are discharged. Non-point sources are more diffuse, often consisting of many small sources. Power plants and factories act as stationary point sources, whereas millions of automobiles on the roadways—each one a tiny point source—together create a massive, mobile non-point source of pollutants.

Once pollutants are in the atmosphere in sufficient concentrations, they may do harm directly, or they may induce chemical reactions that produce harmful compounds. **Primary pollutants**, such as soot and carbon monoxide, are pollutants emitted into the troposphere in a form that can be directly harmful or that can react to form harmful substances. Harmful substances produced when primary pollutants interact or react with constituents of the atmosphere are called **secondary pollutants**. Secondary pollutants include tropospheric ozone, sulphuric acid, and other examples we will explore below.

Arguably the greatest human-induced air pollution problem today is our emission of greenhouse gases that contribute to global climate change. Addressing our release of excess carbon dioxide, methane, and other gases that warm the atmosphere stands as one of our civilization's primary challenges. We will discuss this issue separately and in depth in the next chapter, *Global Climate Change*.

CEPA identifies harmful airborne substances

The *Canadian Environmental Protection Act (CEPA)* (1999) provides a list of air pollutants that are subject to legislative control and management. These pollutants differ widely in their chemical composition, chemical reactivity, emission sources, residence time (how long they remain in various environmental reservoirs, including organisms), persistence (how long they last before breaking down), transportability (their ability to be moved long or short distances), and impacts on the natural and built environments, and on human and ecosystem health. Environment Canada groups the pollutants of greatest concern into four categories:[5]

1. Criteria air contaminants
2. Persistent organic pollutants
3. Heavy metals
4. Toxic air pollutants

Criteria air contaminants Criteria air contaminants (CACs) are produced in varying quantities by a number of processes, including the burning of fossil fuels. In Canada, the list of CACs includes sulphur oxides, nitrogen oxides, particulate matter, volatile organic compounds, carbon monoxide, ammonia, and tropospheric ozone. They are referred to as "criteria" contaminants because they were the first to come under government regulations, because of concerns about their potential impacts on human health.

Sulphur dioxide (SO_2) is a colourless gas with a strong odour. The vast majority of SO_2 and other sulphur oxide (SO_x or SOX) pollution results from the combustion of coal for electricity generation and industry. During combustion, elemental sulphur (S) in coal reacts with oxygen gas (O_2) to form SO_2. Once in the atmosphere, SO_2 may react to form sulphuric acid (H_2SO_4), which may then fall back to Earth as acid precipitation.

Nitrogen dioxide (NO_2) is a highly reactive, foul-smelling reddish brown gas that contributes to smog and acid precipitation. Along with nitric oxide (NO), NO_2 belongs to a family of compounds called *nitrogen oxides* (NO_x or NOX). Nitrogen oxides result when atmospheric nitrogen and oxygen react at the high temperatures created by combustion engines. More than half of NO_x emissions result from combustion in motor vehicle engines; electrical utility and industrial combustion accounts for most of the rest.

Particulate matter (PM) is composed of solid or liquid particles small enough to be suspended in the atmosphere. References to PM often include a number, specifying the size of the particles. PM_{10}, for example, refers to particles less than 10 μm (microns) in diameter; $PM_{2.5}$ refers to extremely fine particles, with diameters less than 2.5 μm; and so on. Particulate matter (which can also be called *suspended particulates, SP*) includes primary pollutants, such as dust and soot, as well as secondary pollutants, such as sulphates and nitrates, which form as a result of the alteration of primary sulphur and nitrous oxides. Particulates can damage respiratory tissues when inhaled. Most particulate matter (60%) in the atmosphere is wind-blown dust; human activity accounts for much of the rest. Along with SO_2, it was largely the emission of particulate matter from coal combustion that produced London's 1952 killer smog.

Volatile organic compounds (VOCs or VOX) are carbon-containing chemicals used in and emitted by vehicle engines and a wide variety of solvents and industrial processes, as well as many household chemicals and consumer items. One group of VOCs consists of hydrocarbons, such as methane (CH_4, the primary component of natural gas), propane (C_3H_8, used as a portable fuel), butane (C_4H_{10}, found in cigarette lighters), and octane (C_8H_{18}, a component of gasoline). Human activi-

weighing the issues

BAD AIR DAYS

Are you sensitive to smog? Do you suffer from itchy eyes, burning lungs, or other symptoms on "bad air days"? Do you think there is a smog problem in your area?

If you visit the website of the National Air Pollution Surveillance Network (NAPS), maintained by Environment Canada, you can watch animations of severe smog events in which ground-level ozone exceeded the accepted air quality standard levels over very large areas of both Canada and the United States (www.etc-cte.ec.gc.ca/NAPS/naps_smog_e.html).

ties account for about half of VOC emissions, and the remainder comes from natural sources. For example, plants produce isoprene (C_5H_8) and terpene ($C_{10}H_{15}$).

Carbon monoxide (CO) is a colourless, odourless gas produced by the incomplete combustion of fuel. Vehicles and engines are the main source, but others include industrial processes, combustion of waste, and residential wood burning. Carbon monoxide poses risk to humans and other animals, even in low concentrations. It can bind to hemoglobin in red blood cells, preventing it from becoming oxygenated.

Ammonia (NH_3) is a colourless gas with a pungent odour—it is the smell associated with urine. Most NH_3 is generated from livestock waste and fertilizer production. Ammonia is poisonous if inhaled in great quantities and is irritating to the eyes, nose, and throat in lesser concentrations. In the atmosphere it combines with sulphates and nitrates to form secondary fine particulate matter ($PM_{2.5}$). NH_3 can also contribute to the nitrification and eutrophication of aquatic systems.

Tropospheric ozone (O_3) is also called *ground-level ozone* to distinguish it from the ozone in the stratosphere, which shields us from the dangers of UV radiation. In contrast to stratospheric ozone, O_3 from human activity forms and accumulates at ground level as a pollutant. In the troposphere, this colourless gas results from the interaction of sunlight, heat, nitrogen oxides, and carbon-containing chemicals; it is therefore a secondary pollutant. A major component of smog, ozone can pose health risks because of its instability as a molecule; this triplet of oxygen atoms will readily release one, leaving a molecule of oxygen gas (O_2) and a free oxygen atom. The free oxygen atom may then participate in reactions that can injure living tissues and cause respiratory problems. Tropospheric ozone is the pollutant that most frequently exceeds its air quality standard.

Persistent organic pollutants   Persistent organic pollutants (POPs) can last in the environment for long periods of time. They are capable of travelling great distances by air because they are *volatile*, which means that they evaporate readily. The term **persistent** refers to substances that have long residence times, because they remain in environmental reservoirs for a long time, or because they take a long time to degrade or break down, or both.

POPs are of particular concern because they can enter the food supply, bioaccumulate in body tissues, and have significant impacts on human health and the environment, even in low concentrations. They have few natural sources and come primarily from human activity. Examples include industrial chemicals, such as PCBs (polychlorinated biphenyls); pesticides, such as DDT (dichloro-diphenyl-trichloroethane, **FIGURE 11.11**), chlordane, and toxaphene; and contaminants and byproducts, such as dioxins and furans, which come from incomplete combustion processes.

The indiscriminate spraying and persistent buildup of DDT caused widespread deaths of birds and other fauna in the 1950s and 1960s, leading Rachel Carson to write her famous book *Silent Spring*, one of the pivotal events in the modern environmental movement. DDT was banned for agricultural use in most developed nations in the 1970s and 1980s, but its use continues today in some parts of the developing world. As recently as 2002, DDT and its byproducts were still widely detectable in human blood, tissue, and breast milk samples from subjects in North America.[6]

Heavy metals   **Heavy metals** can be transported by the air, enter our water and food supply, and reside for long periods in sediments. Metals tend to be associated with

FIGURE 11.11
Learning about the persistence and negative ecological impacts of some chemical pesticides catalyzed the public and helped launch the modern environmental movement in the late 1960s and early 1970s. Here, a farmer sprays pesticide on his field without adequate personal protection against chemical exposure.

particulate matter, either occurring in particulate form or attaching to small particles that can then be transported atmospherically. Heavy metals are poisonous, even in low concentrations, and can bioaccumulate in body tissues. These pollutants occur even in Canada's far north—they are carried from the industrial south by continent-scale atmospheric currents—where they are deposited on land and water surfaces. This is called *long-range transport of atmospheric pollutants (LRTAP)*, and it has been a concern in Canada since at least the early 1970s.

Mercury is a heavy metal of considerable concern in Canada. Mercury is *volatile* (evaporates readily) and occurs in a number of different chemical forms, some more toxic than others. It has natural as well as human sources. It has been used for a variety of industrial purposes, partly because of its unusual property of remaining liquid at surface temperatures and pressures. Like other heavy metals, mercury can enter the food chain, accumulate in body tissues, and cause central nervous system malfunction and other ailments. Mercury is *lipophilic*, which can be translated as "fat-loving"; it is chemically capable of binding to fatty tissues in organisms. Mercury is also of concern as a pollutant in surface water bodies.

Lead, also a heavy metal, enters the atmosphere as a particulate pollutant. The lead-containing compounds tetraethyl lead and tetramethyl lead, when added to gasoline, improve engine performance. However, exhaust from the combustion of leaded gasoline emits lead into the atmosphere, from which it can be inhaled or deposited on land or water. Like mercury, lead is bioaccumulative and can cause damage to the central nervous system. Once people recognized the dangers of lead, leaded gasoline began to be phased out in most industrialized nations in the 1970s. The use of leaded gas ended in Canada in 1993.[7] Today the greatest source of atmospheric lead pollution in developed nations is industrial metal smelting. However, many developing nations still add lead to gasoline and experience significant lead pollution.

Toxic air pollutants Toxic air pollutants are a broad category of "other" pollutants identified by *CEPA* as being harmful or toxic, and therefore subject to regulation, control, and monitoring. They include substances known to cause cancer, reproductive defects, or neurological, developmental, immune system, or respiratory problems in people. Some also negatively affect the health of animals and plants. This category overlaps with the other types of air pollutants (for example, lead, mercury, dioxins, furans, and ozone all appear on the list of toxic pollutants, as well as in their other categories), but it includes additional substances such as asbestos. Chlorofluorocarbons (CFCs) are also on the list. Most toxic air pollutants are produced by human activities, such as metal smelting, sewage treatment, and industrial processes.

Government agencies share in dealing with air pollution

In Canada the management of air-related issues is the responsibility of the federal government—primarily, but not exclusively, Environment Canada—and the provincial and territorial governments, through their environment ministries. For the most part, municipal governments do not have direct regulatory control over activities that affect air quality. However, municipal governments manage so many activities that influence air quality that their role is central to the collaborative effort.

Federal The principal federal legislation under which air quality is regulated is the *Canadian Environmental Protection Act* (1999), described officially as "an Act respecting pollution prevention and the protection of the environment and human health in order to contribute to sustainable development."[8] Although *CEPA* gives the lead responsibility for air quality to Environment Canada, it also defines an important role for Health Canada, which we will investigate in greater detail in the chapter on *Environmental Health and Hazards*. Federal agencies, such as Transport Canada and Natural Resources Canada, also have programs and activities with important linkages to air quality issues.

The federal government is also responsible for entering Canada into international agreements concerning air quality. The *Montreal Protocol* and the *Kyoto Protocol* are examples of multilateral agreements that address air pollution issues of global concern (stratospheric ozone depletion and global warming, respec-

weighing the issues

INVESTIGATING YOUR REGION'S AIR QUALITY

How polluted is the air near where you live? Go to the National Pollutant Release Inventory (NPRI) website at www.ec.gc.ca/pdb/npri/npri_home_e.cfm. Use the *Google Earth* mapping tool to check on the amounts of pollutants released in your own province or local area. Are there any specific facilities in your area that are major emitters of atmospheric pollutants?

tively). In 2011 Canada became the first signatory nation from the developed world to announce that it would withdraw from the Kyoto Protocol.

Canada has a long history of international agreements with the United States to control transboundary pollution. For air quality, these date back to agreements made in the early 1900s, although the modern era began in 1979 with agreements concerning the long-range transport of pollutants related to acid deposition. The present bilateral international agreement on transboundary air pollution, coordinated primarily through the International Joint Commission, is the *Canada–United States Air Quality Agreement*, signed in 1991. This agreement has three annexes, the first dealing with acid rain precursors, the second with coordination of international scientific research, and the third with ground-level ozone.

Provincial/territorial   Each provincial and territorial government approaches air quality issues with its own agenda and set of rules, through its environment ministry. This makes sense—not just politically but scientifically, too—since issues vary dramatically from one region to another. For example, as discussed in "Central Case: The Rain and the Big Nickel," acid deposition caused by both local pollution and pollutants transported from the industrial midwestern states is the major air pollution issue in Ontario. In Saskatchewan, in contrast, air quality issues associated with the handling of grain, feed, and livestock are of greater concern.

Regional differences in the handling of air quality issues can lead to problems, though. For example, in the past the standards for acceptable levels and the protocols of measurement for pollutants have varied significantly from one jurisdiction to another. The government has been trying to bring these standards into conformity across the nation, by working through the Canadian Council of Ministers of the Environment (CCME). In 1998 the federal government, provinces, and territories signed an agreement to enhance effectiveness, accountability, and clarity in the management of environmental issues throughout Canada. Roles and responsibilities are assigned, on a case-by-case basis, to the government agency best situated to deal with the matter, but each level of government still retains its legal authority in the matter. The CCME has signed several agreements on harmonized standards for water quality, but those for air quality, the *National Ambient Air Quality Objectives*, have yet to be formally enacted.[9]

Municipal   Only two municipalities in Canada—Montreal and Greater Vancouver—have been given direct regulatory authority over sources of air pollution by their respective provincial governments. However, all munici-

palities manage programs and activities that directly influence air quality on a daily basis—public transportation and land use zoning come to mind, for example.

Therefore, most municipalities have programs aimed at improving air quality and raising public awareness of air quality issues. The top concerns differ from one location to another, and air quality may or may not be the top issue in a given municipality. For example, in Mississauga, Ontario—a geographically spread-out, largely suburban city—transportation and related air quality concerns are the central environmental issue, both for government decision makers and for the general public. In Halifax, with a smaller population, shorter travel distances, and fewer cars, wastewater management takes priority over air quality concerns. Pollution sources differ, too, from one locality to another. In Sudbury, smelters are a central concern; in Mississauga, the issue is cars and coal-fired power plants. Elsewhere, pulp-and-paper mills are of primary concern, or grain-handling operations, or large feedlots, or dust from cement manufacturers.

Monitoring shows that many forms of air pollution have decreased

CEPA not only lists the pollutants of interest but also requires that any releases of these pollutants be reported to the National Pollutant Release Inventory (NPRI), which is maintained by Environment Canada. The NPRI is thus one important vehicle that can be used to keep track of air quality in Canada. The data on NPRI are submitted, under law, directly by those who emit harmful substances into the atmosphere.

Pollutants also are measured and monitored through a nationwide network of monitoring stations that compose the National Air Pollution Surveillance (NAPS) Network, coordinated by Environment Canada (**FIGURE 11.12**). Many of the stations in the network are NAPS-designated sites; however, stations managed by other federal agencies (such as the Meteorological Service of Canada), as well as provincial, territorial, municipal, or other types of agencies (such as universities), also contribute data to the network.

The main focus of air quality monitoring is on the criteria air contaminants, but other categories of pollutants are monitored at some stations. Specialized and regional networks often contribute to the monitoring of these other pollutants. Examples include the Canadian Air and Precipitation Monitoring Network (non-urban air quality); Surface Ozone Monitoring Network; and Mercury Deposition Network.

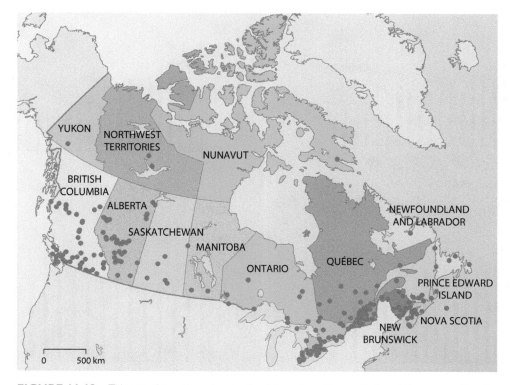

FIGURE 11.12 This map shows the network of real-time air quality monitoring stations across Canada.

In the decades since the first modern anti-pollution actions in North America in the early 1970s, emissions of some criteria air contaminants have decreased substantially. This has resulted in declining levels of these pollutants, as measured at air quality monitoring stations throughout Canada (**FIGURE 11.13**). The most dramatic decrease can be seen in atmospheric lead. Even though Canada did not phase out leaded gas until 1993, the cessation of leaded gas use in the United States in the early 1970s had a clear impact on atmospheric lead in Canada. In contrast, O_3 shows an increase over the same period, whereas NO_2 and PM show only minimal decreases (see also **FIGURE 11.14** on page 325). Not surprisingly, these three pollutants are the core indicators for Canada's Air Quality Health Index.

There are several reasons for the declines in some pollutants, which have occurred in spite of increases in population, energy use, vehicle use, and economic productivity in North America. Cleaner-burning motor vehicle engines and automotive technologies such as catalytic converters have played a large part in decreasing emissions of carbon monoxide and several other pollutants. Sulphur dioxide permit-trading and clean coal technologies have reduced SO_2 emissions. Technologies, such as electrostatic precipitators and **scrubbers** (**FIGURE 11.15** on page 325), which chemically convert or physically remove airborne pollutants before they are emitted

from smokestacks, have allowed factories, power plants, and refineries to decrease emissions of several pollutants.

Other industrialized nations have also succeeded in reducing emissions and improving air quality, thanks to improved technologies and targeted federal policies. Between 1996 and 2005, London, England, achieved a 56% reduction in CO emissions, a 41% drop in NO_x emissions, a 28% decline in particulate matter release, and an impressive 73% decrease in SO_2 emissions. Only tropospheric ozone showed an increase, rising 33%.

We will complete our look at outdoor air pollution with an examination of three specific issues: photochemical smog; acidic deposition; and stratospheric ozone depletion, along with a brief consideration of air quality issues in rural areas and in the rapidly industrializing nations of the developing world.

Smog is the most common, widespread air quality problem

In response to the increasing incidence of fogs polluted by the smoke of Britain's Industrial Revolution, an early British scientist coined the term **smog**. Today the term is used worldwide to describe unhealthy mixtures of air pollutants that often form over urban areas.

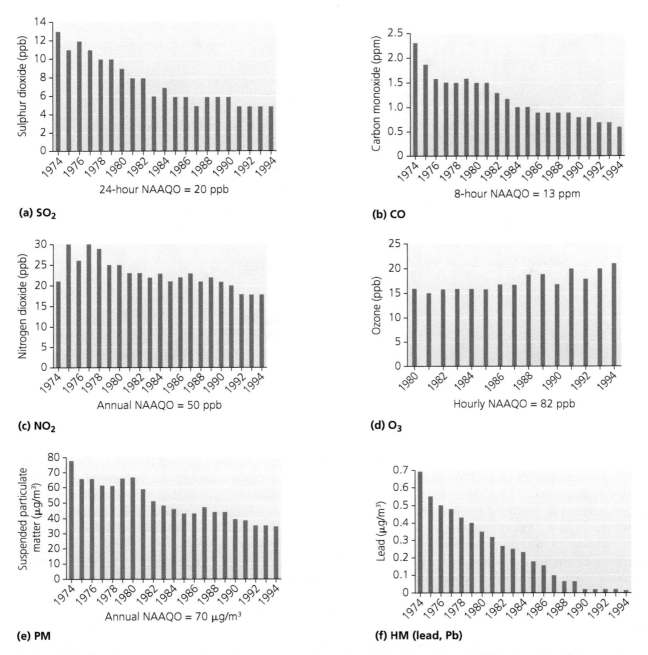

(a) SO₂

24-hour NAAQO = 20 ppb

(b) CO

8-hour NAAQO = 13 ppm

(c) NO₂

Annual NAAQO = 50 ppb

(d) O₃

Hourly NAAQO = 82 ppb

(e) PM

Annual NAAQO = 70 μg/m³

(f) HM (lead, Pb)

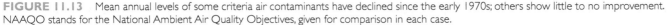

FIGURE 11.13   Mean annual levels of some criteria air contaminants have declined since the early 1970s; others show little to no improvement. NAAQO stands for the National Ambient Air Quality Objectives, given for comparison in each case.

The deadly smog that enveloped London in 1952 was what we today call **industrial smog**, or grey-air smog. When coal or oil is burned, some portion is completely combusted, forming CO_2; some is partially combusted, producing CO; and some remains unburned and is released as soot, or particles of carbon. Moreover, coal contains varying amounts of contaminants, including mercury and sulphur. Sulphur reacts with oxygen to form sulphur dioxide, which can undergo a series of reactions to form sulphuric acid and ammonium sulphate (**FIGURE 11.16A** on page 326). These chemicals and

others produced by further reactions, along with soot, are the main components of industrial smog and give the smog its characteristic grey colour.

Industrial smog is far less common today in developed nations than it was 50–100 years ago. In the wake of the 1952 London episode and others, the governments of most developed nations began regulating industrial emissions to minimize the external costs they impose on citizens. However, in regions that are industrializing today, such as China, India, and Eastern Europe, heavy reliance on coal burning (by industry and by citizens

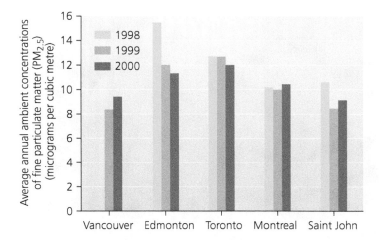

FIGURE 11.14
Levels of fine particulate matter are still a problem in Canadian cities. Based on data from National Air Pollution Surveillance Network, Environment Canada.

heating and cooking in their homes), combined with lax pollution controls, produces industrial smog that poses significant health risks in many areas.

Although coal combustion supplies the chemical constituents for industrial smog, weather also plays a role, as it did in London in 1952. A similar event occurred four years earlier in Donora, Pennsylvania. Here, air near the ground cooled during the night, and because Donora is located in hilly terrain, too little morning sun reached the valley floor to warm and disperse the cold air. The resulting thermal inversion trapped smog containing particulate matter emissions from a steel and wire factory; 21 people were killed, and more than 6000 people—nearly half the town—became ill (**FIGURE 11.16B**).

Hilly topography, such as Donora's, is a factor in the air pollution of many other cities where surrounding mountains trap air and create inversions. This is true for Mexico City, which has long symbolized the smog

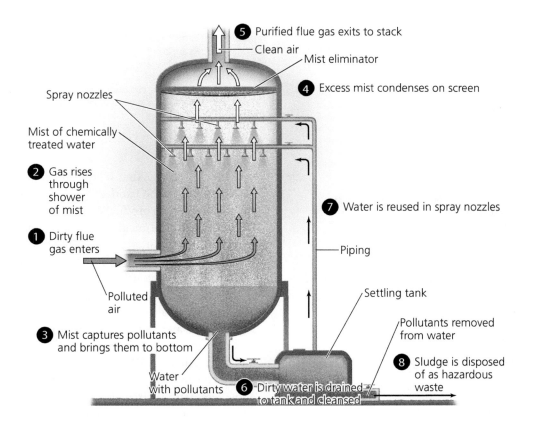

FIGURE 11.15
In this spray-tower wet scrubber, polluted air (1) rises through a chamber while arrays of nozzles spray a mist of water mixed with lime or other active chemicals (2). The falling mist captures pollutants and carries them to the bottom of the chamber (3), essentially washing them out of the air. Excess mist is captured on a screen (4), and air emitted from the scrubber has largely been cleansed (5). Periodically, the dirty water is drained from the chamber (6), cleansed in a settling tank, and recirculated (7) through the spray nozzles. The resulting sludge must be disposed of (8) as hazardous waste. Scrubbers and other pollution control devices come in many designs; the type shown here typically removes at least 90% of particulate matter and gases, such as sulphur dioxide.

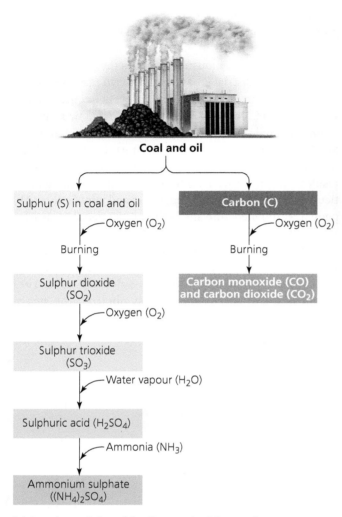

Coal and oil

Sulphur (S) in coal and oil → Oxygen (O_2) → Burning → Sulphur dioxide (SO_2) → Oxygen (O_2) → Sulphur trioxide (SO_3) → Water vapour (H_2O) → Sulphuric acid (H_2SO_4) → Ammonia (NH_3) → Ammonium sulphate (($NH_4)_2SO_4$)

Carbon (C) → Oxygen (O_2) → Burning → Carbon monoxide (CO) and carbon dioxide (CO_2)

(a) Burning sulphur-rich oil or coal without adequate pollution control technologies

(b) Smog event of 1948, midday in Donora, Pennsylvania

FIGURE 11.16
Emissions from the combustion of coal and oil in plants without pollution control technologies can create industrial smog. Industrial smog consists primarily of sulphur dioxide and particulate matter, as well as carbon monoxide and carbon dioxide from the carbon component of fossil fuels. When fossil fuels are combusted, sulphur contaminants give rise to sulphur dioxide, which in the presence of other chemicals in the atmosphere can produce several other sulphur compounds **(a)**. Under certain weather conditions, industrial smog can blanket whole towns or regions, as it did in Donora, Pennsylvania, shown here in the daytime during its deadly 1948 smog episode **(b)**.

problems of modern cities. Modern-day Mexico City, however, suffers from a different type of smog, called photochemical smog.

Photochemical smog is produced by a complex series of reactions

A photochemical process is one whose activation requires light. **Photochemical smog**, or brown-air smog, is formed through light-driven chemical reactions of primary pollutants and normal atmospheric compounds that produce a mix of more than 100 different chemicals, tropospheric ozone often being the most abundant among them (**FIGURE 11.17A**). High levels of NO_2 cause photochemical smog to form a brownish haze over cities (**FIGURE 11.17B**). Hot, sunny, windless days in urban areas provide perfect conditions for the formation of pho-

tochemical smog. Exhaust from morning traffic releases large amounts of NO and VOCs into a city's air. Sunlight then promotes the production of ozone and other constituents of photochemical smog. Levels of photochemical pollutants in urban areas typically peak in midafternoon and can irritate people's eyes, noses, and throats.

The cities most afflicted by photochemical smog are those with weather and topography that promote it. The geographic area associated with a particular air mass is called an **airshed**. People who live within the same airshed tend to experience similar weather and "bad air" days. Airsheds that are topographically constrained, such as those that occupy topographical basins or valleys, allow less natural circulation and renewal of the air, and are more prone to inversions and prolonged smog events.

Some provinces have cut emissions leading to photochemical smog through vehicle inspection programs, such as AirCare in British Columbia or Drive Clean in Ontario, where drivers are required to have their vehicle exhaust inspected regularly at check stations to maintain their registrations. Although a failed "smog check" means inconvenience for the car owner, these programs help maintain vehicle condition and make the air measurably cleaner for all of us.

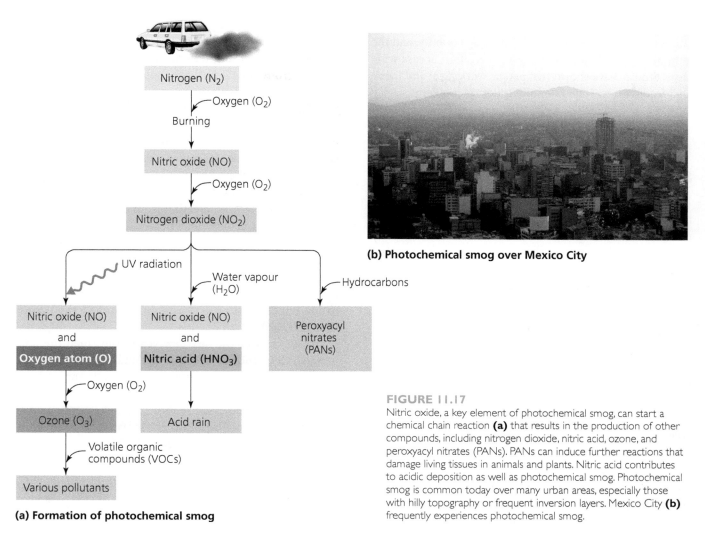

(b) Photochemical smog over Mexico City

(a) Formation of photochemical smog

FIGURE 11.17

Nitric oxide, a key element of photochemical smog, can start a chemical chain reaction **(a)** that results in the production of other compounds, including nitrogen dioxide, nitric acid, ozone, and peroxyacyl nitrates (PANs). PANs can induce further reactions that damage living tissues in animals and plants. Nitric acid contributes to acidic deposition as well as photochemical smog. Photochemical smog is common today over many urban areas, especially those with hilly topography or frequent inversion layers. Mexico City **(b)** frequently experiences photochemical smog.

In 2003, London, England, instituted a "congestion-charging" program. People driving into central London during weekdays were required to pay £8 (about $15) per day. The money was to be used to enhance bus service and encourage transport by rail, taxi, bicycle, and foot. Many citizens were outraged, arguing that the fees were too high or that the system discriminated against poor people. Others complained that it would not work or that the promised improvements in public transport were too slow in coming. However, many Londoners supported the program, and business support grew as the benefits became clearer. Traffic congestion in the zone decreased by nearly 30%, and there were 40–70 fewer injuries from traffic accidents per year. The air became cleaner, as well. In the first year, particulate matter in the charging zone declined by 15.5%, nitrogen oxide emissions decreased by 13.4%, and carbon dioxide emissions fell by 16.4%. The charges are still in place, although the congestion charge zone is now smaller. Similar congestion-charging schemes have been successfully implemented in other cities, such as Singapore. London's most recent (2010) Air Quality Strategy focuses on getting older, more polluting vehicles off the roads, and utilizing cleaner hybrid vehicles for transit routes.

Air quality is a rural issue, too

Air quality is not only an urban issue. In rural areas, people suffer from drift of airborne pesticides from farms, as well as industrial pollutants transported from cities, factories, and power plants. A great deal of rural air pollution emanates from feedlots, where cattle, hogs, or chickens are raised in dense concentrations. The huge numbers of animals at feedlots and the voluminous amounts of waste they produce release dust as well as methane, hydrogen sulphide, and ammonia. These gases create objectionable odours, and the ammonia contributes to nitrogen deposition across wide areas. Studies have shown that people working at and living near feedlots have high rates of respiratory problems.

Industrializing nations are suffering increasing air pollution

Although industrialized nations have been improving their air quality, outdoor air pollution is growing worse in many industrializing countries. In these societies, rapidly proliferating factories and power plants are releasing emissions with little effort to control pollution, and citizens continue to burn traditional sources of fuel, such as wood and charcoal, for cooking and home heating. Thus, just as occurred in England during its period of industrialization, new pollution sources are added to traditional sources while populations rise.

China has some of the world's worst air pollution. Four out of five Chinese cities surveyed by the World Bank in 2000 experienced SO_2 or NO_2 emissions above the threshold set by the World Health Organization. Air pollution became a serious concern for both the health and the performance of athletes during the Beijing Olympics of 2008. Together, China and India suffer 58% of the 1.8 million premature deaths that the World Bank estimates occur each year globally as a result of outdoor air pollution.

Southern Asia has a persistent 3-km-thick layer of pollution that hangs over the subcontinent throughout the dry season each December through April. Dubbed the *Asian Brown Cloud*, this massive layer of pollution is thought to reduce the sunlight reaching Earth's surface in that region by 10–15%, influence climate, decrease rice productivity by 5–10%, and account for many thousands of deaths each year.

Synthetic chemicals deplete stratospheric ozone

A pollutant in the troposphere, ozone is a highly beneficial gas at altitudes of about 25 km in the lower stratosphere, where it is concentrated in the stratospheric *ozone layer* (SEE FIGURE 11.2). Here, concentrations of ozone are only about 12 parts per million. However, ozone molecules are so effective at absorbing incoming ultraviolet radiation from the Sun that this concentration helps to protect life on Earth's surface from the damaging effects of ultraviolet (UV) radiation.

In the 1960s, atmospheric scientists began wondering why their measurements of stratospheric ozone were lower

than theoretical models predicted. Researchers hypothesizing that natural or artificial chemicals were depleting ozone finally pinpointed a group of human-made compounds derived from simple hydrocarbons, such as ethane and methane, in which hydrogen atoms are replaced by chlorine, bromine, or fluorine. One class of such compounds, **chlorofluorocarbons (CFCs)**, was being mass-produced by industry at a rate of 1 million metric tons per year in the early 1970s, and this rate was growing by 20% a year.

Soon researchers showed that CFCs could deplete stratospheric ozone by releasing chlorine atoms that split ozone molecules, creating from each of them an O_2 molecule and a ClO molecule (see "The Science Behind the Story: Identifying CFCs as the Main Cause of Ozone Depletion"). Then in 1985, scientists announced that stratospheric ozone levels over Antarctica had declined by 40–60% in the previous decade, leaving a thinned ozone concentration that was soon dubbed the **ozone hole** (FIGURE 11.18).

Research over the next few years confirmed the link between CFCs and ozone loss in the Antarctic and indicated that depletion was also occurring in the Arctic and perhaps globally. The depletion was shown to be growing both in severity and in areal extent, almost without exception, year to year. Already concerned that increased UV radiation would lead to more skin cancer, scientists were becoming anxious over possible ecological effects as well, including harm to crops and to the productivity of ocean phytoplankton, the base of the marine food chain.

There are still many questions to be resolved about ozone depletion

Although significant progress has been made in understanding stratospheric ozone depletion since the initial discovery of the role of CFCs, many questions remain.

roots
OZONE

The word *ozone*, coined in 1840 by German chemist Christian Friedrich Schönbein, derives from the Greek (and later, German) word *ozon* (from *ozein*), meaning "to smell." The name was chosen to reflect the pungent smell of ozone, which some people liken to an electrical smell, like sparks from fireworks, and others to clean bed sheets or a forest. You can smell ozone immediately after a lightning storm.

For example, will ozone depletion spread from the polar regions, where it is most severe, to encompass mid-latitude and even low-latitude regions (and if so, how quickly)? What is the actual relationship between ozone depletion and human health impacts, such as skin cancer? What are the other potential impacts of ozone depletion, for example, on marine and terrestrial ecosystems and on other types of materials? And—importantly, for policy

decisions—are the substitute chemicals that are being proposed in international agreements definitely less damaging to the stratospheric ozone layer, or do they raise concerns of their own?

The question of polar ozone depletion is of particular interest, especially to Canadian scientists working in the Arctic. The answer to why ozone depletion is most severe over the poles probably lies in a more refined understanding of the physical processes involved in ozone-depleting reactions. For example, scientists now believe that the ozone-depleting chemical reactions may find ideal sites on tiny ice crystals that are found only where the air is extremely cold. These conditions are optimal over Antarctica, where a circular wind pattern called the *polar vortex* traps extremely cold air over the pole.

There are many other interesting questions waiting to be answered. For example, Dr. Ralf Staebler and colleagues from the Air Quality Research Division of Environment Canada are investigating a unique form of ozone depletion that occurs near the ground in the polar regions, as the sun rises in the spring after the long darkness of winter. Here, a sudden loss of ozone is caused by reactions with bromine, another type of halogen, which can deplete ozone at ground level in much the same manner as the chlorine from the CFCs in the upper atmosphere. The scientists measure this ozone loss using a mobile measurement platform—basically, a temperature-controlled box full of instruments and a meteorological mast mounted on a sled—which they call OOTI ("Out On The Ice") (FIGURE 11.19). They wanted a platform that would be self-contained, self-sufficient, and mobile, with which to measure ozone, the chemicals implicated in ozone-destroying chemistry, and the associated *micrometeorology*. As part of the Canadian contribution to the International Polar Year, this sled has been deployed near Alert, NU, Barrow, AK, and Kuujjuarapik (Hudson Bay) and from the Canadian icebreaker Amundsen on the frozen ocean south of Banks Island.

The researchers are particularly interested in finding out whether the ozone-depleting chemistry is occurring near the ground or directly at the ice–atmosphere interface. The OOTI sleds, combined with instruments operated by other researchers on the Amundsen Icebreaker, have allowed them to measure ozone depletion processes. Ozone-depleting reactions are of further interest to these researchers because they have an impact on the fate of mercury (Hg) in the Arctic. Ozone controls the oxidation state of the atmosphere. Once the ozone is gone, a new chemical regime is entered in which halogens emitted from the ocean take over this role. In an ozone-controlled atmosphere, the residence time of Hg vapour is quite long (on the order of a year). In a halogen-controlled regime, Hg is more efficiently

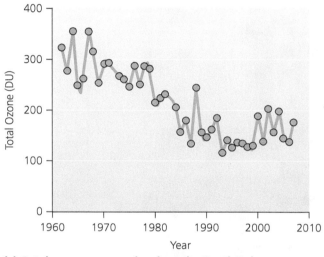

(a) October mean ozone levels at the South Pole

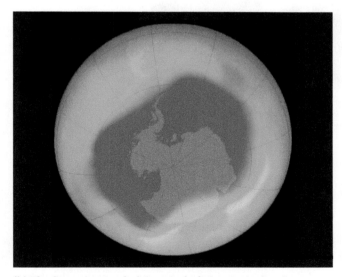

(b) The largest recorded "ozone hole" over Antarctica, September 24, 2006

FIGURE 11.18

The "ozone hole" consists of a region of thinned ozone density in the stratosphere over Antarctica and the southernmost ocean regions. It has reappeared seasonally each September in recent decades. Data from Antarctica **(a)** show a steady decrease in stratospheric ozone concentrations from the 1960s to 1990. Ozone-depleting CFCs began to be regulated under the Montreal Protocol in 1987, and ozone concentrations stopped declining. Satellite imagery from September 24, 2006 **(b)**, shows the "ozone hole" (blue) at its largest-ever recorded extent to date. Data in (a) Earth System Research Laboratory Global Monitoring Division, NOAA www.esrl.noaa.gov

FIGURE 11.19
Researchers from the Air Quality Research Division of Environment Canada employ a mobile lab-on-a-sled called OOTI to measure ozone and ozone-depleting chemicals in the Arctic environment.

converted to more chemically reactive forms, which can then enter the snow and ice and possibly the biosphere, with ensuing negative consequences.

The Montreal Protocol addressed ozone depletion

Scientists all over the world continue to address problems like these in an attempt to refine our understanding of the complex chemical process of ozone depletion. In the meantime, though, the international community has been unwilling to wait for catastrophe and has moved forward to strike an agreement to reduce and eventually eliminate the production of known ozone-depleting substances, also known as *ODS*.

In response to the scientific concerns, international policy efforts to restrict CFC production finally bore fruit in 1987 with the **Montreal Protocol**. In this treaty, signatory nations (eventually numbering 197) agreed to cut CFC production in half. Five follow-up agreements strengthened the pact by deepening the cuts, advancing timetables for compliance, and addressing related ozone-depleting chemicals. Today the production and use of ozone-depleting compounds has fallen by 95% since the late 1980s, and scientists can discern the beginnings of long-term recovery of the stratospheric ozone layer. Industry has been able to shift to alternative chemicals that have largely turned out to be cheaper and more efficient.

There are still challenges to overcome. Much of the 5 billion kilograms of CFCs emitted into the troposphere has yet to diffuse up into the stratosphere, and CFCs are slow to dissipate or break down. Thus, we can expect a considerable lag time between the implementation of policy and the desired environmental effect. (This is one reason scientists often argue for proactive policy guided by the precautionary principle, rather than reactive policy that may respond too late.) Moreover, nations can plead for some ozone-depleting chemicals to be exempted from the ban; for example, the United States recently was allowed to continue using methyl bromide, a fumigant used to control pests on strawberries.

Despite the remaining challenges, the Montreal Protocol and its follow-up amendments are widely considered the biggest success story so far in addressing any global environmental problem. Environmental scientists have attributed this success primarily to two factors:

1. Policy makers engaged industry in helping to solve the problem, and government and industry worked together on developing replacement chemicals. This cooperation reduced the battles that typically erupt between environmentalists and industry.
2. Implementation of the Montreal Protocol followed an adaptive management approach, altering strategies midstream in response to new scientific data, technological advances, or economic figures.

Because of its success in addressing ozone depletion, the Montreal Protocol is widely seen as a model for international cooperation in addressing other pressing global problems, such as persistent organic pollutants, climate change, and biodiversity loss.

Acidic deposition is another transboundary pollution problem

As discussed in "Central Case: The Rain and the Big Nickel," **acidic deposition** refers to the settling, or deposition, of acidic or acid-forming pollutants from the atmosphere onto Earth's surface. This can take place either by **acidic precipitation** (commonly referred to as **acid rain**, but also including acid snow, sleet, and hail), by fog, by gases, or by the deposition of dry particles. Acidic deposition is one type of **atmospheric deposition**, which refers more broadly to the wet or dry deposition on land of a wide variety of pollutants, including mercury, lead, nitrates, organochlorides, and others.

Acidic deposition originates primarily with the emission of sulphur dioxide and nitrogen oxides, largely through fossil fuel combustion by automobiles, electric utilities, and industrial facilities like the Inco and Falconbridge smelters in Sudbury. Once airborne, these primary pollutants can react with water, oxygen, and oxidants to produce secondary compounds of low pH, primarily sulphuric acid and nitric acid. Suspended in the troposphere, droplets of these acids may travel for days or weeks, sometimes covering hundreds or thousands of kilometres in a particular airshed before falling in precipitation (**FIGURE 11.20**).

Natural rainwater is not neutral; in fact, it is slightly acidic, with a typical pH of around 5.6. This is mainly

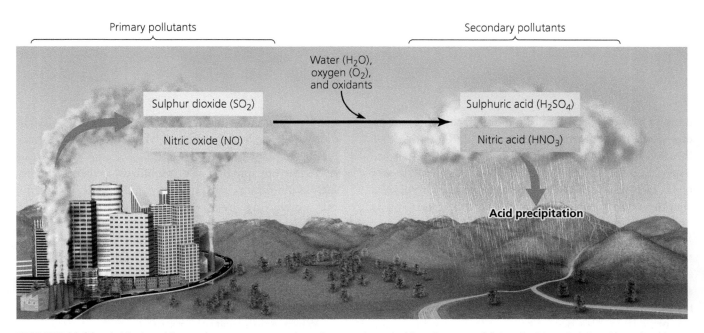

FIGURE 11.20 Acidic deposition can have consequences long distances downwind from its source. Sulphur dioxide and nitric oxide emitted by industries and utilities can be transformed into sulphuric acid and nitric acid through chemical reactions in the atmosphere. These acidic compounds then descend to Earth's surface in rain, snow, fog, and dry deposition.

THE SCIENCE BEHIND THE STORY

Identifying CFCs as the Main Cause of Ozone Depletion

Drs. F. Sherwood Rowland (left), Mario Molina (centre), and Paul Crutzen (right) jointly received the 1995 Nobel Prize in chemistry.

Ozone was discovered in 1839, and its presence in the upper atmosphere was first proposed in the 1880s. In 1924, British scientist G. M. B. Dobson built an instrument that could measure ozone concentrations by sampling incoming sunlight at ground level and comparing the intensities of wavelengths that ozone does and does not absorb. By the 1970s, the Dobson ozone spectrophotometer was being used by a global network of observation stations.

Research on CFCs has also had a long history. First invented in 1928, CFCs were useful as refrigerants, fire extinguishers, and propellants for aerosol spray cans. Starting in the 1960s, CFCs also found wide use as cleaners for electronics and as a part of the process of manufacturing rigid polystyrene foams. Research on the chemical properties of CFCs showed that they were almost completely inert; that is, they rarely reacted with other chemicals. Therefore, scientists surmised that, at trace levels, CFCs would be harmless to both people and the environment.

However, in June 1974, chemists F. Sherwood Rowland and Mario Molina published a paper in the journal *Nature*, arguing that the inertness that made CFCs so ideal for industrial purposes could also have disastrous consequences for the ozone layer.

Whereas reactive chemicals are broken down in the lower atmosphere, CFCs reach the stratosphere unchanged. Once CFCs reach the stratosphere, intense ultraviolet radiation from the Sun breaks them into their constituent chlorine and carbon atoms. In a two-step chemical reaction (see the figure), a chlorine atom can split an ozone molecule and then ready itself to split another one. Over its lifetime, each free chlorine atom, it was calculated, can catalyze the destruction of as many as 100 000 ozone molecules.

Rowland and Molina were the first to assemble a complete picture of the threat posed by CFCs, but they could not have reached their conclusions without the contributions of other scientists. British researcher James Lovelock had developed an instrument to measure extremely low concentrations of atmospheric gases. American scientists Richard Stolarski and Ralph Cicerone had shown that chlorine atoms can catalyze the destruction of ozone. Dutch meteorologist Paul Crutzen had shown that naturally produced nitrous oxide breaks down ozone. And American researcher James McDonald had predicted that ozone loss, by allowing more UV radiation to reach the surface, would result in thousands more skin cancer cases each year.

Rowland and Molina's analysis earned them the 1995 Nobel Prize in chemistry jointly with Crutzen. It also helped spark discussion among scientists, policy makers, and industry leaders over limits on CFC production. As a result, several nations banned the use of CFCs in aerosol spray cans in 1979. Other uses continued, however, and by the early 1980s global production of CFCs was increasing.

Then, a new finding shocked scientists and spurred the international community to take further action. Scientists at a British

---

because rainwater reacts with naturally occurring carbon dioxide in the air, forming carbonic acid. Rain and other forms of precipitation with pH less than about 5.1 are considered to be acidified. Acidification can occur as a result of natural processes, such as sulphur-rich volcanic eruptions, but the main cause of acid precipitation is human-generated air pollution.

Acidic deposition can have wide-ranging, cumulative detrimental effects on ecosystems and on our built environment (TABLE 11.1). Acids leach nutrients, such as calcium, magnesium, and potassium, from the topsoil, altering soil chemistry and harming plants and soil organisms. This occurs because hydrogen ions from acidic precipitation take the place of calcium, magnesium,

and potassium ions in soil compounds, and these valuable nutrients leach into the subsoil, where they become inaccessible to plant roots.

Acidic precipitation also "mobilizes" toxic metal ions, such as aluminum, zinc, mercury, and copper, by chemically converting them from insoluble forms to soluble forms. Elevated soil concentrations of metals, such as aluminum, hinder water and nutrient uptake by plants. In some regions of Britain and the United States, acid fog with a pH of 2.3 (equivalent to vinegar) has enveloped forests for extended periods, leading to widespread tree mortality.

When acidic water runs off from land, it affects streams, rivers, and lakes. In fact, thousands of lakes in

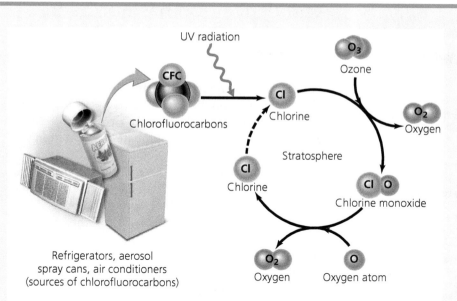

UV radiation

CFC

Chlorofluorocarbons

Cl
Chlorine

O₃
Ozone

O₂
Oxygen

Stratosphere

Cl
Chlorine

Cl O
Chlorine monoxide

Refrigerators, aerosol
spray cans, air conditioners
(sources of chlorofluorocarbons)

O₂
Oxygen

O
Oxygen atom

A chlorine atom released from a CFC molecule in the presence of UV radiation reacts with an ozone molecule, forming one molecule of oxygen gas and one chlorine monoxide (ClO) molecule. The oxygen atom in the ClO molecule will then bind with a stray oxygen atom to form oxygen gas, leaving the chlorine atom to begin the destructive cycle anew. In this way, any given chlorine atom may destroy up to 100 000 ozone molecules.

research station in Antarctica had been recording ozone concentrations since the 1950s. In May 1985, Joseph Farman and colleagues reported in *Nature* that Antarctic ozone concentrations had declined dramatically since the 1970s. The decline exceeded even the worst-case predictions.

To determine what was causing the "ozone hole" over Antarctica, expeditions were mounted in 1986 and 1987 to measure trace amounts of atmospheric gases by using ground stations and high-altitude balloons and aircraft. Together with other researchers, Crutzen analyzed data col-

lected on the expeditions and concluded that the ozone hole resulted from a combination of Antarctic weather conditions and human-made chemicals.

In the frigid Antarctic winter, high-altitude—or polar stratospheric—clouds form. In the spring, those clouds provide ideal conditions for CFC-derived chlorine and other chemicals to catalyze the destruction of massive amounts of ozone. The problem is made worse by the fact that prevailing air currents largely isolate Antarctica's atmosphere from the rest of Earth's atmosphere.

In subsequent years, scientists used data from ground stations and satellites to show that ozone levels were declining globally. In 1987, those findings helped convince the world's nations to agree on the Montreal Protocol, which aimed to cut CFC production in half by 1998. Within two years, however, further scientific evidence and computer modelling showed that more drastic measures would be needed if serious damage to the ozone layer was to be avoided. In 1990, the Montreal Protocol was strengthened to include a complete phaseout of CFCs by 2000. By 1998, the amount of chlorine in the atmosphere appeared to be levelling off.

Canada, Scandinavia, the United States, and elsewhere now have lost their fish because acid precipitation leaches aluminum out of soil and rock and into waterways in a form that can be deadly to aquatic life. Aluminum can kill fish by damaging their gills and disrupting their salt balance, water balance, breathing, and circulation.

Besides altering natural ecosystems, acid precipitation also damages agricultural crops. Moreover, it erodes stone buildings, corrodes cars, and erases the writing from tombstones. Ancient cathedrals, monuments, temples, and stone statues in many parts of the world are experiencing irreversible damage as their features gradually wear away.

Because the pollutants leading to acid deposition can travel long distances, their effects may be felt far from their sources—a situation that has led to political bickering among the leaders of states and nations. For instance, much of the pollution from power plants and factories in Pennsylvania, Ohio, and Illinois falls out in southeastern Canada, as well as in states farther to the east. The bedrock geology and soil chemistry of the area that is receiving the acidic deposition also play a large role in the acid tolerance and the ecological response to acidification. As **FIGURE 11.21** shows, many regions in southeastern Canada have experienced acid deposition in excess of their critical loads.

Table 11.1   Effects of Acidic Deposition on Ecosystems in Northeastern North America

Acidic deposition in northeastern forests has

- Accelerated leaching of base cations (ions that counteract acidic deposition) from soil
- Allowed sulphur and nitrogen to accumulate in soil
- Increased dissolved inorganic aluminum in soil, hindering plant uptake of water and nutrients
- Caused calcium to leach from needles of red spruce, leading to tree mortality from wintertime freezing
- Increased mortality of sugar maples because of leaching of base cations from soil and leaves
- Acidified many lakes, especially those situated on soils and bedrock of granitic composition
- Lowered lakes' capacity to neutralize further acids
- Elevated aluminum levels in surface waters
- Reduced species diversity and abundance of aquatic life, and negatively affected entire food webs

Source: Adapted from Driscoll, C.T., et al. (2001). Acid rain revisited. Hubbard Brook Research Foundation.

Acid deposition has not been reduced as much as scientists had hoped

Reducing acid precipitation involves reducing the pollution that contributes to it. New technologies, such as scrubbers, have helped. As a result of declining emissions of SO$_2$, average sulphate precipitation has decreased in northeastern North America since the early 1980s (**FIGURE 11.22A**). However, because of increasing NO$_x$ emissions, average nitrate precipitation has changed little in the same period (**FIGURE 11.22B**). This may partly account for the trends in **FIGURE 11.23**, which suggest that although sulphate levels in many lakes in Ontario, Québec, and Atlantic Canada have declined, acidification has continued or even worsened in some of the lakes.

A report by scientists at Hubbard Brook Experimental Forest has disputed the notion that the problem of acid deposition is being solved (see "The Science Behind

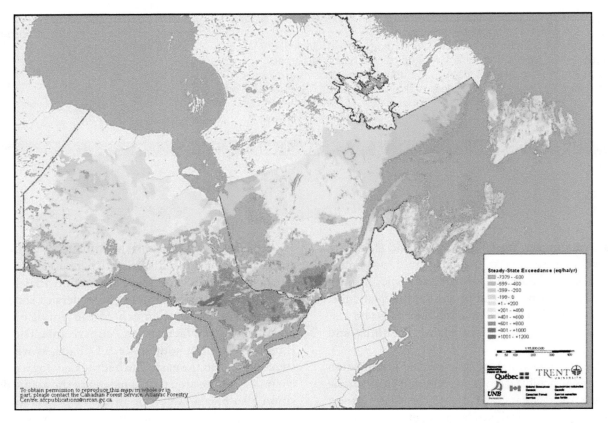

FIGURE 11.21   The maximum amount of acid deposition that a region can receive without damage to its ecosystems—its critical load—depends on the acid rain neutralizing capacity of water, rocks, and soils. This map shows areas of eastern Canada where the levels of acid deposition have exceeded the capacity of the soils to neutralize the acid. From Environment Canada, *Acid Rain and Forests*, www.ec.gc.ca/acidrain/images/Exceedance_E.jpg

the Story: Acid Rain at Hubbard Brook Experimental Forest"). Instead, the report said, the effects are worse than first predicted, and existing clean air legislation and limits on sulphate and nitrate emissions will be insufficient to solve the problem.

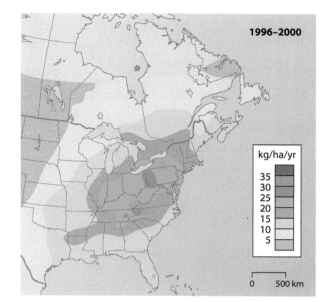

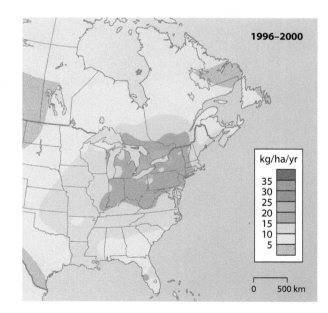

(a) Wet sulphate deposition down since early 1980s

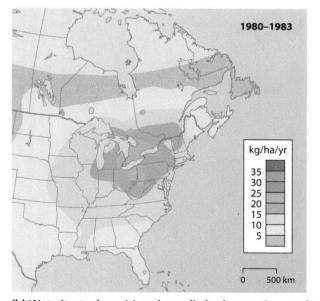

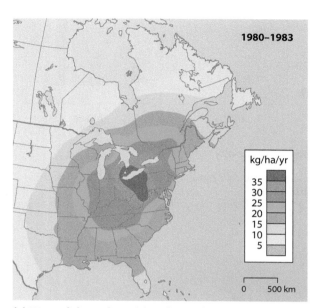

(b) Wet nitrate deposition shows little change since early 1980s

FIGURE 11.22 Acidic deposition of wet sulphates **(a)** and wet nitrates **(b)** has declined slightly in recent years in eastern North America. From Canadian National Atmospheric Chemistry Database, Meteorological Service of Canada, Environment Canada.

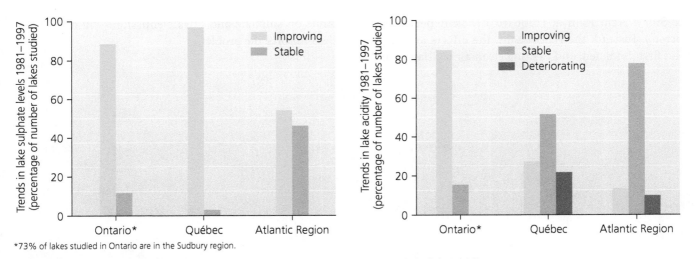

*73% of lakes studied in Ontario are in the Sudbury region.

(a) Trends in lake sulphate levels

(b) Trends in lake acidity

FIGURE 11.23   Although sulphate levels in many lakes in Ontario, Québec, and Atlantic Canada have shown improvement **(a)**, acid conditions in many of the lakes have not improved, and some have even continued to deteriorate **(b)**.

Source: State of the Environment Infobase Acid Rain, Environment Canada, Ontario, Atlantic, and Quebec Regions, adapted by National Indicators and Reporting Office, www.ec.gc.ca/soer-ree/English/Indicator_series/new_issues.cfm?issue_id=3&tech_id=10#bio_pic

12 Fossil Fuels: Energy Use and Impacts

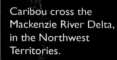

Caribou cross the Mackenzie River Delta, in the Northwest Territories.

Upon successfully completing this chapter, you will be able to

- Identify the principal energy sources that we use
- Describe the nature and origin of coal and evaluate its extraction and use
- Describe the nature and origin of natural gas and evaluate its extraction and use
- Describe the nature and origin of oil and evaluate its extraction, use, and future availability
- Describe the nature, origin, and potential of alternative fossil fuel types and technologies

- Outline and assess environmental impacts of fossil fuel use
- Evaluate political, social, and economic impacts of fossil fuel use
- Specify strategies for conserving energy and enhancing efficiency

The wildlife of the Mackenzie Delta and environs is sure to be affected by the proposed pipeline.

Arctic Ocean
Greenland (DENMARK)
Mackenzie Delta
Northwest Territories
Hudson Bay
CANADA

CENTRAL CASE:
ON, OFF, ON AGAIN? THE MACKENZIE VALLEY NATURAL GAS PIPELINE

"We've embarked on the beginning of the last days of the age of oil."

—MIKE BOWLIN, FORMER CEO (RETIRED), ARCO

"I listened to a brief by northern businessmen in Yellowknife who favour a pipeline through the North. Later, in a native village far away, I heard virtually the whole community express vehement opposition to such a pipeline. Both were talking about the same pipeline; both were talking about the same region—but for one group it is a frontier, for the other a homeland."

—JUSTICE THOMAS BERGER, *NORTHERN FRONTIER, NORTHERN HOMELAND*, 1977

The Mackenzie Valley Gas Project is a proposal to develop three major natural gas fields located in the Mackenzie Delta, Northwest Territories, and deliver the natural gas to southern markets through a 1196-km pipeline system to be constructed along the Mackenzie Valley (see maps).[1]

The idea of a major pipeline running from the Beaufort Sea down the Mackenzie Valley is not new. A pipeline was proposed and examined seriously in the early 1970s; it was called, at the time, "the biggest project in the history of free enterprise."[2]

In 1974 the federal government appointed Justice Thomas Berger to carry out an inquiry into the potential impacts of the project on the people of Canada's North, since the proposed route crosses four Aboriginal regions. Berger travelled throughout the North, meeting with Dene, Inuit, Métis, and white residents and leaders. The report of the inquiry (released in 1977) was called *Northern Frontier, Northern Homeland*. It recommended that pipeline development in the North be delayed by at least 10 years because of deep opposition by native

These maps show the location of the proposed Mackenzie River Valley natural gas pipeline.

leaders and the potential for negative impacts. The report further recommended that such development not proceed until native land claims in the area had been successfully resolved.

Among the main concerns were the potential impacts on people and animals that would result from the infrastructure (roads, airports, towns) likely to accompany the construction of the pipeline. As reported by CBC News, "Some dismissed the impact of a pipeline, saying it would be like a thread stretched across a football field. Those close to the land said the impact would be more like a razor slash across the Mona Lisa."[3]

In the end, the pipeline project was delayed for much longer than 10 years. The idea was on-again, off-again for many years, but was revitalized at the turn of the twenty-first century. Interestingly, many of the native leaders who vehemently opposed the pipeline in the 1970s had by that time become supporters, realizing that it would bring much-needed jobs and revenue to the North. Chief Frank T'Seleie of Fort Good Hope, Northwest Territories, was a vocal opponent of the project as a young man in the 1970s. He now supports the pipeline, since many of the land claims in the area have been settled. He even participated in project negotiations on behalf of native communities.[4]

The partners in the current project are four major Canadian oil and gas companies—Imperial Oil Resources Ventures, ConocoPhillips Canada, Shell Canada, and ExxonMobil Canada, known collectively as the "Producer Group"—and Aboriginal Pipeline Group, representing the interests of Aboriginal people in the project.[5]

The project has been equally controversial on its second go-around. In October 2006, Alternatives North (a social justice group based in Yellowknife) estimated that Imperial Oil and its partners will earn billions of dollars from the project and should not receive federal subsidization. However, principal partner Imperial Oil claims that the project is only marginally economic and will not proceed without assurance of at least $1.2 billion from the federal government. According to Imperial Oil, the cost of the project has increased to $16.2 billion, and the scheduled start date for production (originally 2010) has been delayed until 2014.[6]

According to Nature Canada, the pipeline has the potential to transform the valley into an industrial landscape; fragment habitat for bears, caribou, and wolves; harm fish and fish habitat by increasing sediment deposition into rivers; permanently damage breeding areas for millions of geese, tundra swans, and other migratory birds; require forests to be cut and heavy machinery deployed for infrastructure; trigger a rush of oil and gas development in the Mackenzie Valley (this was also predicted by the Berger report); and increase greenhouse gas emissions.[7] It remains to be scientifically proven or observed whether these impacts will occur, and to what degree.

An interesting side issue concerns the ultimate fate of the gas itself. Much of the natural gas produced in the Mackenzie Delta gas fields may never make it to the southern Canadian and American consumers for whom it was originally intended. This is because of the enormous acceleration in development of tar sand deposits in Alberta. Tar sand production requires significant inputs of energy, and the complete, successful development of these deposits is dependent on the production and delivery of natural gas from the North. The first 20 years' worth of natural gas from the Mackenzie Delta may go straight into the production of oil from Alberta's tar sands. The Mackenzie pipeline would transport natural gas, but pipelines are also used to transport oil. Oil pipelines are subject to at least as much controversy as natural gas pipelines, primarily because of the risk of leaks. In July of 2010 an oil pipeline owned by Enbridge, Inc., which carries oil from Griffith, Indiana, to Sarnia, Ontario, ruptured and spilled more than 800 000 U.S. gallons (about 3000 m^3) of oil into a tributary of the Kalamazoo River in Michigan. In 2011

the U.S. State Department delayed indefinitely a decision to approve the construction of the Keystone XL oil pipeline, proposed to carry oil from the Alberta tar sands to oil refineries along the Gulf Coast of the United States. The planned route for the controversial pipeline was to cross a particularly sensitive ecosystem overlying an important aquifer in Nebraska, and many residents feared that a spill would permanently damage their principal source of water. Since then, the Government of Canada has actively pursued plans to move ahead with the construction of the Northern Gateway Pipelines, a set of twin pipelines that would carry natural gas to the east and oil to the west from Alberta to B.C., opening up new possibilities for the sale of oil from the tar sands to China and other Asian markets.

Sources of Energy

Humanity has devised many ways to harness the renewable and nonrenewable forms of energy available on our planet. We use a wide variety of energy sources to heat and light our homes, power our machinery, fuel our vehicles, and provide the comforts and conveniences to which we've grown accustomed in the modern industrial age.

We use a variety of energy sources

A great deal of energy emanates from Earth's core, making geothermal power available for our use. Energy also results from the gravitational pull of the Moon and Sun, and we are just beginning to harness the power from the ocean tides that these forces generate. An immense amount of energy resides within the bonds among protons and neutrons in atoms, and this energy provides us with nuclear power.

Most of our energy, however, comes ultimately from the Sun. We can harness energy from the Sun's radiation directly in a number of ways. Solar radiation also helps drive wind patterns and the hydrologic cycle, making possible such forms of energy as wind power and hydroelectric power. And of course, sunlight drives photosynthesis and the growth of plants, from which we take wood and other biomass as a fuel source. Finally, when plants die and are preserved in sediments under particular conditions, they may impart their stored chemical energy to **fossil fuels**, highly combustible substances formed from the remains of organisms from past geologic ages. The three fossil fuels we use widely today are oil, coal, and natural gas.

Since the Industrial Revolution, fossil fuels have replaced biomass as our society's dominant source of energy. Global consumption of the three main fossil fuels has risen steadily for years and is now at its highest level ever (**FIGURE 12.1A**). The high energy content of fossil fuels makes them efficient to burn, ship, and store. Besides providing for transportation, heating, and cooking, these fuels are used to generate *electricity*, a secondary form of energy that is easier to transfer over long distances and apply to a variety of uses.

Canada's energy stream is complex; we use energy in different forms for different purposes (**FIGURE 12.1B**). We also both import and export energy—in some cases, different grades of the same form of energy (such as coal, which is both imported and exported). But overall Canada is a net exporter of energy.

Energy sources such as sunlight, geothermal energy, and tidal energy are considered perpetually **renewable** or inexhaustible because their supplies will not be depleted by our use. Other sources, such as timber, are renewable

roots

ENERGY

The term **energy**, with the scientific meaning of "a source of power," first appeared in the late sixteenth century. Before that, the Middle French *énergie* meant "force or vigor of expression" and was used to describe writing or speaking. The word originates from the Latin *energia* and, earlier, Greek *en* ("at") plus *ergon* ("work").

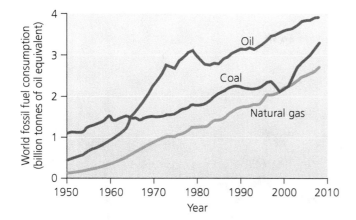

(a) Global consumption of fossil fuels

FIGURE 12.1
Global consumption of fossil fuels **(a)** has risen greatly over the past half century. Oil use rose steeply during the 1960s to overtake coal, and today it remains our leading energy source. Canada's energy mix **(b)** illustrates our fundamental dependence on fossil fuels, as well as the importance of uranium (for nuclear energy) and hydropower in our energy mix. Data for (a) from U.S. Energy Information Administration and International Energy Agency. Graphic in (b) from Natural Resources Canada. (2006).
Source: Report of the National Advisory Panel on Sustainable Energy Science and Technology, Office of Energy Research and Development.

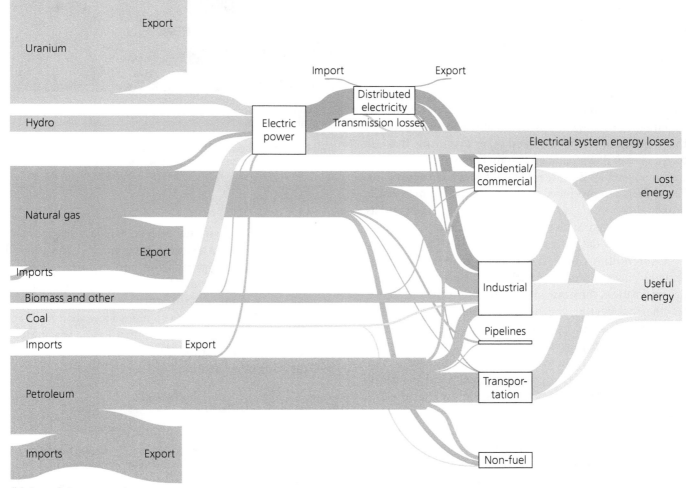

(b) Canada's energy stream

only if we do not harvest them at too great a rate. In contrast, such energy sources as oil, coal, and natural gas are considered **nonrenewable** because at our current rates of consumption we will use up Earth's accessible store of them in a matter of decades to centuries. Nuclear power as currently harnessed through fission of uranium can be

considered nonrenewable to the extent that uranium ore is in limited supply.

Although these nonrenewable fuels result from ongoing natural processes, the timescales on which they are created are so long that once the fuels are depleted, they cannot be replaced within any time span useful to our civilization. It takes a thousand years for the biosphere to generate the amount of organic matter that must be buried to produce a single day's worth of fossil fuels for our society. To replenish the fossil fuels we have depleted so far would take many millions of years. For this reason, and because fossil fuel use exerts severe environmental impacts, renewable energy sources increasingly are being developed as alternatives to fossil fuels, as we will see in a subsequent chapter.

Fossil fuels are indeed fuels created from "fossils"

The fossil fuels we burn today in our vehicles, homes, industries, and power plants were formed from the tissues of organisms that lived 100 million to 500 million years ago. The energy these fuels contain came originally from the Sun and was converted to chemical-bond energy as a result of photosynthesis. The chemical energy in these organisms' tissues then became concentrated as these tissues decomposed and their hydrocarbon compounds were altered and compressed.

Most organisms, after death, do not end up as part of a coal, gas, or oil deposit. A tree that falls and decays as a rotting log undergoes mostly **aerobic** decomposition; in the presence of air, bacteria and other organisms that use oxygen break down plant and animal remains into simpler carbon molecules that are recycled through the ecosystem. Fossil fuels are produced only when organic material is broken down in an **anaerobic** environment, one that has little or no oxygen. Such environments include the bottoms of shallow seas, deep lakes, and swamps (**FIGURE 12.2**).

Over millions of years, organic matter that accumulates at the bottoms of such water bodies undergoes decomposition, forming an oil precursor called **kerogen**. Geothermal heating then acts on the kerogen to create crude oil and natural gas. Natural gas can also be produced nearer the surface by anaerobic bacterial decomposition of organic matter. Oil and gas come to reside in porous rock layers beneath dense, impervious layers. Coal is formed when plant matter is compacted so tightly that there is little decomposition. The specific type of fuel that forms in any given place is dependent on the chemical composition of the starting material, the temperatures and pressures to which the material is subjected, the presence or absence of anaerobic decomposers, and the passage of time.

Fossil fuel reserves are unevenly distributed

Fossil fuel deposits are localized and unevenly distributed over Earth's surface, so some regions have substantial reserves of fossil fuels whereas others have very few. How

FIGURE 12.2
Tropical swamps, like the Okefenokee Swamp in Florida, shown here, are one type of environment in which the formation of fossil fuels would have begun 100 million to 150 million years ago. Fossil fuels begin to form when organisms die and end up in oxygen-poor conditions, such as when trees fall into bogs and are buried by sediment, or when marine phytoplankton and zooplankton drift to the seafloor and are buried.

long each nation's fossil fuel reserves will last depends on how much the nation extracts, how much it consumes, and how much it imports from and exports to other nations. Nearly two-thirds of the world's proven reserves of crude oil lie in the Middle East. The Middle East is also rich in natural gas, but Russia contains more than twice as much natural gas as any other country. Russia is also rich in coal, as is China, but the United States possesses more coal than any other nation (**TABLE 12.1**).

Table 12.1   Nations with the Largest Proven Reserves of Fossil Fuels

Oil (% world reserves)	Natural gas (% world reserves)	Coal (% world reserves)
Saudi Arabia, 19.8	Russian Federation, 23.7	United States, 28.9
Iran, 10.3		Russian Federation, 19.0
Iraq, 8.6	Iran, 15.8	
Kuwait, 7.6	Qatar, 13.5	China, 13.9
Venezuela, 6.6	Turkmenistan, 4.3	Australia, 9.1
	Saudi Arabia, 4.2	India, 7.1

Source: Data from British Petroleum. (2010). Statistical review of world energy 2010.

Developed nations consume more energy than developing nations

Citizens of developed regions generally consume far more energy than do those of developing regions (FIGURE 12.3). Per person, the most-industrialized nations use up to 100 times as much energy as do the least-industrialized nations. The United States, with only 4.6% of the world's population, accounts for 22.5% of the world's energy use. Even so, Canada's per capita energy use is higher. This is partly a result of the cold climate and long distances that characterize our nation, but careless use patterns are part of the story, too.

Moreover, developed and developing nations tend to apportion their energy use differently. Industrialized nations use roughly one-third of their energy on transportation, one-third on industry, and one-third on all other uses. Developing nations devote a greater proportion of their energy to subsistence activities, such as agriculture, food preparation, and home heating, and substantially less on transportation. In addition, people in developing countries often rely on manual or animal energy sources instead of automated ones. For instance, rice farmers in Bali plant rice by hand, but industrial rice growers in California use airplanes. Because industrialized nations rely more on equipment and technology, they use more fossil fuels. In Canada, where hydroelectric resources are particularly abundant,

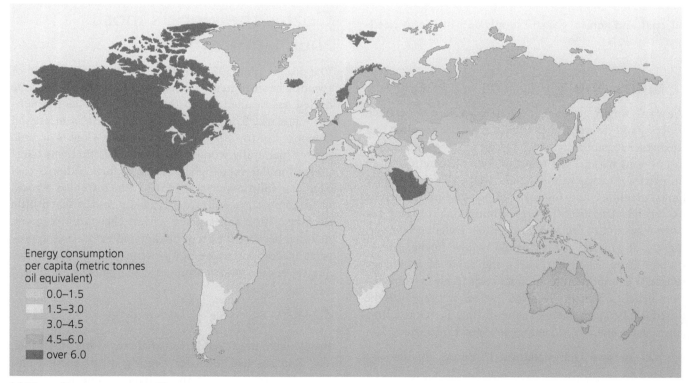

Energy consumption per capita (metric tonnes oil equivalent)
- 0.0–1.5
- 1.5–3.0
- 3.0–4.5
- 4.5–6.0
- over 6.0

(a) Map of energy consumption per person

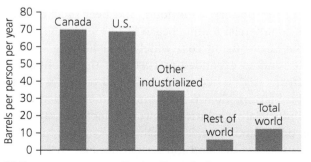

(b) Energy use per capita, in oil equivalents

FIGURE 12.3
Regions vary greatly in their consumption of energy per person **(a)**. People in industrialized nations consume the most. The map combines all types of energy, standardized to metric tonnes of "oil equivalent," that is, the amount of fuel needed to produce the energy gained from combusting one metric tonne of crude oil. The bar graph **(b)** compares energy use in oil equivalents in Canada and the United States—world "leaders" in energy use—to other nations of the world.
Source: Data from British Petroleum. 2007. Statistical review of world energy 2007.

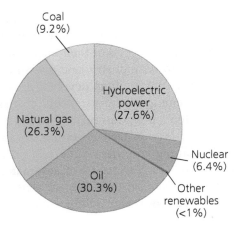

FIGURE 12.4
Fossil fuels dominate energy consumption in Canada, as in other industrialized nations.
Source: Data from BP 2010 Statistical Review of World Energy.

oil, coal, and natural gas still supply 66% of energy needs (**FIGURE 12.4**).

It takes energy to make energy

We don't simply get energy for free. To harness, extract, process, and deliver the energy that we use requires that we invest substantial inputs of energy. Drilling and extracting oil and natural gas requires the construction of an immense infrastructure of roads, wells, vehicles, storage tanks, pipelines, housing for workers, and more—which necessitates the use of energy. Piping and shipping the natural gas out of the Mackenzie River Delta and delivering it to the market for use would require further energy inputs. Thus, when evaluating the value of an energy source, it is important to subtract costs in energy invested from benefits in energy received. **Net energy** expresses the difference between energy returned (that is, the resulting consumable energy) and energy invested to achieve it:

Net Energy = Energy Returned − Energy Invested

When comparing energy sources, it is useful to use a ratio often denoted as **EROI**, or *energy returned on investment*. EROI ratios are calculated as follows:

EROI = Energy Returned/Energy Invested

Higher ratios mean that we receive more energy from each unit of energy that we invest; when EROI = 1, it means that the amount of energy invested is the same as the amount of energy extracted. Fossil fuels are widely used because their EROI ratios have historically been high. However, EROI ratios can change over time. For instance, those for oil and natural gas declined from more than 100:1 in the 1940s to about 30:1 in the 1970s, and today they are less than 15:1 globally. The EROI ratios have declined because we extracted the easiest deposits first and now must work harder and harder to extract the remaining amounts. Canadian tar sands, for comparison, have EROI ratios of 5:1 to 3:1; ethanol produced from corn has an EROI of less than 2:1. Solar panels have an EROI of approximately 1:1 unless the calculation extends for the lifetime of the technology, which greatly raises the EROI for technologies, like solar, that require the biggest energy (and financial) inputs up front.

Coal, Natural Gas, and Oil

The three principal fossil fuels, on which our modern industrial society has been founded, are coal, natural gas, and oil. Let us consider each of them, in turn.

Coal is the world's most abundant fossil fuel

The proliferation 300 million to 400 million years ago of swampy environments where organic material could be buried has resulted in substantial coal deposits throughout the world. The precursor to coal is *peat*, a moist soil composed of compressed organic matter. **Coal** is organic matter (generally woody plant material) that was compressed under very high pressure to form a dense, carbon-rich solid material (**FIGURE 12.5**). Coal is a rock, whereas peat is a soil. Coal typically results when little decomposition takes place within the parent organic material because it cannot be digested or because appropriate decomposers are not present. Coal provides one-quarter of the world's commercial energy consumption.

Coal use has a long history

People have used coal longer than any other fossil fuel. The Romans used coal for heating in the second and third centuries in Britain, as have people in parts of China for 2000–3000 years. Native Americans of the Hopi Nation still follow ancestral traditions by using coal to fire pottery, cook food, and heat their homes. Once commercial mining began in Europe in the 1700s, people began using coal widely as a heating source. Coal found an expanded market after the invention of the steam engine because it was used to boil water to produce steam. Coal-fired steam engines helped drive the Industrial Revolution, powering factories, agriculture, trains, and ships. The birth of the steel industry in 1875 increased demand still further because coal fuelled the furnaces used to produce steel.

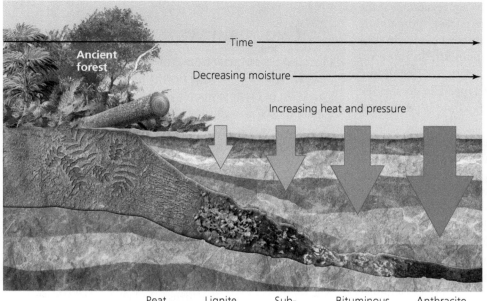

FIGURE 12.5
Coal forms as a result of the compaction of ancient plant matter underground. Scientists categorize coal into several types, depending on the amount of heat, pressure, and moisture involved in its formation. Anthracite coal is formed under the greatest pressure, where temperatures are high and moisture content is low. Lignite coal is formed under conditions of much less pressure and heat but more moisture. Peat is also part of this continuum, representing plant matter that is minimally compacted.

In the 1880s, people began to use coal to generate electricity. In coal-fired power plants, coal combustion converts water to steam, which turns a turbine to create electricity (see "The Science Behind the Story: Clean Coal for Electricity Generation"). Today coal provides more than 30% of the electrical-generating capacity of Canada. Canada hosts approximately 10 billion tonnes of coal reserves—more than our oil and natural gas reserves combined. China and the United States are the primary producers and consumers of coal (**TABLE 12.2**).

Coal is mined from the surface and from below ground

We extract coal by using two major methods. We reach underground deposits with **subsurface mining**. Shafts are dug deep into the ground, and networks of tunnels are dug or blasted out to follow coal seams. The coal is removed systematically and shipped to the surface. Today less than

2% of Canada's coal is extracted by underground mining. The history of underground mining in Nova Scotia demonstrates the hazards posed to miners who go deep under the ground to mine When coal deposits are at or near the surface, open-pit or strip-mining methods are used. Open-pit mining involves large excavations, which are deepened and widened as mining proceeds. This type of coal mining is common in Alberta and British Columbia. In **strip-mining**, heavy machinery removes earth in long, horizontal strips to expose the layers, or *seams*, and extract the coal. The pits are subsequently refilled with the soil that had been removed. Strip-mining is most common in the Prairies and in New Brunswick.[8] Strip-mining operations can occur on immense scales; in some cases entire mountaintops are lopped off.

Coal varies in its qualities

Coal varies from deposit to deposit in many ways, including in its water content and the amount of potential energy it contains. The starting material, peat, is essentially organic material that is broken down anaerobically but remains wet, near the surface, and not well compressed. Peat has been widely used as a fuel in Britain and other locations. Canada is home to some of the most extensive peat deposits in the world, and 90% of our exported peat goes to the United States. As you learned in our chapter on *Soil Resources*, peat is also of interest as a northern soil, and scientists are closely tracking its response to global climate change.

As peat decomposes further, as it becomes buried more deeply under sediment, as pressure and heat

Table 12.2 Top Five Producers and Consumers of Coal

Production (% world production)	Consumption (% world consumption)
China, 45.6	China, 46.9
United States, 15.8	United States, 15.2
Australia, 6.7	India, 7.5
India, 6.2	Japan, 3.3
Indonesia, 4.6	South Africa, 3.0

Data from British Petroleum. (2010). Statistical review of world energy 2010.

increase, and as time passes, water is squeezed out of the material, and carbon compounds are packed more tightly together, forming coal. Scientists classify coal into four types: *lignite*, *sub-bituminous*, *bituminous*, and *anthracite*. Lignite is the least-compressed type of coal, and anthracite is the most-compressed type. The greater the compression, the greater the energy content per unit of volume.

Most coal contains impurities, including sulphur, mercury, arsenic, and other trace metals, and coal deposits vary in the amounts of impurities they contain. Sulphur content depends in part on whether the coal was formed in freshwater or saltwater sediment. Coal from eastern provinces of Canada tends to be relatively high in sulphur (e.g., 2%) because it was formed from marine sediment, where sulphur from seawater was present. In comparison, coal from Alberta and British Columbia is typically lower in sulphur content, ranging down to about 0.5%, whereas coal from China can be very sulphur-rich (and thus more polluting), ranging up to about 3%.

When high-sulphur coal is burned, it produces sulphate air pollutants, which contribute to industrial smog and acidic deposition; China's use of high-sulphur coal deposits has contributed to severe air-quality problems in that country. Combustion of coal high in mercury content emits mercury that bioaccumulates in organisms' tissues, poisoning animals as it moves up food chains. Such pollution problems commonly occur downwind of coal-fired power plants. Scientists and engineers are seeking ways to cleanse coal of its impurities so that it can continue to be used as an energy source while minimizing impact on health and the environment. Reducing pollution from coal is important because society's demand for this relatively abundant fossil fuel may soon rise as supplies of oil and natural gas decline.

Natural gas is the fastest-growing fossil fuel in use today

Natural gas consists primarily of methane (CH_4) and typically includes varying amounts of other volatile hydrocarbons. (Natural "gas" is actually something of a misnomer, as the material can be liquid at the ambient pressures and temperatures in subsurface reservoirs.) Natural gas provides one-quarter of global commercial energy consumption. It is a much cleaner-burning fuel than coal or oil, so it produces less pollution. World supplies of natural gas are projected to last for at least 60 more years (proven global reserves, at current levels of production), and much longer if more unconventional sources, such as shale gas, are brought into production.

Natural gas is formed in two main ways

Natural gas can arise from either of two processes. *Biogenic* gas is created at shallow depths by the anaerobic decomposition of organic matter by bacteria. An example is the "swamp gas" you can sometimes smell when stepping into the muck of a swamp.

In contrast, *thermogenic* gas results from compression of organic material, accompanied by heating deep underground. The organic precursor materials come most commonly from animal and plant matter, such as zooplankton and phytoplankton in shallow marine waters. As the organic matter is buried more and more deeply under sediments, the pressure exerted by the overlying sediments grows, and temperatures increase; this process is called *maturation*. Carbon bonds in the organic matter begin breaking, and the organic matter turns into kerogen, which acts as a source material for both natural gas and crude oil. Further heat and pressure act on the kerogen to degrade complex organic molecules into simpler hydrocarbon molecules. At very deep levels—below about 3 km—the high temperatures and pressures tend to form natural gas. Whereas biogenic gas is nearly pure methane, thermogenic gas contains small amounts of other gases as well as methane.

Thermogenic gas may be formed directly, along with coal or crude oil, or from coal or oil that is altered by heating. Most gas extracted commercially is thermogenic and is found above deposits of crude oil or seams of coal, so its extraction often accompanies the extraction of those fossil fuels. The natural gas found in the Mackenzie River Delta, discussed in "Central Case: On, Off, On Again? The Mackenzie Valley Natural Gas Pipeline," originated from the thermogenic decomposition of organic matter in shallow marine sediments.

Often, natural gas goes to waste as it escapes from coal mines or oil wells. Methane from coal seams, called *coalbed methane*, commonly leaks to the atmosphere during mining. To avoid this waste, and because methane is a potent greenhouse gas that contributes to climate change, mining engineers are now trying to capture more of this gas for energy. Likewise, in most remote oil-drilling areas, where the transport of natural gas remains prohibitively expensive, natural gas is flared—wasted by simply being burned off. Gas captured during oil drilling is expensive to export, but in some cases it can be reinjected into the ground for potential future extraction or to maintain the pressure needed to bring the oil to the surface.

One source of biogenic natural gas is the decay process in landfills, and many landfill operators are now capturing this gas to sell as fuel. This practice decreases energy waste, can be profitable for the operator, and helps reduce the atmospheric release of methane.

Natural gas has only recently been widely used

Throughout history, naturally occurring seeps of natural gas would occasionally be ignited by lightning and could be seen burning in parts of what is now Iraq, inspiring the Greek essayist Plutarch around 100 CE. to describe their "eternal fires." The first commercial extraction of natural gas took place in 1821, but until recently its use was localized because technology did not exist to pipe gas safely over long distances. Natural gas was used to fuel streetlamps, but when electric lights replaced most gas lamps in the 1890s, gas companies began marketing gas for heating and cooking. The first major commercial natural gas development in Canada was at Bow Lake, Alberta, southwest of Medicine Hat, in 1908.[10] After the Second World War, wartime improvements in welding and pipe building made gas transport safer and more economical, and during the 1950s and 1960s, thousands of kilometres of underground pipelines were laid throughout North America.

Today natural gas is increasingly favoured because it is versatile and clean-burning, emitting just half as much carbon dioxide per unit of energy produced as coal and two-thirds as much as oil. Converted to a liquid at low temperatures (*liquefied natural gas*, or *LNG*), it can be shipped long distances in refrigerated tankers, although this poses risks of catastrophic explosions. Natural gas deposits are greatest in Russia and the Middle East, and Russia and the United States lead the world in gas production and gas consumption, respectively (TABLE 12.3); Canada is the world's third-largest producer of natural gas.

Natural gas extraction becomes more challenging with time

To access some natural gas deposits, prospectors need only drill an opening because pressure and low molecular weight drive the gas upward naturally. The first gas fields

to be tapped were of this type. Most fields remaining today, however, require that gas be pumped to Earth's surface. In Alberta as well as parts of the United States, it is common to see a device called a *horsehead pump* (FIGURE 12.6). This pump moves a rod in and out of a shaft, creating pressure to pull both natural gas and crude oil to the surface.

As with oil and coal, many of the most accessible natural gas reserves have already been exhausted, causing their production to decline. Thus, deposits located in more remote areas, such as the Mackenzie River Delta, are becoming more attractive economically. Much extraction today also makes use of sophisticated techniques to break into rock formations and pump gas to the surface. One such "fracturing technique" is to pump salt water or another fluid under high pressure into the rocks to crack them. Sand or small glass beads are inserted to hold the cracks open once the water is withdrawn. This type of extraction (called *fracking*) has extensive environmental impacts, and it is very water-intensive (FIGURE 12.7). Fracking is used to recover *shale gas*, natural gas produced from shale, which is the fastest growing part of the natural gas industry.

Offshore drilling produces much of our gas and oil

Drilling for natural gas, as well as for oil, takes place not just on land but also in the seafloor on the continental shelves. Offshore drilling has required developing technology that can withstand the forces of wind, waves, and ocean currents. Some drilling platforms are fixed standing platforms built with unusual strength. Others are resilient floating platforms anchored in place above the drilling site. Most of the

Production (% world production)	Consumption (% world consumption)
United States, 20.1	United States, 22.2
Russian Federation, 17.6	Russian Federation, 13.2
Canada, 5.4	Iran, 4.5
Iran, 4.4	Canada, 3.2
Norway, 3.5	China, 3.0

Table 12.3   Top Five Producers and Consumers of Natural Gas

Source: Data from British Petroleum. (2010). Statistical review of world energy 2010.

FIGURE 12.6
Horsehead pumps, like this one in Drayton Valley, Alberta, are used to extract natural gas as well as oil. They are a common feature of the landscape in Alberta and parts of the United States. The pumping motion of the machinery draws gas and oil upward from below ground.

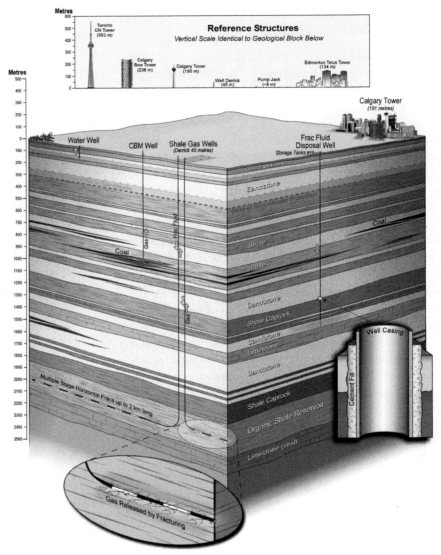

FIGURE 12.7

Fracking is used to extract natural gas, some types of oil, and bitumen from tar sands, as shown here. It involves injecting a fluid (usually water) into the ground under pressure to induce the rock to fracture, as shown here, and release the petroleum that it holds.

offshore gas and oil development in Canada is located in the Beaufort Sea and in the North Atlantic Ocean off the coasts of Newfoundland, Labrador and Nova Scotia (**FIGURE 12.8**). These are very risky environments because of stormy weather and icy waters, as well as the extreme depths of drilling (more than 2.5 km, in the case of Newfoundland).

Oil is the world's most-used fuel

Oil has dominated world energy use since the 1960s, when it eclipsed coal. It now accounts for 37% of the world's commercial energy consumption. Its use worldwide over the past decade has risen more than 17%.

People have used solid forms of oil (such as tar and asphalt) from deposits easily accessible at Earth's surface

FIGURE 12.8

The Hibernia Offshore Drilling Platform, shown here, is located in the North Atlantic about 300 km off the coast of Newfoundland in the Grand Banks. It is the world's largest offshore platform and began production in 1997.

for at least 6000 years. The modern extraction and use of petroleum for energy began in the 1850s, when miners drilling for groundwater or salt occasionally encountered oily rocks instead. At first, entrepreneurs bottled the crude oil from these deposits and sold it as a healing aid, unaware that crude oil is carcinogenic when applied to the skin and poisonous when ingested. Soon, however, it was realized that this "rock oil" could be used to light lamps and lubricate machinery. Edwin Drake is generally credited with drilling the world's first oil well, in Titusville, Pennsylvania, in 1859. In fact, however, the first oil well was drilled a full year earlier, in 1858, at Oil Springs, Ontario, by James Miller Williams, who struck free liquid oil only 20 m below the surface while attempting to drill a water well.[11]

Today our global society produces and consumes nearly 750 L of oil each year for every man, woman, and child. The United States consumes nearly one-fourth of the world's oil and shows little sign of abating. For our part, Canadians—less than 0.5% of the world's population—consume 2.5% of the oil. TABLE 12.4 shows the top oil-producing and oil-consuming nations.

Heat and pressure underground form petroleum

The sludgelike liquid we know as oil, crude oil, or petroleum (a term that includes both oil and natural gas) tends to form within a window of temperature and pressure conditions often found 1.5–3 km below the surface. Like natural gas, most of the crude oil we now extract was formed

Table 12.4   Top Ten Producers and Consumers of Oil

Production (% world production)	Consumption (% world consumption)
Russian Federation, 12.9	United States, 21.7
Saudi Arabia, 12.0	China, 10.4
United States, 8.5	Japan, 5.1
Iran, 5.3	India, 3.8
China, 4.9	Russian Federation, 3.2
Canada, 4.1	Saudi Arabia, 3.1
Mexico, 3.9	Germany, 2.9
Venezuela, 3.3	South Korea, 2.7
United Arab Emirates, 3.2	Brazil, 2.7
Iraq, 3.2	Canada, 2.5

Source: Data from British Petroleum. (2010). Statistical review of world energy 2010.

roots

PETROLEUM

The word **petroleum**, which includes both oil and natural gas in its modern usage, comes from a combination of the Latin words *petra* ("rock") and *oleum* ("oil"). Until about 1300 CE, **oil** was used exclusively in reference to "olive oil," and it derived much earlier from the Greek *elaion*, "olive tree."

when dead plant material (and small amounts of animal material) drifted down through shallow coastal marine waters millions of years ago and was buried in sediments on the ocean floor.

Crude oil is a mixture of hundreds of different types of hydrocarbon molecules characterized by carbon chains of different lengths. The specific properties of the oil depend on the chemistry of the organic starting materials, the characteristics of the geologic environment of formation, and the details of the maturation process. A hydrocarbon chain's length affects its chemical properties, which has consequences for human use, such as whether a given fuel burns cleanly in a car engine. Oil refineries sort the various hydrocarbons of crude oil, separating those intended for use in gasoline engines from those, such as tar and asphalt, used for other purposes.

Petroleum geologists infer the location and size of deposits

Because petroleum forms only under certain conditions, it occurs in isolated deposits. Once geothermal heating separates hydrocarbons from their source material and produces crude oil, this liquid migrates upward through rock pores, sometimes assisted by seismic faulting. It tends to collect in porous layers beneath dense, impermeable layers.

Geologists searching for oil (or other fossil fuels) drill rock cores and conduct ground, air, and seismic surveys to map underground rock formations, understand geologic history, and predict where fossil fuel deposits might lie. One method is to create powerful vibrations (by exploding dynamite, thumping the ground with a large weight, or using an electric vibrating machine) at the surface in one location and then measure how long it takes the seismic waves to reach receivers at other surface locations. Density differences in the substrate cause waves to reflect off layers, refract, or bend. Scientists and engineers interpret the

THE SCIENCE BEHIND THE STORY

Clean Coal for Electricity Generation

A worker checks a furnace at a coal-fired power plant.

We use coal—lots of it—to generate electricity, in a process that dates back more than a century (see the figure). Once mined, coal is hauled to power plants, where it is pulverized. The crushed coal is blown into a boiler furnace on a superheated stream of air and burned in a blaze of intense heat—typical furnace temperatures often flare at 815°C.

Water circulating around the boiler absorbs the heat and is converted to high-pressure steam. This steam is injected into a **turbine**, a rotary device that converts the kinetic energy of a moving substance, such as steam, into mechanical energy. As steam from the boiler exerts pressure on the blades of the turbine, they spin, turning the turbine's drive shaft.

The drive shaft is connected to a generator, which features a *rotor* that rotates and a *stator* that remains stationary. Generators make use of a phenomenon that you may have experimented with in your high school physics class: Moving magnets adjacent to coils of copper wire causes electrons in the wires to move, generating alternating electric current. The current flows into transmission lines that travel from the power plant out to the customers who use the plant's electricity.

As we try to balance growing demand for electricity with rising concerns about environmental and health impacts of coal combustion, power plants continue to rely heavily on coal while scientists work to limit the pollution that use of this fuel creates. **Clean coal** technologies largely focus on approaches to rid the generation process of toxic chemicals before or after the coal is burned.

There are two principal clean-coal pathways being investigated by researchers internationally. These involve technologies that are aimed at (1) a cleaner combustion process and (2) *gasification* and the production of clean synthetic fuels from coal.[9]

Combustion-focused technologies start with the pulverized-coal process and apply improvements aimed at making combustion more efficient and more complete, and thus cleaner. One example is *fluidized bed* technologies, which bathe the finely pulverized coal in jets of air during combustion. This leads to a turbulent, fluid-like environment, which allows the temperature to be increased and raises the efficiency of the chemical reactions that occur during combustion. Gasification technologies are less well developed; they involve creating clean synthetic fuels, including hydrogen, from coal.

Either approach can be combined with technologies aimed at cleaning the coal prior to combustion; cleaning emissions after burning and before they leave the smokestack; cogeneration technologies; and carbon capture and storage technologies. For example, some precombustion technologies utilize sulphur-metabolizing bacteria to remove sulphur from the coal prior to burning. Technologies that clean emissions before they leave the stack include *scrubbers*, which utilize calcium- or sodium-based materials to absorb and remove sulphur dioxide (SO_2) from the emissions. Other types of scrubbers use chemical reactions to strip away nitrogen oxides (NO_X), breaking them down into elemental nitrogen and water. Multilayered filtering devices can be used to capture tiny ash particles before they leave the stack.

---

patterns of wave reception to infer the density, thickness, and location of underlying geologic layers—which in turn provide clues about the location and size of fuel deposits.

Over the past few decades, geologists have greatly improved their methods for locating new deposits; however, with their scientific understanding of Earth processes, geologists are generally quick to acknowledge that petroleum is ultimately a finite and nonrenewable resource.

Some portion of oil that is located by geologists will be impossible to extract by using current technology and will need to wait for future advances in extraction equipment or methods. Thus, estimates are generally made of *technically recoverable* oil. However, oil companies will not be willing to extract these entire amounts. Some oil would be so difficult to extract that the expense of doing so would exceed the income the company would receive from the oil's sale. Thus, the amount a company chooses to drill for will be determined by the costs of extraction (and transportation), together with the current price of oil on the world market. Because the price of oil fluctuates, the portion of oil from a given deposit that is *economically recoverable* fluctuates as well.

Thus, technology sets a limit on the amount that *can* be extracted, whereas economics determines how much *will* be extracted. The amount of oil, or any other fossil fuel, in a deposit that is technologically and economically feasible to remove under current conditions is the *proven recoverable reserve* of that fuel.

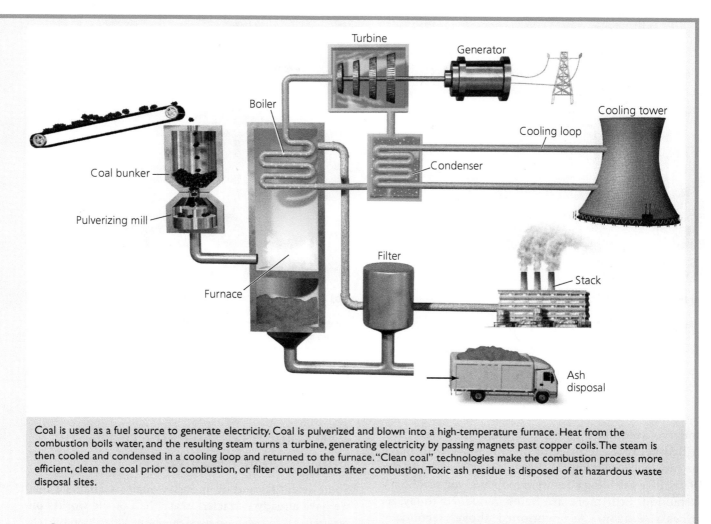

Coal is used as a fuel source to generate electricity. Coal is pulverized and blown into a high-temperature furnace. Heat from the combustion boils water, and the resulting steam turns a turbine, generating electricity by passing magnets past copper coils. The steam is then cooled and condensed in a cooling loop and returned to the furnace. "Clean coal" technologies make the combustion process more efficient, clean the coal prior to combustion, or filter out pollutants after combustion. Toxic ash residue is disposed of at hazardous waste disposal sites.

Some energy analysts and environmental advocates question a policy emphasis on clean coal. Coal, they maintain, is an inherently dirty means of generating power and should be replaced outright with cleaner energy sources. However, with coal-fired power plants still generating a significant proportion of Canada's electricity—as well as Canada's greenhouse gas emissions—the push to clean up coal-based technologies makes sense.

We drill to extract oil

Once geologists have identified an oil deposit, an oil company will typically conduct exploratory drilling. Holes drilled during this phase are usually small in circumference and descend to great depths. If enough oil is encountered, extraction begins. Just as you would squeeze a sponge to remove its liquid, pressure is required to extract oil from porous rock. Oil is typically already under pressure—from above by rock or trapped gas, from below by groundwater, or internally from natural gas dissolved in the oil. All these forces are held in place by surrounding rock until drilling reaches the deposit, whereupon oil will often rise to the surface of its own accord.

Once pressure is relieved, however, both oil and natural gas become more difficult to extract and may need to be pumped out. Even after pumping, a great deal of oil remains stuck to rock surfaces. As much as two-thirds of a deposit may remain in the ground after **primary extraction**, the initial drilling and pumping of available oil (**FIGURE 12.9A**). Companies may then begin **secondary extraction**, in which solvents are used or underground rocks are flushed with water or steam to remove additional oil (**FIGURE 12.9B**).

Even after secondary extraction, quite a bit of oil can remain; we lack the technology to remove every last drop. Secondary extraction is more expensive than primary extraction, so many oil deposits did not

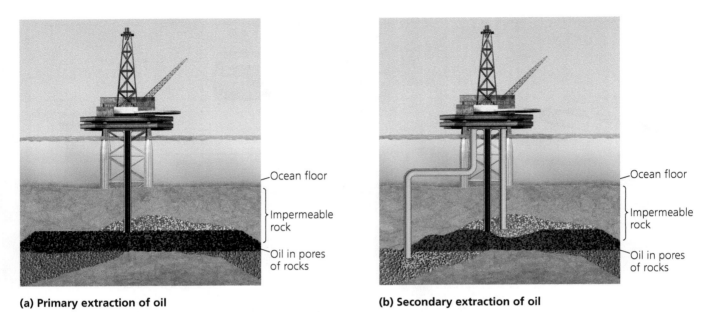

(a) Primary extraction of oil   **(b) Secondary extraction of oil**

FIGURE 12.9   In primary extraction **(a)**, oil is drawn up through the well by keeping pressure at the top lower than pressure at the level of the oil deposit. Once the pressure in the deposit drops, however, material must be injected into the deposit to increase the pressure. Thus, secondary extraction **(b)** involves injecting seawater beneath the oil and/or gases just above the oil to force more oil up and out of the deposit.

undergo secondary extraction when they were first drilled because the price of oil was too low to make the procedure economical. When oil prices rose in the 1970s, many drilling sites were reopened for secondary extraction. Still more are being reopened today, as prices rise again. As mentioned above, secondary extraction also can be harder on the environment than primary extraction.

Petroleum products have many uses

Once crude oil is extracted, it is put through **refining** processes (see "The Science Behind the Story: How Crude Oil Is Refined"). Because crude oil is a complex mix of hydrocarbons, we can create many types of petroleum products by separating its various components. Since the 1920s, refining techniques and chemical manufacturing have greatly expanded our uses of petroleum to include a wide array of products and applications, from lubricants to plastics to fabrics to pharmaceuticals. Today, petroleum-based products are all around us in our everyday lives (**FIGURE 12.10**).

Because petroleum products have become so central to our lives, many fossil fuel experts today are voicing concern that oil production may soon decline as we continue to deplete the world's recoverable oil reserves.

We may have already depleted half our oil reserves

Some scientists and oil industry analysts calculate that we have already extracted nearly half of the world's oil reserves. So far we have used up about 1.1 trillion barrels of oil, and most estimates hold that somewhat more than 1 trillion barrels remain. (A barrel is not a metric unit of measurement, but it is still commonly used in the oil industry. It is equivalent to 0.158987 cubic metres, or 159 litres, or 42 U.S. gallons.)

To estimate how long this remaining oil will last, analysts calculate the *reserves-to-production ratio*, or *R/P ratio*, by dividing the amount of total remaining reserves by the annual rate of production (i.e., extraction and processing). At current levels of production (30 billion barrels globally per year), 1.2 trillion barrels would last about 40 more years.

Unfortunately, this does not mean that we have a full 40 years in which to figure out what to do once the oil runs out. A growing number of scientists and analysts insist that we will face a crisis not when the last drop of oil is pumped, but when the rate of production first begins to decline. They point out that when production declines as demand continues to increase (because of rising global population and consumption), we will experience an oil shortage immediately. Because production tends to decline once reserves are depleted halfway, most of these experts calculate that this crisis will likely begin within the next several years.

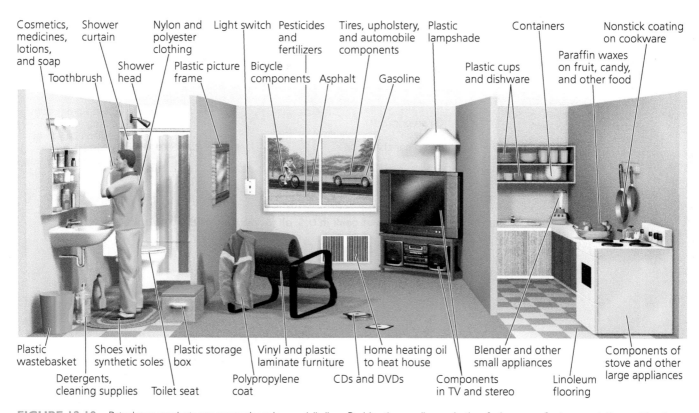

FIGURE 12.10   Petroleum products are everywhere in our daily lives. Besides the gasoline and other fuels we use for transportation and heating, petroleum products include many of the fabrics that we wear and most of the plastics that help make up countless items we use every day.

To understand the basis of these concerns, we need to turn back the clock to 1956. In that year, Shell Oil geologist M. King Hubbert calculated that U.S. oil production would peak around 1970. His prediction was ridiculed at the time, but it proved to be accurate; U.S. production peaked in that very year and has continued to fall since then (**FIGURE 12.11A**). The peak in production came to be known as **Hubbert's peak**.

In 1974, Hubbert analyzed data on technology, economics, and geology, predicting that global oil production would peak in 1995. It grew past 1995, but many scientists using newer, better data today predict that at some point in the coming decade, production will begin to decline (**FIGURE 12.11B**). Oil geologist Kenneth Deffeyes even contends that we have already passed the peak—that we did so in December 2005—and he is not alone in this belief. Indeed, because of year-to-year variability in production, we will be able to recognize that we have passed the peak of oil production only several years after it has happened.

Predicting an exact date for **"peak oil"** and the coming decline in production is difficult. Many companies and governments do not reveal their true data on oil reserves, and estimates differ as to how much oil we can extract secondarily from existing deposits. Moreover, a recent U.S. Geological Survey report estimated 2 trillion barrels remaining in the world, rather than 1 trillion, and some estimates predict still

greater amounts. A report by the U.S. General Accounting Office reviewed 21 studies and found that estimates for the timing of the oil production peak ranged from 2005 through 2040. Regardless of the exact timing, it seems certain that a peak in global oil production will occur. Discoveries of new oil fields peaked 30 years ago, and since then we have been extracting and consuming more oil than we have been discovering. Meanwhile, global demand continues to rise, particularly as China and India industrialize rapidly.

The coming divergence of demand and supply will likely have momentous economic, social, and political

weighing the issues

THE END OF OIL

How do you think your life would be affected if our society were to suffer a 50% decrease in oil availability over the next 10 years, as some observers have predicted? What steps would you take to adapt to these changes? What steps should our society take to deal with the coming depletion of oil? Do you think the recent surges in the price of oil and gasoline are an indication that such changes are beginning?

FIGURE 12.11

Because fossil fuels are nonrenewable resources, supplies at some point pass the midway point of their depletion, and annual production begins to decline. U.S. oil production peaked in 1970, just as geologist M. King Hubbert predicted decades previously; this high point is referred to as Hubbert's peak **(a)**. Today many analysts believe global oil production is about to peak. Shown is the latest projection **(b)**, from a 2007 analysis by scientists at the Association for the Study of Peak Oil. Data in (a) from Deffeyes, K. S. (2001). *Hubbert's Peak: The Impending World Oil Shortage*. Princeton, NJ: Princeton University Press; and U.S. Energy Information Administration. Data in (b) from Campbell, C. J., and the Association for the Study of Peak Oil and Gas. (2007).

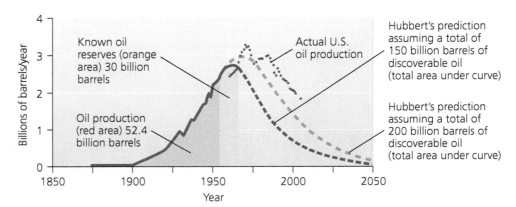

(a) Hubbert's prediction of peak in U.S. oil production, with actual data

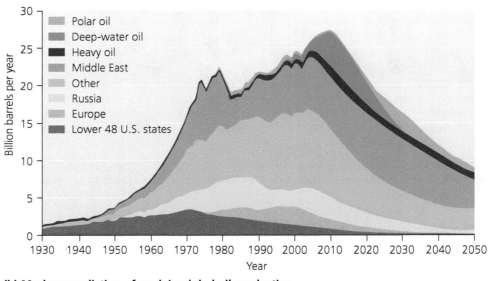

(b) Modern prediction of peak in global oil production

consequences that will profoundly affect the lives of each and every one of us. Pessimists predict the collapse of modern industrial society as fossil fuel supplies become increasingly insufficient. More optimistic observers argue that as oil supplies dwindle, rising prices will create powerful incentives for businesses, governments, and individuals to conserve energy and develop alternative energy sources, and that these developments will save us from major disruptions caused by the coming oil peak.

Indeed, to achieve a sustainable society, we will need to switch to renewable energy sources. Energy conservation can extend the time we have in which to make this transition. However, the research and development needed to construct the infrastructure for a new energy economy depend on having cheap oil, and the time we will have to make this enormous transition will be quite limited.

"Unconventional" Fossil Fuels

As oil production declines, we will rely more on natural gas and coal—yet these in turn will also peak and decline in future years. Are there other fossil fuels that can replace them and stave off our day of reckoning? At least three types of alternative fossil fuels exist in large amounts in deposits of tar sands, shale oil and gas, and methane hydrates.

Canada owns massive deposits of tar sands

Tar sands (also called **oil sands**) are deposits of moist sand and clay containing 1–20% **bitumen**, a thick and heavy form of petroleum that is rich in carbon and poor

FIGURE 12.12
In Alberta, companies strip-mine tar sands with the world's largest dump trucks and power shovels. On average, two metric tonnes of tar sands are required to produce one barrel of synthetic crude oil.

that add hydrogen or remove carbon can upgrade it into more valuable synthetic crude oil.

Three-quarters of the world's tar sands lie in two areas: eastern Venezuela and northeastern Alberta. Tar sands in each region hold at least 175 billion barrels of oil. In Alberta, strip-mining began in 1967, but as rising crude oil prices make tar sands more profitable, dozens of companies are now angling to begin 100 or more mining projects in the region. In 2010, tar sands produced 1.5 million barrels of oil per day, contributing 54% of Canada's petroleum production. If all planned projects go through, production could reach 3.5 million barrels per day by 2025. The tar sands move Canada into a strong position for proven oil reserves in the international context (**FIGURE 12.13**).

Oil shale is abundant in the American West

Oil shale is sedimentary rock that contains abundant *kerogen*, which can be processed to produce liquid petroleum. Oil shale is formed by the same processes that form crude oil but occurs when kerogen was not buried deeply enough or subjected to enough heat and pressure to form oil.

in hydrogen. Tar sands represent crude oil deposits that have been degraded and chemically altered by water erosion and bacterial decomposition.

Because bitumen is too thick to extract by conventional oil drilling, tar sands are generally removed by strip-mining (**FIGURE 12.12**), using methods similar to coal strip-mining. For deposits 75 m or more below ground, a variety of *in situ* extraction techniques are being devised. Most of these involve fracking—injecting steam or chemical solvents to crack the rock and liquefy the bitumen so it can be extracted through conventional wells. After extraction, bitumen may be sent to specialized refineries, where several types of chemical reactions

Oil shale is mined by using strip-mines or subsurface mines. Once mined, oil shale can be burned directly like coal, or it can be baked in the presence of hydrogen and in the absence of air to extract liquid petroleum (a process called *pyrolysis*). Currently, industry is developing *in situ* extraction processes in which rock is heated underground to liquefy and release oil into conventional wells.

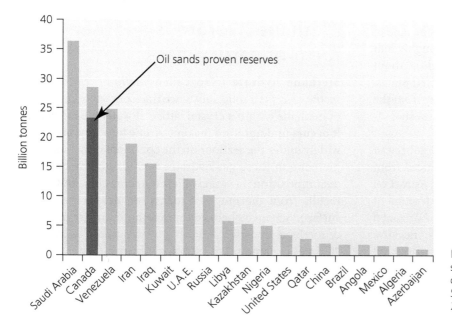

FIGURE 12.13   Canada's tar sands are a significant proven oil reserve, even in an international context.
Source: Based on BP Statistical Review of World Energy, 2010.

THE SCIENCE BEHIND THE STORY

How Crude Oil Is Refined

These workers are at a Citgo oil refinery in Lemont, Illinois.

Crude oil is a complex mixture of thousands of kinds of hydrocarbon molecules. Through the process of *refining*, these hydrocarbon molecules are separated into classes of different sizes and chemically transformed to create specialized fuels for heating, cooking, and transportation and to create lubricating oils, asphalts, and the precursors of plastics and other petrochemical products. To maximize the production of marketable products while minimizing negative environmental impacts, petroleum engineers have developed a variety of refining techniques.

The first step in processing crude oil is *distillation*, or *fractionation*. This process is based on the fact that different components of crude oil boil at different temperatures. In refineries, the distillation process takes place in tall columns filled with perforated horizontal trays (see figure). The columns are cooler at the top than at the bottom. When heated crude oil is introduced into the column, lighter components rise as vapour to the upper trays, condensing into liquid as they cool, while heavier components sink to the lower trays. Light gases, such as butane, boil at less than 32°C, and heavier oils, such as industrial fuel oil, boil only at temperatures above 343°C.

Since the early twentieth century, light gasoline, used in automobiles, has been in much higher demand than most other derivatives of crude oil. The demand for high-performance, clean-burning gasoline has also risen. To meet these demands, refiners have developed several techniques to convert heavy hydrocarbons into gasoline.

The general name for processes that convert heavy oil into lighter oil is *cracking*. One of the simplest methods is thermal cracking, in which long-chained molecules are broken into smaller chains by heating in the absence of oxygen. (The oil would ignite if oxygen were present.) Catalytic cracking, a related method, uses *catalysts*—substances that promote chemical reactions without being consumed by them—to control the cracking process. The result is an increase in the amount of a desired lighter product from a given amount of heavy oil. The products of cracking are then fed into a distillation column.

Refiners can also change the chemical composition of oil through a process called *catalytic reforming*. Catalytic reforming uses catalysts to promote chemical reactions that transform certain hydrocarbons that are slightly heavier than gasoline so that they can be blended with gasoline to obtain higher octane ratings. The octane rating reflects the amount of compression gasoline can undergo before it spontaneously ignites.

Besides distilling crude oil and altering the chemical structure of some of its components, refineries also remove contaminants. Sulphur and nitrogen compounds, which can be harmful when released into the atmosphere, are the two most common contaminants in crude oil. Government regulations have forced refiners to implement scrubbers and other methods of removing such contaminants, particularly sulphur. Some methods successfully remove up to 98% of sulphur.

As a result of all these approaches, crude oil is eventually converted into gasoline and a wide variety of other petroleum products.

The world's known deposits of oil shale may be able to produce more than 600 billion barrels of oil (roughly half as much as the crude oil remaining in the world). About 40% of global oil shale reserves are in the United States. Low prices for crude oil have kept investors away from the more costly oil shale, but as crude prices rise, oil shale is again attracting attention.

An increasingly important unconventional source of fossil fuel is **shale gas**. Natural gas can be produced from shale units by fracking, the same method used to extract oil from tar sands. When fracking is used for the extraction of shale gas, however, it is typical for a much larger horizontal area to be fractured, leading to significantly greater negative environmental impacts. It is likely that the amount of natural gas available to be extracted from shale and other unconventional sources will turn out to be overwhelmingly larger than the amount of oil that may be derived from these sources.

Methane hydrate is another form of natural gas

Methane hydrate (also called *methane clathrate* or *methane ice*) is a solid substance that consists of molecules of methane within a crystal lattice of water ice molecules. It occurs underground in some Arctic locations and more widely under the seafloor on the continental shelves. Most methane in these gas hydrates was formed by bacterial decomposition in anaerobic environments, but some results from thermogenic formation deeper below the surface. Scientists believe there to be immense amounts of methane hydrate on Earth—from perhaps as much as 20 times the amount of natural gas from all other sources.

However, there is currently no technology to extract methane hydrate safely, avoiding the risk of destabilizing these deposits during extraction. Such destabilization could

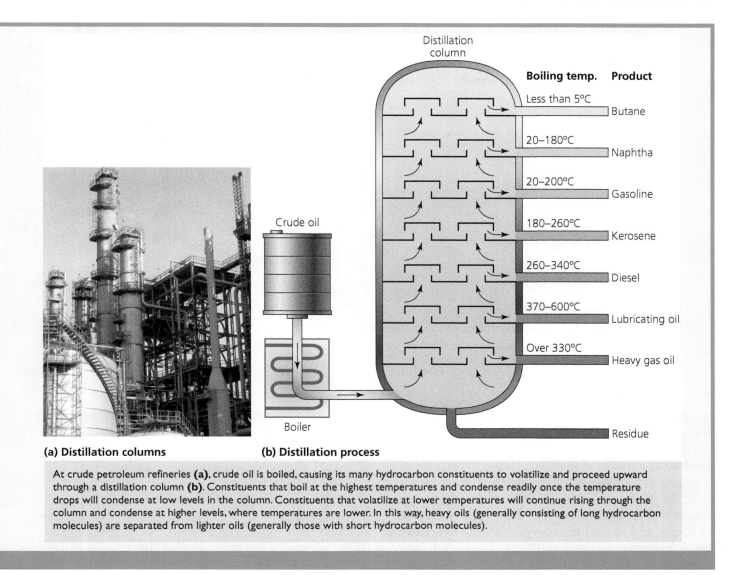

Distillation column

(a) Distillation columns   **(b) Distillation process**

Boiling temp.	Product
Less than 5°C	Butane
20–180°C	Naphtha
20–200°C	Gasoline
180–260°C	Kerosene
260–340°C	Diesel
370–600°C	Lubricating oil
Over 330°C	Heavy gas oil
	Residue

Crude oil

Boiler

At crude petroleum refineries **(a)**, crude oil is boiled, causing its many hydrocarbon constituents to volatilize and proceed upward through a distillation column **(b)**. Constituents that boil at the highest temperatures and condense readily once the temperature drops will condense at low levels in the column. Constituents that volatilize at lower temperatures will continue rising through the column and condense at higher levels, where temperatures are lower. In this way, heavy oils (generally consisting of long hydrocarbon molecules) are separated from lighter oils (generally those with short hydrocarbon molecules).

lead to underwater landslides, tsunamis, and the release of large amounts of methane, a potent greenhouse gas.

Alternative fossil fuels have significant environmental impacts

Alternative and unconventional fossil fuels are abundant, but they are no panacea for our energy challenges. For one thing, their net energy values are low because they are expensive to extract and process. Thus the energy returned on energy invested (EROI) ratio is low. For instance, at least 40% of the energy content of oil shale is consumed in its production, and oil shale's EROI is only about 2:1 or 3:1, compared with a 5:1 or greater ratio for conventional crude oil. Natural gas extracted from the gas fields of the Mackenzie River Delta might never make it all the way to

southern consumers if it must be sidetracked to support the extraction of oil from the Athabasca tar sands.

Second, these fuels exert severe environmental impacts. Tar sands and oil shale require extensive strip-mining and/or fracking, which utterly devastates landscapes over large areas and pollutes waterways that run into other areas. Although most governments require mining companies to restore mined areas to their original condition, regions denuded by the very first oil sand mine in Alberta 30 years ago have still not recovered.

Canadian environmentalists also are worried about the intensive water use that typically accompanies the extraction of unconventional fossil fuels through methods such as fracking, as well as the impacts on water quality in surrounding regions. The impacts on wildlife are also of concern; this concern was brought into stark focus in 2008 when hundreds of migratory birds died when their feathers

FIGURE 12.14
Concerns about the impacts of tar sand exploitation on wildlife came to a head in 2008 when hundreds of migratory birds died after landing in an oily, toxic tailings pond at Fort McMurray, Alberta, similar to the one shown here **(a)**. Only a few of the oiled sea ducks managed to survive **(b)**.

(a) An oil sand tailings pond in Alberta

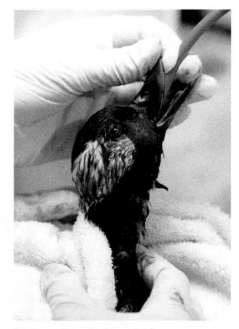

(b) Rescuing oiled sea ducks

became fouled with oil after landing on Syncrude's massive tailings pond near Fort McMurray, Alberta (FIGURE 12.14). A similar event happened in 2010, just days after Syncrude agreed to pay a penalty of $3 million for the previous event.

To give you an idea of the magnitude of these ponds, which can hold up to 540 000 000 m^3 of oily sludge, consider that the Syncrude tailings dam is the largest dam in Canada, and second in the world only to the Three Gorges hydroelectric dam in China. Canada's largest hydroelectric dam, the Gardiner, has just slightly more than one-tenth the capacity of the Syncrude tailings dam.[12]

Besides impacts from their extraction, our combustion of alternative fossil fuels would emit at least as much carbon dioxide, methane, and other air pollutants as does our use of coal, oil, and gas. Thus, they will worsen the effects that fossil fuels are already causing, including air pollution, global climate change, and ocean acidification.

Environmental Impact of Fossil Fuel Use

Our society's love affair with fossil fuels and the many petrochemical products we have developed from them has boosted our material standard of living beyond what our ancestors could have dreamed, has eased constraints on travel, and has helped lengthen our life spans. It has, however, also caused harm to the environment and human health. Concern over these impacts is a prime reason many scientists, environmental advocates, businesspeople, and

policy makers are increasingly looking toward renewable sources of energy that exert less impact on natural systems.

Fossil fuel emissions cause pollution and drive climate change

When we burn fossil fuels, we alter flux rates in Earth's carbon cycle. We essentially take carbon that has been retired into a long-term reservoir underground and release it into the air. This occurs as carbon from within the hydrocarbon molecules of fossil fuels unites with oxygen from the atmosphere during combustion, producing carbon dioxide (CO_2). Carbon dioxide is a greenhouse gas, and CO_2 released from fossil fuel combustion warms our planet and drives changes in global climate. Because global climate change may have diverse, severe, and widespread ecological and socioeconomic impacts, carbon dioxide pollution (FIGURE 12.15) is becoming recognized as the greatest environmental impact of fossil fuel use.

Fossil fuels release more than carbon dioxide when they burn. Methane is a potent greenhouse gas, and other air pollutants resulting from fossil fuel combustion can have serious consequences for human health and the environment. Deposition of mercury and other pollutants from coal-fired power plants is increasingly recognized as a substantial health risk. The burning of fossil fuels in power plants and vehicles releases sulphur dioxide and

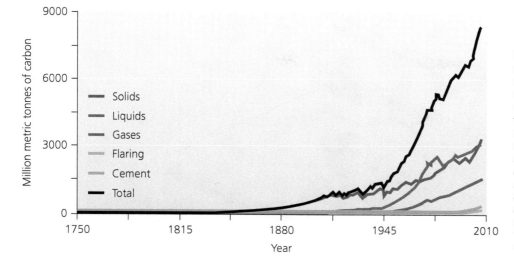

FIGURE 12.15   As industrialization has proceeded, and as population and energy consumption have grown, emissions from fossil fuels have risen dramatically. Here, worldwide emissions of carbon are subdivided by their source (liquid oil, solid coal, or natural gas). Also included are cement manufacture and flaring of natural gas. *Data are from Boden, T.A., G. Marland, and R.J. Andres (2010)* Global, Regional, and National Fossil-Fuel CO_2 Emissions. *Carbon Dioxide Information Analysis Center, Oak Ridge National Laboratory, U.S. Department of Energy, Oak Ridge, Tenn., U.S.A. doi 10.3334/CDIAC/00001_V2010*

nitrogen oxides, which contribute to industrial and photochemical smog and to acidic deposition.

We have already employed technologies, such as catalytic converters, to cut down on vehicle exhaust pollution. Gasoline combustion in automobiles releases pollutants that irritate the nose, throat, and lungs. Some hydrocarbons, such as benzene and toluene, are carcinogenic to laboratory animals and likely also to people. In addition, gases, such as hydrogen sulphide, can evaporate from crude oil, irritate the eyes and throat, and cause asphyxiation. Crude oil also often contains trace amounts of known poisons, such as lead and arsenic. As a result, workers at drilling operations, refineries, and other jobs that entail frequent exposure to oil or its products can develop serious health problems, including cancer.

Fossil fuels can pollute water as well as air. Atmospheric deposition of pollutants exerts many impacts on freshwater ecosystems. Moreover, oil from non-point sources—such as industries, homes, automobiles, gas stations, and businesses—runs off roadways and enters rivers and sewage treatment facilities to be discharged eventually into the ocean. Although most spilled oil results from these non-point sources, large catastrophic oil spills can have significant impacts on the marine environment. Crude oil's toxicity to most plants and animals can lead to high mortality. This was the case with the massive British Petroleum *Deepwater Horizon* oil spill and leak of 2010, which caused the immediate deaths and injuries of thousands of birds, turtles, fish, and shellfish, as well as harming marine mammals and corals. Longer-term concerns centre on the ultimate fate of the oil as well as the *dispersants*—chemicals (also toxic) that were used to induce the oil slicks to break up and disperse through the water column.

Oil can also contaminate groundwater supplies, such as when leaks from oil operations penetrate deeply into soil. Of even greater concern are the thousands of underground storage tanks containing petroleum products that

have leaked, threatening drinking water supplies. In 2011, such concerns led the U.S. State Department to impose a significant delay on the multi-billion-dollar Keystone XL oil pipeline project.

Some emissions from fossil fuel burning can be "captured"

One relatively new technology for "cleaning up" carbon-based fuel sources is **carbon capture and storage (CCS)** or *carbon capture and sequestration*. Recall from our discussion of biogeochemical cycles that **sequestration** is a term that refers to the storage of materials in geologic reservoirs on a long timescale. In this case, the material of interest is carbon—primarily in the form of CO_2—and the goal is to prevent some of the carbon generated by the burning of fossil fuels from entering the atmosphere and contributing to global warming.

In a nutshell, what would happen is that the CO_2 emitted by, for example, a traditional coal-burning power plant would be captured before it reached the atmosphere and then diverted to a storage reservoir. The most likely reservoirs are the deep ocean, which already acts as a reservoir for atmospheric carbon dioxide, and geologic formations deep underground (**FIGURE 12.16**).

Industry analysts predict that 80–90% of the carbon dioxide emissions from large emitters like coal-fired generators could be captured and diverted, as compared with a power plant without CCS technology. This would go a long way toward helping Canada meet its commitments in the Kyoto Protocol—at least in the short term, while we attempt to transition to more renewable energy sources.

Many environmentalists are skeptical about CCS, arguing that the technology is unproven and that the true environmental impacts of reinjecting carbon dioxide into the ground or into ocean water are not known. Some

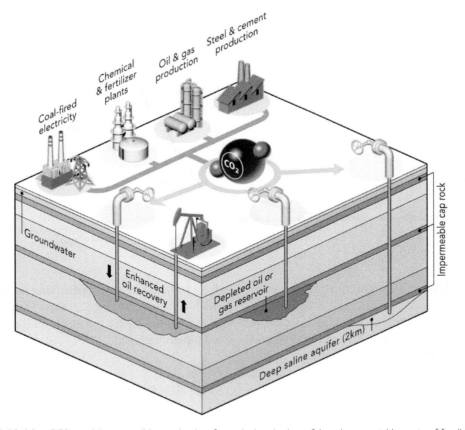

FIGURE 12.16   CCS provides a possible mechanism for reducing the harmful environmental impacts of fossil fuel use.

point to the possibility of further acidification of ocean water (because carbon dioxide mixed with water yields carbonic acid). Additionally, underwater capture and storage would be temporary; deep water does not stay in place but moves, mixes, and ultimately upwells to the surface as part of the global thermohaline circulation. With regard to storage underground, some experts have expressed concern that extraction processes (fracking) have so extensively fractured rock units near Alberta's tar sands that they would no longer be suitable for the purpose of CCS. Still others argue that the approach is fundamentally flawed because it takes the burden off large emitters and serves only to prolong our dependence on fossil fuels rather than facilitating a shift to renewables.

Coal mining affects the environment

The mining of coal also has substantial impacts on natural systems and human well-being. Surface strip-mining can destroy large swaths of habitat and cause extensive soil erosion. It also can cause chemical runoff into waterways through the process of **acid drainage**. This occurs when

sulphide minerals in newly exposed rock surfaces react with oxygen and rainwater to produce sulphuric acid. As the sulphuric acid runs off, it leaches metals from the rocks, many of which are toxic to organisms in high concentrations. Acid drainage is a natural phenomenon, but its rate accelerates greatly when mining exposes many new rock surfaces at once.

Government regulations require mining companies to restore strip-mined land following mining, but impacts can be severe and long-lasting just the same. Mountaintop removal (**FIGURE 12.17**) can have even greater impacts than conventional strip-mining. When countless tonnes of rock and soil are removed from the top of a mountain, it is difficult to keep material from sliding downhill, where immense areas of habitat can be degraded or destroyed and creek beds can be polluted and clogged.

Whereas mountaintop removal threatens the welfare of nearby residents, subsurface mining raises health concerns for miners. Underground coal mining is one of our society's most dangerous occupations. Besides risking injury or death from collapsing shafts and tunnels and from dynamite blasts and coal dust or methane explosions, miners constantly inhale coal dust in the enclosed spaces of mines, which can lead to respiratory diseases, including fatal black lung disease.

FIGURE 12.17
Strip-mining in some areas is taking place on massive scales, such that entire mountain peaks are levelled, as at this site in West Virginia. Such "mountaintop removal" can cause enormous amounts of erosion into waterways that flow into surrounding valleys, affecting ecosystems over large areas, as well as the people who live there.

The costs of alleviating all these health and environmental impacts are high, and the public eventually pays them in an inefficient manner. The reason is that the costs are generally not accounted for in the market prices of fossil fuels, which are kept low through government subsidies to extraction companies.

Oil and gas extraction also alter the environment

Much more than drilling is involved in the development of an oil or gas field. Road networks must be constructed, and many sites may be explored in the course of prospecting. The extensive infrastructure needed to support a full-scale drilling operation typically includes housing for workers, access roads, transport pipelines, and waste piles for removed soil. Ponds may be constructed for collecting the toxic sludge that remains after the useful components of oil have been removed. At extraction sites for coalbed methane, groundwater is pumped out to free gas to rise, but salty groundwater dumped on the surface can contaminate soil and kill vegetation over large areas.

Many onshore North American oil reserves are located in Arctic or semi-arid areas. Plants grow slowly in tundra and semi-desert ecosystems, so even minor impacts can have long-lasting repercussions. Tundra vegetation at some northern oil developments, such as Prudhoe Bay in Alaska, still has not fully recovered from temporary roads last used 30 years ago during the exploratory phase of development. Studies at Prudhoe Bay also show that female caribou and their calves avoid all parts of the oil complex, including its roads, sometimes detouring many kilometres to do so. These studies also show that the reproductive rate of female caribou in the Prudhoe Bay region is lower than for those in undeveloped areas in Alaska. As a result, although the herd near Prudhoe Bay has increased over the past 25 years, it has not increased as much as have herds in some other parts of Alaska.

There is no way of knowing how the Prudhoe Bay herd would have performed in the absence of development; that is, there is no control, as there would be for a manipulative experiment. It is difficult, therefore, to draw conclusions about the impacts of oil development on caribou and other wild animals, such as the grizzly bear (**FIGURE 12.18**), at remote oil developments in places like Prudhoe Bay or the Mackenzie River Valley. It can be anticipated that activities like road building, oil pad construction, worker presence, oil spills, accidental fires, trash buildup, permafrost melting, offroad vehicle trails, and dust from roads would have a significant impact on both vegetation and wildlife.

Political, Social, and Economic Aspects

The political, social, and economic consequences of fossil fuel use are numerous, varied, and far-reaching. Our discussion focuses on several negative consequences of fossil fuel use and dependence, but it is important to bear in mind that their use has enabled much of the world's population to achieve a higher material standard of living than ever before. It is also important to ask in each case whether switching to more renewable sources of energy would solve existing problems.

FIGURE 12.18
Like the Mackenzie River Valley, Alaska's North Slope is home to a variety of large mammals, including grizzly bears, polar bears, wolves, Arctic foxes, and large herds of caribou. How oil development may affect these animals is a controversial issue, and scientific studies are ongoing. Grizzly bears, such as the ones shown here, have been found near, or even walking atop, the Trans-Alaska Pipeline.

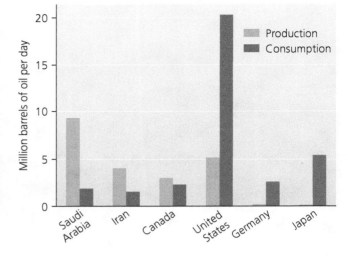

FIGURE 12.19
Japan, Germany, and the United States are among nations that consume far more oil than they produce. Iran, Saudi Arabia, and Canada are among countries that produce more oil than they consume and are able to export oil to high-consumption countries. Data from U.S. Energy Information Administration. 2007. *Annual Energy Review 2006.* Washington, DC.

Oil supply and prices affect the economies of nations

Virtually all our modern technologies and services depend in some way on fossil fuels. Putting all of one's eggs in one basket is always a risky strategy. The fact that our economies are utterly tied to fossil fuels means that we are vulnerable to supplies' becoming suddenly unavailable or extremely costly. Nations that lack adequate fossil fuel reserves of their own are especially vulnerable. For instance, Germany, France, South Korea, and Japan consume far more energy than they produce and thus rely almost entirely on imports for their continued economic well-being (**FIGURE 12.19**). Canada is both an importer and an exporter of fossil fuels in different forms, but imports are outweighed by exports.

Reliance on foreign oil means that seller nations can control energy prices, forcing buyer nations to pay more and more as supplies dwindle. This became clear in 1973, when the *Organization of the Petroleum Exporting Countries (OPEC)* resolved to stop selling oil to the United States as a consequence of U.S. support of Israel. The embargo created panic in the West and caused oil prices to skyrocket (**FIGURE 12.20**), spurring inflation.

When Hurricanes Katrina and Rita slammed into the Gulf Coast in 2005, they damaged offshore platforms and refineries, causing oil and gas prices to spike significantly. The economic ripple effects served to remind us yet again how much we rely on a steady and ever-increasing supply of petroleum.

With the majority of world oil reserves located in the politically volatile Middle East, political instabilities there are

a concern for policy makers. The world's third-largest holder of oil reserves, at 10%, is Iraq, which is why many people around the world believe that the American-led invasion of that nation in 2003 was motivated primarily to secure access to oil. Major petroleum trade relations among nations and regions of the world are depicted in **FIGURE 12.21**.

Residents may or may not benefit from fossil fuel resources

The extraction of fossil fuels can be extremely lucrative; many of the world's wealthiest corporations deal in fossil fuel energy or related industries. These industries provide jobs to millions of employees and supply dividends to millions of investors. Development can potentially yield economic benefits for people who live in petroleum-bearing areas, as well. In addition to the potential for jobs from the Mackenzie River Valley gas pipeline project, for example, the federal government has promised at least $500 million in assistance to residents of the area. Supporters argue that income and federal assistance related to the project could pay for health care, police and fire protection, and other services that are currently scarce in this remote region.

In many parts of the world where fossil fuels have been extracted, local residents have not seen great benefits but instead have suffered. When multinational corporations extract oil or gas in developing countries, paying those countries' governments for access, the money often does not

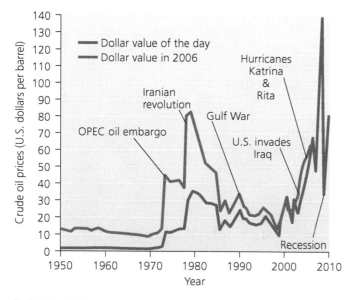

FIGURE 12.20
World oil prices have fluctuated greatly over the decades, often because of political and economic events in oil-producing countries. The greatest price hikes in recent times have resulted from wars and unrest in the oil-rich Middle East. Data from U.S. Energy Information Administration.

trickle down to residents of the regions where the extraction takes place. Moreover, oil-rich developing countries, such as Ecuador, Venezuela, and Nigeria, tend to have few environmental regulations, and existing regulations may go unenforced if a government does not want to risk losing the large sums of money associated with oil development.

In Nigeria, oil was discovered in 1958 in the territory of the Ogoni, one of Nigeria's native peoples, and the Shell Oil Company moved in to develop oil fields. Although Shell extracted $30 billion of oil from Ogoni land over the years, the Ogoni still live in poverty, with no running water or electricity. The profits from oil extraction on Ogoni land went to Shell and to the military dictatorships of Nigeria. The development resulted in oil spills, noise, and constantly burning gas flares, all of which caused illness among people living nearby. From 1962 until his death in 1995, Ogoni activist and leader Ken Saro-Wiwa worked for fair compensation to the Ogoni for oil extraction and environmental degradation on their land. After years of persecution by the Nigerian government, Saro-Wiwa was arrested in 1994, given a trial universally regarded as a sham, and put to death by a military tribunal.

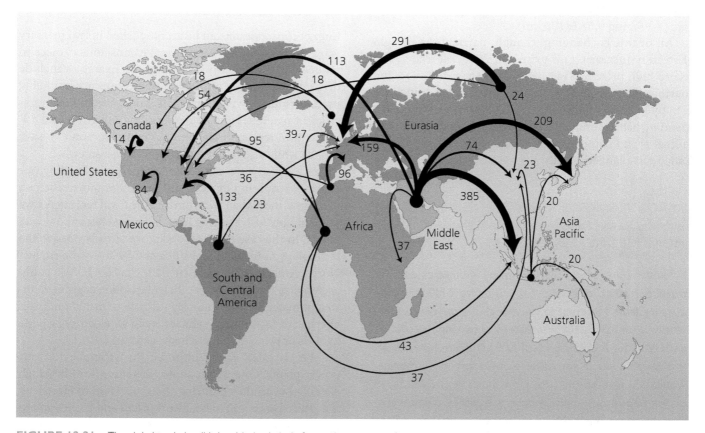

FIGURE 12.21   The global trade in oil is lopsided; relatively few nations account for most exports, and some nations are highly dependent on others for energy. Canada imports some North Sea oil while exporting more to the United States. Numbers in the figure represent millions of metric tons. Data from British Petroleum. 2007. *Statistical review of world energy 2007*.

We need to conserve energy and find renewable sources

Fossil fuel supplies are limited, and their use and our continued dependence on them have health, environmental, political, and socioeconomic consequences. Until our society makes the transition to renewable energy sources, we will need to find ways to minimize the expenditure of energy from our dwindling fossil fuel resources. **Energy conservation** is the practice of reducing energy use to extend the lifetimes of our nonrenewable energy supplies, to be less wasteful, and to reduce our environmental impact.

Many people first saw the value of conserving energy following the OPEC embargo of 1973–1974. In the subsequent three decades, however, many of the conservation initiatives that followed the oil crisis were abandoned. Without high market prices and an immediate threat of shortages, people lacked economic motivation to conserve. Government funding for research into alternative energy sources decreased, speed limits increased, and countless proposals to raise the mandated average fuel efficiency of vehicles failed. The average fuel efficiency of new vehicles worsened, from 10.64 L/100 km in 1988 to 11.21 L/100 km in 2006, primarily as a result of increased sales of light trucks and sport utility vehicles (SUVs)(averaging 12.79 L/100 km) relative to cars (averaging 9.57 L/100 km).

All of this is changing, though, particularly in light of steadily increasing oil prices. In 2008, oil traded at a record high price of $147 per barrel (then declining, but soaring again in 2011), and increases were translated directly to gas station pumps. A 2008 survey of Canadian spending habits conducted by Investors Group, the largest mutual group company in Canada, revealed that 83% of Canadians planned to buy a more fuel-efficient car next time around, 51% had been cutting down on driving, and 44% planned to change their holiday plans in response to high fuel prices.[13] These types of consumer changes are happening with equal fury in the United States, and as a result the light truck and SUV industry in North America underwent a sudden, severe contraction, with a number of production facilities closing.

Transportation accounts for two-thirds of oil use and more than a quarter of energy use in Canada, and passenger vehicles consume more than half this energy. The vast distances of the Canadian landscape add to the problem. Thus, the failure to improve vehicular fuel economy over the past 20 years, despite the existence of technology to do so, has added greatly to oil consumption. This is unfortunate because the inefficient use of gasoline in auto engines wastes oil that we could put to better use in manufacturing countless products that enhance our lives. Transportation also accounts for about a third of Canada's greenhouse gas emissions, an increasing concern as we strive to meet our international commitments regarding climate change.[14]

Personal choice and increased efficiency are two routes to conservation

Energy conservation can be accomplished in two primary ways. As individuals, we can make conscious choices to reduce our own energy consumption. Examples include driving less, turning off lights when rooms are not being used, turning down thermostats, and investing in more-efficient machines and appliances. For any given individual or business, reducing energy consumption can save money while also helping to conserve resources.

As a society, we can conserve energy by making our energy-consuming devices and processes more efficient. Currently, more than two-thirds of the fossil fuel energy we use is simply lost, as waste heat, in automobiles and power plants. In the case of automobiles, we already possess the technology to increase fuel efficiency far above the current North American average of 900 km/100 L. We could accomplish this with more efficient gasoline engines, lightweight materials, continuously variable transmissions, and alternative technology vehicles, such as electric/gasoline hybrids or vehicles that use hydrogen fuel cells.

We can also vastly improve the efficiency of our power plants. One way is to use **cogeneration**, in which excess heat produced during the generation of electricity is captured and used to heat workplaces and homes and to produce other kinds of power. Cogeneration can almost double the efficiency of a power plant. The same is true of *coal gasification* and *combined cycle* generation. In this

weighing the issues

MORE KILOMETRES, LESS GAS

If you drive an automobile, how many kilometres does it travel per 100 L of gasoline? If you drove 2400 km (the distance from Montreal to Winnipeg) in a car with a fuel efficiency of 8.33 L/100 km, instead of making the trip in an SUV with a fuel efficiency of 12.5 L/100 km, how much less gasoline would you have to buy? How much money would you save on the trip? How much would you save on the amount you typically drive in a year? Do you think that the government should raise taxes on gasoline sales as an incentive to consumers to conserve energy?

CANADIAN ENVIRONMENTAL PERSPECTIVES

Mary Griffiths

Mary Griffiths spent much of her career at the Pembina Institute looking for ways to reduce the environmental impacts of fossil fuels and raise awareness about the need for wise management.

■ **Environmental policy analyst**
■ **Energy researcher**
■ **Author**

Circumstances and opportunities have led Mary Griffiths to "reinvent" herself and her career a number of times in her life. Throughout it all, however, she has maintained her childhood love of nature and her commitment to raising awareness about the interrelationships between people and the natural environment.

In the 1960s—before there was such as thing as a degree in environmental science—Griffiths earned a Ph.D. in geography and subsequently taught the subject for a number of years at the University of Exeter, England. She remembers teaching about the decline of the Ogallala Aquifer beneath the High Plains of the United States and thinking, at the time, how short-sighted it was to be depleting this critical resource. Many years later when she learned about the enormous quantities of

fresh water that were being used in Alberta to get oil out of the ground, she felt that it was very important to make sure that the aquifers were not being adversely affected.

Moving with her young family to the Netherlands, Griffiths helped set up a small environmental group to educate individuals and municipalities on the harmful effects of pesticides. "I have always believed in sound research as the basis for action, as well as in the power of leading by example. If one municipal authority could successfully manage its public open spaces without using pesticides, others could do it, too," she says.

The family's next move, to Canada this time, found Griffiths working with the environment and other portfolios for the Liberal Caucus at the Alberta Legislature. Occasionally she sought advice from staff at the Pembina Institute, whose mandate "is to advance sustainable energy solutions through innovative research, education, consulting and advocacy."[15] An opening at Pembina for a new policy analyst gave Griffiths the opportunity to focus entirely on environmental issues once more and to devote her research efforts to finding sustainable energy solutions.

As a senior policy analyst in the Energy Solutions group at Pembina, Griffiths became an expert on the environmental impacts of fossil fuel use, especially the impacts on water. She contributed to evaluations of the environmental impacts of energy projects, including oil sands developments and coal-fired power plants. She has written several books, including *When the Oilpatch Comes to Your Backyard: A Citizens' Guide* (2004), and has co-authored numerous reports on topics ranging from landowner rights to coalbed methane development, the use of water by the oil industry, and carbon

capture and storage. She has served on several government committees, including the Alberta Minister of the Environment's Environmental Protection Advisory Committee and Alberta Environment's Advisory Committee on Water Use Practice and Policy. In 2002, Griffiths received a Canadian Environment Award for her work on clean air issues and was awarded the Alberta Centennial Medal in 2005.[16]

Now retired from the Pembina Institute, Griffiths continues to carry out research on energy and water. She is convinced that water resources will come under increasing pressure in the future and hopes to encourage more and better research and the formulation of strong policies to ensure that freshwater aquifers are protected and managed in a sustainable manner. Her overall goal is to raise awareness about the need for wise management—in all sectors—to protect the environment. "We must scrutinize all our corporate, government, and individual planning decisions, to see if they meet our long-term goal of sustainability. And we should start planning for 2020 today."[17]

"Knowledge is the foundation for environmental action."[18]*—**Mary Griffiths***

Thinking About Environmental Perspectives

Do you agree with Mary Griffiths that all environmental action should be founded on research and knowledge? Why is research so important in making environmental decisions and formulating environmental policies? How can researchers in science and social science communicate their findings to policy makers in understandable ways?

process, coal is treated to create hot gases that turn a gas turbine, while the hot exhaust of this turbine heats water to drive a conventional steam turbine.

In homes and public buildings, a significant amount of heat is lost in winter and gained in summer because of inadequate insulation (**FIGURE 12.22**). Improvements in the design of homes and offices can reduce the energy

required to heat and cool them. Such design changes can involve the building's location, the colour of its roof (light colours keep buildings cooler by reflecting the Sun's rays), and its insulation.

Among consumer products, scores of appliances, from refrigerators to light bulbs, have been reengineered through the years to increase energy efficiency. Energy-efficient

FIGURE 12.22
Many of our homes and offices could be made more energy-efficient. One way to determine how much heat a building is losing is to take a photograph that records energy in the infrared portion of the electromagnetic spectrum. In such a photograph, or *thermogram* (shown here), white, yellow, and red signify hot and warm temperatures at the surface of the house, whereas blue and green shades signify cold and cool temperatures. The white, yellow, and red colours indicate areas where heat is escaping.

lighting, for example, can reduce energy use by 80%, and new energy-efficient appliances have already reduced per-person home electricity use below what it was in the 1970s. Even so, there remains room for further improvement.

While manufacturers can improve the energy efficiency of appliances, consumers need to "vote with their wallets" by purchasing these energy-efficient appliances. Decisions by consumers to purchase energy-efficient products are crucial in keeping those products commercially available. For the individual consumer, studies show that the slightly higher cost of buying energy-efficient washing machines is rapidly offset by savings on water and electricity bills. On the national level, France, Great Britain, and many other developed countries have standards of living equal to that of Canada, but they use much less energy per capita. This disparity indicates that Canadian citizens could significantly reduce their energy consumption without decreasing their quality of life.

Conclusion

It is often said that reducing our energy use is equivalent to finding a new oil reserve. Indeed, conserving energy is better than finding a new reserve because it lessens impacts on the environment while extending our access to fossil fuels.

However, energy conservation does not add to our supply of available fuel. Regardless of how much we conserve, we will still need energy, and it will need to come from somewhere. The only sustainable way of guaranteeing ourselves a reliable long-term supply of energy is to ensure sufficiently rapid development of renewable energy sources, which we will consider in greater detail in the next chapter.

Over the past 200 years, fossil fuels have helped us build the complex industrialized societies we enjoy today. However, we are now approaching a turning point in history: Our production of fossil fuels will begin to decline. We can respond to this new challenge in creative ways, encouraging conservation and developing alternative energy sources. Or we can continue our current dependence on fossil fuels and wait until they near depletion before we try to develop new technologies and ways of life. The path we choose will have far-reaching consequences for human health and well-being, for Earth's climate, and for our environment.

The ongoing debates over projects like the Mackenzie River Valley natural gas pipeline are microcosms of this debate over our energy future. Fortunately, there is not simply a trade-off between benefits of energy for us and harm to the environment, climate, and health. Instead, as evidence builds that renewable energy sources are becoming increasingly feasible and economical, it becomes easier to envision giving up our reliance on fossil fuels and charting a win–win future for humanity and the environment.

REVIEWING OBJECTIVES

You should now be able to:

Identify the principal energy sources that we use

- A variety of renewable and nonrenewable energy sources are available to us.
- Since the Industrial Revolution, nonrenewable fossil fuels—including oil, natural gas, and coal—have become our primary sources of energy.

- Fossil fuels are formed very slowly as buried organic matter is chemically transformed by heat, pressure, and/or anaerobic decomposition.
- In evaluating energy sources, it is important to compare the amount of energy obtained from them with the amount invested in their extraction and production.

Describe the nature and origin of coal and evaluate its extraction and use

- Coal is our most abundant fossil fuel. It results from organic matter that undergoes compression but little decomposition.
- The first fossil fuel to be widely used for heating homes and powering industry, coal is used today principally to generate electricity.
- Coal is mined underground and strip-mined from the land surface.
- Coal comes in different types and varies in its composition. Combustion of coal that is high in contaminants emits toxic air pollution.

Describe the nature and origin of natural gas and evaluate its extraction and use

- Natural gas consists mostly of methane and can be formed in two ways.
- Use of natural gas is growing rapidly, and it is cleaner burning than coal or oil.
- Natural gas often occurs with oil and coal deposits, is extracted in similar ways, and becomes depleted in similar ways.

Describe the nature and origin of oil and evaluate its extraction, use, and future availability

- Crude oil is a thick, liquid mixture of hydrocarbons that is formed underground under certain temperature and pressure conditions.
- Scientists locate fossil fuel deposits by analyzing subterranean geology. Geologists estimate total reserves, as well as the technically and economically recoverable portions of those reserves.
- Oil drilling often involves primary extraction followed by secondary extraction, in which gas or liquid is injected into the ground to help force up additional oil.
- Petroleum-based products, from gasoline to clothing to plastics, are everywhere in our daily lives.
- Components of crude oil are separated in refineries to produce a wide variety of fuel types.
- We have depleted nearly half the world's oil. Once we pass the peak and production slows, the gap between rising demand and falling supply may pose immense economic and social challenges for our society.

Describe the nature, origin, and potential of alternative fossil fuel types and technologies

- Tar sands, abundant in Canada's West, can be mined and processed into synthetic oil.
- Oil shale is abundant in the western United States.
- Methane hydrate is another type of methane gas.

Outline and assess environmental impacts of fossil fuel use

- Emissions from fossil fuel combustion pollute air, pose human health risks, and drive global climate change.
- Oil is a major contributor to water pollution.
- Strip-mining and mountaintop removal can devastate ecosystems locally or regionally, and acid drainage from coal mines pollutes waterways.
- Development for oil and gas extraction exerts various environmental impacts.

Evaluate political, social, and economic impacts of fossil fuel use

- Today's societies are so reliant on fossil fuel energy that sudden restrictions in oil supplies can have major economic consequences.
- Nations that consume more fossil fuels than they produce are especially vulnerable to supply restrictions.
- People living in areas of fossil fuel extraction do not always benefit from their extraction.

Specify strategies for conserving energy and enhancing efficiency

- Energy conservation involves both personal choices and efficient technologies. These two forces interact through the market power of consumer choice.
- Increases in automotive fuel efficiency and efficiency in power plant combustion could help us conserve immense amounts of oil.
- Conservation helps lengthen our access to fossil fuels and reduce environmental impact, but to build a sustainable society we will also need to shift to renewable energy sources.

TESTING YOUR COMPREHENSION

1. Why are fossil fuels our most prevalent source of energy today? Why are they considered nonrenewable sources of energy?
2. How are fossil fuels formed? How do environmental conditions determine what type of fossil fuel is formed in a given location? Why are fossil fuels often concentrated in localized deposits?
3. Describe how net energy differs from energy returned on investment (EROI). Why are these concepts important when evaluating energy sources?
4. Describe how coal is used to generate electricity.
5. Why is natural gas often extracted simultaneously with other fossil fuels? What constraints on its extraction does it share with oil?
6. How do geologists estimate the total amount of oil reserves that remain underground? How is the "tech-nically recoverable" oil different from the "economi-cally recoverable" oil?
7. How do we create petroleum products? Provide examples of several of these products.
8. What is Hubbert's peak? Why do many experts think we are about to pass the global production peak for oil? What consequences could there be for our society if we do not transition soon to renewable energy sources?
9. List three environmental impacts of fossil fuel production and consumption. Compare some of the contrasting views of scientists regarding the environmental impacts of the Mackenzie River Valley natural gas pipeline.
10. Describe two main approaches to energy conservation; give specific examples of each.

THINKING IT THROUGH

1. Roughly how much oil is left in the world, and how much longer can we expect to use it? What steps should we take to avoid energy shortages in the future?
2. Compare the effects of coal and oil consumption on the environment. Which process do you think has ultimately been more detrimental to the environment, oil extraction or coal mining, and why? What steps could governments, industries, and individuals take to reduce environmental impacts?
3. If Canada and other developed countries reduced dependence on foreign oil and on fossil fuels in general, do you think that their economies would benefit or suffer? Might your answer be different for the short term and the long term? What factors come into play in trying to make such a judgment?
4. Do some additional research and contrast the experiences of the Ogoni people of Nigeria with those of the citizens of the Northwest Territories. How have they been similar and different, thus far? Do you think businesses or governments should take steps to ensure that local people benefit from oil-drilling operations? How could they do so?
5. You have been elected to be a negotiator on behalf of Aboriginal interests in the ongoing discussions about the development of the Mackenzie River Valley natural gas pipeline. What will your position be? Explain it to another negotiator who disagrees with you.
6. Would it be more difficult to contain and remediate a major oil spill, like the BP *Deepwater Horizon* spill of 2010, if it were to happen in the Beaufort Sea or in deep water off the coast of Newfoundland, compared to the Gulf of Mexico? What would be some of the important differences?
7. Throughout this book we have asked you to imagine yourself in various roles. This time we ask you simply to be yourself. Given the information in this chapter on petroleum supplies, consumption, and depletion, what actions, if any, do you plan to take to prepare yourself for changes in our society that may come about as oil production declines? Describe in detail how you think your life may change, and suggest one thing you could do to help reduce negative impacts of oil depletion on our society.

INTERPRETING GRAPHS AND DATA

The fossil fuels that we burn today were formed long ago from buried organic matter. However, only a small fraction of the original organic carbon remains in the coal, oil, or natural gas that is formed. Thus, it requires approximately 90 metric tonnes of ancient organic matter—so-called paleoproduction—to result in just 3.8 L of gasoline. The graph presents estimates of the amount of paleoproduction required to produce the fossil fuels humans have used each year over the past 250 years.

1. Estimate in what year the annual consumption of paleoproduction, represented by our combustion of fossil fuels, surpassed Earth's current annual net primary production (NPP).
2. In 2000, approximately how many times greater than global NPP was our consumption of paleoproduction?
3. If on average it takes 7000 units of paleoproduction to produce 1 unit of fossil fuel, estimate the total carbon content of the fossil fuel consumed in 2000. How does this amount compare to global NPP?

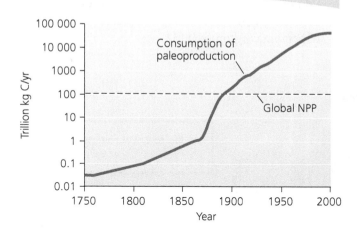

Annual human consumption of paleoproduction by fossil fuel combustion (red line), 1750–2000. The dashed line indicates current annual net primary production (NPP) for the entire planet.
Source: Data from Dukes, J. 2003. Burning buried sunshine: Human consumption of ancient solar energy. Climatic Change 61:31–44.

CHAPTER ENDNOTES

1. Mackenzie Gas Project, www.mackenziegasproject. com/theProject/index.html#
2. CBC News In-depth, *The Mackenzie Valley Pipeline*, www.cbc.ca/news/background/mackenzievalley_pipeline/index.html, updated March 12, 2007.
3. CBC News In-depth, *The Mackenzie Valley Pipeline*, www.cbc.ca/news/background/mackenzievalley_pipeline/index.html, updated March 12, 2007.
4. CBC News In-depth, *The Mackenzie Valley Pipeline*, www.cbc.ca/news/background/mackenzievalley_pipeline/index.html, updated March 12, 2007.
5. Mackenzie Gas Project, www.mackenziegasproject. com/whoWeAre/index.htm
6. CBC News In-depth, *The Mackenzie Valley Pipeline*, www.cbc.ca/news/background/mackenzievalley_pipeline/index.html, updated March 12, 2007.
7. Nature Canada: Take Action! The Mackenzie River Gas Project, www.naturecanada.ca/take_action_raise_voice_protect.asp
8. Coal Association of Canada, www.coal.ca/content/index.php?option=com_content&task=view&id=43&Itemid=40
9. CCTRM Canada's Clean Coal Technology Roadmap, Natural Resources Canada, 2005, www.cleancoaltrm.gc.ca
10. Petroleum History Society, *Six Historical Events in the First 100 Years of Canada's Petroleum Industry*, www.petroleumhistory.ca/history/wells.html#springs
11. Petroleum History Society, *Six Historical Events in the First 100 Years of Canada's Petroleum Industry*, www.petroleumhistory.ca/history/wells.html#springs
12. Tariq Piracha, Natural Resources Canada, *Natural Elements: Squeezing Water from Oil Sands—Resources Management in Petroleum Development*, modified 2008-05-06, www.nrcan-rncan.gc.ca/com/elements/issues/22/wateau-eng.php
13. Canwest News Service, June 17, 2008, as referenced in the *Montreal Gazette*.
14. The State of Energy Efficiency in Canada, *Office of Energy Efficiency Report 2006*, Natural Resources Canada, www.oee.nrcan.gc.ca/publications/statistics/see06/transportation.cfm?attr=0
15. The Pembina Institute, *About Pembina: Our Mission*, www.pembina.org

16. Pembina Institute, *Bio: Mary Griffiths,* http://re.pembina.org/author/43

17. *The Edmonton Journal,* p. 1, 2005, "What Will Edmonton Look Like in 2015?" posted on Pembina Institute Renewable Energy Op-Ed page, http://re.pembina.org/op-ed/1152

18. *Canadian Geographic,* from the citation for the Canadian Environment Award, Mary Griffiths, www.canadiangeographic.ca/cea/archives/archives_individual.asp?id=54

MyEnvironmentPlace

Go to **www.myenvironmentplace.ca** where you will find quizzes, animations, your Pearson eText, and more.

13 Energy Alternatives

(a) Low tide

(b) High tide

The Bay of Fundy is shown here at low tide (a) and high tide (b).

Upon successfully completing this chapter, you will be able to

- Discuss the reasons for seeking alternatives to fossil fuels
- Summarize the contributions to world energy supplies of conventional alternatives to fossil fuels
- Describe the scale, methods, and environmental impacts of hydroelectric power, nuclear power, and biomass energy
- Outline the major "new renewable" alternative sources of energy and assess their potential for growth

- Describe a variety of new biomass, solar, wind, geothermal, and ocean energy technologies, and outline their advantages and disadvantages
- Explain the benefits of hydrogen and fuel cells and assess future options for energy storage and transportation

Hudson
Bay

CANADA

Bay of
Fundy

CENTRAL CASE:
HARNESSING TIDAL ENERGY AT THE BAY OF FUNDY

"I believe that water will one day be employed as fuel, that hydrogen and oxygen which constitute it, used singly or together, will furnish an inexhaustible source of heat and light. . . . Water will be the coal of the future."

—JULES VERNE, IN *THE MYSTERIOUS ISLAND*, 1874

"Not only will atomic power be released, but someday we will harness the rise and fall of the tides and imprison the rays of the Sun."

—THOMAS A. EDISON, 1921

"EXTREME HAZARD," reads the posted sign. "Incoming tide rises 5 feet [1.5 m] per hour and may leave you stranded for 8 hours." Not only do ocean tidewaters rise quickly, but nowhere else in the world is the difference between low tide and high tide as great

as here, in the Bay of Fundy on Canada's Atlantic coast (see chapter-opening photo).

The Bay of Fundy is a long, narrow bay that separates the provinces of Nova Scotia and New Brunswick, just touching the U.S. state of Maine. The name "fundy" is thought to have come from early Portuguese explorers, who called it the "deep river," or *rio fundo*.

The long, narrow, deep configuration of the bay is responsible for its extreme tidal variation. When the tide comes in, a large volume of ocean water (about 100 billion tonnes) rushes in, against the outgoing freshwater flow, up the length of the narrowly constricted bay (see satellite photos). This phenomenon is called a *tidal bore*. The result is a very large vertical difference between high and low tide (up to 17 m near the extreme head of the bay, but more typically about 12 m in the main part of the bay). The large tidal range makes this one of the most suitable locations in the world for generating power from ocean tides.

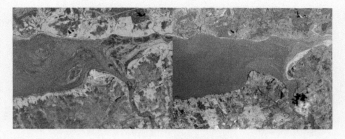

(a) Low Tide   **(b) High Tide**

Satellite images show low tide (a) and high tide (b) in the Bay of Fundy.

The Bay of Fundy is the site of one of only three operating tidal power plants in the world. The Annapolis Royal Tidal Power Generating Station, owned by Nova Scotia Power, is located on a small side-basin on the Nova Scotia side of the main bay, by the town of Annapolis Royal. The power station, which opened in 1984, works on the same principle as normal hydroelectric power generation—the movement of rushing water turns the blades of a turbine, which, in turn, runs a generator to produce electricity.

In the case of tidal power, a *sluice*—like a dam with movable openings—is constructed across a narrow part of the water body. When the tide comes in, the sluice gates are opened and the water flows through. At high tide, the gates are closed. When the tide starts to go out, the water above the sluice is held behind the closed gates. Once there is a sufficient difference in water level (1 m, in the case of the Annapolis power station), the gates are opened. The water rushes out from behind the sluice to join the rest of the outgoing tide (see photo), turning the turbine blades in the process. At this station, Nova Scotia Power generates enough power to run about 4000 homes.[1]

Many of the negative impacts of traditional hydroelectric power generation are associated with the creation of large reservoirs of standing water behind dams; tidal power does not entail these negative impacts, because the water has to be retained behind the sluice gates only for brief periods. The few negative environmental impacts of tidal power generation are mainly associated with interference in the normal currents of the water body. In one case, for example, a whale is thought to have died after following some fish through the sluice gates and becoming trapped.

Nova Scotia Power and its partners are among those working on new *in-stream* tidal power technologies. These approaches involve underwater turbines—like underwater windmills—that would eliminate the need to construct a visible dam or sluice across the waterway. As new in-stream technologies are developed, the environmental impacts of tidal power will become even less significant.

Alternatives to Fossil Fuels

Fossil fuels helped drive the Industrial Revolution and create the unprecedented material prosperity we enjoy today. Our global economy is largely powered by fossil fuels: 80% of the world's energy comes from oil, coal, and natural gas, and these three fuels generate two-thirds of the world's electricity. However, these nonrenewable energy sources will not last forever. Oil production is thought to be peaking now, and easily extractable supplies of oil and natural gas may not last half a century more. Moreover, the use of coal, oil, and natural gas entails substantial environmental impacts.

For these reasons, most scientists and energy experts, and many economists and policy makers, accept that we will need to shift from fossil fuels to energy sources that are less easily depleted and gentler on our environment. Developing alternatives to fossil fuels has the added benefit of helping to diversify an economy's mix of energy, lessening price volatility and dependence on foreign fuel imports.

There is a wide range of alternatives to fossil fuels. Most of these energy sources are renewable, and most have less impact on the environment than oil, coal, or natural gas. However, at this time most remain more costly than fossil fuels, at least in the short term, and many depend on technologies that are not yet fully developed. In this chapter we will explore the "conventional" alternatives to fossil fuels; then we will look more closely at some "new renewable" alternatives.

Hydro, nuclear, and biomass are "conventional" alternatives

Three alternative energy sources are currently the most developed and widely used worldwide; they are hydroelectric power, nuclear power, and energy derived from biomass. Each of these well-established energy sources plays substantial roles in the energy and electricity budgets of nations today. We therefore call them "conventional" alternatives to fossil fuels.

Fuelwood and other biomass sources provide 10.0% of the world's energy; nuclear power provides 6.3%; and hydropower provides 2.2%. In some respects, this trio of conventional energy alternatives is an odd collection. They are generally considered to exert less environmental impact than fossil fuels, but more than the "new renewable" alternatives we will discuss later in this chapter. Yet, as you will see, they each involve a complex mix of benefits and drawbacks for human well-being and the environment.

Although their global contributions to overall energy supply are relatively minor, the conventional alternatives to fossil fuels contribute significantly to the generation of electricity. Nuclear and hydropower each account for nearly one-sixth of the world's electricity generation.

Canada's energy mix is somewhat different from that of the rest of the world, because almost 60% of our electricity is generated from hydroelectric power (**FIGURE 13.1**). In the United States, for comparison, it is much more common for electricity to be generated by coal-fired power plants or nuclear energy than by running water. Hydropower is the source of approximately 25% of Canada's total primary energy.

Hydroelectric Power

People worldwide draw more energy from the motion of water than from any other renewable source except biomass. In **hydroelectric power** (or *hydropower*), the kinetic energy of moving water is used to turn turbines and generate electricity.

Modern hydropower uses two approaches

People have long harnessed the power of moving water. Waterwheels spun by river water powered mills in past centuries. Today we utilize the kinetic energy of water in two major ways: with large dams and with "run-of-river" technologies.

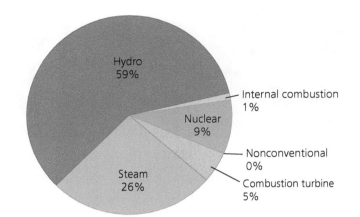

(a) Electricity generation in Canada, by fuel type

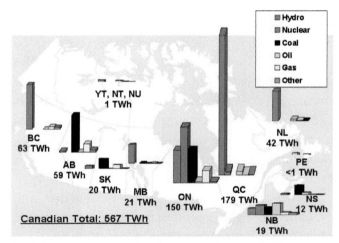

(b) Total power generation by energy type, in 2003

FIGURE 13.1
(a) In Canada we depend heavily on abundant hydropower sources for electricity generation. **(b)** This map shows regional variations in the type of energy source used to generate electricity in Canada; the units are terrawatt hours (TWh).
Source: Energy Information Administration, U.S. Department of Energy, Country Analysis Briefs: Canada, www.eia.doe.gov/emeu/cabs/Canada/Full. html

Most hydroelectric power today comes from impounding water in reservoirs behind large concrete dams that block the flow of river water and then controlling the flow of water through the dam. Because the water is held in reservoirs behind dams, this approach is variously referred to as a *reservoir, storage,* or *impoundment* approach. If you have ever seen the Gardiner Dam on the South Saskatchewan River (Canada's largest hydroelectric dam), the Ottawa-Holden Dam on the Ottawa River (**FIGURE 13.2A**), the Hoover Dam on the Colorado River, or any other large dam, you have seen an impoundment approach being used for hydroelectric power generation.

When reservoir water passes through a dam, it turns the blades of turbines, causing a generator to generate electricity (**FIGURE 13.2B, C**). Electricity generated in the

(a) Beck II Generating Station

(b) Turbine generator

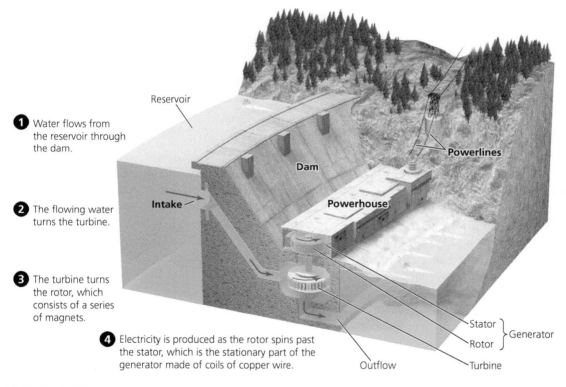

1 Water flows from the reservoir through the dam.

2 The flowing water turns the turbine.

3 The turbine turns the rotor, which consists of a series of magnets.

4 Electricity is produced as the rotor spins past the stator, which is the stationary part of the generator made of coils of copper wire.

Reservoir

Dam

Intake

Powerhouse

Powerlines

Stator ⎱ Generator
Rotor ⎰

Outflow

Turbine

(c) **Hydroelectric power**

FIGURE 13.2   Large dams, such as the Ottawa-Holden Dam on the Ottawa River between Ontario and Québec **(a)**, generate substantial amounts of hydroelectric power. Inside these dams, flowing water is used to turn turbines similar to the one shown here **(b)**. As shown in **(c)**, water is funnelled through a portion of the dam (1) to rotate the turbine (2), which turns rotors containing magnets (3). The spinning rotors generate electricity (4) as their magnets pass coils of copper wire. Electrical current is transmitted through power lines, and the river's water flows out through the base of the dam.

powerhouse of a dam is transmitted to the electric grid by transmission lines, and the water is allowed to flow into the riverbed below the dam to continue downriver. The amount of power generated depends on the distance the water falls and the volume of water released. By storing water in reservoirs, dam operators can ensure a steady and predictable supply of electricity at all times, even during seasons of naturally low river flow.

An alternative to large dams is the **run-of-river** (or *diversion*) approach, which generates electricity without water impoundment and without greatly disrupting the flow of river water. On the one hand, this approach sacrifices the reliability of water flow that the storage approach guarantees, but on the other hand it minimizes many of the negative impacts of large dams. Run-of-river can use various methods, one of which diverts a portion of a river's flow through a pipe or channel, passing it through a powerhouse and then returning it to the river (**FIGURE 13.3**). The pipe or channel can be run along the surface or underground. Another method involves the river

FIGURE 13.3
Run-of-river systems divert a portion of a
river's water for electricity generation. Some
designs involve piping water downhill through
a powerhouse and releasing it downriver, and
some involve using water as it flows over
shallow dams.

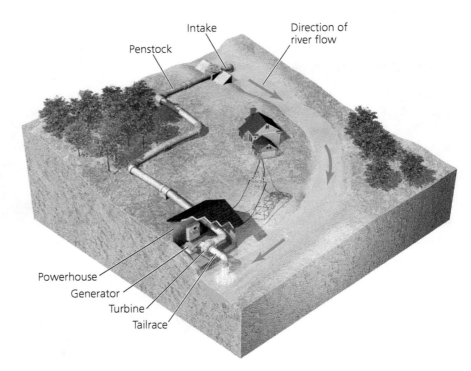

water flowing over a dam small enough not to impede
fish passage, using the water to turn turbines and then
returning the water to the river.

Run-of-river systems are particularly useful in areas
remote from established electrical grids and in regions
without the economic resources to build and maintain
large dams. Run-of-river is often called *small hydro* or
even *micro-hydro* (referring to installations that produce
less than 1000 kW of power), in contrast to the *large
hydro* of traditional hydroelectric dams. Some environmentalists worry that the impacts of run-of-river systems
on water flow and other aspects of the aquatic system are
not sufficiently understood, but the impacts are surely
less than those of large dams.

Hydropower generates relatively little air pollution

The great age of dam building for hydroelectric power
(as well as for flood control and irrigation) began in the
1930s, when the U.S. federal government constructed
dams as public projects. Dam construction in the United
States peaked in 1960, when 3123 dams were completed in
a single year. American engineers subsequently exported
dam-building technologies to the developing world.
Indian Prime Minister Pandit Nehru commented in 1963
that "dams are the temples of modern India," referring to
their central importance in the development of energy
capacity in that nation.

Hydropower now accounts for 2.2% of the world's
energy supply but 16.0% of electricity production (and
considerably more than this in Canada). For nations with
large amounts of river water and the economic resources
to build dams, hydroelectric power has been a keystone
of their development. The largest producing region is
Europe but Eastern Asia, led by China, is rapidly developing its capacity (**FIGURE 13.4**).

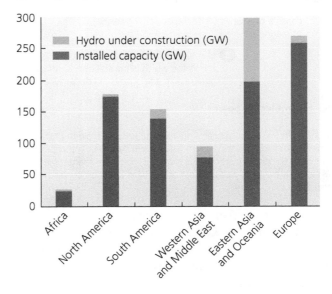

FIGURE 13.4
Europe currently has the highest installed capacity for hydropower,
but Asia—led by China—is rapidly developing its capacity; units are
gigawatts (GW).
Source: Data are for 2009. from International Hydropower Association
Activity Report, *2010.*

Hydropower has two clear advantages over fossil fuels for the production of electricity. First, it is renewable: as long as precipitation falls from the sky and fills rivers and reservoirs, we can use water to turn turbines. The second advantage is cleanliness. Because no combustion is involved, no carbon dioxide or other pollutants are emitted during the production of hydropower. Fossil fuels *are* used in constructing and maintaining dams, and recent evidence indicates that large reservoirs release the greenhouse gas methane as a result of anaerobic decay in deep water. But overall, hydropower creates only a small fraction of the greenhouse gas emissions typical of fossil fuel combustion.

Hydropower is also efficient, with an EROI (*energy returned on investment*) of 10:1 or more, at least as high as any other modern-day energy source. Fossil fuels had higher EROI in the past, but as the cost of reaching remaining deposits has increased, their EROI values have dipped below that of hydropower.

Hydropower has many negative impacts, too

Although it is renewable, efficient, and produces little air pollution, hydropower does have other negative impacts. Damming rivers destroys habitat for wildlife as riparian areas above dam sites are submerged and those below are starved of water. Because water discharge is regulated to optimize electricity generation, the natural flooding cycles of rivers are disrupted. Suppressing floods prevents floodplains from receiving fresh nutrient-laden sediments. Instead, sediments become trapped behind dams, where they gradually fill the reservoir.

Dams also cause **thermal pollution**, because water downstream may become warmer if water levels are kept unnaturally shallow. Moreover, periodic flushes of cold water occur from the release of reservoir water; such thermal shocks, together with habitat alteration, have damaged many native fish populations in dammed waterways. Dams also block the passage of fish and other aquatic creatures, effectively fragmenting the river and reducing biodiversity.

The weight of water in a large reservoir can cause geological impacts, such as earthquakes, particularly where water has seeped into fractures in the bedrock underlying the reservoir. Dam collapses—whether as a result of earthquakes or landslides or from degradation of the construction materials—are regrettably not uncommon, and have resulted in many deaths in the decades since the great surge in large dam construction. These ecological and physical impacts also translate into negative social and economic impacts on local communities.

There has also been recent concern about the generation of greenhouse gases in large hydroelectric reservoirs. As mentioned above, large reservoirs release methane, as well as carbon dioxide, as a result of anaerobic decay in deep water, particularly in warm climates.

The most controversial hydroelectric installation in Canada is the James Bay Project in northern Québec, an extremely complicated, multi-phase project that began in 1970. James Bay has been controversial for environmental, political, social, and economic reasons, as well as being intimately connected with the modern history of Aboriginal land claims in Canada. The project has involved significant river diversions, resulting in the merging of several major watersheds on the eastern shore of the Hudson Bay, from the southern tip of James Bay to Ungava Bay in the north. Just two of these diversions, of the Caniapiscau and Eastmain rivers, inundated about 11 000 km² of boreal forest, with major impacts on water resources in nearby Cree villages.

Additional environmental impacts associated with the James Bay Project have included massive changes to the landscape, seismic tremors, fluctuating water levels, and loss of wetlands, with consequent ecological impacts. The decomposition of organic matter killed as a result of flooding has also proven problematic, and flooding is thought to have contributed to higher levels of methylmercury in local waterways. (*Methylmercury* is a particularly toxic and bioaccumulative form of mercury, which forms in aquatic systems through bacterially mediated processes. These occur most readily in oxygen-poor conditions, which are created by reservoir flooding and the subsequent decay of flooded organic matter.) The river diversions associated with the James Bay Project also have interfered with animal migration patterns (e.g., caribou) and fish spawning habitats (e.g., salmon).

Hydropower may not expand much more

China's recently completed Three Gorges Dam is the world's largest hydroelectric installation. When fully operational, Three Gorges will have 32 generators producing as much electricity as dozens of coal-fired or nuclear plants. The reservoir required the displacement of over a million people, and there are concerns about its ecological impacts.

Hydropower is not likely to expand much more in North America. One reason is that most of the large rivers that offer excellent opportunities for hydropower are already dammed. Another reason is that people have grown more aware of the negative environmental impacts of dams. In some regions residents are resisting dam construction, or even (primarily in the United States) proposing to dismantle some dams and restore river habitats. Hydropower will likely continue to increase substantially in Asia, however, as China develops its capacity.

Nuclear Power

Nuclear power—usable energy extracted from the force that binds atomic nuclei together—occupies a conflicted position in our modern debate over energy. It is free of the air pollution produced by fossil fuel combustion, so it has been put forth as an environmentally friendly alternative to fossil fuels. Yet nuclear power's great promise has been clouded by nuclear weaponry, by the challenge of radioactive waste disposal, and by the long shadow of Chernobyl and other power plant accidents. Public safety concerns and the costs of addressing them have constrained the development and spread of nuclear power in Canada and many other nations.

First developed commercially in the 1950s, nuclear power has expanded 15-fold worldwide since 1970. The United States generates the most electricity from nuclear power—nearly a third of the world's production—followed by France and Japan. Although the United States is the leader in quantity of electricity generated, only about 20% of its total electricity comes from nuclear sources. A number of other nations rely more heavily on nuclear power (TABLE 13.1); France leads the list, obtaining 75% of its electricity from nuclear power. Canada generates approximately 15% of its electricity with nuclear power. The province of Ontario leads the

roots

FISSION

The term **fission** was first used in physics to describe the splitting of a nucleus quite recently—in 1939. This was only a few years after the discovery of neutrons, and during a time when there was frantic scientific and political effort to manufacture and deploy the first atomic bomb. Previously the term had been used to apply to the process of cell division, and it derives much earlier than that from the Latin word *findere*, "to cleave, split, or divide."

nuclear industry in Canada, with about half of the electricity used in the province coming from its 16 operating nuclear generators; Québec and New Brunswick have one operating reactor each.

Fission releases nuclear energy

Strictly defined, *nuclear energy* is the energy that holds together protons and neutrons in the nucleus of an atom. We harness this energy by converting it to thermal energy, which can then be used to generate electricity.

The reaction that drives the release of nuclear energy in power plants is **fission**, the splitting apart of atomic nuclei (FIGURE 13.5). To induce fission, the nuclei of large, heavy atoms, such as uranium or plutonium, are bombarded with neutrons, causing them to break apart. Each split nucleus produces heat, radiation, and multiple

Nation	Nuclear power produced*	Operating plants†	Percentage of electricity from nuclear power*
United States	796.8	104	20.2
France	390.0	58	75.2
Japan	260.1	54	28.9
Russia	153.0	32	17.8
South Korea	141.1	21	34.8
Germany	127.6	17	26.1
Canada	85.3	18	14.8
Ukraine	77.8	15	48.6
China	70.1	13	1.9
United Kingdom	62.9	19	17.9
World Total	2559.7	441	14.0

Table 13.1   Top Producers of Nuclear Power

*In billion kilowatt-hours (BkWh) for 2009.

†As of August 2010. Data from the Nuclear Energy Institute (www.nei.org/).

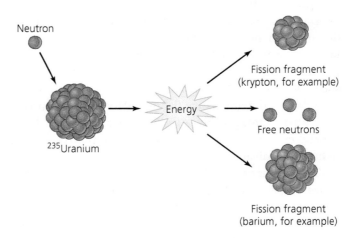

FIGURE 13.5

In nuclear fission, an atom of fissionable material (in this case, ^{235}U) is bombarded with a neutron. The collision splits the uranium atom into smaller atoms and releases two or three neutrons, radiation, and energy. The neutrons can continue to split other uranium atoms in a chain reaction. Engineers at nuclear plants use control rods to absorb excess neutrons and regulate the rate of the reaction.

neutrons, as well as the leftover fragments of the original nucleus. The emitted neutrons then bombard other nearby *fissionable* (or *fissile*) atomic nuclei, resulting in a self-sustaining chain reaction.

If not controlled, this chain reaction becomes a runaway process that releases enormous amounts of energy; it is responsible for the explosive power of a nuclear bomb. Inside a nuclear power plant, however, fission is controlled so that, on average, only one of the two or three neutrons emitted with each fission event goes on to induce another fission event. In this way, the chain reaction maintains a constant output of energy at a controlled rate.

Enriched uranium is used as fuel in nuclear reactors

We generate electricity from nuclear power by controlled fission in **nuclear reactors**, facilities contained within nuclear power plants. This is just one step in a longer process called the *nuclear fuel cycle*, which begins when the naturally occurring element uranium is mined from underground deposits.

Uranium minerals are uncommon, and uranium ore is in finite supply; it must be mined, which is why nuclear power is generally considered to be a nonrenewable energy source. However, Canada is particularly rich in uranium resources, and currently produces about one-third of the world's uranium. Canada also has developed reactor technologies that are used in many countries.

Uranium is useful for nuclear power because it is radioactive. Radioactive isotopes, or *radioisotopes*, emit subatomic particles and high-energy radiation as they decay into lighter radioisotopes, until they ultimately become stable isotopes. The isotope uranium-235 decays into a series of daughter isotopes, eventually forming stable lead-207. Each radioisotope decays at a rate determined by that isotope's *half-life*, the time it takes for half of the atoms to give off radiation and decay.

Over 99% of the uranium in nature occurs as the isotope uranium-238; uranium-235 (with three fewer neutrons) makes up less than 1% of the total. Because ^{238}U does not emit enough neutrons to maintain a chain reaction when it splits, ^{235}U is more commonly used for commercial nuclear power. Mined uranium ore therefore must be processed or *enriched*, so that the concentration of ^{235}U is at least 3%. The enriched uranium is formed into pellets of uranium dioxide (UO_2), which are then incorporated into *fuel rods* (**FIGURE 13.6**) that are used in nuclear reactors.

After several years in a reactor, the uranium fuel will have decayed to the point where it can no longer generate

FIGURE 13.6
Enriched uranium fuel is formed into pellets and then packaged into fuel rods, shown here. The fuel rods are encased in metal and inserted into the cores of nuclear reactors.

adequate energy, and must be replaced with new fuel. In some countries (not Canada and the United States), the spent fuel is reprocessed to recover what usable energy may be left. Most spent fuel, however, is disposed of as radioactive waste.

Fission takes place in nuclear power plants

The neutrons bombarding uranium fuel in a reactor are slowed down with a substance called a *moderator*, most often water. As fission proceeds, it becomes necessary to soak up the excess neutrons produced when uranium nuclei divide, so that on average only a single neutron from each nucleus goes on to split another nucleus. For this purpose, *control rods*, made of a material that absorbs neutrons, are placed into the reactor among the fuel rods. Engineers move these control rods into and out of the water to maintain the fission reaction at the desired rate.

All this takes place within the reactor core and is the first step in the electricity-generating process of a nuclear power plant (**FIGURE 13.7**). The reactor core is housed within a reactor vessel, and the vessel, steam generator, and associated plumbing are protected within a containment building. Containment buildings, with their metre-thick concrete and steel walls, are constructed to prevent leaks of radioactivity due to accidents or natural catastrophes such as earthquakes.

Instead of using ^{235}U-enriched fuel, some reactors (including the Canadian CANDU reactor) are designed to make use of ^{238}U and other fissile materials present in natural (unenriched) ores. Some of these are so-called

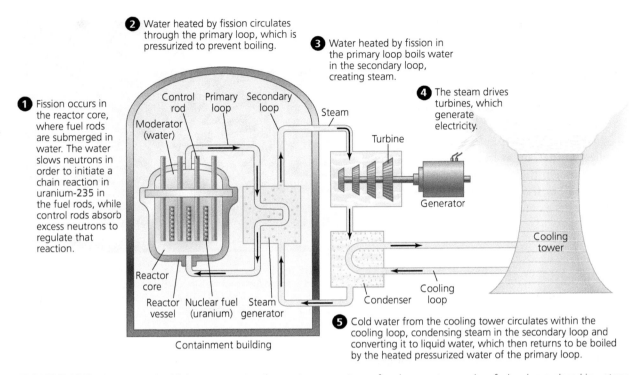

FIGURE 13.7   In a pressurized light water reactor, the most common type of nuclear reactor, uranium fuel rods are placed in water, a moderator that slows neutrons so fission can occur (1). Control rods are moved into and out of the reactor core to absorb excess neutrons and regulate the chain reaction. Water heated by fission circulates through the primary loop (2) and warms water in the secondary loop, which turns to steam (3). Steam drives turbines to generate electricity (4). The steam is then cooled in the cooling tower by water from an adjacent water body and returns to the containment building (5) to be heated again in the primary loop.

breeder reactors, which generate new fissile material at a faster rate than they use it up. Because 99% of all uranium is ^{238}U, breeder reactors make better use of fuel, produce less waste for a given amount of energy generation, and eliminate the costly necessity to enrich nuclear fuels. However, breeder reactors are more expensive to construct than conventional reactors, and some technologies may be more susceptible to explosive accidents.

Nuclear power generates little air pollution

Nuclear power plants generate electricity without creating air pollution from stack emissions. In contrast, combusting coal, oil, or natural gas emits sulphur dioxide that contributes to acidic deposition and particulate air pollution, as well as greenhouse gases.

Scientists from the International Atomic Energy Agency (IAEA) have calculated that nuclear power produces emissions up to 150 times lower than those from fossil fuel combustion. They conducted a "cradle-to-grave" analysis that included emissions not just from power generation, but also from the mining, processing, and transport of fuel; manufacturing of equipment; construction of power plants; disposal of wastes; and

decommissioning of plants. The results showed that, per unit of energy produced, fossil fuels produce much higher emissions than either renewable energy sources or nuclear energy.

Because the IAEA is responsible for promoting nuclear energy, critics point out that the agency is motivated to show nuclear power in a favourable light. However, few experts would argue with the conclusion that nuclear and renewable energy sources are cleaner than fossil fuels.

Nuclear power has additional environmental advantages over fossil fuels—coal in particular. Because uranium generates far more power than coal by weight or volume, less of it needs to be mined, so uranium mining (which is commonly done in underground mines) causes less damage to landscapes and generates less solid waste than coal mining (which is often, though not always, done at the surface by strip-mining). Moreover, in the course of normal operation, nuclear power plants are safer for workers than coal-fired plants.

Nuclear power also has serious drawbacks, though. One is that the waste it produces is radioactive; it must be handled with great care, and disposed of in a way that minimizes danger to present and future generations. A second major concern is that if an accident occurs at a power plant, or if a plant is sabotaged, or if a government were to use its nuclear capabilities for aggressive purposes,

Environmental Impacts of Coal-Fired and Nuclear Power		
Type of Impact	Coal	Nuclear
Land and ecosystem disturbance from mining	Extensive, on surface or underground	Less extensive
Greenhouse gas emissions	Considerable emissions	None from plant operation; much less than coal over the entire life cycle
Other air pollutants	Sulphur dioxide, nitrogen oxides, particulate matter, and other pollutants	No pollutant emissions
Radioactive emissions	No appreciable emissions	No appreciable emissions during normal operation; possibility of emissions during severe accident
Occupational health among workers	More known health problems and fatalities	Fewer known health problems and fatalities
Health impacts on nearby residents	Air pollution impairs health	No appreciable known health impacts under normal operation
Effects of accident or sabotage	No widespread effects	Potentially catastrophic widespread effects
Solid waste	More generated	Less generated
Radioactive waste	None	Radioactive waste generated
Fuel supplies remaining	Should last several hundred more years	Uncertain; supplies could last for a longer or shorter time than coal supplies

FIGURE 13.8 Coal-fired power plants and nuclear power plants pose very different risks and impacts to human health and the environment. This chart compares the major impacts of each mode of electricity generation. The more severe impacts are indicated by red boxes.

the consequences can be catastrophic. Given this mix of advantages and disadvantages (**FIGURE 13.8**), many governments (although not necessarily most citizens) have judged the good to outweigh the bad, and today the world has 436 operating nuclear plants in 30 nations.

Nuclear power poses small risk of large accidents

Although nuclear power poses fewer chronic health risks than does fossil fuel combustion, the possibility of catastrophic accidents has spawned a great deal of public anxiety over nuclear power. As plants around the world

weighing the issues

CHOOSE YOUR RISK

Given the choice of living next to a nuclear power plant or living next to a coal-fired power plant, which would you choose? What kinds of information would inform your choice?

age, they require more maintenance. New concerns have also surfaced that nuclear plants could become targets for terrorism, or radioactive material could be stolen and used in terrorist attacks. This possibility is especially worrisome in countries of the former Soviet Union, where former nuclear sites have gone without adequate security for years.

Three significant events have been most influential in shaping public opinion about nuclear energy. They are Three Mile Island, Chernobyl, and Fukushima Dai-ichi.

Three Mile Island The first took place at the Three Mile Island plant in Pennsylvania, where in 1979 the United States experienced its most serious nuclear power plant accident. Through a combination of mechanical failure and human error, coolant water drained from the reactor vessel, temperatures rose inside the reactor core, and metal surrounding the uranium fuel rods began to melt, releasing radiation. This process, called a **meltdown**, proceeded through half of one reactor core at Three Mile Island. Area residents stood ready to be evacuated, but fortunately most radiation remained trapped inside the containment building.

The accident was brought under control within days, the damaged reactor was shut down, and a multibillion-dollar cleanup lasted for years. Three Mile Island is regarded as a near-miss; the emergency could have been far worse had the meltdown proceeded through the entire stock of uranium fuel, or had the containment building not contained the radiation. Although residents have shown no significant health impacts in the years since, the event put safety concerns squarely on the map for both citizens and policy makers.

Chernobyl   In 1986 an explosion at the Chernobyl plant in Ukraine (then part of the Soviet Union) caused the most severe nuclear power plant accident the world has yet seen. Engineers had turned off safety systems to conduct tests. Human error, combined with technological failures and unsafe reactor design, led to explosions that destroyed the reactor and sent clouds of radioactive debris into the atmosphere. For 10 days radiation escaped from the plant while emergency crews risked their lives (some later died from radiation exposure) to put out fires. Most residents of the surrounding countryside remained at home for these 10 days, exposed to radiation, before the Soviet government belatedly began evacuating more than 100 000 people.

In the months and years afterwards, workers erected a gigantic concrete sarcophagus around the demolished reactor, scrubbed buildings and roads, and removed irradiated materials (FIGURE 13.9). However, the landscape for at least 30 km around the plant remains contaminated today. An international team plans to build a larger sarcophagus around the original one, which is seriously deteriorating.

The accident killed 31 people directly and sickened or caused cancer in thousands more. Exact numbers are uncertain because of inadequate data and the difficulty of determining long-term radiation effects. Health authorities estimate that most of the over 4000 cases of thyroid cancer since diagnosed in people who were children at the time resulted from the accident. Estimates for the total number of cancer cases attributable to Chernobyl, past and future, vary widely, ranging from several thousand, on the conservative side, to as many as 200 000 fatal cancers.

Atmospheric currents carried radioactive fallout from Chernobyl across much of the Northern Hemisphere, particularly Ukraine, Belarus, and parts of Russia and Europe (FIGURE 13.10). Fallout was greatest where rainstorms brought radioisotopes down from the radioactive cloud. Parts of Sweden received high amounts of fallout, and the accident reinforced the Swedish public's fears about nuclear power. A survey taken after the event asked, "Do you think it was good or bad for the country to invest in nuclear energy?" The proportion of respondents answering "bad" jumped from 25% before Chernobyl to 47% afterward.

(a) The Chernobyl sarcophagus

(b) Technicians measuring radiation

FIGURE 13.9
The world's worst nuclear power plant accident unfolded in 1986 at Chernobyl, in present-day Ukraine. As part of the extensive cleanup operation, the destroyed reactor was encased in a massive concrete sarcophagus **(a)** to contain further radiation leakage. Technicians scoured the landscape surrounding the plant **(b)**, measuring radiation levels, removing soil, and scrubbing roads and buildings.

Fukushima Dai-ichi   On Friday, March 11, 2011, a megathrust earthquake of magnitude 9.0—one of the largest earthquakes ever measured—struck in a subduction zone just off the northeast coast of Tōhoku, Japan. The earthquake, devastating in its own right, also generated a massive tsunami that swept ashore, killing more than 15 000 people, injuring many more, and wiping whole villages off the map.

The tsunami also inundated the Fukushima Dai-ichi power plant, located on the coast of Japan, not far from the earthquake's epicentre. (Nuclear power plants are commonly located near the ocean or large lakes, because they require large volumes of water to use as coolant fluid.) The nuclear reactors at Fukushima Dai-ichi shut down

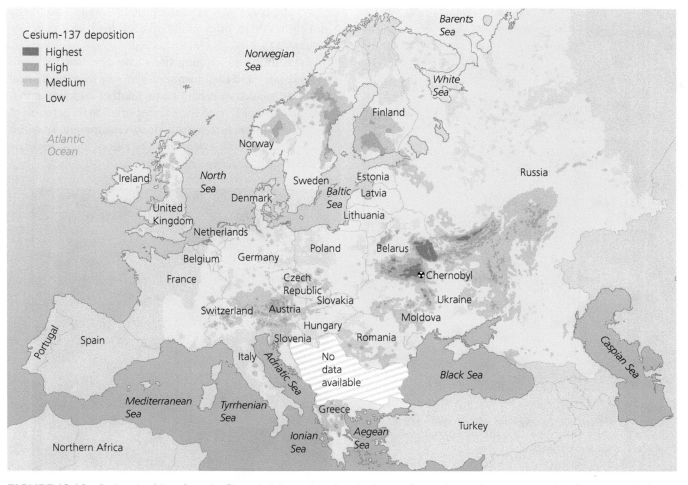

FIGURE 13.10 Radioactive fallout from the Chernobyl disaster was deposited across Europe in complex patterns resulting from atmospheric currents and rainstorms in the days following the accident. Darker colours in this map of ^{137}Cs deposition indicate higher levels of radioactivity. Although Chernobyl produced 100 times more fallout than the U.S. bombs dropped on Hiroshima and Nagasaki in World War II, it was distributed over a much wider area. Thus, levels of contamination outside of Ukraine, Belarus, and western Russia were relatively low.   *Source: Data from Swiss Agency for Development and Cooperation, Bern, 2005.*

automatically as a result of the earthquake, as they were intended to do; however, fission continues in the reactor cores, requiring constant cooling to maintain a manageable temperature. The back-up generators that should have kept the coolant fluids circulating were flooded and incapacitated by the tsunami. The subsequent overheating of the reactor cores set off a series of fires, explosions, and core meltdowns, accompanied by several releases of radioactive materials (**FIGURE 13.11**). These events required significant interventions, and the radioactive releases resulted in public health warnings; for example, food grown in the area had to be taken off the market.

The International Atomic Energy Agency introduced a scale for the measurement of nuclear accidents, called the *International Nuclear and Radiological Event Scale.* The scale ranges from 0 (a "deviation" from normal procedures, with no safety significance), through 1–3 ("incidents" of increasing severity) and 4–7 ("accidents"). Three Mile Island is one of several events given a rating of

5, an "accident with wider consequences," which includes limited release of radioactive material and severe damage to the reactor core. Both Chernobyl and Fukushima (as a whole, although each reactor was given its own individual rating) have been rated as 7, the most severe level on this scale. A level 7 accident involves "major release of radioactive material with widespread health and environment effects, requiring implementation of planned and extended counter-measures."

Radioactive waste disposal remains problematic

Even if nuclear power generation could be made completely safe, and accidents like those at Chernobyl and Fukushima Dai-ichi were completely avoidable, we would be left with the conundrum of what to do with spent fuel rods and other radioactive waste. Recall that fission

FIGURE 13.11
This photo from March, 2011, shows some of the nuclear reactor buildings at Fukushima Dai-ichi that were damaged by the massive Tōhoku earthquake and tsunami.

utilizes ^{235}U as fuel, leaving as waste the 97% of uranium that is ^{238}U. This ^{238}U, as well as all irradiated material and equipment that is no longer being used, is radioactive and must be disposed of in a location where radiation will not escape. Because the half-lives of uranium, plutonium, and many other radioisotopes are far longer than human lifetimes, this *high-level waste* will continue emitting radiation for many thousands of years. Thus, radioactive waste must be placed in unusually stable and secure locations and monitored for many, many years to protect future generations.

Currently, nuclear waste from power generation is held in temporary storage at nuclear power plants in Canada and other places around the world. Spent fuel rods are sunken in pools of cooling water to minimize radiation leakage (FIGURE 13.12A). However, plants have only a limited capacity for this type of on-site storage.

FIGURE 13.12
Spent uranium fuel rods are stored on-site at nuclear power plants and will likely remain at these scattered sites until a central repository for commercial radioactive waste is fully developed. Spent fuel rods are most often kept in "wet storage" in pools of water **(a)**, which keep them cool and reduce radiation release. Alternatively, radioactive waste may be kept in "dry storage" in thick-walled casks layered with lead, concrete, and steel **(b)**.

Many plants are now expanding their storage capacity by storing waste in thick casks of steel, lead, and concrete (FIGURE 13.12B).

In addition to keeping the waste dry, isolated from groundwater and the biosphere, and safe from geological disruptions such as earthquakes, another concern is that nuclear waste will need to be transported to its permanent repository. Because this would involve shipment by rail or truck, many people worry that the risk of an accident or of sabotage is unacceptably high.

(a) Wet storage

(b) Dry storage

Storing waste at many dispersed sites creates a large number of potential hazards, so it is desirable to send the waste to a central repository that can be heavily guarded. Even transporting high-level waste to a central repository poses risks, however; it is a dangerous cargo and derailments, accidents, and terrorist attacks are all concerns.

Sweden has established a single repository for low-level waste near one power plant, and is searching for a single disposal site deep within bedrock for spent fuel rods and other high-level waste. In the United States, a multi-year search for a disposal site homed in on Yucca Mountain, in the desert of southern Nevada; however, the project is now all but dead as a result of political delays and funding cutbacks. No site has yet been chosen in Canada, but at a research facility in Lac du Bonnet, Manitoba scientists are testing proposals for long-term storage deep underground in the stable, ancient crystalline rocks of the Canadian Shield. This approach is called **geological isolation** (FIGURE 13.13), and it is the disposal method of choice among nations that are seeking permanent repositories for high-level waste.

Multiple dilemmas have slowed nuclear power's growth

Dogged by concerns over waste disposal, safety, and cost overruns, nuclear power's growth has slowed. Many plants have been much more expensive than anticipated, and public anxiety in the wake of Chernobyl has made utilities less willing to invest in new plants. In addition, some plants have aged more quickly than expected because of problems that were underestimated, such as corrosion in coolant pipes. Decommissioning a plant can sometimes be more expensive than the original construction.

As a result of these economic issues, electricity from nuclear power today remains more expensive than electricity from coal and other sources. Nonetheless, nuclear power remains one of the few currently viable alternatives to fossil fuels with which we can generate large amounts of electricity in short order.

Many experts predict nuclear power will decrease because three-quarters of Western Europe's capacity is

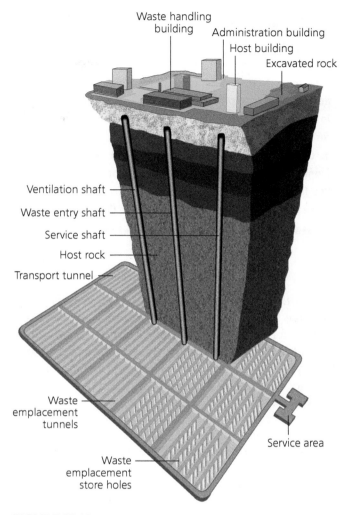

FIGURE 13.13
There is no permanent repository for high-level radioactive waste in Canada. Scientific testing of various proposals is ongoing. At a site similar to the Lac du Bonnet research facility in Manitoba, waste could be buried in a network of tunnels deep underground in the stable, crystalline rocks of the Canadian Shield, as shown here.

scheduled to be retired by 2030, and Germany, Belgium, and Sweden have declared an intention to phase out nuclear power altogether. Asian nations, in contrast, are adding nuclear capacity. China, India, and South Korea are expanding their nuclear programs to help power their rapidly growing economies. Japan is so reliant on imported oil that it is eager to diversify its energy options. Asia hosts two-thirds of the most recent nuclear plants to go into operation, and more than half of the plants now under construction.

Fusion remains a dream

For as long as scientists and engineers have generated power from nuclear fission, they have tried to figure out how they might use nuclear fusion instead. **Fusion**—the

weighing the issues

MORE NUCLEAR POWER?

Do you think Canada as a whole, or your province in particular, should expand its nuclear power program? Why, or why not?

roots

FUSION

The term **fusion** was applied to the merging of two atomic nuclei by physicists researching these processes in the 1930s and 1940s. It comes from the Latin word *fusus*, "to spread out or flow," and it has the same root as the English word *fuse*, "to melt." Both probably come from a much earlier Indo-European root *gheu-*, meaning "to flow or pour." Interestingly, this root may also have something to do with the origins of the English word *god*.

---

process that drives our Sun's vast output of energy and the force behind hydrogen or thermonuclear bombs—involves forcing together the small nuclei of lightweight elements under extremely high temperature and pressure. The hydrogen isotopes deuterium and tritium can be fused together to create helium, releasing a neutron and a tremendous amount of energy.

Overcoming the mutually repulsive forces of protons in a controlled manner is difficult, and fusion typically requires extremely high temperatures. Researchers have not yet developed "cold" fusion for commercial power generation; fusion experiments still require scientists to input more energy than they produce from the process. Fusion's potentially huge payoffs, though, make many scientists eager to keep trying.

If one day we were to find a way to control fusion in a reactor, we could produce vast amounts of energy using water as a source of hydrogen for fuel. The process would create only low-level radioactive wastes, without polluting emissions or the risk of dangerous accidents, sabotage, or weapons proliferation. A consortium of industrialized nations, including Canada, is collaborating to build a prototype fusion reactor called the International Thermonuclear Experimental Reactor (ITER) in southern France. Even if this multibillion-dollar effort succeeds, however, power from fusion seems likely to remain a dream until many years in the future.

Traditional Biomass Energy

Although technologies for many renewable energy sources are still early in their stages of development, biomass energy is widely used. Worldwide, it is a "conventional" alternative to fossil fuels. Indeed, biomass was the very first source of energy used by our human ancestors, whose mastery of fire represents one of the first great steps toward the control of the environment. Today, traditional biomass accounts for about 10% of energy use globally.

Biomass energy means different things to different users

When people use the term **biomass energy**, they can mean very different things. To a subsistence farmer in Africa, biomass energy means cutting wood from trees or collecting livestock manure and burning it to heat and cook for her family. To an industrialized farmer in Saskatchewan, biomass energy might mean shipping his grain to a high-tech refinery that converts it into liquid fuel to run automobiles.

People harness biomass energy from many types of plant matter, including wood from trees, charcoal (which is actually charred wood, not coal), and agricultural crops, as well as combustible animal waste products such as cattle manure. Fossil fuels are not considered biomass energy sources because their organic matter has not been part of living organisms for millions of years and has undergone considerable chemical alteration.

Traditional biomass sources are widely used in the developing world

Over 1 billion people still use wood from trees as their principal energy source. In developing nations, especially in rural areas, families gather fuelwood to burn in their homes for heating and cooking (FIGURE 13.14). In these nations, the direct combustion of fuelwood, charcoal, and manure accounts for fully 35% of energy use—in the poorest nations, up to 90%.

Fuelwood and other traditional biomass sources constitute nearly 80% of all renewable energy used worldwide. Many new approaches and technologies are being developed to make biomass energy more efficient and most sustainable, but these still constitute a very small proportion of overall energy use. As developing nations industrialize, fossil fuels are replacing traditional energy sources (FIGURE 13.15); as a result, traditional biomass use is growing more slowly worldwide than overall energy use. However, the total use of fuelwood in the developing world continues to increase, and the International Energy Agency estimates that by the year 2030, 2.6 billion people will be using traditional fuels for heating and cooking in unsustainable ways.

Traditional biomass energy has environmental pros and cons

Biomass energy has one overarching environmental benefit: It is essentially *carbon-neutral*, releasing no net carbon into the atmosphere. Although burning biomass emits plenty of carbon, it is simply the carbon that photosynthesis had pulled from the atmosphere to create the biomass in the first place. That is, the carbon that biomass combustion emits is balanced by the carbon that photosynthesis had sequestered within the biomass just years, months, or weeks before. Therefore, when we replace fossil fuels with bioenergy, we reduce net carbon flux to the atmosphere, helping to mitigate global climate change.

However, this holds only if biomass sources are not overharvested. Harvesting fuelwood at an unsustainably rapid rate leads to deforestation, soil erosion, and desertification, damaging landscapes, diminishing biodiversity, and impoverishing human societies. Deforestation increases the carbon flux to the atmosphere, because less vegetation means less carbon uptake by plants for photosynthesis. In arid regions that are heavily populated and support meagre woodlands, fuelwood harvesting can have enormous impacts; such is the case with many regions of Africa and Asia. Burning fuelwood and other biomass in traditional ways for cooking and heating also leads to health hazards from indoor air pollution.

FIGURE 13.14
Over a billion people in developing countries rely on fuelwood for heating and cooking. Wood cut from trees remains the major source of biomass energy used in the world today. In theory, biomass is renewable; in practice, it may not be renewable if forests are overharvested.

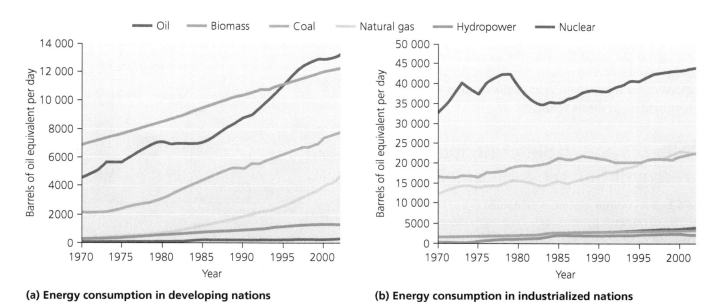

(a) Energy consumption in developing nations

(b) Energy consumption in industrialized nations

FIGURE 13.15 Energy consumption patterns vary greatly between developing nations **(a)** and wealthier industrialized nations, here represented by nations of the Organisation for Economic Cooperation and Development (OECD) **(b)**. Note the large role that traditional biomass (primarily fuelwood) plays in supplying energy to developing countries. Note also that the y axes differ; people in developing nations consume far less energy than those in industrialized nations. *Source: Data from Energy Information Administration, U.S. Department of Energy.*

"New" Renewable Energy Sources

Next we will explore a group of alternative energy sources that are often called the "new renewables." These include energy from sunlight, wind, Earth's geothermal heat, ocean water, and hydrogen, as well as new technologies for biomass energy. Most of these energy sources are not truly new; they are as old as our planet, and people have used them for millennia. They are referred to as "new" because they are not yet used on a wide scale in our modern industrial society. These energy sources are harnessed using technologies that are still in a rapid phase of development, and they will likely come to play a much larger role in the future.

There are three major applications for new renewables in the world's energy market today:

- Power generation (using wind, solar, and other energy sources to generate electricity)
- Space heating (using solar or terrestrial energy sources to heat buildings or factories) and *district heating/cooling* (distributing heated or cooled air to many buildings throughout a community or urban area)
- Fuel (using hydrogen fuels, or using crops, crop residues, or waste materials to manufacture ethanol and biodiesel for use in transportation)[2]

All of these applications are very important in Canada, and promising alternative energy resources are available for all three. Electricity generation powers our modern lifestyle and industry; space heating is important in our northern climate; and fuel for transportation is vital, given the need for mobility in our large country. Energy solutions and new technologies for these applications differ from one region of the country to another, depending on available resources.

"New" renewable contributions are small but growing quickly

As a global community, we obtain only half of one percent (0.5%) of our energy from new renewable energy sources. Only 18% of our electricity worldwide comes from renewable energy, and traditional "large hydro" accounts for nearly 90% of this. In Canada, only about 6% of electricity generation comes from renewable sources *other* than traditional large hydro (TABLE 13.2). Most non–large hydro renewable electricity generation in Canada now comes from wind, followed by small hydro (run-of-river) installations and biomass.

Table 13.2 Renewable* Generation Capacity in Canada† (2009)	
Technology	**Installed capacity (MW)**
Wind	3549
Small hydro	2000
Solar PV	95
Biomass	1628
Landfill gas	5
Geothermal	1 (experimental)
Tidal energy	20

*Not including large hydro

†Data sources: Canadian Wind Energy Association (www.canwea.ca); International Small Hydro Atlas (www.small-hydro.com); Canadian Solar Industries Association (www.cansia.ca); Pembina Institute (www.pembina.org); Centre for Energy (www.centreforenergy.com); Canadian Geothermal Energy Association (www.cangea.ca); Nova Scotia Power (www.nspower.ca).

Although they comprise only a minuscule proportion of our energy budget, the new renewable energy sources are growing at much faster rates than conventional energy sources. Over the past three decades, solar, wind, and geothermal energy sources have grown far faster than the overall energy supply (FIGURE 13.16). The leader in growth is wind power, which has expanded by nearly 50% *each year* since the 1970s. Because these sources started from such low levels of use, however, it will take them some time to catch up to conventional sources. For instance, the absolute amount of energy added by a 50% increase in wind power is still far less than the amount added by just a 1% increase in oil, coal, or natural gas.

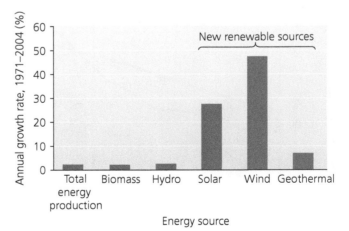

FIGURE 13.16
Globally, the "new" renewable energy sources are growing substantially faster than the total primary energy supply. Solar power has grown by 28% each year since 1971, and wind power has grown by 48% each year. Because these sources began from such low starting levels, however, their overall contribution to our energy supply is still small.
Source: Data from International Energy Agency Statistics, 2007.

Use of new renewables has been expanding quickly because of growing concerns over diminishing fossil fuel supplies (causing both high prices and national security concerns) and the substantial environmental impacts of fossil fuel combustion. Unlike fossil fuels, renewable sources are inexhaustible on timescales relevant to human societies. Advances in technology are also making it easier and less expensive to harness renewable energy sources. Developing renewables can diversify an economy's mix of energy, lowering price volatility and protecting against supply restrictions.

New energy sources also can create employment opportunities and sources of income and property tax for communities, especially in rural areas passed over by other economic development. Developing technologies require more labour per unit of energy output than do established technologies, and it has been calculated that photovoltaic (PV) solar, wind, and biomass energy implementation supports more jobs than natural gas and coal, per unit of energy generated. This means that shifting to renewable energy could actually support more employment than remaining with a fossil fuel economy.[3]

Rapid growth in renewable energy sectors seems likely to continue as population and consumption grow, global energy demand expands, fossil fuel supplies decline, and people demand cleaner environments. More governments, utilities, corporations, and consumers are now promoting and using renewable energy, and, as a result, the prices of renewables are falling.

The transition won't happen overnight

We cannot switch to renewable energy sources overnight, because there are technological, economic, and social barriers. Currently, most renewables lack adequate technological development and infrastructure. However, rapid advances in recent years suggest that most remaining barriers are political. For decades, research and development of renewable sources have received far less in subsidies, tax breaks, and other incentives from governments than have conventional sources. For example, in the United States, by one estimate, of the $150 billion in federal government subsidies provided to nuclear, solar, and wind power in the past half century, the nuclear industry received 96%, solar received 3%, and wind less than 1%.

The funding situation has not been much different in Canada (FIGURE 13.17). As recently as 2006, the Report of the National Advisory Panel on Sustainable Energy Science and Technology[4] included the somewhat surprising statement that "renewable and nuclear technologies

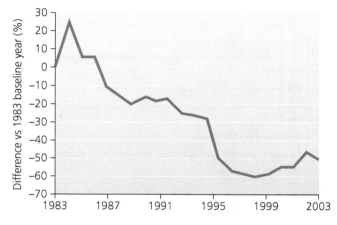

FIGURE 13.17
Federal funding for energy research and development (R&D) has plummeted in Canada over the past 20 years. Some of the gap has been filled by increases in funding from provinces and the private sector. Of federal energy R&D funds, a very small proportion has gone to the development of alternative energy technologies, primarily nuclear.

were not considered by the Panel to be key priorities for a national energy science and technology effort."

In light of continuing short-term profits and unclear policy signals, companies have not been eager to invest in the transition from fossil fuels to renewable energy. Under these circumstances, our best hope may be for a gradual shift driven largely by economic supply and demand. If the transition proceeds too slowly—if we wait for the market to do its work, without government encouragement—then fossil fuel supplies could dwindle faster than we are able to develop new sources, and we could find our economies disrupted and our environment highly degraded. Encouraging the development of renewable energy alternatives holds promise for a vigorous and sustainable energy economy without the environmental impacts of fossil fuels.

Biofuels and Biopower

As discussed earlier, biomass is widely used as a traditional energy source, especially in the developing world. Today biomass energy sources are becoming increasingly diverse and innovative (TABLE 13.3), providing great potential for addressing our energy challenges.

Biomass can be processed to make vehicle fuels

An important use of biomass energy is for conversion into **biofuels**. The two principal types of biofuels developed

Table 13.3 New Sources of Biomass Energy

Biofuels for powering vehicles

- Corn grown for ethanol
- *Bagasse* (sugarcane residue) grown for ethanol
- Soybeans, rapeseed (canola), and other crops grown for biodiesel
- Used cooking oil for biodiesel
- Plant matter treated with enzymes to produce cellulosic ethanol
- Algae fuels

Biopower for generating electricity

- Crop residues (such as cornstalks) burned at power plants
- Forestry residues (such as wood waste from logging) burned at power plants
- Processing wastes (such as solid or liquid waste from sawmills, pulp mills, and paper mills) burned at power plants
- "Landfill gas" burned at power plants
- Livestock waste from feedlots for gas from anaerobic digesters
- Organic components of municipal solid waste from landfills

FIGURE 13.18

An increasing proportion of the corn crop in Canada, as in the United States, is used to produce ethanol. Brazil produces most of the rest of the world's ethanol, from *bagasse* (sugarcane residue). Production of ethanol in Canada and worldwide has grown rapidly in the last decade.

so far are *ethanol* (for gasoline engines) and *biodiesel* (for diesel engines).

Ethanol is the alcohol that is in beer, wine, and liquor. It is produced as a biofuel by fermenting biomass, generally from carbohydrate-rich crops, in a process similar to brewing beer. The carbohydrates contained in the plants are converted to sugars and then to ethanol. Ethanol is now widely added to gasoline in the United States to reduce automotive emissions, spurred by the 1990 U.S. Clean Air Act. In 2008 in the United States, more than 9.2 billion litres of ethanol were produced, mostly from corn (**FIGURE 13.18**). The total production capacity for ethanol in Canada, as of 2009, was approximately 1.4 billion litres.

Any vehicle with a gasoline engine runs well on gasoline blended with up to 10% ethanol. Many automakers are now producing *flexible-fuel vehicles* that run on E-85, a mix of 85% ethanol and 15% gasoline. Few gas stations offer E-85, so drivers generally are forced to fill these cars with conventional gasoline; however, increasing infrastructure for ethanol will change this. In Brazil, for many years, sugarcane residue has been crushed to make *bagasse*, a material that is then used to make ethanol. Half of all new Brazilian cars are flexible-fuel vehicles, and ethanol from sugarcane accounts for 40% of all automotive fuel that Brazil's drivers use.

Vehicles with diesel engines can run on **biodiesel**, produced from vegetable oil mixed with small amounts of ethanol or methanol (wood alcohol). In Canada and in Europe, where most biodiesel is used, rapeseed (canola)

oil is the oil of choice, whereas U.S. biodiesel producers use mostly soybean oil. Biodiesel producers can even utilize animal fats and used grease and cooking oil from restaurants.

Most frequently, biodiesel is mixed with conventional *petrodiesel* (petroleum-based diesel fuel); a 20% biodiesel mix (called B20) is common today. To run on straight vegetable oil, a diesel engine needs to be modified. Although the parts needed for these modifications can be bought for as little as $800, it remains to be seen whether using straight vegetable oil might entail further costs, such as reduced longevity or greater engine maintenance. Biodiesel cuts down on emissions compared with petrodiesel (**FIGURE 13.19**). Its fuel economy is almost as good, and it costs just slightly more, at today's oil prices. It is also nontoxic and biodegradable.

Growing crops specifically to produce ethanol or biodiesel may not be sustainable, so researchers are refining some new techniques for biofuel production. So-called second-generation biofuel technologies use enzymes to produce ethanol from the cellulose that gives structure to all plant material. If we can produce this *cellulosic ethanol* in commercially feasible ways, ethanol could be made from low-value crop waste (indigestible residues, such as corn stalks and husks), rather than from high-value crops (**FIGURE 13.20A**).

Other research projects are underway that aim to produce biofuels from algae, called third-generation biofuels. Lipids and carbohydrates from several species of photosynthetic algae can be converted into a variety of biofuels. Algae can be grown for the purpose in open ponds or in closed transparent tubes called *photobioreactors* (**FIGURE 13.20B**). Algae grow much faster than terrestrial crops, can be harvested every other day, and

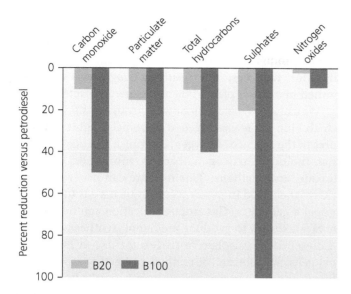

FIGURE 13.19

Burning biodiesel in a diesel engine emits less pollution than burning conventional petroleum-based diesel. Shown are the percentage reductions in several major automotive pollutants that one can attain by using B20 (a mix of 20% biodiesel and 80% petrodiesel) and B100 (pure biodiesel).
Source: Data from U.S. Environmental Protection Agency.

produce many times more biofuel than other crops. Algae farms can be set up just about anywhere, and can use waste water or saltwater. Because algae need nutrients, waste water from sewage treatment plants can be a good source of water. And because carbon dioxide is required for algal growth, algae farms can even be used to capture smokestack emissions. Production of algal fuels is still expensive, but the cost will likely come down as technologies improve.

Electricity can be generated from biomass

We can harness biomass energy by combusting biomass to generate electricity. Many of the sources used for this **biopower** are the waste products of existing industries. For instance, the forest products industry generates large amounts of woody debris in logging operations and at sawmills, pulp mills, and paper mills (FIGURE 13.21A), which can be used for biopower. Other waste sources include organic waste from municipal landfills, animal waste from agricultural feedlots, and crop residues (such as cornstalks and husks). Some crops are grown specifically to produce biopower. These include fast-growing trees, such as willows and poplars (FIGURE 13.21B), and fast-growing grasses, such as bamboo, fescue, and switchgrass.

(a) Switchgrass for cellulosic ethanol

(b) Algae for third-generation biofuels

FIGURE 13.20

(a) Switchgrass, a fast-growing plant native to the North American prairies, provides fuel for biopower and is being studied as a crop to provide cellulosic ethanol. **(b)** Algae are a leading candidate for a next-generation biofuel. Here algae are growing in networks of lighted tubes at a demonstration facility. Algae grow quickly, can be farmed in many places, and can be used to produce biodiesel, ethanol, and other fuels.

Power plants built to combust biomass operate similarly to those fired by fossil fuels; the combustion heats water, creating steam to turn turbines and generators, thereby generating electricity. Much of the biopower produced so far comes from power plants that generate both electricity and heating through *cogeneration*. These plants are often located where they can take advantage of forestry waste.

Biomass is also increasingly being combined with coal in coal-fired power plants in a process called *co-firing*. Wood chips, wood pellets, or other biomass is introduced with coal into a high-efficiency boiler that uses one of

(a) Forestry residues

(b) Fast-growing poplars

FIGURE 13.21
(a) Forestry residues (here from a Swedish logging operation on Vancouver Island) are a major source material for the production of biopower. **(b)** Hybrid poplars are specially bred for fast growth, and they are harvested for use in biopower production. The monocultural plantations, which may replace natural systems over large areas, do not function ecologically as forests.

several technologies. Biomass can substitute for up to 15% of the coal with only minor equipment modification and no appreciable loss of efficiency. Co-firing can be a relatively easy and inexpensive way for fossil-fuel-based utilities to expand their use of renewable energy.

The anaerobic bacterial breakdown of waste by microbes in landfills produces methane and other gases. This **landfill gas** is now being captured and used as fuel, generating both electricity and profits while avoiding harmful greenhouse gas emissions from the landfill (see "The Science Behind the Story: Energy from Landfill Gas at Beare Road"). Landfill gas utilization solves local

environmental problems by cutting down on odours and limiting the possibility of fires and explosions caused by escaping methane gas. Methane and other gases can also be produced in a more controlled way in anaerobic digestion facilities. The resulting *biogas* can then be burned in a power plant's boiler to generate electricity.

We can also harness biopower through *gasification*, in which biomass is vaporized at extremely high temperatures in the absence of oxygen, creating a gaseous mixture that includes hydrogen, carbon monoxide, carbon dioxide, and methane. This mixture can generate electricity when used in power plants to turn a gas turbine to propel a generator. Gas from gasification can be treated in various ways to produce methanol, synthesize a type of diesel fuel, or isolate hydrogen for use in hydrogen fuel cells. An alternative method of heating biomass in the absence of oxygen can produce a liquid fuel called *pyrolysis oil*, which can be burned to generate electricity.

Biofuels have environmental and economic benefits

Adding biofuels such as ethanol and biodiesel to gasoline or petrodiesel helps those fuels to combust more completely, reducing pollution. Replacing gasoline or petrodiesel with biofuels reduces emissions of nitrogen oxides, greenhouse gases, and other pollutants. When used instead of coal in co-firing and direct combustion, biopower reduces emissions of sulphur dioxide because plant matter, unlike coal, contains no appreciable sulphur content.

Shifting from fossil fuels to biomass energy also can have economic benefits. The forest products industry in North America now obtains much of its energy by combusting the waste it recycles, including woody waste from pulp mill processing. Biomass tends to be the least expensive type of fuel for burning in power plants, and improved energy efficiency brings lower prices for consumers. As a resource, biomass tends to be well spread geographically, so using it should help support rural economies and reduce many nations' dependence on imported fuels.

Biofuels also have drawbacks

Growing crops to produce biofuels exerts tremendous impacts on ecosystems. Although crops grown for energy typically receive lower inputs of pesticides and fertilizers than those grown for food, cultivating biofuel crops is land-intensive and brings with it all the impacts of monocultural agriculture. Biofuel crops take up land that might

THE SCIENCE BEHIND THE STORY

Energy from Landfill Gas at Beare Road

Many municipalities utilize passive flaring systems like this one to dispose of landfill gases, preventing the gas from collecting and exploding catastrophically.

Methane (CH_4) is the main component of **landfill gas**, gas generated by the decomposition of waste in landfills. (Carbon dioxide, CO_2, is typically a close second.) The capture, recovery, and use of landfill gas for electricity generation can yield from 50% to 70% of the energy of natural gas, in addition to cutting down greenhouse gas emissions that would otherwise result from its release into the atmosphere.[5] Capture is particularly important in the case of methane, which is approximately 21 times more effective than carbon dioxide as a greenhouse gas.

Municipalities around the world have long captured and burned off the gases that are naturally generated by garbage accumulating in landfills. In the past, this has been undertaken mainly to avoid odours, fires, and the potential for explosions. For

years at Beare Road Landfill in Toronto, as at many other sites, the gas was allowed to leak from the landfill via pipes called "candlesticks"—vertical pipes that allow the gas to flow passively out of the ground, with flames occasionally flaring from the tops of the pipes (see photo).

The passive flaring system at Beare Road has been replaced by over 80 vertical wells designed to extract approximately 40 m^3 of landfill gas per minute from the ground.[6] The gas—almost 50% methane—is brought to the Beare Landfill Power Plant, where particulate matter and moisture are removed (see second photo). The gas then goes to a series of reciprocating gas furnaces, where it is burned to generate electricity. Electricity generation began at the site in 1996.[7]

The Beare Landfill Power Plant currently produces enough electricity to service 4000 homes. The total cost of this *LFGTE (landfill gas-to-electricity)* facility was about $8.5 million. It has a 10-year anticipated life span, based on the amount of garbage in the landfill, and generates approximately $2 million in revenues each year for its owner, E.S. Fox, which has an agreement with Ontario Power Generation to purchase the electricity. Other LFGTE projects in Canada, including the Keele Valley Landfill in Toronto, Saint Michel Landfill near Montréal, and Clover Bar Landfill near Edmonton, have even higher gas and electricity outputs, longer projected life spans, and greater potential profits for the owners of the projects.

This is the landfill gas cleanup room at the Beare Landfill Power Plant, where particulates and moisture are removed from the methane gas, prior to bringing it to the furnaces.

Although LFGTE sounds like a win-win idea (reusing waste materials, cutting back on greenhouse gas emissions and air pollution), some environmentalists are fundamentally opposed to its development. They fear that generating something positive from a pile of garbage will derail attempts to get people to cut down on the amount of waste that they generate. This is a reasonable concern. However, in the case of old sites like Beare Road, which hasn't received any new garbage since 1983, the pollution-reducing benefits seem to make it a winning proposition.

As of 2003 there were 44 LFGTE systems in Canada,[8] mostly in Ontario, British Columbia, and Québec. These facilities will likely play an increasingly important role as Canada strives to reduce greenhouse gas emission.

otherwise be left in its natural condition or developed for other purposes.

If we were to try to produce all the automotive fuel currently used in North America with ethanol from corn, we would need to expand the already immense corn acreage by more than 60%, with no loss of productivity and without producing any additional corn for food. Even at current levels of production, biofuel is competing with food production. As farmers shift more corn crops to ethanol, corn supplies for food have dropped, and international corn prices have skyrocketed. In Mexico,

where corn tortillas are a staple food, average citizens found themselves struggling and protests erupted across the country over the inflated price of corn.

Growing bioenergy crops also requires substantial inputs of energy. We currently operate farm equipment using fossil fuels, and farmers apply petroleum-based pesticides and fertilizers to increase yields. Moreover, fossil fuels are used in refineries to heat water so that we can distil pure ethanol. Thus, shifting from gasoline to ethanol for our transportation needs would not eliminate our reliance on fossil fuels.

Furthermore, growing corn for ethanol yields only a modest amount of energy relative to the energy that needs to be input. Recall our discussion of *energy returned on investment* (EROI). The EROI, or ratio of energy returned to energy invested, for corn-based ethanol is controversial, but the best recent estimates place it around 1.5:1. This means that to gain 1.5 units of energy from ethanol, we need to expend 1 unit of energy. The EROI of Brazilian *bagasse* ethanol is much higher, but the low ratio for corn-based ethanol makes this fuel quite inefficient. For this reason, many critics do not view ethanol as an effective path to sustainable energy use.

Future advances in cellulosic ethanol may ease the environmental impacts of biofuel crops considerably. Third-generation biofuels such as algal fuels are promising and should take up far less space than growing corn. In the meantime, until these technologies develop and costs decline, biomass energy use involves a complex mix of advantages and disadvantages.

Solar Energy

The Sun provides energy for almost all biological activity on Earth by converting hydrogen to helium through nuclear fusion. On average, each square metre of Earth's surface receives about 1 kilowatt of solar energy—17 times the energy of a light bulb. As a result, a typical house has enough roof area to generate all its power needs with rooftop panels that harness **solar energy**. The amount of energy Earth receives from the Sun *each day*, if it could be collected in full for our use, would be enough to power human consumption for a quarter of a century.

The potential for using sunlight to meet our energy needs is tremendous. However, we are still in the process of developing solar technologies and learning the most effective and cost-efficient ways to put the Sun's energy to use. Most solar technologies rely on the collection and, in some cases, concentration, of the Sun's rays. The principal uses for solar energy today are heating and cooling air; heating water for home and industrial uses; drying crops, such as tea, coffee, fruit, and others; generating electricity for off-grid and distributed energy applications; detoxifying water and air; cooking food; and, of course, daytime lighting.

Passive solar heating is simple and effective

The most commonly used way to harness solar energy is through **passive solar** energy collection. In this approach, buildings are designed and building materials are chosen to maximize absorption of sunlight in winter, even as they keep the interior cool in the summer.

Passive solar design usually involves installing south-facing windows to maximize sunlight capture in the winter (in the Northern Hemisphere; north-facing windows are used in the Southern Hemisphere). Overhangs block light from above, shading windows in the summer when the Sun is high in the sky and when cooling is needed. Passive solar techniques also include the use of heat-absorbing construction materials (called *thermal mass*) that absorb heat, store it, and release it later. Thermal mass made of straw, brick, concrete, or other materials most often is used in floors, ceilings, and walls.

Thermal mass is strategically located to capture sunlight in cold weather and radiate heat to the interior of the building. In warm weather the mass absorbs warm air in the interior to cool the building. Passive solar design can also involve planting vegetation in particular locations around a building. By heating buildings in cold weather and cooling them in warm weather, passive solar methods conserve energy and reduce energy costs.

Active solar energy can heat air and water in buildings

Active solar approaches make use of technological devices to focus, move, and store solar energy. One active technology involves using **solar panels** or *flat-plate solar collectors*, most often installed on rooftops. The panels generally consist of dark-coloured, heat-absorbing metal plates mounted in flat boxes covered with glass panes. Water, air, or antifreeze solutions are run through tubes that pass through the collectors, transferring heat throughout a building. Heated water can be pumped to tanks to store the heat for later use. Active solar systems are especially effective for heating water, and can be used even in remote areas (**FIGURE 13.22**).

We can magnify the strength of solar energy by gathering sunlight from a wide area and focusing it on a single point. This is the principle behind *solar cookers*, simple portable ovens that use reflectors to focus sunlight onto food and cook it. Such cookers are proving extremely useful in parts of the developing world.

Utilities have put the solar cooker principle to work in large-scale, high-tech approaches to generating electricity. In one approach, mirrors concentrate sunlight onto a receiver atop a tall "power-tower" (**FIGURE 13.23**). From the receiver, heat is transported by fluids that are piped to a steam-driven generator to create electricity. These solar power plants can harness light from large mirrors spread across many hectares of land. The largest such plant—a

FIGURE 13.22
Engineers in Gaviotas, a remote highland town in Colombia, developed inexpensive solar panels that provide residences and businesses active solar power for heating, cooling, and water purification.

collaboration among government, industry, and utility companies in the California desert—produces power for 10 000 households.

An interesting combination of active and passive solar technologies is the "Solarwall" that provides heating and cooling at the Bombardier's Canadair plant in Montreal. This is a south-facing cladding wall with millions of tiny holes, each about 1 mm in diameter, which allow outside air to pass through. Behind the cladding is a space for air flow. The air passing along the back of the wall absorbs solar-generated heat and rises to the roof, where it is

FIGURE 13.23
At the Solar Two facility in the desert of southern California, the largest such facility in the world, mirrors are spread across wide expanses of land to concentrate sunlight onto a receiver atop a "power-tower." Heat is then transported through fluid-filled pipes to a steam-driven generator that produces electricity.

collected and circulated through the building. This installation, the largest in the world, eliminated the need for fossil fuels at this facility, thereby cutting atmospheric emissions, and improved interior air quality in the plant as well.

Active solar technology dates from the eighteenth century, but it was pushed to the sidelines as fossil fuels came to dominate our energy economy. Largely because of lack of investment, solar energy contributes only a minuscule portion of energy production in Canada and worldwide. However, the growth in solar energy use worldwide has been second only to that of wind power. Since 1995, solar energy use in Canada has grown by an estimated 25% per year.[9] The federal government and some provincial/territorial governments have provided financial incentives for homeowners and business owners to switch to solar technologies.

PV cells generate electricity directly

A direct approach to producing electricity from sunlight involves **photovoltaic (PV) cells**, which collect sunlight and convert it to electrical energy by making use of the *photovoltaic* or *photoelectric effect*. This effect occurs when light strikes one of a pair of metal plates in a PV cell, causing the release of electrons, which are attracted by electrostatic forces to the opposing plate. The flow of electrons from one plate to the other creates an electrical current (direct current, DC), which can be converted into alternating current (AC) and used for residential and commercial electrical power (**FIGURE 13.24**).

The plates of a typical PV cell are made of silicon, which conducts electricity. One silicon plate (the *n-type layer*) is rich in electrons; the other (the *p-type layer*) is electron-poor. When sunlight strikes the PV cell, it knocks electrons loose from some of the silicon atoms. Connecting the two plates with wires generates electricity as electrons flow from the n-type layer back to the p-type layer. Photovoltaic cells can be connected to batteries that store the accumulated charge until it is needed.

You may be familiar with small PV cells that power your watch or solar calculator. Atop the roofs of homes and other buildings, PV cells can be arranged in arrays. Increasingly, PV roofing tiles are being used in place of these arrays. In some remote areas, PV systems are used in combination with wind turbines and a diesel generator to power entire villages. The use of PV cells is growing fast, and should continue to increase as prices fall, technologies improve, and governments enact economic incentives to spur investment.

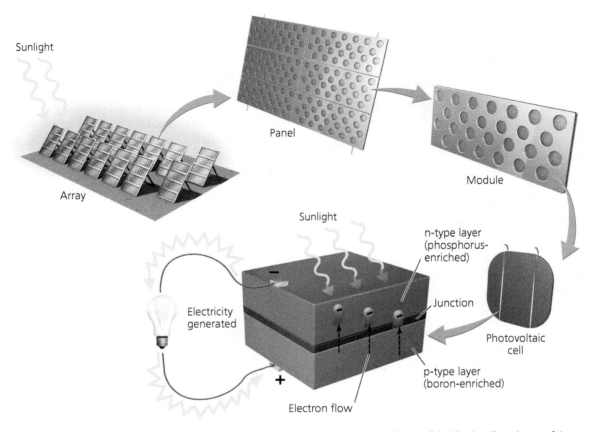

FIGURE 13.24   A photovoltaic (PV) cell converts sunlight to electrical energy. When sunlight hits the silicon layers of the cell, electrons are knocked loose and move from layer to layer. Connecting the layers with wiring allows electrical current to flow between them. This direct current (DC) is converted to alternating current (AC) to produce usable electricity. PV cells are grouped in modules, which comprise panels that can be erected in arrays.

Solar power offers many benefits

The Sun is effectively inexhaustible as an energy source for human civilization. Moreover, the amount of solar energy reaching Earth's surface should be enough to power our civilization once the technology is adequately developed. These primary benefits of solar energy are clear, but the technologies themselves also provide benefits. PV cells and other solar technologies use no fuel, are quiet and safe, contain no moving parts, require little maintenance, and do not even require a turbine or generator to create electricity. An average unit can produce energy for 20 to 30 years.

Solar systems allow for local, decentralized power. Homes, businesses, and isolated communities can use solar power to produce their own electricity without being near a power plant or connected to the power grid. In developing nations, solar cookers enable families to cook food without gathering fuelwood, lessening the daily workload and reducing deforestation. The low cost of solar cookers has made them available to many impoverished areas.

In the developed world, most PV systems are connected to the regional electric grid. This may enable owners of houses with PV systems to sell their excess solar energy to their local power utility. In this process, called **net metering**, the value of the power the consumer sells to the utility is subtracted from the consumer's monthly utility bill. As of this writing, net metering is available in most Canadian provinces.

Another advantage of solar power is that its development is producing new jobs. Currently, among major energy sources, PV technology employs the most people per unit of energy output. Finally, a major advantage of solar power over fossil fuels is that once a PV system is up and running, it produces no greenhouse gases or other polluting emissions.

Location and cost can be drawbacks

Solar energy currently has two major disadvantages. One is that not all regions are sunny enough to provide adequate power, given current technology. Daily or seasonal variation in sunlight can also pose problems for stand-alone solar systems if storage capacity in batteries or fuel cells is not adequate or if backup power is not available from a municipal power grid. In far northern locations, for example, although the total number of bright sunshine hours is very high over the course of a year, seasonal variations in the number of hours of daylight can make solar power more difficult to utilize (FIGURE 13.25). Intermittent supply is an argument that is also commonly levied against wind and other alternative energy sources. This can be mitigated against by having backup systems available, and by coupling different energy sources together. The use of alternative energy sources doesn't have to be an all-or-nothing venture; even if solar is only supplying 50% of the energy to a building, for example, GHG emissions will still be cut in half.

The primary disadvantage of current solar technology is the up-front cost of equipment. Proponents of solar power argue that decades of government promotion of fossil fuels and nuclear power have made solar power unable to compete. However, decreases in price and improvements in energy efficiency of solar technologies so far are encouraging, even in the absence of significant financial commitment from government and industry.

At their advent in the 1950s, solar technologies had efficiencies of around 6% while costing $600 per watt (the cost is now closer to $7 per watt). Recent single-crystal silicon PV cells are showing 15% efficiency commercially and 24% efficiency in lab research, suggesting that future solar technologies may be more efficient than any energy technologies we have today. Solar systems have become much less expensive over the years and now can pay for themselves within 10 to 20 years. After that time, they provide energy virtually for free as long as the equipment lasts. With future technological advances, some experts believe that the time to recoup investment could fall to one to three years.

Wind Energy

Wind energy—energy derived from moving air masses— is an indirect form of solar energy, because it is the Sun's differential heating of air masses that causes wind to blow. We can harness power from wind using **wind turbines**, mechanical assemblies that convert wind's kinetic energy, or energy of motion, into electrical energy.

Today's wind turbines have their historical roots in Europe, where windmills have been used for 800 years to drain wetlands, irrigate crops, and grind grain into flour. Wind causes the windmill's blades to turn, driving a shaft connected to several cogs that turn wheels, which perform the required work. In North America, countless ranches in the Prairies and the Great Plains have long used windmills to draw groundwater up for thirsty cattle.

After the 1973 oil crisis, governments in North America and Europe began funding research and development for wind power. This moderate infusion of funding boosted technological progress, and the cost of wind power was

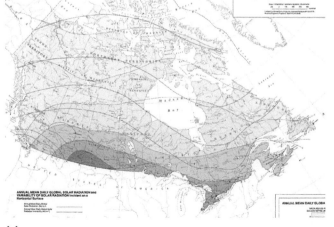

(a)

(b)

FIGURE 13.25 Because some locations receive more sunlight than others, harnessing solar energy is more profitable in some areas than in others. The yearly solar average of Canada's populated areas **(a)** exceeds that in both Germany and Japan, the world's solar leaders. Solar energy can be used to power remote applications, as in this solar installation in Nunavut **(b)**.   *Source: Based on* The Canadian Atlas Online, *Canadian Geographic www. canadiangeographic.ca/atlas/themes.aspx?id=weather&sub=weather_power_solarpower&lang=En*

cut in half within 10 years. Today wind power at favourable locations generates electricity for nearly as little cost per kilowatt-hour as conventional sources. The first wind power producer in Canada was Cowley Ridge Wind Plant in Alberta, the first phase of which opened in 1993. The largest is the Le Nordais project in the Gaspé Peninsula.

Modern wind turbines convert kinetic energy to electrical energy

In modern wind turbines, the wind turns blades that rotate machinery inside a compartment called a *nacelle*, which sits atop a tall tower (**FIGURE 13.26**). Inside the nacelle are a gearbox, a generator, and equipment to monitor and control the turbine's activity. Most towers range from 40 to 100 m tall. Higher is generally better, to minimize turbulence and maximize wind speed. Most rotors consist of three blades and measure 42 to 80 m across. Turbines are designed to yaw, or rotate back and forth, in response to changes in wind direction, ensuring that the motor faces into the wind at all times. Turbines can be erected singly, but they are often erected in groups called **wind farms**. The world's largest wind farms contain hundreds of turbines spread across the landscape.

Slight differences in wind speed yield substantial differences in power output. The energy content of a given amount of wind increases as the square of its velocity; for this reason, if wind velocity doubles, energy quadruples. Some turbines are designed to generate low levels of electricity by turning in light breezes; others are programmed to rotate only in stronger winds, operating less frequently but generating large amounts of electricity in short time periods.

Wind power is the fastest-growing energy sector

Like solar energy, wind provides only a small proportion of the world's power needs, but wind power capacity is growing fast—by 26% per year globally between 2000 and 2005, and then quadrupling between 2006 and 2009. Germany has been the world leader in installed wind capacity; however, in Denmark a series of wind farms supplies over 20% of the nation's electricity needs, the highest proportion in the world. Experts agree that wind power's rapid growth will continue. Meteorological evidence suggests that wind power could be expanded in Canada to about 30 000 MW, sufficient to meet 15% of the nation's electrical needs. To date, Canada's wind power leaders are Québec, Alberta, and Saskatchewan.[10]

Offshore and high-altitude sites are particularly promising. Wind speeds on average are roughly 20% greater over water than over land, and there is less air turbulence over water. It is clear from **FIGURE 13.27** that wind conditions over Hudson's Bay are stronger than anywhere over land in Canada, for example. Costs to erect and maintain offshore wind turbines are higher, but the stronger, less turbulent winds produce more power and make them potentially more profitable. Currently, offshore wind farms are limited to shallow water, where towers are sunk into sediments to stabilize them. In the future, towers may be placed on floating pads anchored to the seafloor in deep water. There are as yet no operational offshore wind installations in Canada.

Winter weather also promotes stronger wind conditions, as do high elevations. Studies in the Yukon Territory, for example, have found many elevated sites suitable for wind power development, and the territory

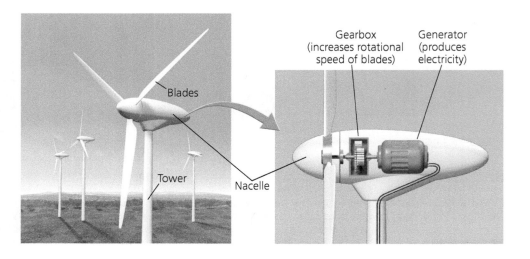

FIGURE 13.26
A wind turbine converts wind's energy of motion into electrical energy. Wind causes the blades to spin, turning a shaft that extends into the nacelle, perched atop the tower. Inside the nacelle, a gearbox converts the rotational speed of the blades, which can be up to 20 revolutions per minute (rpm) or more, into much higher rotational speeds (over 1500 rpm). These high speeds provide motion for a generator inside the nacelle to produce electricity.

Mean Wind Speed at 50 m above ground
Vitesse moyenne du vent à 50 m au dessus du sol

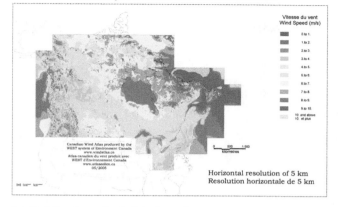

(a) Distribution of wind in Canada

(b) Cowley Ridge Wind Plant, Alberta

FIGURE 13.27 Southern Alberta and Saskatchewan enjoy some of Canada's best conditions for wind power, but offshore wind speeds are highest **(a)**. Cowley Ridge Wind Plant in southwestern Alberta **(b)** was Canada's first commercial wind power plant, opened in 1993. *Source: Based on Canadian Geographic,* The Canadian Atlas Online, *"Wind Power" www.canadiangeographic.ca/atlas/themes.aspx?id=WEATHER&sub=WEATHER_POWER_WINDPOWER&lang=En*

has recently invested in new installations (**FIGURE 13.28**). Wind turbines in cold climates face specific challenges, however, such as icing of the turbine blades.

Wind power has many benefits

Like solar power, wind produces no emissions once the necessary equipment is manufactured and installed. The graph in **FIGURE 13.29** shows emissions per kWh of

FIGURE 13.28
Winter winds and high elevations combine to make conditions that are appropriate for wind power generation in Yukon Territory, although icing of the turbine blades can be a challenge.

electricity produced over the entire installed lifetime of various technologies. Emissions of CO_2 (the main greenhouse gas associated with global warming), SO_2 (the main precursor of acid rain), and NO_x (the main precursor of photochemical smog) are significantly lower for wind and other renewables, as well as nuclear and hydro, compared to fossil-fuel-based electricity generation. Other types of harmful emissions also can be avoided; for example, the U.S. Environmental Protection Agency (EPA) calculates that running a 1-megawatt wind turbine for 1 year prevents the release of approximately 30 kg of mercury, in comparison to the generation of electricity by a typical coal-fired power plant.

Wind power, under optimal conditions, is considerably more efficient than conventional power sources in its energy returned on investment (EROI). One study found that wind turbines produce 23 times more energy than they consume. For nuclear energy, the ratio was 16:1; for coal it was 11:1; and for natural gas it was 5:1.

Wind turbine technology can be used on many scales, from a single tower for local use to fields of hundreds that supply large regions. Small-scale turbine development can help make local areas more energy self-sufficient. Farmers and ranchers can lease their land for wind development, which provides extra revenue while increasing property tax income for rural communities. Because each turbine takes up only a small area, most of the land can still be used for farming, ranching, or other uses.

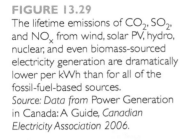

FIGURE 13.29
The lifetime emissions of CO_2, SO_2, and NO_x from wind, solar PV, hydro, nuclear, and even biomass-sourced electricity generation are dramatically lower per kWh than for all of the fossil-fuel-based sources.
Source: Data from Power Generation in Canada: A Guide, *Canadian Electricity Association 2006.*

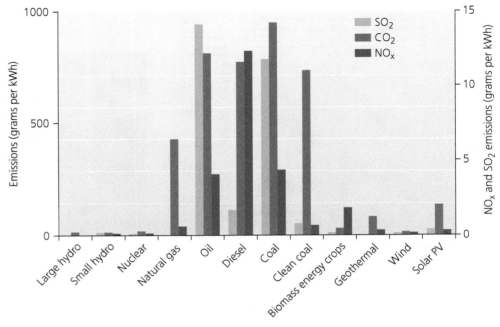

Wind power has some downsides—but not many

Wind is an intermittent resource; we have no control over when wind will occur, and this unpredictability is a major limitation in relying on it as an electricity source. However, this poses little problem if wind is only one of several sources contributing to a utility's power generation. Moreover, several new technologies are being developed to store energy generated by wind and release it later when needed.

Wind varies from place to place. Global and regional wind systems combine with local topography to create local wind patterns, and the best wind resources are not always near population centres that need the energy. Transmission networks would need to be greatly expanded to get wind power to where people live. When wind farms *are* proposed near population centres, local residents often oppose them. Some people object to wind farms for aesthetic reasons, feeling that the structures clutter the landscape. Although polls show wide public approval of existing wind projects and of the concept of wind power in general, newly proposed wind projects often elicit the **"not-in-my-backyard" (NIMBY)** syndrome among people living nearby.

Wind turbines may also pose a threat to birds and bats, which can be killed by flying into rotating blades or by encountering pockets of negative pressure in the lee side of the rotating blades. Studies at several sites suggest that bird deaths may be a less severe problem

weighing the issues
WIND AND NIMBY

How would you react if your electric utility proposed to build a wind farm atop a ridge running in back of your neighbourhood, such that the turbines would be visible from your house? Would you support or oppose the development? Why? If you would oppose it, where would you suggest the farm be located? Do you think anyone might oppose it in that location?

than was initially feared; for instance, one European study indicated that migrating seabirds fly past offshore turbines without problem. However, other data show that resident seabird densities decline near turbines. The key for protecting birds and bats may be selecting sites that are not on flyways or in the midst of prime habitat.

Geothermal Energy

Geothermal energy is one form of renewable energy that does not originate from the Sun; it is generated deep within Earth. The radioactive decay of elements deep in the interior of our planet generates heat that rises to the surface, heating rock and groundwater, and generating steam. Geysers and submarine hydrothermal vents are the surface manifestations of these processes.

One country that has abundant geothermal resources is Iceland (**FIGURE 13.30A**). It is an island built from magma that extruded above the ocean's surface and cooled—magma from the Mid-Atlantic Ridge, the area of volcanic activity along the spreading boundary of two tectonic plates. Because of the geothermal heat in this region, volcanoes and geysers are numerous in Iceland. In fact, the word *geyser* (a natural spring that discharges hot water or steam) originated from the Icelandic *Geysir*, the island's largest geyser.

Geothermal power plants use the energy of naturally heated underground water and steam for direct heating and to turn turbines and generate electricity (**FIGURE 13.30B**). Geothermal energy is renewable, in principle, because its use does not affect the amount of heat produced in Earth's interior.

The geothermal power plants may not be capable of operating indefinitely. If a geothermal plant uses heated water more quickly than the groundwater is recharged, the plant will eventually run out of water. This is occurring at The Geysers, in Napa Valley, California, a very early geothermal application where the first generator was built in 1960. In response, operators have begun injecting municipal wastewater into the ground to replenish the supply. More geothermal plants are now reinjecting water after it is used, to help maintain pressure in the aquifer and thereby sustain the resource.

![geothermal power station photo]

(a) Nesjavellir, Iceland

FIGURE 13.30

At the Nesjavellir geothermal power station in Iceland **(a)**, steam is piped from four wells to a condenser at the plant, where cold water pumped from lakeshore wells 6 km away is heated. The water, heated to 83°C, is sent through an insulated 270-km pipeline to Reykjavik, where residents use it for washing and space heating. **(b)** At a typical geothermal site, magma heats groundwater deep underground (1), some of which escapes naturally through surface vents such as geysers (2). Geothermal facilities tap into heated water below ground and channel steam through turbines in buildings to generate electricity (3). After being used, the steam is often condensed, and the water pumped back into the aquifer to maintain pressure (4).

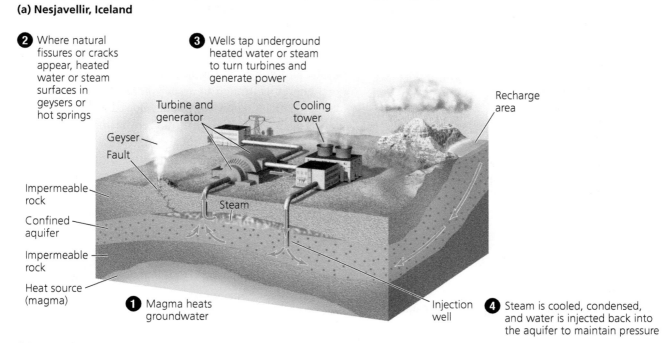

(b) A geothermal power plant

We can harness geothermal energy for heating and electricity

Geothermal energy can be harnessed directly from geysers at the surface, but most often wells must be drilled down hundreds or thousands of metres toward heated groundwater. Water at temperatures of 150–370°C or more is brought to the surface and converted to steam by lowering the pressure in specialized compartments. The steam is then employed in turning turbines to generate electricity.

Hot groundwater can also be used directly for heating homes, offices, and greenhouses; for driving industrial processes; and for drying crops. Iceland heats most of its homes through direct heating with piped hot water. Iceland began using geothermal energy in the 1940s, and today 30 municipal district heating systems and 200 small private rural networks supply heat to 86% of the nation's residences.

Geothermal **ground-source heat pumps** (GSHPs) use thermal energy from near-surface land and water (see "The Science Behind the Story: Water and Earth Energy for Heating and Cooling in Toronto and Ottawa"). Soil varies in temperature from season to season less than air does, so the pumps heat buildings in the winter by transferring heat from the ground into buildings, and they cool buildings in the summer by transferring heat from buildings into the ground. Both types of heat transfer are accomplished by a network of underground plastic pipes that circulate water. Because heat is simply moved from place to place rather than being produced using outside energy inputs, heat pumps can be highly energy-efficient.

Natural Resources Canada estimates that there are at least 30 000 GSHPs making use of Earth energy to heat offices, institutions (such as hospitals and universities), factories, and residences in Canada. This is significant because more than half of the energy demand in institutional and commercial settings in Canada is for space heating. Compared to conventional electric heating and cooling systems, GSHPs heat spaces 50–70% more efficiently, cool them 20–40% more efficiently, can reduce electricity use by 25–60%, and can reduce emissions by up to 70%.

Use of geothermal power is growing

Geothermal energy provides less than 0.5% of the total energy used worldwide and remains largely unexploited in Canada. Worldwide it provides more power than solar and wind combined, but only a small fraction compared to hydropower and biomass. In Canada the geologic settings are such that true geothermal energy is commercially viable only in British Columbia because of its proximity to the boundary of the Juan da Fuca tectonic plate.

In the right setting, geothermal power can be among the cheapest sources of electricity. Currently Japan, China, and the United States lead the world in use of geothermal power. However, at the world's largest geothermal power plants, The Geysers in northern California, generating capacity has declined by more than 50% since 1989 as steam pressure has declined.

Geothermal power has benefits and limitations

Like other renewable sources, geothermal power greatly reduces polluting emissions, relative to fossil fuel combustion. Geothermal sources can release variable amounts of gases dissolved in their water, including carbon dioxide, methane, ammonia, and hydrogen sulphide. However, these gases are generally in very small quantities, and geothermal facilities using the latest filtering technologies produce even fewer emissions. By one estimate, each megawatt of geothermal power prevents the emission of 7.0 million kg of carbon dioxide emissions each year.

On the negative side, geothermal sources, as we have seen, may not always be truly sustainable. In addition, the water of many hot springs is laced with salts and minerals that corrode equipment. These factors may shorten the lifetime of plants, increase maintenance costs, and add to pollution. Moreover, use of geothermal energy is limited to areas where the energy can be tapped. Unless technology is developed to penetrate far more deeply into the ground, geothermal energy use will remain extremely localized. Nonetheless, many hydrothermal resources remain unexploited, awaiting improved technology and governmental support for their development.

Ocean Energy

The ocean hosts several underexploited energy sources. Each involves continuous natural processes that could potentially provide sustainable, predictable energy. Of the four approaches being developed, three involve motion, and one involves temperature.

THE SCIENCE BEHIND THE STORY

Water and Earth Energy for Heating and Cooling in Toronto and Ottawa

The Enwave Deep Lake Water Cooling Plant in Toronto takes advantage of the cold, deep waters of Lake Ontario to provide district cooling.

A forward-looking plan utilizes the cold, deep waters of Lake Ontario to provide air conditioning to more than 2.5 million m² of downtown office and living spaces in Toronto. The Enwave Deep Lake Water Cooling project is a district cooling technology that takes advantage of low-temperature lake water immediately adjacent to the downtown area. The project is coordinated by Enwave Energy, which was set up (originally as a nonprofit corporation) to develop the application more than 20 years ago.

The system works by taking cold water in through three large intake pipes that lie 83 m below the surface of the lake and extend 5.1 km from the shore. Each day, millions of litres of water at 4°C are pumped to the Toronto Island filtration plant, where the water is treated and circulated for normal distribution into the city drinking water supply via a pumping station. Before leaving the pumping station, the cold water is diverted through a series of heat exchangers. The coldness of the water is used to remove the thermal energy from warm water passing through pipes on the other side of the heat exchangers. The newly cooled water moves through a system of many kilometres of underground pipes, providing cooling to customers in more than 140 buildings. The water is then returned to the pumping station, and the circuit is repeated.

The chilled water and the city's drinking water always remain on opposite sides of the heat exchanger and thus never come into contact with each other. The chilled water is recirculated and recooled through a closed loop system (see diagram). By using the deep lake water to provide district cooling, the project saves approximately 128 million kWh annually in electricity, reducing CO_2 emissions by 79 000 tons and reducing electricity consumption by 90% compared to conventional air conditioning technologies.[11]

Geothermal or terrestrial ("Earth energy") heat pumps also utilize fluids to store, transport, and supply thermal energy. During the winter months, when the temperature just a few metres under the surface is considerably warmer than the air temperature, heat pumps are used to extract this near-surface thermal energy from groundwater travelling through underground pipes. This heat is primarily solar energy that was absorbed and stored in subsurface soil layers, rather than "true" geothermal energy originating from the hot inner layers of Earth.

Once extracted, the heat is distributed. The cooled fluid is then returned to its underground reservoir to be reheated. Heat pumps are reversible, so the same process can provide cooling. During the summer months, groundwater is used to cool buildings (in a process similar to the Enwave Deep Lake Water Cooling process) and is then returned to its underground reservoir to be recooled. Both heating and cooling by this method are cyclic processes that can be repeated indefinitely.

Closed-loop systems continuously recirculate the fluid through a pipeline circuit (see diagram) without discharging it back into the aquifer or water body from which it was obtained. In district heating systems in Canada, this fluid is typically a mixture of antifreeze and water, but plain water or air can work in some circumstances. In an open-loop system, in contrast, heat energy is acquired from the water via heat exchangers, and the water is then discharged back into the aquifer or water body. Open-loop systems can be less expensive, but they require a suitable water supply and must be designed to mitigate

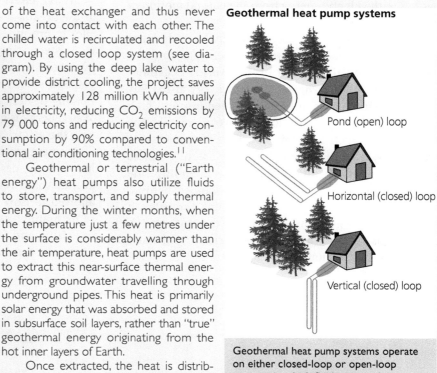

Geothermal heat pump systems

Pond (open) loop

Horizontal (closed) loop

Vertical (closed) loop

Geothermal heat pump systems operate on either closed-loop or open-loop systems, in which fluids are used to carry, supply, and store thermal energy. Heat pumps extract energy from the fluids, which are then returned to the underground reservoir.

environmental impacts.[12] Injecting water into an aquatic system at a temperature that differs from its original temperature may damage organisms in the ecosystem.

There are thousands of heat pump installations throughout Canada, some for individual buildings and others used in district heating or cooling. One example is the Underground Thermal Energy Storage (UTES) system, which relies on underground reservoirs to store heat during the summer and provide heat during the winter. The UTES technology has been in use at Carleton University in Ottawa since 1990. Environment Canada estimates that the UTES system reduces cooling costs by 80% and heating costs by 40% or more, in addition to significant reductions in the polluting emissions that would otherwise be associated with space heating and cooling.[13]

We can harness energy from tides, waves, and currents

Just as dams on rivers use the kinetic energy of flowing water to generate hydroelectric power, some scientists, engineers, businesses, and governments are developing ways to use the kinetic energy from the natural motion of ocean water to generate electrical power.

The rising and falling of ocean tides twice each day at coastal sites throughout the world moves large amounts of water past any given point on the world's coastlines (see "Central Case: Harnessing Tidal Energy at the Bay of Fundy"). Differences in height between low and high tides are especially great in long, narrow bays like the Bay of Fundy. Such locations are best for harnessing **tidal energy**, which is accomplished by erecting sluices across the outlets of tidal basins. The incoming tide flows through the sluice gates, and is trapped behind. Then, as the outgoing tide passes through the gates, it turns turbines to generate electricity (FIGURE 13.31). Some designs allow for generating electricity from water moving in both directions.

The world's largest tidal generating facility is the La Rance facility in France, which has operated for over 40 years. Smaller facilities operate in China and Russia and in Canada at the Bay of Fundy. Tidal stations release few or no pollutant emissions, but they can have impacts on the ecology of estuaries and tidal basins.

Wave energy, harnessed from wind-driven waves at the ocean's surface, could be developed at a variety of sites to produce electricity. Many designs for machinery to harness wave energy exist, but few have been adequately tested and no commercial facilities are operating yet. Some designs are for offshore facilities and involve floating devices that move up and down with the waves. Wave energy is greatest at deep-ocean sites, but transmitting the electricity to shore would be expensive. Other wave-energy technologies are designed for coastal installation. Some designs funnel waves into narrow channels and elevated reservoirs from which the water is then allowed to flow out, generating electricity in much the same manner as hydroelectric dams do. Other designs use rising and falling waves to push air into and out of chambers, turning turbines to generate electricity.

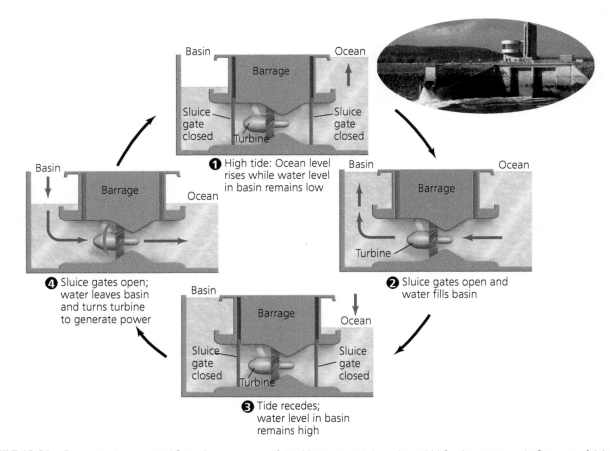

FIGURE 13.31 Energy can be extracted from the movement of the tides at coastal sites where tidal flux is great enough. One way of doing so involves using bulb turbines in concert with the outgoing tide. At high tide (1), ocean water is let through the sluice gates, filling an interior basin (2). At low tide (3), the basin water is let out into the ocean, spinning turbines to generate electricity (4). This technology is similar to what has been used at the Annapolis Tidal Power Station since 1984.

In addition to tides and waves, a third potential source of marine kinetic energy is the flow of ocean currents, such as the Gulf Stream. Devices that look essentially like underwater wind turbines have been erected in European waters to test the intriguing idea of harnessing the energy from the flow of surface currents.

The ocean stores thermal energy

Each day the tropical oceans absorb an amount of solar radiation equivalent to the heat content of 250 billion barrels of oil—enough to provide about 100 000 times the electricity used daily in Canada. The ocean's sun-warmed surface is higher in temperature than its deep water, and **ocean thermal energy conversion (OTEC)** is based on this gradient in temperature.

In a closed-cycle approach (similar to the systems discussed in "The Science Behind the Story: Water and Earth Energy for Heating and Cooling in Toronto and Ottawa"), warm surface water is piped into a facility to evaporate chemicals, such as ammonia, that boil at low temperatures. These evaporated gases spin turbines to generate electricity. Cold water piped in from ocean depths then condenses the gases so they can be reused. In the open-cycle approach, warm surface water is evaporated in a vacuum, and its steam turns turbines and then is condensed by cold water. Because ocean water loses its salts as it evaporates, the water can be recovered, condensed, and sold as desalinized fresh water for drinking or agriculture.

OTEC systems require not only a large temperature difference between the surface and deeper waters, but also a rapid dropoff of underwater topography near the coast, so that sufficiently cold temperatures can be accessed within a reasonable distance of the shore. Research on OTEC systems has been conducted in Hawaii and Japan, where conditions are optimal, but costs remain high, and as of yet no facility is commercially operational.

Hydrogen Fuel and Power Storage

At the beginning of the chapter we mentioned that there are three main categories of applications for renewables: electricity generation, space heating (and cooling), and fuels. All the renewable energy sources we have discussed so far can be used to generate electricity more cleanly than can fossil fuels. Many of them can be applied locally, to provide space heating or cooling for buildings and districts.

As useful as these applications are to us, however, a major drawback is that the energy and electricity generated by them cannot be stored and transported easily in large quantities for use when and where they are needed. This is why vehicles still rely on fossil fuels for power. The development of hydrogen shows fuel, fuel cells, and related energy storage technologies shows promise for storing and transporting energy conveniently.

In the "hydrogen economy" that many energy experts believe will be the next big energy wave worldwide, hydrogen fuel—together with electricity— believe will be the next big energy wave would serve as the basis for a clean, safe, and efficient energy system. This system would use as fuel the universe's simplest and most abundant element. Electricity generated from renewable sources that are intermittent, such as wind or solar energy, could be used to produce hydrogen. **Fuel cells**—which utilize chemical energy, like batteries—could then employ the hydrogen to produce electrical energy as needed to power vehicles, computers, cell phones, home heating, and countless other applications (**FIGURE 13.32**).

Basing an energy system on hydrogen could alleviate dependence on foreign fuels and help fight climate change. For these reasons, many governments, including the federal and provincial governments in Canada, are funding research into hydrogen and fuel cell technology. Automobile companies and other private corporations also are investing significant amounts in research and development to produce vehicles that run on hydrogen and to develop fuel cell technologies and infrastructure.

Hydrogen may be produced from water or from other matter

Hydrogen gas (H_2) does not tend to exist freely on Earth; rather, hydrogen atoms bind to other molecules, becoming incorporated in everything from water to organic molecules. To obtain hydrogen, we must force these substances to release their hydrogen atoms, and this requires an input of energy. Several ways of producing hydrogen are being studied. In **electrolysis**, electricity is input to split hydrogen atoms from the oxygen atoms of water molecules:

$$2H_2O \rightarrow 2H_2 + O_2$$

Whether this strategy for producing hydrogen would cause pollution over its entire life cycle depends on the source of the electricity used for the electrolysis. If coal is burned to create the electricity, then the process may not reduce emissions compared with fossil fuels. If, however,

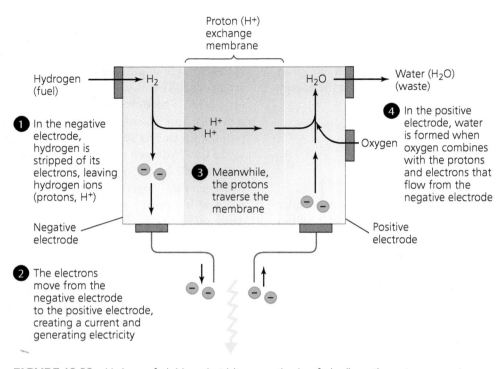

Proton (H+)
exchange
membrane

Hydrogen → H₂
(fuel)

H₂O ← Water (H₂O)
(waste)

1 In the negative
electrode,
hydrogen is
stripped of its
electrons, leaving
hydrogen ions
(protons, H⁺)

H⁺
H⁺

4 In the positive
electrode, water
is formed when
oxygen combines
with the protons
and electrons that
flow from the
negative electrode

Oxygen

3 Meanwhile,
the protons
traverse the
membrane

Negative
electrode

Positive
electrode

2 The electrons
move from the
negative electrode
to the positive electrode,
creating a current and
generating electricity

FIGURE 13.32   Hydrogen fuel drives electricity generation in a fuel cell, creating water as a waste product. There are many different types of fuel cells. In this example, atoms of hydrogen first are stripped of their electrons (1). The electrons move from a negative electrode to a positive one, creating a current and generating electricity (2). Meanwhile, the hydrogen ions pass through a proton exchange membrane (3) and combine with oxygen to form water molecules (4).

the electricity is produced by a less-polluting renewable source, then hydrogen production by electrolysis would create much less pollution than fossil fuels. The "cleanliness" of a future hydrogen economy, therefore, depends largely on the source of electricity used in electrolysis.

The environmental impact of hydrogen production also depends on the source material for the hydrogen. Besides water, hydrogen can be obtained from biomass and fossil fuels. Obtaining hydrogen from these sources generally requires less energy input, but results in emissions of carbon-based pollutants. For instance, extracting hydrogen from the methane (CH_4) in natural gas entails producing one molecule of the greenhouse gas carbon dioxide for every four molecules of hydrogen gas:

$$CH_4 + 2H_2O \rightarrow 4H_2 + CO_2$$

Thus, whether a hydrogen-based energy system would be environmentally cleaner than a fossil fuel system will depend on how the hydrogen is extracted and on its source. Other questions about the lifetime environmental impacts of hydrogen fuel are still being investigated.

Fuel cells can be used to produce electricity

Once isolated, hydrogen gas can be used as a fuel to produce electricity within fuel cells. The chemical reaction involved in a fuel cell is simply the reverse of that shown for electrolysis; an oxygen molecule and two hydrogen molecules each split so that their atoms can bind and form two water molecules:

$$2H_2 + O_2 \rightarrow 2H_2O$$

The way this occurs in one common type of fuel cell is shown in **FIGURE 13.32**. Hydrogen gas (usually compressed and stored in an attached fuel tank) is allowed into one side of the cell, whose middle consists of two electrodes that sandwich a membrane that only protons (hydrogen ions) can move across. One electrode, helped by a chemical catalyst, strips the hydrogen gas of its electrons, creating two hydrogen ions that begin moving across the membrane. Meanwhile, on the other side of the cell, oxygen molecules from the open air are split into their component atoms along the other electrode. These oxygen ions soon bind to pairs of hydrogen ions travel-

CANADIAN ENVIRONMENTAL PERSPECTIVES

David Keith

David Keith has made a lifetime commitment to solving problems related to energy and climate change.

- **Sustainable energy advisor** and **energy systems expert**
- **Physicist** and **Canada Research Chair in Energy and Environment** at the University of Calgary
- **Canadian Geographic Environmental Scientist of the Year** for 2006

In 2001, *Canadian Geographic* created the Canadian Environment Awards, recognizing a variety of contributions to better understanding and management of the environment, from a wide spectrum of people. In 2006 the magazine also began to recognize the contributions of Canadian scientists, and the very first Canadian Environmental Scientist of the Year was David Keith.

As an undergraduate, Keith won first prize in Canada's National Physics Prize exam. As a graduate student, he won a departmental prize for excellence in experimental physics at the Massachusetts Institute of Technology (MIT). He is now a professor appointed to both the Department of Chemical and Petroleum Engineering and the Department of Economics at the University of Calgary. These seemingly incongruent postings reflect the interdisciplinary nature of Keith's research interests, which lie at the intersections between climate science, energy technology, and public policy. His technical and policy work focuses on technologies for the capture and storage of CO_2, the economics and climatic impacts of large-scale wind power, the use of hydrogen as a transportation fuel, and the technology and implications of *geoengineering*[14]—that is, large-scale interventions in or modifications of Earth's climate system.

Keith, who chairs the Energy and Environmental Systems Group at the University of Calgary, has a reputation for being somewhat blunt, and for challenging entrenched beliefs. He has been known to reject some widely accepted ideas about energy and the environment—both those of the traditional energy sectors and those of the environmental movement. This prompted *Canadian Geographic* to call him a "contrarian" in his citation for Environmental Scientist of the Year.[15] For example, Keith spends a lot of time working out the economics of alternative, non–carbon-based energy technologies, such as wind power. "When it comes to climate change, I'm interested in technologies and social solutions that could take a big bite out of the problem," he says; but he also stresses that, in his opinion, "Economically, it's not even clear that global warming is all negative. It's just not true that the climate we have is automatically the best one—and you have to be straight about this."[16]

Much of Keith's commitment to solving problems related to climate change arises from his deep love of the Arctic. "One of the most fundamental reasons for working on the climate problem is to protect some remaining natural wilderness in the world ... There are places, like the Arctic and Central Australia, we haven't yet messed with much. These are important, not just biologically but spiritually."[17] Keith comes by this commitment to environmental science naturally—his father, Anthony Keith, began his career as a Canadian Wildlife Service scientist in the 1960s, and was instrumental in convincing then-prime minister Pierre Trudeau to support a widespread ban on DDT use in Canada.

"We don't yet know how to manage the planet, and we don't have the institutions and governing structures for doing so."[18]
—David Keith

Thinking About Environmental Perspectives

David Keith's career has combined a number of seemingly unrelated disciplines (physics, economics, and engineering) into a research focus that makes a lot of sense in today's complicated environmental landscape. Try to identify some of your own cross-disciplinary interests. What about psychology and energy conservation (How do you get people to change their energy-using behaviour?)? Or ethics and waste disposal (Is it right to transport someone's garbage a long distance, to dispose of it in someone else's backyard?)? Or economics, political science, and water resources (Can you use laws or pricing structures to effect a change in the way we use and manage our water resources?)?

---

ling across the membrane, forming molecules of water that are expelled as waste, along with heat. While this is occurring, the electrons from the hydrogen atoms have travelled to a device that completes an electric current between the two electrodes. The movement of the hydrogen's electrons from one electrode to the other creates the output of electricity.

Hydrogen and fuel cells have many benefits

As a fuel, hydrogen offers a number of benefits. We will never run out of hydrogen; it is the most abundant element in the universe. It can be clean and nontoxic to use, and—depending on the source of the hydrogen and the source of electricity for its extraction—it may produce few greenhouse gases and other pollutants. Pure water and heat may be the only waste products from a hydrogen fuel cell, along with negligible traces of other compounds. In terms of safety for transport and storage, hydrogen can catch fire, but if kept under pressure it is probably no more dangerous than gasoline in tanks.

Hydrogen fuel cells are energy-efficient. Depending on the type of fuel cell, 35% to 70% of the energy released in the reaction can be used. If the system is designed to capture heat as well as electricity, then the energy efficiency of fuel cells can rise to 90%. These rates are comparable or superior to most nonrenewable alternatives.

Fuel cells are also silent and nonpolluting. Unlike batteries (which also produce electricity through chemical reactions), fuel cells will generate electricity whenever hydrogen fuel is supplied, without ever needing recharging. For all these reasons, hydrogen fuel cells are being used to power vehicles, including the buses now operating on the streets of many European, North American, and Asian cities.

Conclusion

The coming decline of fossil fuel supplies and the increasing concern over air pollution and global climate change have convinced many people that we will need to shift to renewable energy sources that will not run out and will pollute far less. Hydropower is a renewable, pollution-free alternative, but it is not without its own negative ecological impacts. Nuclear power showed promise, but high costs and public fears over safety stalled its growth. Biomass energy sources include traditional fuelwood, as well as newer biofuels and biopower. These sources can be carbon-neutral but are not all strictly renewable, especially if biomass sources are overharvested.

New renewable sources with promise for sustaining our civilization far into the future with gentler environmental impacts include solar energy, wind energy, geothermal energy, and ocean energy. By using electricity from renewable sources to produce hydrogen fuel, we may be able to use fuel cells to produce electricity when and where it is needed, helping to convert our transportation sector to a nonpolluting, renewable basis.

Most renewable energy sources have been held back by inadequate funding for research and development, and by artificially cheap market prices for nonrenewable resources that do not include external costs. Despite these obstacles, renewable technologies have progressed far enough to offer hope that we can shift from fossil fuels to renewable energy with a minimum of economic and social disruption. Whether we can also limit environmental impact will depend on how soon and how quickly we make the transition and to what extent we put efficiency and conservation measures into place.

REVIEWING OBJECTIVES

You should now be able to:

Discuss the reasons for seeking alternatives to fossil fuels

- Fossil fuels are nonrenewable resources, and we are gradually depleting them.
- Fossil fuel combustion causes air pollution that results in many environmental and health impacts and contributes to global climate change.

Summarize the contributions to world energy supplies of conventional alternatives to fossil fuels

- Biomass provides 10.0% of global primary energy use, nuclear power provides 6.3%, and hydropower provides 2.2%.
- Nuclear power generates 15.2% of the world's electricity, and hydropower generates 16.0%. In Canada, hydro accounts for almost 60% of electricity generation.

- "Conventional" energy alternatives are the alternatives to fossil fuels that are most widely used. They include hydroelectric power, nuclear power, and biomass energy.

Describe the scale, methods, and environmental impacts of hydroelectric power, nuclear power, and biomass energy

- Hydroelectric power is generated when water from a river runs through a powerhouse and turns turbines. Hydropower produces little air pollution, but dams and reservoirs can greatly alter riverine ecology. Run-of-river is an alternative approach.
- Nuclear power comes from converting the energy of subatomic bonds into thermal energy. Uranium is mined, enriched, processed, and used as fuel for controlled fission reactions. This process, carried out in nuclear reactors, produces heat that powers electricity generation.

- Many advocates of "clean" energy support nuclear power because it lacks the polluting emissions of fossil fuels, but for many people the risks, costs, and challenges outweigh the benefits.
- Traditional biomass energy sources, mainly fuelwood, charcoal, and animal waste, are widely used, especially in the developing world. Biomass can only be considered truly renewable if it is not overharvested.

Outline the major "new" renewable alternative sources of energy and assess their potential for growth

- "New" renewable energy sources include solar, wind, geothermal, ocean, and new biomass technologies, as well as hydrogen fuels and fuel cells. Most of these are not truly "new," but they are currently in a stage of rapid development of modern technologies.
- The new renewables currently provide far less energy and electricity than fossil fuels and other conventional energy sources. However, their use is growing quickly, and this growth is expected to continue as people move away from fossil fuels.

Describe a variety of new biomass, solar, wind, geothermal, and ocean energy technologies, and outline their advantages and disadvantages

- Biofuels, including ethanol and biodiesel, are used to power automobiles. Some crops are grown specifically for this purpose, and waste oils are also used. There are some concerns about the impacts of using food crops to produce biofuels.
- We use biomass to generate electrical power (biopower) from special crops, waste products from agriculture and forestry, and landfill gas. The use of biomass energy theoretically adds no net carbon to the atmosphere.
- Energy from the Sun's radiation can be harnessed using passive methods or by active methods involving powered technology. Solar energy is perpetually renewable, creates no emissions, and enables decentralized power.
- Wind energy is harnessed using turbines mounted on towers. They are often erected in arrays at wind farms on land or offshore, in locations with optimal wind conditions. Wind energy is renewable and creates no emissions. The cost is competitive with that of electricity from fossil fuels, but wind energy is an intermittent source and may face local opposition.
- Thermal energy from inside the planet rises toward the surface and heats groundwater. Use of geothermal energy and Earth energy for direct heating of water, for electricity generation, and in heat pumps for space heating and cooling can be efficient and clean, but may be exhausted if water is overpumped.
- Major ocean energy sources include the motion of tides, waves, and currents, and the thermal heat of ocean water. Ocean energy is perpetually renewable, but so far technologies have seen only limited development.

Explain the benefits of hydrogen and fuel cells and assess future options for energy storage and transportation

- Hydrogen can serve as a fuel to store and transport energy, so that electricity generated by renewable sources can be made portable and used to power vehicles.
- Hydrogen can be produced through electrolysis, or by using fossil fuels—in which case its environmental benefits are reduced.
- Fuel cells create electricity by controlling an interaction between hydrogen and oxygen, and they produce only water as a waste product. Fuel cells are silent, nonpolluting, and do not need recharging.

TESTING YOUR COMPREHENSION

1. How much of our global energy supply do nuclear power, biomass energy, and hydroelectric power contribute? How much of our global electricity do these three conventional energy alternatives generate?

2. Describe how nuclear fission works. How do nuclear plant engineers control fission and prevent a runaway chain reaction? What has been done so far about disposing of radioactive waste?

3. In terms of greenhouse gas emissions, how does nuclear power compare to coal, oil, and natural gas? How do hydropower and biomass energy compare?

4. Contrast the two major approaches to generating hydroelectric power, and compare their environmental impacts.

5. List five sources of biomass energy. What is the world's most-used source of biomass energy? How

does biomass energy use differ between developed and developing nations?

6. About how much of our energy now comes from renewable sources? What is the most prevalent form of renewable energy we use? What form of renewable energy is most used to generate electricity? Which renewable source is experiencing the most rapid growth?

7. Contrast passive and active solar heating. Describe how each works, and give examples of each. What are the environmental and economic advantages and disadvantages of solar power?

8. How do modern wind turbines generate electricity? How does wind speed affect the process? What factors affect where wind turbines are placed? What are the environmental and economic benefits and drawbacks of wind power?

9. Define geothermal energy, and explain how it is used. In what ways is it renewable, or not renewable? How does it differ from what Natural Resources Canada calls "Earth energy"?

10. List and describe four approaches to obtaining energy from ocean water.

THINKING IT THROUGH

1. Given what you have learned about some of the conventional alternatives discussed in this chapter, do you think it is important for us to minimize our use of fossil fuels and maximize our use of these alternatives? What challenges or obstacles would we need to overcome, in order to transition smoothly to alternative sources of energy?

2. Nuclear power has by now been widely used for over three decades, and the world has experienced only one major accident (Chernobyl) responsible for a significant number of deaths. Would you call this a good safety record? Why might safety at nuclear power plants be better in the future? Why might it be worse?

3. There are many different sources of biomass and many ways of harnessing energy from biomass. Discuss one that seems particularly beneficial to you, and one with which you see problems. What biomass energy sources and strategies do you think our society should focus on investing in?

4. One of the greatest challenges in operationalizing new renewable energy sources is to find effective ways of storing and transporting the energy, to even out inconsistencies in supply. One possible solution is to convert solar, wind, or biomass energy into a fuel, such as hydrogen, that can be stored for later use. How is hydrogen fuel produced? Is it a clean process? What factors determine the amount of pollutants hydrogen production will emit?

5. Imagine that you are an investor, and you would like to invest in alternative energy. You are considering buying stock in companies that (1) construct nuclear reactors, (2) construct turbines for hydroelectric dams, (3) operate pulp mills, (4) build ethanol refineries, and (5) supply farm waste to co-fired power plants. What questions would you research about each of these companies before deciding how to invest your money? How do you expect you might apportion your investments, and why? Do you expect there may be ways in which you will feel torn between doing what seems financially wise and what seems best for the environment or for energy security? Explain.

6. Let's say that you are the CEO of a company that develops wind farms. Your staff is presenting you with three options, listed below, for sites for your next development. Describe at least one likely advantage and at least one likely disadvantage you would expect to encounter with each option. What further information would you like to know before deciding which to pursue?

   ▪ Option A: A remote rural site in Yukon Territory
   ▪ Option B: A ridge-top site among the suburbs of Saskatoon
   ▪ Option C: An offshore site off the Nova Scotia coast

INTERPRETING GRAPHS AND DATA

It is not clear that growing crops such as corn for the purpose of producing ethanol is the most efficient use of crop lands. David Pimentel and Tad Patzek have estimated that replacing just one-third of the gasoline used in North America with ethanol would require more cropland than is needed to feed the population![19] They calculate that 0.6 hectares of corn will yield enough ethanol to displace one-third of the gasoline needed to run one average North American car for one year; for comparison, it would require 0.5 hectares of corn to feed one person for one year.

As shown on the graph, the area of corn planted in Canada peaked at about 1 315 000 hectares in 2001. Given that Pimentel and Patzek estimate that it would take 1.8 hectares of corn ethanol to displace the need for gasoline to run one car for a year, and given that there are approximately 12 650 000 cars in Canada, how much would the hectares planted in corn need to be increased in order to run all of the cars in Canada on ethanol? One-third of the cars? One-fourth of the cars?

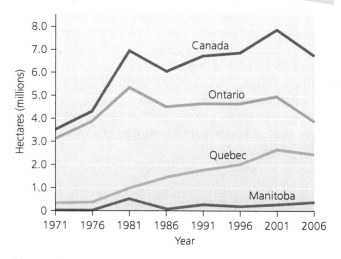

This graph shows the corn area planted in Canada, over time.
Source: Pimentel, David, and Tad W. Patzek (March 2005) Ethanol production using corn, switchgrass, and wood; Biodiesel production using soybean and sunflower. Natural Resources Research, 14(1).

CHAPTER ENDNOTES

1. Nova Scotia Power Environment > Renewable Energy > Tidal, www.nspower.ca/environment/green_power/tidal/technology.shtml

2. Pembina Institute, Renewable Energy, http://re.pembina.org/global/support

3. Worldwatch Institute and Center for American Progress (2006) *American Energy: The Renewable Path to Energy Security.* Washington, D.C.

4. *Powerful Connections: Priorities and Directions in Energy Science and Technology in Canada* (2006) The Report of the National Advisory Committee on Sustainable Energy Science and Technology, Office of Energy Research and Development, Natural Resources Canada, www.nrcan.gc.ca/eps/oerd-brde/report-rapport/toc_e.htm

5. Canadian Biogas Industry Overview, Ken Hogg (October 27, 2005) New Era Renewable Energy Solutions, www.ptac.org/eea/dl/eeaf0501p04.pdf

6. Canadian Biogas Industry Overview, Ken Hogg (October 27, 2005) New Era Renewable Energy Solutions, www.ptac.org/eea/dl/eeaf0501p04.pdf

7. Environment Canada, Municipal Solid Waste, Landfill Gas, Beare Road Project, www.ec.gc.ca/wmd-dgd/default.asp?lang=En&n=3438B2E7-1

8. Environment Canada, Methane to Markets Partnership Landfill Subcommittee (October 2005) Landfill Gas Management in Canada, www.methanetomarkets.org/resources/landfills/docs/canada_lf_profile.pdf

9. Canadian Geographic, The Canadian Atlas Online, *Solar Power,* www.canadiangeographic.ca/atlas/themes.aspx?id=weather&sub=weather_power_solarpower&lang=En

10. Canadian Geographic, The Canadian Atlas Online, *Wind Power,* www.canadiangeographic.ca/atlas/themes.aspx?id=WEATHER&sub=WEATHER_POWER_WINDPOWER&lang=En

11. C40 Large Cities Climate Summit 2007, *Case Studies: Energy*, www.nycclimatesummit.com/casestudies/energy/energy_CANADA.html

12. Canadian Centre for Energy, www.centreforenergy.com/silos/geothermal/geothermalOverview03.asp

13. Environment Canada Science and the Environment: Earth for Storing Energy, www.ec.gc.ca/science/sand-esept99/article5_e.html

14. Keith, David, *Homepage*, University of Calgary, www.ucalgary.ca/~keith/

15. Bergman, Brian (2006) Environmental scientist of the year: Climate contrarian, *Canadian Geographic* May/June, pp. 74–82.

16. Bergman, Brian (2006) Environmental scientist of the year: Climate contrarian, *Canadian Geographic* May/June, pp. 74–82.

17. Bergman, Brian (2006) Environmental scientist of the year: Climate contrarian, *Canadian Geographic* May/June, pp. 74–82.

18. Bergman, Brian (2006) Environmental scientist of the year: Climate contrarian, *Canadian Geographic* May/June, pp. 74–82.

19. Pimentel, David, and Tad W. Patzek (March 2005) Ethanol production using corn, switchgrass, and wood; Biodiesel production using soybean and sunflower. *Natural Resources Research*, 14(1).

MyEnvironmentPlace

Go to **www.myenvironmentplace.ca** where you will find quizzes, animations, your Pearson eText, and more.

14 Managing Our Waste

These containers are en route to a recycling facility.

Upon successfully completing this chapter, you will be able to

- Summarize and compare the types of waste we generate
- List the major approaches to managing waste
- Delineate the scale of the waste dilemma
- Describe conventional waste disposal methods: landfills and incineration

- Evaluate approaches for reducing waste: source reduction, reuse, composting, and recycling
- Discuss industrial solid waste management and principles of industrial ecology
- Assess issues in managing hazardous waste

After only a couple of years the newly established North Garden at Beare Road, planted by community volunteers, was flourishing. Source: Friends of the Rouge, *About the Rouge Watershed: Geology*, www.frw.ca/rouge.-php?ID=105

CENTRAL CASE:
THE BEARE ROAD LANDFILL: MAKING GOOD USE OF OLD GARBAGE

"An extraterrestrial observer might conclude that conversion of raw materials to wastes is the real purpose of human economic activity."
—GARY GARDNER AND PAYAL SAMPAT, WORLDWATCH INSTITUTE

"We can't have an economy that uses our air, water, and soil as a garbage can."
—DAVID SUZUKI

"The issue will never go away. It's going to be a crisis if we can't find another place for our trash."
—JANE PITFIELD, TORONTO CITY COUNCILLOR

In the eastern part of Toronto, not far from the University of Toronto Scarborough campus, there is a park with a grassy hill. On the hill there are trees, bike trails, and fields of wildflowers. This is the highest spot in the neighbourhood, overlooking the Rouge River. Visitors stroll, chat, admire the view, and walk their dogs. As you hike toward the top, there are few clues that beneath this grassy hill lie 9.6 million tonnes of garbage.[1] This is the old Beare Road Landfill.

The Beare Road site is located on gravel that was deposited some 12 000 years ago. At that time, when the last glaciation was drawing to a close, meltwater from the Laurentide Ice Sheet flowed into the Lake Ontario basin, creating a glacial lake much larger than the present-day Lake Ontario. Geologists refer to this ancient lake as Lake Iroquois (see map).

The coarse sandy and gravelly deposits of the former shoreline of Lake Iroquois are now bluffs, stranded high above the current lake level. These porous and permeable units host significant aquifers, including the aquifer of the Oak Ridges Moraine, as well as the headwaters for hundreds of streams and rivers. The

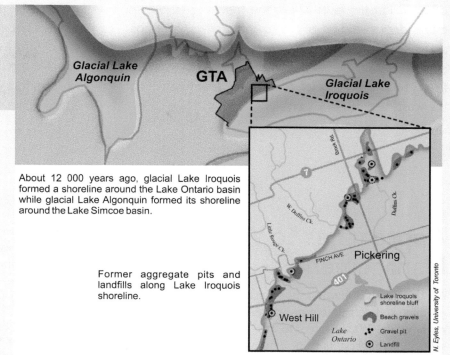

The location of the ancient shoreline of glacial Lake Iroquois is now marked by a series of gravel deposits and bluffs. Old gravel pits show the extent of aggregate extraction from these deposits over the past 100+ years. Many of the worked-out gravel pits were later utilized as dumpsites for municipal solid waste.

About 12 000 years ago, glacial Lake Iroquois formed a shoreline around the Lake Ontario basin while glacial Lake Algonquin formed its shoreline around the Lake Simcoe basin.

Former aggregate pits and landfills along Lake Iroquois shoreline.

deposits have also been profitable for producers of *aggregates*—gravel, sand, and crushed stone used for various construction purposes, including the building of roads and production of concrete. Many of the small towns scattered along the ancient shoreline in Ontario owe their economic beginnings to the exploitation of gravel and sand from these deposits.

Fast-forward to the latter half of the 1900s, when worked-out gravel pits scattered along the ancient shoreline sat empty. Some of the pits filled with water, serving as recreational lakes for fishing and swimming. In other cases, they beckoned to local residents—what better place to dispose of municipal solid waste? In that era, the negative impacts of tossing waste into such a porous and permeable medium were little known, and a number of the pits were used for this purpose (see maps), including the Beare Road gravel pit.

The Beare Road pit officially began receiving municipal garbage in 1968. It began with a capacity of 3 million tonnes, but this was increased several times over the years as the urgency grew for places to put Toronto's ever-increasing garbage. The final increase in capacity was accompanied by a promise of funding from the government to be used toward the rehabilitation of the landscape, ultimately making it available for recreational use by the community.[2]

The landfill was eventually closed down in 1983.[3] At that time a system for passive flaring of landfill gases was installed (see "The Science Behind the Story: Energy from Landfill Gas at Beare Road," Chapter 17). Some landscape restoration was undertaken, by the government and by local residents (see photo), and the site was opened as a park.

In 1996, E.S. Fox, in agreement with the City of Toronto (owner of the site) and Ontario Power Generation, began to collect the methane-rich gas being generated by the decomposing garbage at Beare Road. This type of operation is called *LFGTE* (*landfill gas-to-electricity*), and it makes use of what would otherwise be a harmful by-product of the garbage. Methane gas smells bad, damages vegetation, and is explosive and flammable. It is also a highly effective greenhouse gas, which must be actively managed if Canada hopes to minimize GHG emissions to fulfill its commitment to control global warming in the future.

Some environmental problems persist at the site; they are typical of old dumpsites and will require active management for years. For example, early engineering installations designed to control the collection and movement of leachate failed years ago. The impermeable liner that had been installed to prevent leakage filled with leachate, which then began to seep from the side of the hill at the level where the liner topped out—a classic demonstration of the "bathtub effect." The possibility persists that leachate may one day threaten community developments immediately downstream from the site. The exact content and composition of the waste also are unknown.

In spite of these problems, the Beare Road project provides a hope-inspiring model for the management of old landfill sites. Gas collection and utilization has helped to resolve a number of local environmental problems (such as odour and damage to vegetation) and is contributing to the reduction of GHG emissions for Canada.

Approaches to Waste Management

As the world's human population rises, and as we produce and consume more material goods, we generate more waste. **Waste** refers to any unwanted material or substance that results from a human activity or process. The federal government of Canada has adopted a definition that states, in part, that waste is "any substance for which the owner/generator has no further use."[4] Another popular definition suggests that waste is "resources out of place," emphasizing the fact that most waste still contains a significant proportion of useful materials. These definitions represent a changing perception of waste—that there is much of value that can be recovered from our waste stream.

For management purposes, waste is divided into several main categories. *Municipal solid waste* is nonliquid waste that comes from homes, institutions, and small businesses. *Industrial solid waste* includes waste from production of consumer goods, mining, agriculture, and petroleum extraction and refining. *Hazardous waste* refers to solid or liquid waste that is toxic, chemically reactive, flammable, corrosive, or radioactive. It can include everything from paint and household cleaners to medical waste to industrial solvents. Another type of waste is *wastewater*, water we use in our households, businesses, industries, or public facilities and drain or flush down our pipes, as well as the polluted runoff from our streets and storm drains.

We have several aims in managing waste

Waste can degrade water quality, soil quality, and air quality, thereby degrading human health and the environment. Waste is also a measure of inefficiency, so reducing waste can potentially save industry, municipalities, and consumers both money and resources. In addition, waste is unpleasant esthetically. For these and other reasons, waste management has become a vital pursuit.

There are three main components of **waste management**:

1. Minimizing the amount of waste we generate
2. Recovering waste materials and finding ways to recycle them
3. Disposing of waste safely and effectively

Minimizing waste at its source—called *source reduction*—is the preferred approach. There are several ways to reduce the amount of waste that enters the **waste stream**, the flow of waste as it moves from its sources toward disposal destinations (**FIGURE 14.1**). Manufacturers can use materials more efficiently. Consumers can buy fewer goods, buy goods with less packaging, and use those goods longer. Reusing goods you already own, purchasing used items, and donating your used items for others also help reduce the amount of material entering the waste stream.

Recovery (which includes recycling and composting) is widely viewed as the next best strategy in waste management. *Recycling* involves sending used goods to facilities that extract and reprocess raw materials to manufacture new goods. Newspapers, white paper, cardboard, glass,

roots

WASTE

The early uses of the word **waste**, around the year 1200, referred to a large, uninhabitable space. This makes sense when you consider that the word comes from the Latin root *vastus*; the same root is found in the words *vast* and *devastate*. The meaning "useless expenditure" dates from about 1300, and that of "garbage" from the early 1400s.

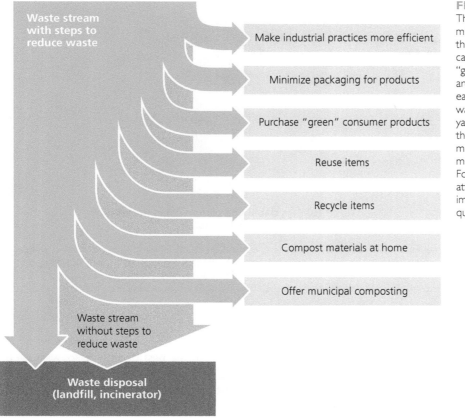

FIGURE 14.1
The most effective way to manage waste is to minimize the amount of material that enters the waste stream. To do this, manufacturers can increase efficiency, and consumers can buy "green" products that have minimal packaging, are designed to make recycling of components easy, or are produced in ways that minimize waste. Individuals can compost food scraps and yard waste at home and can reuse items rather than buying new ones. Many of us can recycle materials and compost yard waste through municipal recycling and composting programs. For all remaining waste, waste managers attempt to find disposal methods that minimize impact on human health and environmental quality.

metal cans, appliances, and some plastic containers have all become increasingly recyclable as new technologies have been developed and as markets for recycled materials have grown. Organic waste can be recovered through *composting*, or biological decomposition. Recycling is not a concept that humans invented; recall that all materials are recycled in ecosystems. Recycling is a fundamental feature of the way natural systems function.

Regardless of how effectively we reduce our waste stream, there will always be some waste left to dispose of. Disposal methods include burying waste in landfills and burning waste in incinerators. In this chapter we first examine how these approaches are used to manage municipal solid waste, and then we address industrial solid waste and hazardous waste.

Municipal Solid Waste

Municipal solid waste is waste produced by consumers, public facilities, and small businesses. It is what we commonly refer to as "trash" or "garbage." Everything from paper to food scraps to roadside litter to old appliances and furniture is considered municipal solid waste.

Patterns in the municipal solid waste stream vary from place to place

In Canada, paper, organics (mainly yard debris and food scraps), and plastics are the principal components of municipal solid waste, together accounting for more than 66% of the waste stream (**FIGURE 14.2**). Even after recycling, paper is the largest component of municipal solid waste. Patterns differ in developing countries; there, food scraps are often the primary contributor to solid waste, and paper makes up a smaller proportion.

Most municipal solid waste comes from packaging and nondurable goods (products meant to be discarded after a short period of use). In addition, consumers throw away old durable goods and outdated equipment as they purchase new products. As we acquire more goods, we generate more waste. According to Statistics Canada, which tracks a variety of social, economic, and environmental indicators, Canadian citizens produced more than 26 million tonnes of municipal solid waste in 2008, for a population of 33 million—almost 1 tonne per person for that year. This means that Canadians generated about

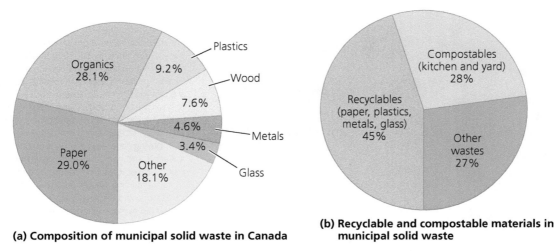

(a) Composition of municipal solid waste in Canada

(b) Recyclable and compostable materials in municipal solid waste

FIGURE 14.2   Paper products are the largest component of the municipal solid waste stream in Canada (a), followed closely by organic wastes (yard trimmings and food scraps) and plastics. In total, each Canadian citizen generates more than 1 tonne (actually, 1037 kg in 2004, including both residential and industrial components)[5] of solid waste each year. Much of the waste generated by Canadians is, in principle, recyclable or compostable (b).   *Source: Data are for 2004, from Environment Canada, Waste Management,* Municipal Solid Waste, *www.ec.gc.ca/wmd-dgd/Default.-asp?lang=En&n=7623F633-1*

800 kg of trash per person that year, or 2.2 kg per person per day.[6]

Surpassing Canada in per capita solid waste generation is the United States, with about 3.3 kg per person per day.[7] Trailing behind is the Netherlands, with 1.4 kg per person per day. Among developed nations, Germany and Sweden produce the least waste per capita, generating just under 0.9 kg per person per day. Differences among nations result in part from differences in the cost of waste disposal; where disposal is expensive, people have incentive to waste less. The wastefulness of the North American lifestyle, with its excess packaging and reliance on nondurable goods, has caused critics to label this as "the throwaway society."

In developing nations, people consume less and generate considerably less waste. One study found that people of high-income nations waste more than twice as much as people of low-income nations. However, wealthier nations also invest more in waste collection and disposal, so they are often better able to manage their waste proliferation and minimize impacts on human health and the environment.

Waste generation is rising in all nations

In North America since 1960, waste generation has increased by almost 300%, and per capita waste generation has risen by about 70%. Plastics, which came into wide consumer use only after 1970, have accounted for the greatest relative increase in the waste stream during the

last several decades. In the past decade or so, waste generation in Canada has kept pace with the growth rate of the population but has lagged slightly behind the growth in real gross domestic product (GDP). This suggests a promising trend of waste diversion and producing more for less, perhaps because of recycling and a shift to more efficient waste management processes.

The intensive consumption that has long characterized wealthy nations is now increasing rapidly in developing nations. To some extent, this trend reflects rising material standards of living, but an increase in packaging is also to blame. Items made for temporary use and poor-quality goods designed to be inexpensive wear out and pile up quickly as trash, littering the landscapes of countries from Mexico to Kenya to Indonesia. Over the past three decades, per capita waste generation rates have more than doubled in Latin American nations and have increased more than fivefold in the Middle East. Like consumers in "the throwaway society," wealthy consumers in developing nations often discard items that can still be used. At many dumps and **landfills** throughout the developing world, in fact, poor people still support themselves by selling items they scavenge (**FIGURE 14.3**).

In many industrialized nations, per capita waste generation rates have levelled off or decreased in recent years. Waste generation has essentially kept pace with population in Canada since 1996, which means that per capita waste production has been essentially stable over this period. This is due largely to the increased popularity of recycling, composting, reduction, and reuse. We will examine these nondisposal approaches to waste management shortly, but let us first assess how we dispose of waste.

FIGURE 14.3
Tens of thousands of people used to scavenge each day from the dump at Payatas, outside Manila in the Philippines, finding items for themselves and selling material to junk dealers for 100–200 pesos ($2–$4) per day. That so many people could support themselves this way testifies to the immense amount of usable material needlessly discarded by wealthier portions of the population. The dump was closed in 2000 after an avalanche of trash killed hundreds of people.

Open dumping of the past has given way to improved disposal methods

Historically, people dumped their garbage wherever it suited them. Until the mid-nineteenth century, New York City's official method of garbage disposal was to dump it off piers into the East River. As population densities increased, municipalities took on the task of consolidating trash into open dumps at specified locations to keep other areas clean. This is how the worked-out gravel pits of the ancient Lake Iroquois shoreline in southern Ontario came to be used as dumpsites. To decrease the volume of trash, the dumps would be burned from time to time. Open dumping and burning still occur throughout much of the world.

As population and consumption rose in developed nations, more packaging and the use of nondegradable materials increased, waste production increased, and dumps accordingly grew larger. At the same time, expanding cities and suburbs forced more people into the vicinity of dumps and exposed them to the noxious smoke of dump burning. Reacting to opposition from residents living near dumps and to a rising awareness of health and environmental threats posed by unregulated dumping and burning, many nations improved their methods of waste disposal. Most industrialized nations now bury waste in lined and covered landfills and burn waste in incineration facilities.

Since the late 1980s, the recovery of materials for recycling has expanded, slightly decreasing the pressure on landfills (**FIGURE 14.4**). The total rate of diversion of municipal solid waste in Canada (that is, diversion away

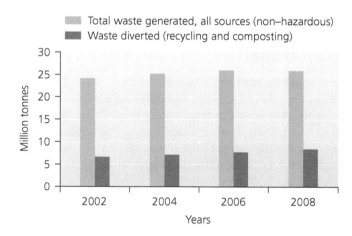

FIGURE 14.4
Waste generation may be levelling off in Canada. The diversion rate (to recycling and composting) has not changed much, hovering around 25–27%.
Source: Statistics Canada (2010) Cansim Table 153-0041.

from disposal or incineration, to recycling or composting) increased from 21% in 2000 to 27% in 2008. Over the same period, the rate of diversion of solid waste from residential sources increased more. Change has been slow, however, and an estimated $1.5 billion worth of recyclable materials were disposed of in 2004.[8]

Waste disposal is regulated by three levels of government

In Canada, municipal governments are responsible for the collection, diversion, and disposal of solid waste from residential and small commercial and industrial sources. If you put waste by the side of the road on garbage collection day and it is picked up by city garbage trucks, then it is municipal solid waste. Many municipalities now also provide drop-off facilities for special categories of waste, including household hazardous wastes, such as leftover paint.

Provincial and territorial governments have control over the movement of waste materials within the jurisdiction and over the licensing of treatment facilities and waste generators. Thus, each province or territory has its own legislation and guidelines regulating the design, siting, licensing, operations, and expansion of landfill sites. The federal government, meanwhile, is responsible for looking after international agreements about waste and regulating transboundary movements of waste materials. Federal involvement in waste management occurs mainly through the *Canadian Environmental Protection Act* and the *Fisheries Act*.

Sanitary landfills are engineered to minimize leakage of contaminants

In a modern **sanitary landfill**, waste is buried in the ground or piled up in large, carefully engineered mounds. In contrast to open dumps, sanitary landfills are designed to prevent waste from contaminating the environment and threatening public health (**FIGURE 14.5**). In a sanitary landfill, waste is partially decomposed by bacteria and

compresses under its own weight to take up less space. Waste is typically interlayered with soil, a method that speeds decomposition, reduces odours, and reduces infestation by pests. Limited infiltration of rainwater allows for biodegradation by aerobic and anaerobic bacteria.

To protect against environmental contamination, landfills must be located away from wetlands and situated well above the local water table. The bottoms and sides of modern sanitary landfills are lined with heavy-duty plastic or other high-tech geo-engineered fabrics. They are typically underlain by a thick layer (a metre or more) of impermeable clay to help prevent contaminants from seeping into aquifers. Sanitary landfills also have systems of pipes, collection ponds, and treatment facilities to collect and treat **leachate**, the liquid that results when substances from the trash dissolve in water as rainwater percolates downward. Leachate collection systems must be maintained throughout the lifetime of the landfill and for many years after closure. Regulations also require that area groundwater and soils be monitored regularly for contamination.

After a landfill is closed, it is capped with an engineered cover that must be maintained. The cap usually consists of a hydraulic barrier that prevents water from seeping down and gas from seeping up; a gravel layer above the hydraulic barrier that drains water, lessening pressure on the hydraulic barrier; a soil barrier that stores water and protects the hydraulic layer from weather extremes; and a topsoil layer that encourages plant growth, helping to prevent erosion.

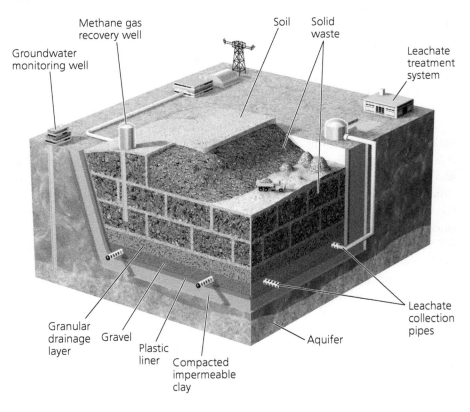

FIGURE 14.5
Sanitary landfills are engineered to prevent waste from contaminating soil and groundwater. Waste is laid in a large, lined depression, underlain by an impervious clay layer designed to prevent liquids from leaching out. Pipes of a leachate collection system draw out these liquids from the bottom of the landfill. Waste is layered along with soil until the depression is filled, and it continues to be built up until the landfill is capped. Landfill gas produced by anaerobic bacteria may be recovered, and waste managers monitor groundwater for contamination.

Methane gas recovery well　Soil　Solid waste　Leachate treatment system

Groundwater monitoring well

Granular drainage layer　Gravel　Plastic liner　Compacted impermeable clay　Aquifer　Leachate collection pipes

At the Beare Road Landfill, some underlying rock and sediment units are naturally clay-rich shales, creating a barrier that appears to slow the subsurface movement of leachate from the site. However, the Iroquois sand and gravel deposits—removed at an earlier stage for aggregate production, forming the pit itself—are much more permeable, providing a pathway for leachate migration.[9] Although it met provincial standards for landfill technology at the time of its construction, the Beare Road Landfill predated most current regulations and guidelines. As a result, it has caused some environmental contamination, and residents of adjacent areas continue to express some concerns about the possibility of gas and leachate migration. There is no functional engineering to control leachate migration at the site, aside from a collection ditch around the perimeter and the gas collection technologies. The refuse mound is surrounded by a number of wells installed for the purpose of monitoring groundwater for any signs of leachate migration into the surrounding areas.[10] The mound was covered after the closure of the site to inhibit the infiltration of rainwater and the production and migration of leachate.

Landfills can be transformed after closure

Today many landfills lie abandoned. One reason is that waste managers have closed many smaller landfills and consolidated the trash stream into fewer, much larger landfills. Meanwhile, growing numbers of cities have converted closed landfills into public parks (FIGURE 14.6), like the Rouge Park in Toronto, which includes the Beare Road Landfill site. Such efforts date back at least to 1938,

FIGURE 14.6
Residents and members of Friends of the Rouge plant wildflowers at the Beare Road North Garden.
Source: Friends of the Rouge, About the Rouge Watershed: Geology, *www.frw.ca/rouge.php?ID=105.*

when an ash landfill at Flushing Meadows, in Queens, New York, was redeveloped for the 1939 World's Fair, and subsequently the 1964–1965 World's Fair. Designated a park in 1967, today the site hosts Shea Stadium, the Queens Museum of Art, the New York Hall of Science, and the Queens Botanical Garden. Shutting down an industrial site and getting it ready for cleanup and post-industrial repurposing is called **decommissioning**.

The Fresh Kills redevelopment endeavour in New York will be the world's largest landfill conversion project. The largest landfill in the world, Fresh Kills was the primary repository of New York City's garbage for half a century. On March 22, 2001, New York City Mayor Rudolph Giuliani and New York Governor George Pataki were on hand to celebrate as a barge arrived on the western shore of New York City's Staten Island and dumped the final load of trash at Fresh Kills. The landfill's closure was a welcome event for Staten Island's 450 000 residents, who had long viewed the landfill as a bad-smelling eyesore, health threat, and civic blemish. The 890 ha landfill featured six gigantic mounds of trash and soil. The highest, at 69 m, was higher than the nearby Statue of Liberty.

New York City planned to transform the old landfill into a world-class public park—a verdant landscape of rolling hills and wetlands teeming with wildlife, a mecca for recreation for New York's residents. Later in 2001, however, the landfill had to be reopened temporarily. After the September 11, 2001, terrorist attacks, the 1.8 million tonnes of rubble from the collapsed World Trade Center towers, including unrecoverable human remains, were taken by barge to Fresh Kills, where the material was sorted and buried. A monument will be erected at the site as part of the new park. Today, plans for the park are forging ahead. The master plan for reclamation of the site involves everything from ecological restoration of the wetlands to construction of roads, ball fields, sculptures, and roller-blading rinks. People will be able to bicycle on trails parallelling tidal creeks of the region's largest estuary and reach stunning vistas atop the hills.

Landfills have drawbacks

Despite improvements in liner and cover technology and landfill siting, many experts believe that leachate will eventually escape even from well-lined landfills. Liners can be punctured, and leachate collection systems eventually cease to be maintained. Moreover, landfills are kept dry to reduce leachate, but the bacteria that break down material thrive in wet conditions. Dryness, therefore, slows waste decomposition. In fact, it is surprising how slowly some materials biodegrade when they are tightly compressed in a landfill. Innovative archeological research has revealed that landfills often contain food that has not decomposed and 40-year-old newspapers that are still legible (see "The Science Behind the Story: Digging Garbage: The Archaeology of Solid Waste").

Another problem is finding suitable areas to locate landfills because most communities do not want them nearby. This *not-in-my-backyard* (*NIMBY*) *syndrome* is one reason why Toronto, New York, and many other cities export their waste and why residents of areas that are receiving the waste are increasingly protesting. The quote from a Toronto city councillor at the beginning of this chapter refers to the ongoing struggle to find somewhere to dispose of Toronto's waste. The past practice—to export Toronto's trash to Michigan—had become increasingly unpopular among residents there. In 2007 an average of 74 truck-loads per day of solid waste (approximately 441 363 tonnes) went to a Michigan landfill from Toronto (down from 142 daily truckloads in 2003). This amount continued to decline as the city surpassed its waste export reduction targets. Toronto's agreement with the receiving landfill in Michigan (by which the city is contractually obligated to continue to deliver garbage to the privately maintained landfill) expired at the end of 2010. In 2007, the City of Toronto acquired the Green Lane Landfill site located southwest of London. This landfill is still about 200 km from downtown Toronto, but it provides an alternative to the Michigan exports. The site features the latest landfill engineering technology, including onsite leachate treatment and methane gas collection and flaring systems.[11]

As a result of the NIMBY syndrome, landfills are rarely sited in neighbourhoods that are home to wealthy and educated people with the political clout to keep them out. Instead, they are disproportionately sited in poor and minority communities, as environmental justice advocates have frequently made clear.

The unwillingness of most communities to accept waste became apparent with the famed case of the "garbage barge," the *Mobro4000*. In Islip, New York, in 1987, the town's landfills were full, prompting town administrators to ship waste by barge to a methane production plant

roots

GARBAGE

The word **garbage**, first used in the late 1500s to mean "refuse" or "filth," probably comes from the Old French word *garbe*, which refers to the entrails or waste parts of an animal. The term *garbology*, the study of garbage as a social science, was coined by William Rathje in the 1970s.

in North Carolina. Prior to the barge's arrival, it became known that the shipment was contaminated with medical waste, including syringes, hospital gowns, and diapers. Because of the medical waste, the methane plant rejected the entire load. The barge sat in a North Carolina harbour for 11 days before heading for Louisiana. However, Louisiana would not permit the barge to dock. The barge travelled toward Mexico, but the Mexican navy prevented it from entering that nation's waters. In the end, the barge travelled 9700 km before eventually returning to New York, where, after several court battles, the waste was finally incinerated at a facility in Queens.

Incinerating trash reduces pressure on landfills

Incineration, or combustion, is a controlled process in which mixed garbage is burned at very high temperatures (**FIGURE 14.7**). At incineration facilities, waste is generally sorted and metals removed. Metal-free waste is chopped into small pieces to aid combustion and then is burned in a furnace. Incinerating waste reduces its weight by up to 75% and its volume by up to 90%.

However, simply reducing the volume and weight does not rid trash of components that are toxic. The ash remaining after trash is incinerated therefore must be disposed of in special landfills for hazardous waste. Moreover, when trash is burned, hazardous chemicals—including dioxins, heavy metals, and PCBs—can be created and released into the atmosphere. Such releases caused a backlash against incineration from citizens concerned about health hazards. Opponents also feel that incineration is incompatible with the more sustainable path of reducing consumption, producing less waste, and diverting more of the waste we produce into recycling and composting.

Most developed nations now regulate incinerator emissions, and some have banned incineration outright. In Canada the ability to ban incineration rests with the provinces and territories. In some provinces where incineration is allowed, such as Ontario (where a previous ban was lifted in 1995), some municipalities continue to ban incineration in their own jurisdictions, or do not include incineration as part of their waste reduction and diversion plans. For example, the City of Toronto's aggressive plan for reducing the amount of waste produced and shipped to Michigan does not include incineration.

As a result of real and perceived health threats from incinerator emissions—and of community opposition to these plants—engineers have developed several technologies to mitigate emissions. *Scrubbers* chemically treat the gases produced in combustion to remove hazardous

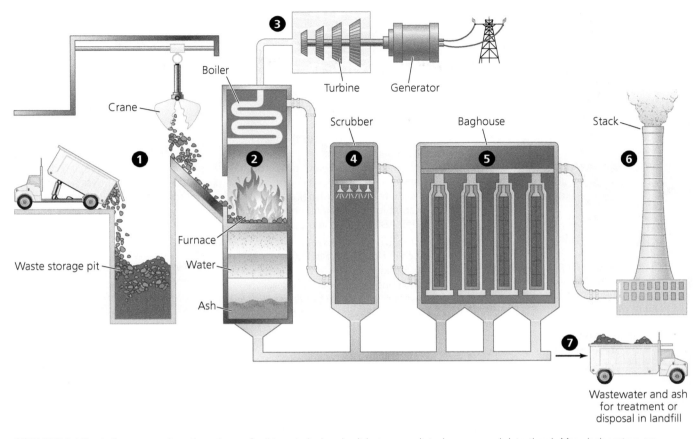

FIGURE 14.7   Incinerators reduce the volume of solid waste by burning it but may emit toxic compounds into the air. Many incinerators are waste-to-energy (WTE) facilities that use the heat of combustion to generate electricity. In a WTE facility, solid waste (1) is burned at extremely high temperatures (2), heating water, which turns to steam. The steam turns a turbine (3), which powers a generator to create electricity. In an incinerator outfitted with pollution-control technology, toxic gases produced by combustion are mitigated chemically by a scrubber (4), and airborne particulate matter is filtered physically in a baghouse (5) before air is emitted from the stack (6). Ash remaining from the combustion process is disposed of (7) in a landfill.

components and neutralize acidic gases, such as sulphur dioxide and hydrochloric acid, turning them into water and salt. Scrubbers generally do this either by spraying liquids formulated to neutralize the gases or by passing the gases through dry lime.

Particulate matter is physically removed from incinerator emissions in a system of huge filters known as a *baghouse*. These tiny particles, called fly ash, often contain some of the worst dioxin and heavy metal pollutants. In addition, burning garbage at especially high temperatures can destroy certain pollutants, such as PCBs. Even all these measures, however, do not fully eliminate toxic emissions.

Many incinerators burn waste to create energy

Incineration was initially practised simply to reduce the volume of waste, but today it often serves to generate electricity as well. Most North American incinerators today are **waste-to-energy (WTE) facilities** that use the heat

produced by waste combustion to boil water, creating steam that drives electricity generation or fuels heating systems. When burned, waste generates about 35% of the energy generated by burning coal, per unit weight.

Revenues from power generation, however, are usually not enough to offset the considerable financial cost of building and running incinerators. Because it can take many years for a WTE facility to become profitable, many companies that build and operate these facilities require communities contracting with them to guarantee the facility a minimum amount of garbage. In a number of cases, such long-term commitments have interfered with communities' later efforts to reduce their waste through recycling and other waste-reduction strategies.

Landfills can produce gas for energy

Combustion in WTE plants is not the only means of gaining energy from waste. Deep inside landfills, bacteria decompose waste in an oxygen-deficient environment.

THE SCIENCE BEHIND THE STORY

Digging Garbage: The Archaeology of Solid Waste

This is Fresh Kills Landfill before its closure.

Garbage and *knowledge* are two words rarely put together. But when scientist William Rathje dons trash-flecked clothes and burrows into a city dump, he gleans valuable information about how we live. By pulling tonnes of trash out of disposal sites over the course of decades, Rathje has turned dumpster diving into a noteworthy field of scientific inquiry that he calls *garbology*. An archaeologist by training, Rathje has brought exacting archaeological techniques to the contents of trashcans.

As a professor at the University of Arizona in the early 1970s, Rathje wanted his students to learn a technique common among archaeologists—sorting through ancient trash mounds to understand past cultures. With few ancient civilizations or their trash close at hand, he arranged for his students to dig through their neighbours' garbage.

In 1973, he gave that effort a name, "The Garbage Project," and began a methodical study of the contents of modern trash. With rakes and notebooks, the researchers sorted, weighed, itemized, and analyzed the refuse. They then visited the homes of the people who had generated the trash and asked residents about their shopping and consumption habits.

Then in 1987, amid growing debates about how quickly landfills were filling up, Rathje decided to see what was taking up space in them. The Garbage Project headed to landfills with a truck-mounted bucket auger—a large drill commonly employed by geologists and construction crews to handle everything from excavating soil samples to creating new water wells. Rathje and his researchers dug into landfills around North America, boring as far as 30 m down in 15 to 20 garbage "wells" at each site, with each well yielding up to 25 tonnes of trash.

Once excavated, landfill contents were sorted, weighed, and identified. Rathje's teams sometimes froze the trash before they worked with it to make the garbage easier to separate and to limit odour and flies. Smaller bits of trash were put through sieves and sometimes washed with water to make them easier to label. Rathje has excavated at least 21 dumps, uncovering a host of interesting things in the process:

■ *Not much rot.* Trash doesn't decay much in closed landfills, Rathje has found. In the dry, low-oxygen conditions inside most closed dumps, trash turns into a sort of time capsule. Rathje's teams have found whole hot dogs in most digs, intact pastries that are decades old, and grass clippings that are still green. Decades-old newspapers are legible and can be used to date layers of trash.

■ *Paper rules.* Paper-based products make up more than 40% of most landfill content, and construction debris makes up about 20%. Newspapers are often a high-volume item, averaging about 14% of landfill space.

■ *Diapers not a problem.* Rathje says that fast-food packaging, polystyrene foam, and disposable diapers aren't a major problem, making up only about 3% of landfill content. (There are other concerns about diapers contributing pathogens to the waste stream, however.) If all plastic packaging were to be replaced by containers made of glass, paper, steel, or similar materials, Rathje maintains, the packaging load to landfills (in weight) would more than double.

■ *Poison in small bottles.* Toxic waste comes in all sizes. If nail polish were sold in large drums, its chemical composition would make it illegal to throw out in a regular dump. Nail polish, however, is discarded in small bottles—hundreds of thousands of them per year. Luckily, however, the potentially toxic ingredients in nail polish don't always spread far, he found. Paper, diapers, and other nontoxic garbage often absorb toxic materials in landfills and keep the poisons from leaching out.

Through garbology, Rathje has gleaned unique insights into how we can change our often wasteful habits. Now a consulting professor at Stanford University, Rathje has emerged as a leading expert on how to reduce waste.

"Garbologist" William Rathje has pioneered the study of our culture through the waste we generate.

Do you know where your trash goes? Where is your landfill or incinerator located? Are the people who live closest to the facility wealthy, poor, or middle class? What race or ethnicity are they? Do you know whether the people of this neighbourhood protested against the introduction of the landfill or incinerator?

This anaerobic decomposition produces *landfill gas*, a mix of gases that consists of roughly half methane. Landfill gas can be collected, processed, and used in the same way as natural gas.

Today more than 40 operational projects in Canada, like the one at Beare Road, collect landfill gas and convert it into energy. Other countries take advantage of this resource as well. In Chile, four facilities in Valparaiso and Santiago supply 40% of the region's demand for natural gas. In the United States, more than 300 facilities convert landfill gas to energy. At landfill sites where gas is not collected for commercial use, it is typically allowed to flow out passively through candlestick pipes, where it is burned off in flares to reduce odours.

Reducing waste is a better option

Reducing the amount of material entering the waste stream avoids costs of disposal and recycling, helps conserve resources, minimizes pollution, and can often save consumers and businesses money. Preventing waste generation in this way is known as **source reduction**.

Much of our waste stream consists of materials used to package goods. Packaging serves worthwhile purposes—preserving freshness, preventing breakage, protecting against tampering, and providing information—but much packaging is extraneous. Consumers can give manufacturers incentive to reduce packaging by choosing minimally packaged goods, buying unwrapped fruit and vegetables, and buying food in bulk. In addition, manufacturers can use packaging that is more recyclable. They can also reduce the size or weight of goods and materials, as they already have with many items, such as aluminum cans, plastic soft drink bottles, and personal computers.

Some governments have recently taken aim at a major source of waste and litter—plastic grocery bags.

These lightweight polyethylene bags can persist for centuries in the environment, choking and entangling wildlife and littering the landscape. Several nations have now banned their use. When Ireland began taxing these bags, their use dropped 90%. The IKEA Company began charging for them and saw similar drops in usage. In 2007 the small Manitoba town of Leaf Rapids became the first municipality in Canada to ban plastic bags, and the City of Toronto approved a per-bag charge of five cents for new plastic bags, which went into effect in 2009.

Increasing the longevity of goods also helps reduce waste. Consumers generally choose goods that last longer, all else being equal. To maximize sales, however, companies often produce short-lived goods that need to be replaced frequently, particularly in electronics and fashion. Thus, increasing the longevity of goods is largely up to the consumer. If demand is great enough, manufacturers will respond.

Reuse is one main strategy for waste reduction

To reduce waste, you can save items to use again or substitute disposable goods with durable ones. Habits as simple as bringing your own coffee cup to coffee shops or bringing sturdy reusable cloth bags to the grocery store can, over time, have substantial impact. You can also donate unwanted items and shop for used items yourself at yard sales and resale centres. Besides doing good for the environment, reusing items is often economically advantageous. Used items are quite often every bit as functional as new ones, and much cheaper. TABLE 14.1 presents a sampling of actions that we all can take to reduce the waste we generate.

Reducing packaging cuts down on the waste stream, but how, when, and how much should we reduce? Packaging can serve very worthwhile purposes, such as safeguarding consumer health and safety. Can you think of three products for which you would *not* want to see less packaging? Can you name three products for which packaging could easily be reduced without ill effect to the consumer? Would you be any more or less likely to buy these products if they had less packaging?

Table 14.1   Some Everyday Things You Can Do to Reduce and Reuse

Donate used items to charity.

Reuse boxes, paper, plastic wrap, plastic containers, aluminum foil, bags, wrapping paper, fabric, packing material, and so on.

Rent or borrow items instead of buying them, when possible ... and lend your items to friends.

Buy groceries in bulk.

Decline bags at stores when you don't need them.

Bring reusable cloth bags shopping.

Make double-sided photocopies.

Bring your own coffee cup to coffee shops.

Pay a bit extra for durable, long-lasting, reusable goods rather than disposable ones.

Buy rechargeable batteries.

Select goods with less packaging.

Compost kitchen and yard wastes in a compost bin or worm bin (often available from your community or waste hauler).

Buy clothing and other items at resale stores and garage sales.

Use cloth napkins and rags rather than paper napkins and towels.

Write to companies to tell them what you think about their packaging and products.

When solid waste policy is being debated, let your government representatives know your thoughts.

Support organizations that promote waste reduction.

Table 14.2   Composting in Canada, 2007

Composted either kitchen or yard waste

	Percent
Canada	**57**
Newfoundland and Labrador	46
Prince Edward Island	98
Nova Scotia	92
New Brunswick	56
Québec	35
Ontario	71
Manitoba	50
Saskatchewan	52
Alberta	54
British Columbia	59

Source: Statistics Canada, Households and the Environment Survey, 2007.

Composting recovers organic waste

Composting is the conversion of organic waste into mulch or humus through natural biological processes of decomposition. The resulting compost can then be used to enrich soil. Householders can place waste in compost piles, underground pits, or specially constructed containers. As wastes are added, heat from microbial action builds in the interior, and decomposition proceeds. Banana peels, coffee grounds, grass clippings, autumn leaves, and countless other organic items can be converted into rich, high-quality compost through the actions of earthworms, bacteria, soil mites, sow bugs, and other detritivores and decomposers. Home composting is a prime example of how we can live more sustainably by mimicking natural cycles and incorporating them into our daily lives.

Centralized composting programs—there are now more than 350 of them in Canada—divert food and yard waste from the waste stream to composting facilities, where they decompose into mulch that community residents can use for gardens and landscaping. Some municipalities now ban yard waste from the municipal

waste stream, helping accelerate the drive toward composting. Approximately 28% of the Canadian solid waste stream is made up of materials that can easily be composted (see FIGURE 14.2). Composting reduces landfill waste, enriches soil and helps it resist erosion, encourages soil biodiversity, makes for healthier plants and more pleasing gardens, and reduces the need for chemical fertilizers. According to Statistics Canada, 57% of Canadian households do some form of composting (TABLE 14.2).

Recycling consists of three steps

Recycling, too, offers many benefits. **Recycling** consists of collecting materials that can be broken down and reprocessed to manufacture new items. In 2008, 8.5 million tonnes of materials were prepared for recycling by waste management organizations and companies. Of this, paper was the main component.[12]

The recycling loop contains three basic steps (FIGURE 14.8). The first step is collecting and processing used recyclable goods and materials. Communities may designate locations where residents can drop off recyclables or receive money for them. Many of these have now been replaced by the more convenient option of curbside recycling, in which trucks pick up recyclable items in front of houses, usually in conjunction with municipal trash pickup. Curbside recycling has grown rapidly, and its convenience has helped boost household recycling rates across Canada.

Items collected are taken to *materials recovery facilities (MRFs)*, where workers and machines sort items, using

FIGURE 14.8
The familiar recycling symbol consists of three arrows to represent the three components of a sustainable recycling strategy: collection and processing of recyclable materials, use of the materials in making new products, and consumer purchase of these products.

automated processes including magnetic pulleys, optical sensors, water currents, and air classifiers that separate items by weight and size. The facilities clean the materials, shred them, and prepare them for reprocessing.

Once readied, these materials are used in manufacturing new goods. Newspapers and many other paper products use recycled paper, many glass and metal containers are now made from recycled materials, and some plastic containers are of recycled origin. Some large objects, such as benches and bridges in city parks, are now made from recycled plastics, and glass is sometimes mixed with asphalt (creating "glassphalt") for paving roads and paths. The pages in this textbook are made from recycled paper that is up to 20% post-consumer waste.

If the recycling loop is to function, consumers and businesses must complete the third step in the cycle by purchasing products made from recycled materials. Buying recycled goods provides economic incentive for industries to recycle materials and for new recycling facilities to open or existing ones to expand. In this arena, individual consumers have the power to encourage environmentally friendly options through the free market. Many businesses now advertise their use of recycled materials, a widespread instance of *ecolabelling*. As markets for products made with recycled materials expand, prices continue to fall.

Recycling has grown rapidly and can expand further

The thousands of curbside recycling programs and MRFs in operation today have sprung up only in the last 20 years. According to Statistics Canada, 95% of Canadian households had access to recycling programs by 2007, and most programs covered all four recyclables: paper, plastic, glass, and metal.[13]

Recycling rates vary greatly from one product or material type to another and from one location to another. Rates for different types of materials and products range from nearly zero to almost 100%. The increase in recycling has been propelled in part by economic forces as established businesses see opportunities to save money and as entrepreneurs see opportunities to start new businesses. It has also been driven by the desire of municipalities to reduce waste and by the satisfaction people take in recycling. These two forces have driven recycling's rise even though it has often not been financially profitable. In fact, many of the increasingly popular municipal recycling programs are run at an economic loss. The expense required to collect, sort, and process recycled goods is often more than recyclables are worth in the market. Furthermore, the more people recycle, the more glass, paper, and plastic are available to manufacturers for purchase, driving down prices.

Recycling advocates, however, point out that market prices do not take into account external costs—in particular, the environmental and health impacts of *not* recycling. For instance, it has been estimated that globally, recycling saves enough energy to power 6 million households per year. And recycling aluminum cans saves 95% of the energy required to make the same amount of aluminum from mined virgin bauxite, its source material.

As more manufacturers use recycled products and as more technologies and methods are developed to use recycled materials in new ways, markets should continue to expand, and new business opportunities may arise. We are still at an early stage in the shift from an economy that moves linearly from raw materials to products to waste to

weighing the issues

COSTS OF RECYCLING AND NOT RECYCLING

Should recycling programs be subsidized by governments even if they are run at an economic loss? What types of external costs—costs not reflected in market prices—do you think would be involved in not recycling, say, aluminum cans? Do you feel these costs justify sponsoring recycling programs even when they are not financially self-supporting? Why or why not?

an economy that moves circularly, using waste products as raw materials for new manufacturing processes. The steps we have taken in recycling so far are central to this transition, which many analysts view as key to building a sustainable economy.

Financial incentives can help address waste

Waste managers have employed economic incentives to reduce the waste stream. The "pay-as-you-throw" approach to garbage collection uses a financial incentive to influence consumer behaviour. In these programs, municipalities charge residents for home trash pickup according to the amount of trash they put out. The less waste the household generates, the less the resident has to pay.

Return-for-refund schemes ("bottle bills" in the United States) represent another approach that hinges on financial incentive. To date, all provinces and territories except Nunavut have such programs. Consumers pay a deposit, return bottles and cans to stores after use, and receive a refund—generally $0.05 to $0.20 per bottle or can. The first bottle bills were passed in the 1970s to cut down on litter, but they have also served to decrease the waste stream. Research by Melissa Felder, Clarissa Morawski, and others has shown that where they have been enacted, these laws have proven profoundly effective and resoundingly popular; they are recognized as among the most successful recycling programs of recent decades. Jurisdictions with bottle and can refund programs have reported that their beverage container litter has decreased by 69–84%, their total litter has decreased by 30–64%, and their per capita container recycling rate has risen 260%.

Edmonton showcases reduction and recycling

Edmonton, Alberta, has one of the world's most advanced waste management programs. As recently as 1998, fully 85% of the city's waste was being landfilled, and space was running out. Today, just 35% goes to the new sanitary landfill, whereas 15% is recycled, and an impressive 50% is composted. Edmonton's citizens are proud of the program, and 88% of them participate in its curbside recycling program. Where blue recycling bins are available at apartments and condominiums, the participation rate of residents is 91%. The goal is to divert 90% of the city's waste from landfill by 2012.[14]

When Edmonton's residents put out their trash, city trucks take it to their new *co-composting* plant, the largest in North America (**FIGURE 14.9A**). The waste is dumped on the floor of the facility, and large items, such as furniture, are removed and landfilled. The bulk of the waste is mixed with dried sewage sludge for one to two days in five large rotating drums, each the length of six buses. The resulting mix travels on a conveyor to a screen that removes nonbiodegradable items. It is aerated for several weeks in the largest stainless steel building in North America (**FIGURE 14.9B**). The mix is then passed through a finer screen and finally is left outside for four to six months. The resulting compost—80 000 tonnes annually—is made available to area farmers and residents. The facility even filters the air it emits with a 1-m layer of compost, bark, and wood chips, which eliminates the release of unpleasant odours into the community. Christmas tree composting and "grasscycling" programs are now included, as well.

(a) Composting facility, Edmonton, Alberta

(b) Aeration building, Edmonton composting facility

FIGURE 14.9
Edmonton boasts one of North America's most successful waste management programs. Edmonton's gigantic composting facility (a) is the size of eight football fields. Inside the aeration building (b), which is the size of 14 professional hockey rinks, mixtures of solid waste and sewage sludge are exposed to oxygen and composted for 14–21 days.

Edmonton's program also includes a state-of-the-art MRF, a leachate treatment plant, a research centre, public education programs, and a wetland and landfill revegetation program. In addition, 100 pipes collect enough landfill gas to power 4000 homes, bringing thousands of dollars to the city and helping power the new waste management centre. Five area businesses reprocess the city's recycled items, including e-wastes. Newsprint and magazines are turned into new newsprint and cellulose insulation, and cardboard and paper are converted into building paper and shingles. Household metal is made into rebar and blades for tractors and graders, and recycled glass is used for reflective paint and signs.

Industrial Solid Waste

In Canada, disposal of wastes from nonresidential sources (industrial, commercial, and institutional) increased from 14.6 million to 17.3 million tonnes between 2002 and 2008.[15] **Industrial solid waste** includes waste from factories, mining activities, agriculture, petroleum extraction, and more. Waste is generated at various points along the process from raw materials extraction to manufacturing to sale and distribution (**FIGURE 14.10**).

Regulation and economics each influence industrial waste generation

Most methods and strategies of waste disposal, reduction, and recycling by industry are similar to those for municipal solid waste. For instance, businesses that manage their own waste onsite most often dispose of it in landfills, and companies must design and manage their landfills in ways that meet provincial/territorial, local, or tribal guidelines. Other businesses pay to have their waste disposed of at municipal disposal sites. Regulation and enforcement vary across provinces and territories and from municipality to municipality.

The amount of waste generated by a manufacturing process is one measure of its efficiency; the less waste produced per unit or volume of product, the more efficient that process is, from a physical standpoint. However, physical efficiency is not always equivalent to economic efficiency. Often it is cheaper for industry to manufacture its products or perform its services quickly but messily. That is, it can be cheaper to generate waste than to avoid generating waste. In such cases, economic efficiency is maximized, but physical efficiency is not. The frequent mismatch between these two types of efficiency is a major reason that the output of industrial waste is so great.

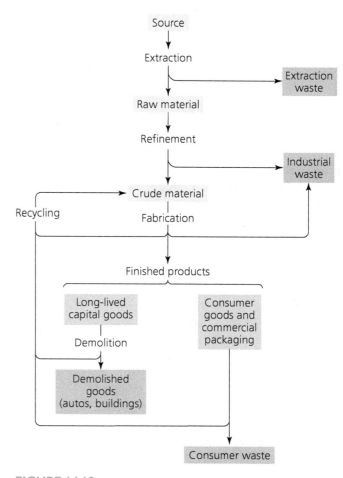

FIGURE 14.10
Industrial and municipal waste is generated throughout the life cycles of products. Waste is first generated when raw materials needed for production are extracted. Further industrial waste is produced as raw materials are processed and as products are manufactured. Waste results from the demolition or disposal of products by businesses and individuals. At each stage, there are opportunities for efficiency improvements, waste reduction, or recycling.

Rising costs of waste disposal, however, enhance the financial incentive to decrease waste and increase physical efficiency. Once either government or the market makes the physically efficient use of raw materials also economically efficient, businesses have financial incentives to reduce their own waste.

Industrial ecology seeks to make industry more sustainable

To reduce waste, growing numbers of industries today are experimenting with industrial ecology. A holistic approach that integrates principles from engineering, chemistry, ecology, and economics, **industrial ecology** seeks to redesign industrial systems to reduce resource inputs and to minimize physical inefficiency while maximizing economic efficiency. Industrial ecologists would reshape industry so that nearly everything produced in a manufacturing process is used, either within that process or in a different one.

The larger idea behind industrial ecology is that industrial systems should function more like ecological systems, in which almost everything produced is used by some organism, with very little being wasted. This principle brings industry closer to the ideal of ecological economists, in which human economies attain sustainability by functioning in a circular fashion rather than a linear one.

Industrial ecologists pursue their goals in several ways. For one, they examine the entire life cycle of a given product—from its origins in raw materials, through its manufacturing, to its use, and finally its disposal—and look for ways to make the process more ecologically efficient. This strategy is called **life-cycle analysis**. In addition, industrial ecologists examine industrial processes with an eye toward eliminating environmentally harmful products and materials. Finally, they study the flow of materials through industrial systems to look for ways to create products that are more durable, recyclable, or reusable. Goods that are currently thrown away when they become obsolete, such as computers, automobiles, and some appliances, could be designed to be more easily disassembled and their component parts reused or recycled. In this way, industrial ecology also helps to close the loop by minimizing wastes at both the industry end and the consumer end of the process.

By applying strategies aimed at reducing waste and preventing pollution at its source—commonly referred to as **pollution prevention (P2) strategies**—companies can significantly reduce their waste output.

Businesses are adopting industrial ecology

Businesses are taking advantage of the insights of industrial ecology to reduce waste and lessen their impact on health and the environment while saving money. A good example is the carpet tile company Interface, which asks customers to return used tiles for recycling and reuse as backing for new carpet. Interface also modified its tile design and its production methods to reduce waste. It adapted its boilers to use landfill gas for its energy needs and has the goal of sourcing all energy from renewable sources by 2020. Through such steps, the company has cut its waste generation by 80%, its fossil fuel use by 45%, and its water use by 70%—all while saving $30 million per year, holding prices steady for its customers, and raising profits by 49%.

Among many other initiatives are such programs as Canadian Tire's auto parts return initiatives and Xerox's take-back/lease programs for its used photocopiers. Programs like these are founded in good business principles, and they have the added benefit of building customer loyalty. An interesting variation of the take-back concept is the ENVIRx program run by the Pharmacists Association of Alberta, in which consumers are able to return unused medications to participating pharmacies for proper disposal. This helps prevent pharmaceuticals from entering the municipal waste stream.

The Swiss Zero Emissions Research and Initiatives (ZERI) Foundation sponsors dozens of innovative projects worldwide that attempt to create goods and services without generating waste. One example involving breweries is currently being pursued in Canada, Sweden, Japan, and Namibia. Brewers in these projects take waste from the beer-brewing process and use it to fuel other processes. Traditional breweries produce only beer while generating much waste, some of which goes toward animal feed. ZERI-sponsored breweries use their waste grain to make bread and to farm mushrooms. Waste from the mushroom farming, along with brewery wastewater, goes to feed pigs. The pigs' waste is digested in containers that capture natural gas and collect nutrients used to nourish algae for growing fish in fish farms. The brewer derives income from bread, mushrooms, pigs, gas, and fish, as well as beer, while producing little waste. Although most ZERI projects are not fully closed-loop systems, they attempt to approach this ideal.

An international initiative that has been adopted in Canada as an overriding strategy for industrial waste minimization is the Extended Producer Responsibility and Stewardship (or EPRS) program. The central goal of the program is to transfer a large part of the responsibility for waste minimization, both physical and financial, to producers.[16] This gives producers the economic incentives to design more environmentally efficient products and processes and to take greater responsibility for the product at the end of its life cycle. It also encourages producers to build the environmental costs of a product into its market price—one of the basic tenets of ecological economics.

Waste exchanges are an offshoot of industrial ecology

The concept of industrial ecology is based on a "closed loop" in which wastes are recycled back through the system. Following the definition of wastes as "resources out of place," industrial ecologists strive to find practical, economical uses for waste materials. To achieve this goal, they try to identify how waste products from one manufacturing process can be used as raw materials for a different process. For instance, used plastic beverage containers cannot be refilled because of the potential for contamination, but they can be shredded and reprocessed to make other plastic items, such as benches, tables, and decks.

Many network services have emerged with the goal of linking producers of waste with industries or individuals that can make use of the waste as raw materials. Such a network is called a **waste exchange**. You can check out an example of a nationwide waste exchange by visiting the website of The Waste Exchange of Canada at www. recyclexchange.net. Other waste exchanges operate locally or internationally.

For businesses, governments, and individuals alike, there are plenty of ways to reduce waste and mitigate the impacts of our waste generation—and quite often, doing so brings economic benefits. This is true both for solid waste and for hazardous waste.

Hazardous Waste

Hazardous wastes are diverse in their chemical composition and may be liquid, solid, or gaseous. In Canada, according to the *Canadian Environmental Protection Act (CEPA)* (1999), **hazardous waste** is waste that has one or more of the following properties:

- **Flammable**. Substances that easily catch fire (for example, natural gas or alcohol)
- **Corrosive**. Substances that corrode metals in storage tanks or equipment
- **Reactive**. Substances that are chemically unstable and readily react with other compounds, often explosively or by producing noxious fumes
- **Toxic**. Substances that harm the health of humans or other organisms when they are inhaled, are ingested, or come into contact with skin

Materials with these characteristics can harm human health and degrade environmental quality. Flammable and explosive materials can cause ecological damage and atmospheric pollution. For instance, fires at tire dumps, such as the one in Hagersville, Ontario, in 1990 (**FIGURE 14.11**), have caused air pollution and highway closures. Toxic wastes in lakes and rivers have caused fish die-offs, endangered aquatic mammals (see "Central Case: The Plight of the St. Lawrence Belugas"), and closed important domestic fisheries.

Certain categories of materials that are clearly "dangerous" are nevertheless not included in the official definition of hazardous waste. An example is biomedical waste, which includes things like human tissues and fluids,

FIGURE 14.11
In 1990 a pile of 15 million discarded tires in Hagersville, Ontario, caught fire and burned for 17 days, releasing thousands of litres of toxic chemicals, such as benzene and toluene, into the air and water.

and discarded medical sharps. These materials are excluded from the definition of hazardous waste not because they are without risk but because they require specialized handling, treatment, and disposal methods and are therefore controlled under different legislation. Similarly, radioactive waste requires a special set of management approaches.

Hazardous wastes have diverse sources

Industry, mining, households, small businesses, agriculture, utilities, and building demolition all create hazardous waste. Industry produces the largest amounts of hazardous waste, but in most developed nations industrial waste generation and disposal is highly regulated. This regulation has reduced the amount of hazardous waste entering the environment from industrial activities. As a result, households currently are the largest source of unregulated hazardous waste.

Household hazardous waste (HHW) includes a wide range of items, such as paints, batteries, oils, solvents, cleaning agents, lubricants, and pesticides. Nine categories of hazardous materials are commonly used by municipalities for the purpose of sorting and disposing of HHW (TABLE 14.3).[17]

Canadians improperly dispose of approximately 27 000 tonnes of HHW each year,[18] and the average home contains close to 45 kg of it in sheds, basements, closets, and garages (TABLE 14.4). Although many hazardous substances become less hazardous over time as they degrade chemically, two classes of chemicals are particularly hazardous because their toxicity persists over time: organic compounds and heavy metals.

Organic compounds and heavy metals can be hazardous

In our day-to-day lives, we rely on the capacity of synthetic organic compounds and petroleum-derived

Table 14.3   Categories of Household Hazardous Waste

- *Antifreeze* (ethylene or propylene glycol used or intended for use as a vehicle engine coolant; materials and their containers)
- *Fertilizers* (materials registered under the Fertilizers Act, packaged in 30-kg quantities or less, including their containers)
- *Lubricating oils* (petroleum-derived or synthetic oils, crankcase, engine and gear oils, and hydraulic, transmission and heat transfer fluids, and lubricating fluids used in machinery; containers of 30 L and less)
- *Paints and coatings* (household and industrial use, including their containers)
- *Pesticides, fungicides, herbicides, insecticides* (and their containers, including domestic, commercial, agricultural, and restricted pesticides)
- *Pressurized containers* (such as propane tanks and cylinders, and oxygen tanks)
- *Single-use dry cell batteries* (alkaline and carbon zinc, mercuric-oxide, silver-oxide and zinc-air, and lithium, including cylindrical, regular and button batteries)
- *Solvents* (and their containers, including turpentine, isopropanol, ethanol, ketones, xylene, toluene, mineral spirits, linseed oils, naphtha, and methylene chloride; these are better known as paint thinners, lacquer thinners, automotive body resin solvents, contact cement thinners, paint strippers, and degreasers)
- *Used oil filters* (from hydraulic, transmission or internal combustion engine applications, including diesel fuel filters, household furnace fuel filter, coolant filter, storage tank diesel fuel filter, sump-type automatic transmission filter, and others)

Source: Stewardship Ontario, Municipal Hazardous or Special Waste, Do What You Can Program; for more information see "What's Included."

compounds to resist bacterial, fungal, and insect activity. Such items as plastic containers, rubber tires, pesticides, solvents, and wood preservatives are useful to us precisely because they resist decomposition. We use these substances to protect our buildings from decay, kill pests that attack crops, and keep stored goods intact. However, the resistance of these compounds to decay is a double-edged sword, for it also makes them persistent pollutants. Many synthetic organic compounds are toxic because they can be absorbed readily through the skin of humans and other animals and can act as mutagens, carcinogens, teratogens, and endocrine disruptors.

Heavy metals, such as lead, chromium, mercury, arsenic, cadmium, tin, and copper, are used widely in industry for wiring, electronics, metal plating, metal fabrication, pigments, and dyes. Heavy metals enter the environment when paints, electronic devices, batteries, and other materials are disposed of improperly. Lead from fishing weights and from hunters' lead shot has accumulated in many rivers, lakes, and forests. In older homes, lead from pipes contaminates drinking water, and lead paint remains a problem, especially for infants. Heavy metals that are fat-soluble and break down slowly are prone to bioaccumulating.

"E-waste" is a new and growing problem

When we first began to conduct much of our business, learning, and communication with computers and other electronic devices, many people predicted that our paper waste would decrease. Instead, the proliferation of computers, printers, VCRs, fax machines, cell phones, GPS devices, MP3 players, and other gadgets has created a substantial new source of waste. These products have short lifetimes before people judge them obsolete, and most are discarded after only a few years.

The amount of **electronic waste**—often called **e-waste**—is growing rapidly. Statistics Canada reports that in 2009, 36% of Canadian households had unwanted electronic devices.[19] Canadians discarded 74 000 tonnes of computer waste in 2002, including 1.7 million desktop computers, 1.9 million cell phones, 2 million television sets, and 1.1 million VCRs (see also TABLE 14.4). The U.S. Environmental Protection Agency reports that 70% of the heavy metals found in U.S. landfills came from discarded electronic products.[20]

Most e-waste is disposed of in landfills as conventional solid waste. However, most electronic products contain heavy metals and toxic flame retardants, and recent research suggests that e-waste should instead be

Table 14.4   Household Hazardous Waste in Canada, 2009

% of households

Had leftover or expired medication to dispose of	**39**
Put them in the garbage	22
Took or sent them to a depot or drop-off centre	6
Returned them to a supplier or retailer	57
Poured them down the drain, sewer, ground, toilet or sink	8
Still had them	15
Other	1
Had leftover paint or solvents to dispose of	**39**
Put them in the garbage	4
Took or sent them to a depot or drop-off centre	62
Returned them to a supplier or retailer	8
Still had them	31
Other	2
Had unwanted engine oil or antifreeze to dispose of	**15**
Put them in the garbage	1
Took or sent them to a depot or drop-off centre	61
Returned them to a supplier or retailer	19
Still had them	18
Other	4
Had dead or unwanted car batteries to dispose of	**12**
Put them in the garbage	[data unreliable]
Took or sent them to a depot or drop-off centre	46
Returned them to a supplier or retailer	31
Still had them	20
Other	5
Had other dead or unwanted batteries to dispose of	**58**
Put them in the garbage	42
Took or sent them to a depot or drop-off centre	35
Returned them to a supplier or retailer	7
Still had them	18
Other	5
Had unwanted electronic devices to dispose of	**36**
Put them in the garbage	11
Took or sent them to a depot or drop-off centre	45
Returned them to a supplier or retailer	5
Donated them or gave them away	22
Still had them	28
Other	2
Had dead or unwanted compact fluorescent lights (CFLs) to dispose of	**22**
Put them in the garbage	56
Took or sent them to a depot or drop-off centre	24
Donated them or gave them away	4
Still had them	13
Other	3

Source: Statistics Canada, Households and the Environment Survey, 2009.

treated as hazardous waste (**FIGURE 14.12**). For instance, more than 6% of a typical computer is composed of lead. The cathode ray tubes in televisions and computer screens can hold up to 5 kg of heavy metals, such as lead and cadmium. These represent the second-largest source of lead in landfills today, behind auto batteries. In Canada there are no federal programs or legislation aimed specifically at dealing with e-waste, although initiatives have been started in most provinces. More and more electronics are now being recycled. The devices are taken apart, and parts are either reused or disposed of more safely. Roughly one-fifth of the nearly 2 million tonnes of electronics discarded in 2005 in the United States was recycled, the EPA estimates.

There are serious concerns about the health risks that recycling may pose to workers doing the disassembly, and wealthy nations ship much of their e-waste to developing countries, where the disassembly is done by poor workers with minimal safety regulations. These environmental justice concerns need to be resolved, but if electronics recycling can be done responsibly, it seems likely to be the way of the future.

In many North American cities, businesses, nonprofit organizations, or municipal services now collect used electronics for reuse or recycling. The next time you upgrade to a new computer, TV, DVD player, VCR, or cell phone, find out about opportunities to recycle your old ones.

(a) Electronic waste

FIGURE 14.12
(a) Discarded electronic waste can leach heavy metals and should be considered hazardous waste, researchers say. **(b)** Some proportion of all electronic devices tested exceeded 5 mg/L, the U.S. EPA's regulatory threshold for lead leachate. (Canada'a threshold for drinking water is 0.010 mg/L.) Devices with higher ferrous metal content tended to leach less lead. Where both standard and modified TCLPs were used, results are averaged. *Source: Data from Townsend, T. G., et al. 2004. RCRA toxicity characterization of computer CPUs and other discarded electronic devices. July 15, 2004, report to the U.S. EPA.*

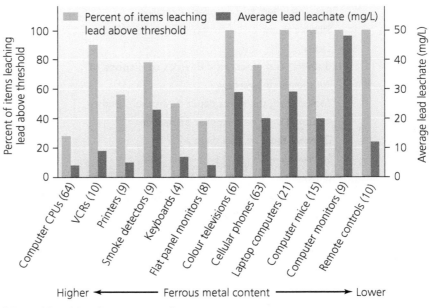

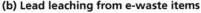

(b) Lead leaching from e-waste items

Several steps precede the disposal of hazardous waste

For many years we discarded hazardous waste without special treatment. In many cases, people did not know that certain substances were harmful to human health. In other cases, the danger posed by these substances was known or suspected, but it was assumed that the substances would disappear or be sufficiently diluted in the environment. The resurfacing of toxic chemicals in a residential area years after their burial at Love Canal in upstate New York provided a dramatic demonstration to the North American public that hazardous waste deserves special attention and treatment.

Since the 1980s, many communities have designated sites or special collection days to gather household hazardous waste or have designated facilities for the exchange and reuse of substances (FIGURE 14.13). Once consolidated in such sites, the waste is transported for treatment and ultimate disposal.

As for municipal solid waste, the management and control of hazardous waste and hazardous recyclable materials is a shared responsibility in Canada. The federal government regulates international agreements and transport. Provincial and territorial governments regulate intraprovincial transport and are responsible for licensing hazardous waste generators, carriers, and treatment facilities.[21] As hazardous waste is generated, transported, and disposed of, the producer, carrier, and disposal facility

FIGURE 14.14
Unscrupulous individuals or businesses sometimes dump hazardous waste illegally to avoid disposal costs.

must each report the type and amount of material generated; its location, origin, and destination; and its handling. This is intended to prevent illegal dumping and encourage the use of reputable waste carriers and disposal facilities. Because it can be quite costly to dispose of hazardous waste, irresponsible companies sometimes illegally and anonymously dump waste, creating health risks for residents and financial headaches for local governments forced to deal with the mess (FIGURE 14.14).

Hazardous waste from industrialized nations is also sometimes dumped illegally in developing nations—a major environmental justice issue. This practice occurs despite the *Basel Convention*, an international treaty to prevent such acts. In 2006, a ship secretly dumped toxic wastes in Abidjan, the capital of Ivory Coast, after being told by Dutch authorities that the Netherlands would charge money to dispose of the waste in Amsterdam. The waste caused several deaths and thousands of illnesses in Abidjan, and street protests forced the government to resign over the scandal. Some jail sentences and fines were eventually handed down in this case, although thousands of victims still have received no compensation for their suffering.

Fortunately, high costs of disposal have also encouraged conscientious businesses to invest in reducing their hazardous waste. Many biologically hazardous materials can be broken down by incineration at high temperatures in cement kilns. Some hazardous materials can be treated by exposure to bacteria that break down harmful components and synthesize them into new compounds. Besides bacterial bioremediation, phytoremediation is also used. Various plants have now been bred or engineered to take

FIGURE 14.13
Many communities designate collection sites or collection days for household hazardous waste. Here, workers handle waste from an Earth Day collection event.

up specific contaminants from soil; they then break down organic contaminants into safer compounds or concentrate heavy metals in their tissues. The plants are eventually harvested and disposed of.

There are three disposal methods for hazardous waste

There are three primary means of hazardous waste disposal: secure landfills, surface impoundments, and injection wells. These do nothing to lessen the hazards of the substances, but they do help keep the waste isolated from people, wildlife, and ecosystems.

Secure landfills   Design and construction standards for landfills that receive hazardous waste are much stricter than those for ordinary sanitary landfills. Hazardous waste landfills, also called **secure landfills**, must have several impervious liners, leachate removal systems, and extensive monitoring wells, and they must be located far from aquifers. Dumping of hazardous waste in ordinary landfills is particularly problematic in closed-down landfills that received wastes prior to the advent of more-secure disposal options for hazardous materials.

Surface impoundments   Liquid hazardous waste, or waste in dissolved form, may be stored in ponds or **surface impoundments**, shallow depressions lined with plastic and an impervious material, such as clay. Water containing dilute hazardous waste is placed in the pond and allowed to evaporate, leaving a residue of solid hazardous waste on the bottom (**FIGURE 14.15**). This process is repeated until the dry material is removed and transported elsewhere for permanent disposal. Impoundments are not ideal. The underlying layer can crack and leak waste. Some material may evaporate or blow into surrounding areas. Rainstorms may cause waste to overflow and contaminate nearby areas. For these reasons, surface impoundments are used only for temporary storage.

The potential for problems with surface impoundment of hazardous wastes became abundantly clear in the small rural town of Elmira, Ontario, in the late 1980s. UniRoyal (now the Crompton Company) had operated a chemical production facility at Elmira since 1942. One of the substances produced at the plant was the so-called Agent Orange, an extremely powerful herbicide used by the United States during the Vietnam War to defoliate large areas of forest. (U.S. and Vietnamese soldiers and civilians later suffered serious health impacts as a result of exposure to this chemical.) Rubber and agrichemicals were also produced at the plant. The waste by-products

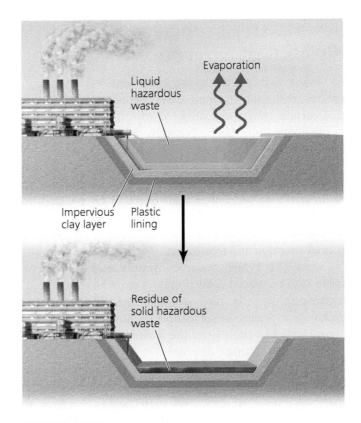

FIGURE 14.15
Surface impoundments are a strategy for temporarily disposing of liquid hazardous waste. The waste, mixed with water, is poured into a shallow depression lined with plastic and clay to prevent leakage. When the water evaporates, leaving a crust of the hazardous substance, new liquid is poured in and the process repeated. This method alone is not satisfactory because waste can potentially leak, overflow, evaporate, or blow away.

of chemical production were disposed of—legally, and within Ontario Ministry of Environment regulations for the day—in a clay-lined surface impoundment pit onsite, starting in the 1960s.

Then, in 1989, traces of chemical markers, notably the carcinogen N-nitrosodimethylamine (NDMA), began to appear in municipal drinking water wells, downslope of the impoundment site. Apparently the clay liner of the impoundment pit had failed, perhaps because it had become saturated, and contaminants were leaking out of the pit and joining the groundwater. The company undertook remediation of both the impoundment pit and the surrounding aquifers in the early 1990s. However, the town of Elmira no longer withdraws its drinking water from these aquifers; instead, it pipes water in from another municipality.

Deep-well injection   The third method is intended for long-term disposal. In **deep-well injection**, a well is drilled deep beneath the water table into porous rock,

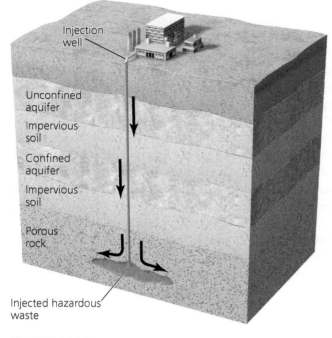

FIGURE 14.16
Liquid hazardous waste may be pumped deep underground, by deep-well injection. The well must be drilled below any aquifers, into porous rock separated by impervious clay. The technique is expensive, and waste may leak from the well shaft into groundwater.

and wastes are injected into it (**FIGURE 14.16**). The waste is meant to remain deep underground, isolated from groundwater and human contact. This idea seems attractive in principle, but in practice wells become corroded and can leak wastes into soil, allowing them to enter aquifers. Alberta accounts for approximately 90% of all deep-well injection of hazardous wastes in Canada.

Radioactive waste is especially hazardous

Radioactive waste is particularly dangerous to human health. It is, by definition, **radioactive** (that is, giving off energetic particles and radiation in the process of spontaneous radioactive decay) and thus potentially hazardous to human and animal health. In addition, some of it is highly toxic, and some of it is extremely persistent. The dilemma of disposal has dogged the nuclear energy industry for decades. There is as yet no identified permanent repository for radioactive waste in Canada. Yucca Mountain in Nevada was approved as the single-site repository for all nuclear waste in the United States but the licence application was withdrawn in 2010. Other countries, including Germany also have designated permanent disposal sites for radioactive waste.

Most proposals for permanent disposal of radioactive waste involve some form of **geologic isolation**; that is, using the absorptive capacity and impermeability of some naturally occurring rock units to block the movement of contaminants away from the disposal site. Canadian proposals focus on disposal in automated facilities located deep underground in the stable, ancient, plutonic igneous rocks of the Canadian Shield. Other geologic settings that are amenable to geologic isolation include salt domes and thick shale units.

Geologic isolation would be combined with the chemical immobilization of the waste, sophisticated engineering design of the facility itself, and multiple-layered impervious containers for storage of the waste. In Canada, this is referred to as a **multiple-barrier approach**—that is, engineering the entire facility to place as many barriers as possible, both physical and chemical, in the pathway of any escaping contaminants.

Contaminated sites are being cleaned up, slowly

Many thousands of former military and industrial sites remain contaminated with hazardous waste in Canada and virtually every other nation on Earth. For most nations, dealing with these messes is simply too difficult, time-consuming, and expensive. Some contaminated sites, especially in the United States, have reached iconic status for the roles they played in raising public awareness, spurring local residents to action, and kick-starting the modern environmental movement. In Love Canal, a residential neighbourhood in Niagara Falls, New York, families were evacuated after toxic chemicals buried by a company and the city in past decades rose to the surface, contaminating homes and an elementary school. In Missouri, the entire town of Times Beach—another name that is practically synonymous with poorly managed toxic waste—was evacuated and its buildings demolished after being contaminated by dioxin from waste oil sprayed on its roads. The beneficial outcome is that these horrific cases led to the establishment of the first legislation to deal with liability, compensation, and cleanup costs associated with contaminated sites in the United States.

In Canada, many contaminated sites have been abandoned and thus fall under federal jurisdiction. Approximately 18 000 sites are currently listed in Canada's Federal Contaminated Sites Inventory and have been assessed or classified under the National Classification System for contaminated sites, developed by the Canadian Council of Ministers of the Environment.[22] Examples of the nearly 1197 priority sites identified for cleanup include the following:[23]

■ *Faro Mine, Yukon:* $14.6 million for the largest and highest priority of the federal contaminated sites, an old lead, zinc, silver, and gold mine that was shut down when the company went into receivership. There are now approximately 70 million tonnes of tailings and 320 million tonnes of waste rock at the site, with consequent acid drainage, wind-blown particulates, and other environmental hazards.[24]

■ *Canadian Forces Base Esquimalt, British Columbia:* $4.56 million for remediation of hydrocarbon and heavy metal–contaminated soil, assessment, and risk management.

■ *Port Radium Mine, Northwest Territories:* $7.1 million funding for sealing of mine openings, covering of areas of elevated radiation levels, stabilization of tailings areas, demolition, and hazardous waste disposal.

■ *Belleville Small Craft Harbour, Ontario:* $6.8 million to treat contaminated soil and prevent contaminants in groundwater from discharging into the adjacent Bay of Quinte. Belleville Harbour was used for more than 50 years for the storage of coal and fuel products, which led to petroleum hydrocarbon and heavy metal contamination.

You can examine the complete Federal Contaminated Sites Inventory for yourself. It is maintained (interestingly, perhaps because of the enormous costs associated with remediation of these sites) by the Treasury Board of Canada Secretariat, and the website is www.tbs-sct.gc.ca/fcsi-rscf.

Sites that have been contaminated but have the potential to be cleaned up and remediated for other purposes are called **brownfields**. However, many sites are contaminated with hazardous chemicals we have no effective way to deal with. In such cases, cleanups simply involve trying to isolate waste from human contact, either by building trenches and clay or concrete barriers around a site or by excavating contaminated material, placing it in industrial-strength containers, and shipping it to a hazardous waste disposal facility. For all these reasons, the current emphasis is on preventing hazardous waste contamination in the first place.

All three North American countries monitor industrial pollutants by using Pollutant Release and Transfer Registers (PRTRs), which combine reports from industrial facilities with information about transfers, off-site treatments, and disposal or recycling of pollutants. In Canada the PRTR is the National Pollutant Release Inventory (NPRI), established in 1992, which covers more than 300 chemicals plus the criteria air contaminants. In Mexico, it is the *Registro de Emisiones y Transferencia de Contaminantes (RETC)*, which covers 100 chemicals, and in the United States it is the Toxics Release Inventory (TRI), started in 1987, which tracks data for more than 600 chemicals.[25] By learning where these pollutants come from, where they end up, and how they are transferred, we may ultimately be in a better position to control them.

Conclusion

Our societies have made great strides in addressing our waste problems. Modern methods of waste management are far safer for people and gentler on the environment than past practices of open dumping and open burning. In many countries, recycling and composting efforts are making rapid progress. Canada has changed in a few decades from a country that did virtually no recycling to a nation in which nearly one-quarter of all solid waste is diverted from disposal. The continuing growth of recycling, composting, and pollution-prevention initiatives, driven by market forces, government policy, and consumer behaviour, shows potential to further alleviate our waste problems.

Despite these advances, our prodigious consumption habits have created more waste than ever before. Our waste management efforts are marked by a number of difficult dilemmas, including the cleanup of highly contaminated sites, safe disposal of hazardous and radioactive waste, and frequent local opposition to disposal sites. These dilemmas make clear that the best solution to our waste problem is to reduce our generation of waste. Finding ways to reduce, reuse, and efficiently recycle the materials and goods that we use stands as a key challenge for this century.

CANADIAN ENVIRONMENTAL PERSPECTIVES

Brennain Lloyd

Brennain Lloyd defends the North against the irresponsible dumping of garbage and other harmful waste materials.

■ **Coordinator** of Northwatch
■ **Peace and environmental activist**
■ **Advisor** on natural resource management

Brennain Lloyd came to environmental activism from the peace movement, where she confronted issues such as poverty, injustice, and violence. As she explains it, "peace work in northeastern Ontario inevitably led to working with environmental groups" on such issues as the impacts of uranium mining and refining, the threat of a nuclear waste dumpsite in the area, and the establishment of a military testing and training corridor for the delivery of air-launched cruise missiles. "These issues had huge peace implications, but also impacts on forest health, wildlife, and human communities."

Lloyd—who is from North Bay, Ontario—is the coordinator of Northwatch, a coalition of citizen organizations and individual members. Founded in 1988, Northwatch brings a northern perspective to regional environmental issues, including

waste dumping; natural resource management, especially mining and logging; and water and air quality concerns. Northwatch also provides support for local citizen groups working to address environmental issues in their communities. Three current focus areas are better forest management, greater community involvement in mine monitoring and management, and preventing northeastern Ontario from becoming a dumping ground.[26]

Today, Lloyd is ubiquitous—speaking about nuclear waste disposal in the Canadian Shield to the Canadian Environmental Assessment Agency; presenting a talk at the University of Waterloo on garbage dumping in the North, as part of the university's Environmentalist-in-Residence series; participating in a task force on mining sector sustainability or running a workshop on forest management for a local citizens' group or advisory committee to the Ministry of Natural Resources; and reviewing and analyzing a proposal for a new biodiesel plant.

A few years ago, she was central to a successful intervention in the City of Toronto's plan to ship municipal garbage hundreds of kilometres for disposal in the old Adams Mine site in Kirkland Lake, Ontario. Northwatch coordinated community opposition to this plan, through the Adams Mine Intervention Coalition. The plan, which would have endangered regional water bodies and groundwater, was eventually overturned by the Toronto City Council in 2000. In 2004, the Province of Ontario passed the *Adams Mine Lake Act*, which revoked all existing approvals for the use of the old mine site as a landfill, prevented the site from ever being used for that purpose, and extended the same protection to all large water bodies in the province.

In addition to the Adams Mine struggle, Lloyd and Northwatch have intervened in a number of other plans to import waste

into Northern Ontario, including Ontario's biomedical waste and PCBs from around the world. Radioactive waste has been a long-term struggle; the coalition opposes any plans to develop a deep geologic isolation disposal site for nuclear waste in the Canadian Shield. It also works to ensure appropriate decommissioning of old mine sites in the North, such as the uranium mines of Elliot Lake (see "Central Case: Mining Denendeh").

Northwatch often finds itself in a reactive position, such as opposing plans to use the North as a dumping ground or withdraw resources in a harmful or negligent manner. But Lloyd and her coalition also take a proactive stance on northern development, stating that "the North must realize a long-term objective of diversifying the economy while maintaining the natural resource base and making best use of those resources which are extracted. To this end, economic and social decisions must be made with the priority of creating and contributing to a 'sustainable' North."

"My work on waste management has been of necessity, in response to repeated efforts to use northeastern Ontario as a dumping ground for 'foreign' wastes."[27] **—Brennain Lloyd**

Thinking About Environmental Perspectives

Toronto reversed its original plan to ship garbage to a dumpsite located in the old Adams Mine near Kirkland Lake, Ontario, partly in response to the enormous opposition from organizations like the Adams Mine Intervention Coalition and Northwatch. What do you think about a city like Toronto shipping its garbage far away? If Toronto or other large cities simply run out of room to dispose of their garbage within their own borders, what realistic alternatives do they have?

REVIEWING OBJECTIVES

You should now be able to:

Summarize and compare the types of waste we generate

- Municipal and industrial solid waste, hazardous waste, and wastewater are major types of waste.

List the major approaches to managing waste

- Source reduction, recovery, and disposal are the three main components of waste management.

Delineate the scale of the waste dilemma

- Developed nations generate far more waste than developing nations do.
- Waste everywhere is increasing as a result of growth in population and consumption.

Describe conventional waste disposal methods: landfills and incineration

- Sanitary landfills guard against contamination of groundwater, air, and soil. Nonetheless, such contamination can occur.
- Incinerators reduce waste volume by burning it. Pollution control technology removes most pollutants from emissions, but some escape, and highly toxic ash needs to be disposed of in landfills.
- We are harnessing energy from landfill gas and generating electricity from incineration.

Evaluate approaches for reducing waste: source reduction, reuse, composting, and recycling

- Reducing waste before it is generated is the best waste management approach. Recovery is the next-best option.

- Consumers can take simple steps to reduce their waste output.
- Composting reduces waste while creating organic matter for gardening and agriculture.
- Recycling has grown slowly in recent years and now removes about 25% of waste from the Canadian waste stream.

Discuss industrial solid waste management and principles of industrial ecology

- Regulations differ, but industrial waste management is similar to that for municipal solid waste.
- Industrial ecology urges industrial systems to mimic ecological systems and provides ways for industry to increase its efficiency.

Assess issues in managing hazardous waste

- Hazardous waste is flammable, corrosive, reactive, or toxic.
- Electronic waste may be considered hazardous.
- Hazardous waste is strictly regulated, yet illegal dumping remains a problem.
- No fully satisfactory method of disposing of hazardous waste has yet been devised.
- Cleanup of hazardous waste sites is a long and expensive process.

TESTING YOUR COMPREHENSION

1. Describe five major methods of managing waste. Why do we practise waste management?
2. Why have some people labelled modern North America as "the throwaway society"? How much solid waste do Canadians generate, and how does this amount compare with that of people from other countries?
3. Name several technologies designed to make sanitary landfills safe places for the disposal of waste. Describe three problems with landfills.

4. Describe the process of incineration or combustion. What happens to the resulting ash? What is one drawback of incineration?
5. What is composting, and how does it help reduce input to the waste stream?
6. What are the three elements of a sustainable process of recycling?
7. What are the goals of industrial ecology?
8. What four criteria are used to define hazardous waste? Why are heavy metals and synthetic organic compounds particularly hazardous?

9. What are the largest sources of hazardous waste? Describe three ways to dispose of hazardous waste.

10. How is waste regulated in Canada? What are some of the similarities and differences between the regulation of nonhazardous wastes and that of hazardous wastes?

THINKING IT THROUGH

1. How much waste do you generate? Look into your waste bin at the end of the day, and categorize and measure the waste there. List all other waste you may have generated in other places throughout the day. How much of this waste could you have avoided generating? How much could have been reused or recycled?

2. Some people have criticized current waste management practices as merely moving waste from one medium to another. How might this criticism apply to the methods now in practice? What are some potential solutions?

3. Of the various waste management approaches covered in this chapter, which ones are your community and campus pursuing, and which are they not pursuing? Would you suggest that your community or campus start pursuing any new approaches? If so, which ones, and why?

4. Could manufacturers and businesses benefit from source reduction if consumers were to buy fewer products as a result? How? Given what you know about industrial ecology, what do you think the future of sustainable manufacturing may look like?

5. You are the CEO of a major corporation that produces containers for soft drinks and a wide variety of other consumer products. Your company's shareholders are asking that you improve the company's image—while not cutting into profits—by taking steps to reduce waste. What steps would you consider taking?

6. Now let's say that you are the president of your college or university. Your trustees want you to engage with local businesses and industries in ways that benefit both the school and the community. Your faculty and students want you to make the school a leader in waste reduction and industrial ecology. Consider the industries and businesses in your community and the ways they interact with facilities on your campus. Bearing in mind the principles of industrial ecology, can you think of any novel ways in which your school and local businesses might mutually benefit from one another's services, products, or waste materials? Are there waste products from one business, industry, or campus facility that another might put to good use? Can you design an eco-industrial park that might work on your campus? What steps would you propose to take as president?

INTERPRETING GRAPHS AND DATA

In 2006, about 90% of all households in Canada reported using some sort of recycling program.[28] This sounds like fantastic news—the "reduce, reuse, recycle" message appears to have reached the population, and the work of protecting the environment is mostly done. Is this true? Find out by taking a closer look at Canadian statistics.

The following table shows how many kilograms of residential waste were produced per person and how much waste was diverted from landfill sites through recycling in 2006. It also shows the percentage of households that used any type of recycling program in 2006.

Definitions:
- **Waste disposed:** waste that is landfilled, incinerated, or treated for final disposal (does not include materials destined for recycling and composting)
- **Recyclable materials diverted:** materials diverted from the waste stream and remanufactured into a new product or used as a raw material substitute
- **Total materials discarded:** the combined total amount of waste disposed and recyclable materials diverted

Disposal and Diversion of Residential Waste and Household Use of Recycling Programs, by Province and Territory, 2006

	1	2	3	4	5
	Total residential waste disposed,[29] per capita	Residential recyclable materials diverted,[30] per capita	Total materials discarded, per capita (Column 1 + Column 2)	Diversion rate	Households that used any recycling program in 2006[31]
	Kilograms per capita			Percent %	
Newfoundland and Labrador	446	x[32]			82
Prince Edward Island	x	x			98
Nova Scotia	181	149			95
New Brunswick	289	44			83
Québec[33]	285	122			86
Ontario	292	119			93
Manitoba	386	60			79
Saskatchewan	300	39			87
Alberta	289	98			85
British Columbia	222	145			93
Yukon	214	x			—
Northwest Territories	347	x			—
Nunavut	x	x			—
Canada	283	115			90

Use the table to answer these questions:

1. For each region, calculate the total materials discarded per capita, including waste disposed and recyclable materials diverted. Record your answers in column 3 of the table.

2. For each region, calculate the diversion rate (the amount of residential recyclable materials diverted, per capita, compared to total materials discarded per capita), using the following formula:

$$\text{Diversion rate} = \frac{\text{Column 2}}{\text{Column 3}} \times 100$$

Record your answers in column 4 of the table.

3. Which province had the highest diversion rate?

4. Do you think there is a connection between the diversion rate and the percentage of households that use a recycling program in the provinces and territories? Explain your answer.

5. Create a scatter plot to compare the percentages of households that used a recycling program (column 5 from the table above) with the diversion rates (column 4). Identify each data point by labelling it with the provincial or territorial abbreviation (e.g., MB for Manitoba, NB for New Brunswick).

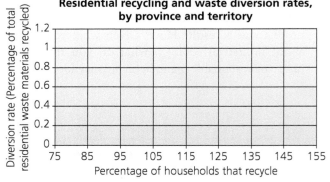

Residential recycling and waste diversion rates, by province and territory

6. Draw the line of best fit (the trend line that fits the majority of data points) for the above graph.

7. Describe the trend in the graph. Does this match your prediction in question 4?

8. How can you explain the connection between the percentage of households that recycle and the diversion rate?

Source: Statistics Canada, Contributed by Angela McCanny, Statistics Canada resource teacher, Ottawa, Ontario, www19.statcan. ca/02/02_051-eng.htm.

CHAPTER ENDNOTES

1. Canadian Biogas Industry Overview, Ken Hogg, October 27, 2005, *New Era Renewable Energy Solutions*, www.ptac.org/eea/dl/eeaf0501p04.pdf

2. City of Toronto Council and Committees, June 1, 1999, *Ontario Hydro Corridor Lands and Beare Road Ski Facility Trust Fund*, www.toronto.ca/legdocs/1999/agendas/committees/sc/sc990622/it035b.htm

3. Environment Canada, Waste Management, *Beare Road Project*, www.ec.gc.ca/wmd-dgd/default.asp?lang=En&n=3438B2E7-1

4. Government of Canada Depository Services Program, *Hazardous Waste Management: Canadian Directions, 1992*, http://dsp-psd.tpsgc.gc.ca/Collection-R/LoPBdP/BP/bp323-e.htm#A.%20Definitions%20and%20Classification(txt)

5. Environment Canada, Waste Management, *Municipal Solid Waste*, www.ec.gc.ca/wmd-dgd/Default.-asp?lang=En&n=7623F633-1

6. Statistics Canada, Environment Accounts and Statistics Product Catalogue (2011) No. 16-257.

7. Simmons, P., et al. (2006) The state of garbage in America. *BioCycle*, Vol. 47, p. 26.

8. Environment Canada, Waste Management, *Municipal Solid Waste*, www.ec.gc.ca/wmd-dgd/Default.-asp?lang=En&n=7623F633-1

9. Desrocher, S., and B. Sherwood-Lollar (1998) Isotopic constraints on off-site migration of landfill CH4, *Ground Water*, Vol. 36, No. 5, pp. 801–809. Research Library Core.

10. Desrocher, S., and B. Sherwood-Lollar (1998) Isotopic constraints on off-site migration of landfill CH4, *Ground Water*, Vol. 36, No. 5, pp. 801–809. Research Library Core.

11. City of Toronto Solid Waste Management, *Facts About Toronto's Trash*, updated November 1, 2007, www.toronto.ca/garbage/facts.-htm

12. Statistics Canada, Summary Tables: Disposal and Diversion of Waste, by Province and Territory www40.statcan.gc.ca/101/cst01/envir32c-eng.htm

13. Statistics Canada, Environment Accounts and Statistics Analytical and Technical Paper Series *Recycling by Canadian Housholds*, 2007.

14. City of Edmonton, 2011, *Recycling Facts*, www.edmonton.ca/for_residents/Environment/City_recycle_factsheet(web).pdf

15. Statistics Canada, Environment Accounts and Statistics Division, Cansim Table 153-0041.

16. Environment Canada, *EPR*, www.ec.gc.ca/epr/Default.-asp?lang=En&n=EEBCC813-1

17. Recycling Council of Ontario, *Household Hazardous Waste Fact Sheet, 1996*, www.rco.on.ca/RCO_files/HHW.pdf.

14. Canadian Institute for Environmental Law and Policy, *Understanding Hazardous Waste in Ontario, 2006*, www.cielap.org/pdf/HazWaste2007.pdf

19. Statistics Canada, Households and the Environment (2009), Highlights.

20. Canadian Institute for Environmental Law and Policy, *Understanding Hazardous Waste in Ontario, 2006*, www.cielap.org/pdf/HazWaste2007.pdf

21. Environment Canada, Waste Management, *Hazardous Waste*, www.ec.gc.ca/wmd-dgd/default.asp?lang=En&n=FDC36D83-1

22. Environment Canada, News Release, July 26, 2007, and Federal Contaminated Sites Inventory, www.tbs-sct.gc.ca/fcsi-rscf/home-accueil.aspx?Language=EN&sid=wu91133413870

23. Environment Canada, *Backgrounder: Federal Contaminated Sites Receiving Funds, 2007*, www.ec.gc.ca/default.asp?lang=En&n=714D9AAE-1&news=81941DCD-F8FA-4012-9266-CE-C4F186B0F7

24. Faro Mine Closure, *Challenges*, www.faromineclosure.yk.ca/project/challenges.html

25. Commission for Environmental Cooperation (2008) *The North American Mosaic: An Overview of Key Environmental Issues: Industrial Pollution and Waste*, www.cec.org/soe/files/en/SOE_IndustrialPollution_en.pdf

26. Northwatch, www.web.net/~nwatch/

27. Brennain Lloyd, from a delegation to the Canadian Environmental Assessment Agency, 2003, www.ceaa.gc.ca/010/0001/0001/0012/0002/0012/s6_e.htm

28. *EnviroStats* "Recycling in Canada" (July 1, 2007). As reported in *The Daily*. Retrieved June 29, 2008 www.statcan.ca/Daily/English/070713/d070713a.htm#tab2ftnote1

29. Statistics Canada (2006) *Waste Management Industry Survey: Business and Government Sectors*. Catalogue no. 16F0023X, Text Table 1: Disposal of waste, by source and by province and territory. Residential nonhazardous wastes disposed includes solid waste produced by all residences and includes waste that is picked up by the municipality (either using its own staff or through contracting firms) and waste

from residential sources that is self-hauled to depots, transfer stations, and disposal facilities.

30. Statistics Canada. Table 153-0042, Materials prepared for recycling, by source, Canada, provinces and territories, every 2 years (tonnes), CANSIM (database), Using E-STAT (distributor). This information covers only those companies and local waste management organisations that reported nonhazardous recyclable material preparation activities and refers only to that material entering the waste stream and does not cover any waste that may be managed on-site by a company or household. Additionally, these data do not include those materials transported by the generator directly to secondary processors such as pulp and paper mills while bypassing entirely any firm or local government involved in waste management activities.

31. Statistics Canada (2006) *Households and the Environment Survey*, Text table 3.7.

32. "x" means data is suppressed to meet the confidentiality requirements of the *Statistics Act*.

33. Waste diversion and residential sector disposal data are derived from a survey administered by RECYC. QUEBEC.

MyEnvironmentPlace

Go to **www.myenvironmentplace.ca** where you will find quizzes, animations, your Pearson eText, and more.

15 Environmental Ethics and Economics: Values and Choices

This is an aerial view of Diavik Diamond Mine, Northwest Territories.

Upon successfully completing this chapter, you will be able to

- Characterize the influences of culture and world view on the choices people make
- Outline the nature, evolution, and expansion of environmental ethics in Western cultures
- Describe some basic precepts of economic theory and summarize their implications for the environment

- Compare the concepts of economic growth, economic health, and sustainability
- Explain the fundamentals of environmental economics, ecological economics, and natural resource accounting

This is the mining settlement at Port Radium, Northwest Territories, in 1930.

CENTRAL CASE:
MINING DENENDEH¹

"This forest is where our people have fished and trapped for generations—so we have this responsibility to take care of it, and that responsibility came from the elders, our ancestors, who told us to do whatever we have to do to protect the land."

—SOPHIA RABLIAUSKAS, GOLDMAN ENVIRONMENT PRIZE WINNER; POPLAR RIVER FIRST NATION COMMUNITY

"Let us not forget that, in the end, all economies, whether new or old, are built on foundations of access to land, natural wealth and resources."

—MATTHEW COON COME, FORMER GRAND CHIEF OF THE CREE NATION AND NATIONAL CHIEF OF THE ASSEMBLY OF FIRST NATIONS

The traditional lands of the Dene and Métis form the Northwest Territories of Canada, known as *Denendeh*. The people of Denendeh have mined, manufactured, and traded metals—especially copper—since long before the arrival of Europeans.

Industrial-scale mining has played a significant role in the history and development of the Northwest Territories since 1930, when the first modern mining operation, Eldorado uranium mine, was established at Port Radium on Great Bear Lake (*Sahtu*, in the Dene language; see map and photo). The Con and Giant gold mines, which began production at Yellowknife in 1938 and 1948, respectively, were important to the economy of the area for more than 50 years. Mining continues today in the North but the emphasis has shifted to diamonds, with the development of new mines like Ekati and Diavik, the first diamond mines in Canada.

Recent staking rushes in the Northwest Territories, particularly for diamonds, have generated concerns over unsettled land claims. For example, the public hearings of the Mackenzie Valley Environmental Impact Review Board for Wool Bay and Drybones Bay in 2003 centred

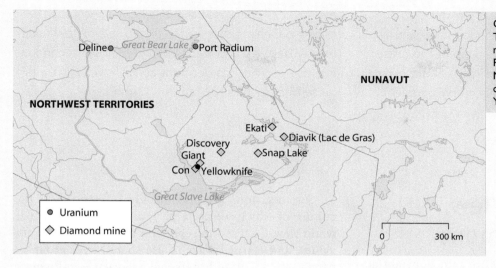

Great Bear Lake in the Northwest Territories was the site of uranium mining at the Eldorado Mine in Port Radium from 1930 until the 1960s. More recent diamond mining centres on an area to the northeast of Yellowknife.

on conflicts between unresolved Aboriginal land claims and mineral claims made by exploration companies. The environmental impact assessments halted exploration. The Dene claimed that their spiritual and cultural use of the land was in jeopardy. This included many practical issues, such as the locations of gravesites, as well as improperly managed waste materials from exploration. In this case, the Aboriginal rights and title to the land were given precedence over mining exploration.

The environmental, social, and economic impacts of past mining development in the North have been considerable, including contamination of land and water; devastating economic boom-and-bust cycles; influxes of large numbers of non-native temporary workers; and persistent health issues for workers and residents. An early case in the Aboriginal rights movement involved Eldorado's alleged discrimination against Dene workers, discussed later in this chapter, which came to light when former mine workers developed health problems that may have resulted from inadequate protection against radiation.

Mines can leave a legacy of contamination, and Canada's North is strewn with closed and abandoned mines. Discovery gold mine, 80 km northeast of Yellowknife (see map), began production in 1944 and closed in 1969. Left behind were uncontrolled tailings and waste rock piles, mercury and cyanide contamination of the nearby lake, and an abandoned and crumbling town site that was finally demolished in 2005.

Mining also can cause profound social and economic changes. The inability to maintain traditional food systems and cultural practices can undermine community health and wellness; impacts can include substance abuse and family breakdown. When Giant closed, the economic impacts on Yellowknife were devastating, causing housing prices to plummet. The recent diamond rush has created a new economic boom in Yellowknife and a construction push to house incoming workers, with the result that rents and housing prices are now some of the highest in Canada.

Today the life cycle of a mine, and the involvement of a mining company with a site and its people, no longer ends when the supply/demand for metal and minerals is depleted. Today, greater care is legally required when new mines are developed, to ensure that they will have minimal environmental, social, and health impacts. Mitigation, closure, and restoration plans, and financing for those plans, must be in place before a mine even begins production. The decision to transform an area into a mine comes with the responsibility of post-operational management and remediation, and a commitment to ongoing quality of life for workers and the community.

The new diamond mines at Ekati, Diavik, and Snap Lake have been designed so that, once mining is finished, the land will be reclaimed and restored. There will be no town, no permanent roads, no waste rock or tailings left behind. The new mines also distinguish themselves in the consideration they give to traditional knowledge, including learning from elders about environmental conditions, and applying this knowledge to construction, aquatic monitoring, and other aspects of mine management.

There is no single perspective or consensus on mining among Dene people today. Some call for greater involvement of Dene leaders in mine development. Some wish for a greater share of economic benefits and reduced risks. Others are concerned about the preservation of their land and culture. Decisions about mining in Canada's North must be based not only on scientific assessments but on social and cultural concerns as well. Mining in Denendeh provides an example of how values, beliefs, lifestyles, and traditions interact with economic interests to influence decisions about how to live within our environment.

Culture, World View, and the Environment

The Dene have an opportunity to gain substantial economic benefits by allowing mining to proceed on their lands, but they are cognizant of the long history of environmental and cultural damage associated with mining in Canada's North. Trade-offs in which economic benefits and social or ethical concerns appear to be in conflict crop up frequently in environmental issues. In this chapter we will examine some of the underlying causes of such conflicts, how they may be resolved, and how they influence the environmental choices we all make every day.

Culture, world view, and values influence our understanding of the environment

Environmental science examines Earth's natural systems, how they affect humans, and how humans affect them. To address environmental problems, however, requires input from disciplines beyond the natural sciences. It is necessary to understand how people perceive their environment, how they relate to it philosophically and pragmatically, and how they value its elements. Ethics and economics are quite different disciplines, but each deals with questions of what we value and how those values influence our decisions and actions. Anyone trying to address an environmental problem must try to understand not only how natural systems work but also how values shape human behaviour. Every action we take affects our environment. Growing food requires soil, cultivation, and irrigation. Building homes requires land, lumber, and metal. Manufacturing and fuelling vehicles require metal, plastic, glass, and petroleum. From nutrition to housing to transportation, we meet our needs by withdrawing resources and altering our surroundings. Decisions about how we manipulate and exploit our environment to meet our needs depend in part on rational assessments of costs and benefits.

Our decisions are also heavily influenced by the culture of which we are a part, and by our particular world view. Culture—the ensemble of knowledge, beliefs, values, and learned ways of life shared by a group of people—together with personal experience, influences each person's perception of the world and his or her place within it, something described as the person's world view. A world view reflects a person's (or group's) beliefs about the meaning, operation, and essence of the world.

People with different world views can study the same situation and review identical data yet draw dramatically different conclusions. For example, many well-meaning people support mining in Canada's North, while many other well-meaning people oppose it. The officers, employees, and shareholders of the mining companies, and the government officials who support mining, view it as a source of jobs, income, energy, and economic growth. They believe mining will benefit the North in general and the Dene in particular. Opponents, in contrast, foresee environmental problems and negative social consequences. They recognize that mining disturbs the landscape and can pollute air and water, while community disruption, substance abuse, and crime can accompany mining booms.

In Australia, too, there have been conflicts between corporations seeking to develop mining operations and Aboriginal people trying to maintain their traditional culture. One such group is the Mirrar Clan (see "The Science Behind the Story: The Mirrar Clan Confronts the Jabiluka Uranium Mine").

Uranium mining is a key contributor to Australia's economy; however, many of Australia's uranium deposits occur on Aboriginal lands in the remote region of Kakadu. When a company proposed to open a new uranium mine on their land, the Mirrar fought back. They saw the mine as a threat not only to their health and the integrity of the environment but also to their culture and religion, which are deeply tied to the landscape. The proposed mine site is near traditional hunting and gathering sites, in the floodplain of a river that provides the clan with food and water. Like many other Aborigines, the Mirrar hold the landscape to be sacred, and they depend on its resources for their daily needs.

THE SCIENCE BEHIND THE STORY

The Mirrar Clan Confronts the Jabiluka Uranium Mine

These protestors rallied against the proposed Jabiluka uranium mine.

"The Jabiluka uranium mine will improve the quality of the environment."—Michael Darby, Australian political commentator

"My country is in danger."—Yvonne Margarula, senior traditional land owner, Mirrar Clan and Goldman Environment Prize winner; to the U.N. World Heritage Committee, 1998

The remote Kakadu region of Australia's Northern Territory is home to several groups of **Aborigines**, the native or **indigenous** people who lived there before British colonization. The region features Kakadu National Park (see photo), a World Heritage Site recognized by the United Nations for its irreplaceable natural

and cultural resources. The land also holds uranium, a naturally occurring radioactive metal valued for its use in nuclear power plants, nuclear weapons, and medical and industrial tools. Uranium mining is a key contributor to the Australian national economy, accounting for 7% of Australia's economic output.

The occurrence of uranium deposits on Aboriginal land has led to conflicts between corporations seeking to develop mining operations and Aboriginal people trying to maintain their traditional culture. One such group is the Mirrar Clan, an extended family of Kakadu-area Aborigines. The Mirrar have been living with the region's first uranium mine, the Ranger mine, since the Australian government approved its development on their land in 1978.

When the corporate owners of Ranger proposed to open another uranium mine, Jabiluka, on their land, the Mirrar launched into an environmental battle that would rage over a number of years and several continents. The Mirrar viewed Jabiluka as a threat to their health and to the integrity of their environment, particularly given repeated radioactive spills at the Ranger mine. Many feared that contaminated water would be released into area creeks and that radioactive radon gas would emanate from stored waste materials. Moreover, mindful of geologic faults

in the area, the Mirrar worried that dams holding mine waste could fail catastrophically in an earthquake. "We are talking about a uranium mine inside our largest national park," said Peter Robertson, coordinator of the Environment Centre of the Northern Territory at the time. "This is not a place to cut corners."[2]

Environmental activists worldwide joined the Mirrar's struggle. In 1998 nearly 3000 people travelled to the Kakadu region to protest Jabiluka. In late 2002 their efforts finally succeeded. Sir Robert Wilson, chief executive officer of Rio Tinto, the corporation holding rights to the ore body, announced the cancellation of mining plans at Jabiluka, citing economic factors (declining world uranium prices) and ethical factors (concerns about developing the mine without Mirrar consent). The company agreed to rehabilitate the site and restore damage done during exploration and assessment.

Since that time, the price of uranium has risen on the world market. The corporation's plans are now in a holding pattern as it waits and hopes that the Mirrar will one day give their consent. In 2007 the new CEO of Rio Tinto, Tom Albanese, reiterated the company's intention not to pressure the government for approval to develop Jabiluka without the prior informed consent of the traditional landowners.[3] **Prior informed consent**, one of the hallmark principles of modern environmental ethics, means that consent or acceptance of an activity (such as land development or waste disposal) is not legally valid unless the consenting person or group has been properly and adequately informed *and* can be shown to have a reasonable understanding of all potential impacts before giving consent.

The Mirrar opposed the mine development despite the economic benefits promised to them in the form of jobs, income, development, and a higher material standard of living. The decision to bypass these economic incentives was not easy; indeed, other Aboriginal groups in the Kakadu region supported the mine development. In formulating their approaches to the mining proposal, they had to weigh economic, social, cultural, and philosophical questions as well as scientific ones.

This is Kakadu National Park, Australia, where Aboriginal residents, environmentalists, and mining companies have battled over mining rights.

weighing the issues

ECOIMPERIALISM?

The Mirrar Clan opposed the development of the Jabiluka uranium mine on their land, in spite of potential economic benefits. They were supported by an extensive international network of environmentalists. How do you think those environmentalists would have reacted if the Mirrar, having gained self-determination over their land, had changed their position and opted to approve the mine? Do you believe that the right to self-determination *obliges* Aboriginal people to retain their traditional way of life and preserve the integrity of their ancestral lands?

(a) Ranger Uranium Mine, Kakadu region, Australia

(b) Voisey's Bay Nickel Mine, northern Labrador, Canada

FIGURE 15.1

The Ranger mine **(a)**, located on Australian Aboriginal lands amid sacred sites, caused enough environmental impacts to spark fierce opposition to the proposed Jabiluka mine nearby. **(b)** The Voisey's Bay mine and concentrator site in northern Labrador faced similar challenges from both Innu Nation and Nunatsiavut Government. The mine's owner, Vale, negotiated special agreements with the two Aboriginal groups prior to the opening of the mine, dealing with land rights, social and economic considerations, and numerous environmental concerns.[5]

Many factors shape our world views and perception of the environment

The traditional culture and world view of the Mirrar Clan helped shape its response to the proposed Jabiluka mine. Australian Aborigines view the landscape around them as the physical embodiment of stories that express the beliefs and values central to their culture. The landscape to them is a sacred text. They believe that spirit ancestors travelled routes called "dreaming tracks," leaving signs and lessons in the landscape. By explaining the origins of specific landscape features, dreaming-track stories assign meaning to notable landmarks and help Aborigines construct detailed mental maps of their surroundings. The stories also teach lessons concerning family relations, hunting, food gathering, and conflict resolution. The Mirrar who opposed the Jabiluka uranium mine believed that it would desecrate sacred sites and compromise their culture (**FIGURE 15.1**).

Similarly, many Aboriginal people of Canada's North, including the Dene and Innu, believe that the landscape is inhabited by spirits, both benevolent and malevolent, and thus must be honoured and protected.[4] They worry that mining may have negative impacts on their lands, traditional hunting routes, water sources, or resource-gathering sites. There is also concern that noise, disruption, and emissions from such operations might cause harm to sacred animals or to sites that have spiritual or cultural significance.

Religion and spiritual beliefs are among many factors that can shape people's world views and perception of the environment. A community may also share a particular view of the environment if its members have lived through

similar experiences. For example, European Christian settlers in both Australia and North America viewed their environment as a hostile force because inclement weather, wild animals, and other natural forces frequently destroyed crops, killed livestock, and took settlers' lives. Such experiences were shared in stories and in songs and helped shape social attitudes in frontier communities. The view of nature as a hostile force and an adversary to be overcome passed from one generation to the next and still influences the way many North Americans and Australians view their surroundings.

Political ideology also shapes a person's worldview and attitude toward the environment. For instance, one's

weighing the issues

MINING IN MECCA . . . ?

Suppose a mining company discovered uranium near the Sacred Mosque at Mecca—or the site in Bethlehem believed to be the birthplace of Jesus, or the Wailing Wall in Jerusalem. What do you think would happen if the company announced plans to develop a mine close to one of these sacred locations, assuring the public that environmental impacts would be minimal and that the mine would create jobs and stimulate economic growth? Which aspects of these unlikely situations resemble that of the Jabiluka case, and which are different?

views on the role of government will influence whether or not one wants government to intervene in a market economy to protect environmental quality. Economic factors also sway how people perceive their environment and make decisions. An individual with a strong interest in the outcome of a decision that may result in his or her private gain or loss is said to have a *vested interest*. Mining company executives and shareholders have a vested interest in a decision to open an area to mining because a new mine can increase profits. Vested interests may lead people to view a proposed mine as a source of economic gain, while minimizing (whether consciously or subconsciously) the potential for negative environmental impacts.

There are many ways to understand the environment

An interesting aspect of the relationship of indigenous peoples with their local environment is **traditional ecological knowledge (TEK)**, or *indigenous ecological knowledge*, intimate knowledge of a particular environment possessed and passed along by those who have inhabited an area for many generations.[6] Examples include knowledge of the medicinal properties of local plants; wintering-over or migration habits of local animals; local geographic and microclimatic variations; or the sequence of tasks required to carry out a traditional task, such as trapping and butchering a large animal. Such a deep understanding is gained through generations of hunters, fishers, gatherers, and harvesters sharing their knowledge of the natural world, usually by way of oral teachings, songs, and storytelling.

In some circumstances, TEK can be assigned a market value. For example, indigenous knowledge of local plants might be extremely valuable to a pharmaceutical company searching for plants with modern medicinal applications. In recent years the value of TEK has become more widely recognized, acknowledged, and remunerated by governments and industry. The Nunavut Wildlife Management Board, which meets annually to set limits on the annual polar bear hunt for Inuit traditional hunters, receives and weighs information from government scientists and from the hunters themselves as part of the decision-making process.

Throughout this book you have encountered scientific data regarding the environmental impacts of our choices (where to make our homes, how to make a living, what to wear, what to eat, how to travel, how to spend our leisure time, and so on). Culture, world views, and values play critical roles in such choices and even can influence the interpretation of scientific data. Thus, acquiring a foundation of scientific understanding is only one part of the search for solutions to environmental problems. Attention to ethics and economics helps us understand why and how we value those things we value.

Environmental Ethics

The field of **ethics** is a branch of philosophy that involves the study of good and bad, right and wrong. The term *ethics* can also refer to the set of moral principles or values held by a person or a society. Ethicists help clarify how people judge right from wrong by elucidating the criteria, standards, or rules that people use in making these judgments. Such criteria are grounded in values— for instance, promoting human welfare, maximizing individual freedom, or minimizing pain and suffering.

People of different cultures or with different world views may differ in their fundamental values and thus may differ in the specific actions they consider to be right or wrong. Ethical standards help differentiate right

roots

ETHICS

The word **ethics**, referring to the study of good and bad, as well as to an individual's or society's set of morals, is thought to derive from the Greek *ethike philosophia*, "moral philosophy." Related words are the Greek *ethikos*, meaning "customs," and *ethos* or *thos*, meaning "character."

weighing the issues

THE ATLANTIC SEAL HUNT

No environmental issue identified with Canada is more emotionally charged than the Atlantic seal hunt. Each year environmentalists and animal activists mobilize to try to stop the hunt, arguing that too many seals are killed, and that the methods used are inhumane. The hunters and supporters counter that they are continuing a way of life that has been practised by Aboriginal people in Canada for at least 4000 years, that it is their right to practise their traditional ways, and that the hunt is vital for the economic well-being and survival of their communities.

What do you think? Who should decide which of these sets of values—animal rights or Aboriginal self-determination—should take precedence?

---

from wrong across different cultures and situations. One classic ethical standard is the *categorical imperative* proposed by philosopher Immanuel Kant, which roughly approximates the "golden rule" common to many of the world's great religions. For example, Hindus learn that they should "not do to others what would cause pain if done to you"; a central tenet of Buddhism is to "hurt not others in ways that you yourself would find hurtful"; and Christians are encouraged to "do unto others as you would have others do unto you." The universality of the golden rule or categorical imperative makes it a fundamental ethical standard.

Another ethical standard is the principle of *utility*, elaborated by British philosopher John Stuart Mill, among others. The **utilitarian principle** holds that something is right when it produces the greatest practical benefits for the most people. For example, a utilitarian might argue that forest biodiversity should be conserved because the possibility exists that a cure for cancer might be found there among the naturally occurring biological compounds. The argument that forest species should be preserved because they have an *intrinsic value*, or an inherent right to exist, would be much less convincing to a utilitarian. This is particularly true in the context of marine protected areas, which are often justified on the basis of utilitarian ends.

Environmental ethics pertains to humans and the environment

The application of ethical standards to relationships between humans and nonhuman entities is known

as **environmental ethics.** This branch of ethics arose once people began to perceive environmental changes brought about by industrialization. Human interactions with the environment frequently give rise to ethical questions that can be difficult to resolve. Consider some examples:

1. Does the present generation have an obligation to conserve resources for future generations? If so, how should this influence our decision making, and how much are we obligated to sacrifice?
2. Are there situations that justify exposing some communities to a disproportionate share of pollution? If not, what actions are warranted in preventing this problem? By extension, if a certain community stands to gain the most from a particular activity, should that community be expected to take on most of the risk associated with the activity?
3. Are humans justified in driving species to extinction? Are we justified in causing other permanent changes in ecological systems? If destroying a forest would drive extinct an insect species few people have heard of, but would create jobs for 10 000 people, would that action be ethically admissible? What if it were an owl species, or an ape, or a whale? What if only 100 jobs would be created? What if it were a species that is harmful to humans, such as mosquitoes? What about a bacterium or a virus?

The intergenerational question—whether we owe consideration to those who will live on this planet and make use of its resources years from now—is of particular interest. The most common definition of **sustainable development** says that we must meet our current needs without compromising the availability of natural resources or the quality of life for future generations. But how can we tell what future generations may need or want, or what they will value or hold sacred?

In 2007 and 2008 construction crews began digging trenches for the laying of an oil pipeline extension through pristine wilderness areas of Jasper National Park and Mount Robson Provincial Park in the Canadian Rockies. The extension, which will allow for the movement of an extra 40 000 barrels of oil each day from Alberta to markets in the United States, was approved in 1952. If the pipeline extension had been requested today, it is highly unlikely that it would have been approved because of the environmental disruption involved. Would it have been possible to know, in 1952, how this decision would be viewed more than 50 years later? And how can we determine how the environmental decisions that we make today will be viewed 50 years into the future?

We extend ethical consideration to non-human entities

Answers to questions like those above depend partly on what ethical standard(s) a person chooses to use. They also depend on the breadth and inclusiveness of the person's domain of ethical concern. A person who feels responsibility for the welfare of insects would answer the third question very differently from a person whose domain of ethical concern ends with humans. Most of us feel moral obligations to some entities in the world but by no means to all.

Throughout the history of Western cultures, people have gradually enlarged the array of entities they feel deserve ethical consideration. The enslavement of human beings by other human beings was common in many societies until recently, for instance. Women were not allowed to vote in Canada until 1916 (even then, only in Manitoba), and many still receive lower pay for equal work. Consider, too, how little ethical consideration citizens of one nation generally extend to those of another on which their government has declared war. Human societies are only now beginning to embrace the principle that all people should be granted equal ethical consideration.

Our expanding domain of ethical concern has begun to include nonhuman entities as well. Mahatma Gandhi reportedly said, "The greatness of a nation and its moral progress can be judged by the way its animals are treated." Concern for the welfare of domesticated animals is evident today in humane societies and in the way many people provide for their pets. Animal-rights activists voice concern for animals that are hunted or used in laboratory testing. Most people now accept that wild animals (at least obviously sentient animals, such as primates and other large vertebrates, with which we share similarities) merit ethical consideration.

Today many environmentalists are concerned not only with certain animals but also with the well-being of whole natural communities. Some have gone still further, suggesting that all of nature—living and nonliving things, even rocks—should be ethically represented (**FIGURE 15.2**). If you think this is a silly idea, consider how you might react if someone put a fast-food restaurant on the top of Mt. Everest, or if a multinational corporation decided to paint a gigantic corporate logo on the Moon. Do the unique landmarks of the natural environment deserve ethical consideration? Do they have any inherent value, or the "right" to exist unaltered? Is their value distinct from the services they may render to humans, or inseparable from human interests? These questions are all worth considering.

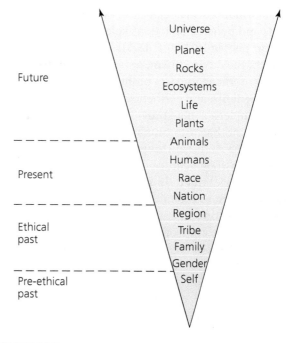

FIGURE 15.2

Through time, people in Western cultures have broadened the scope of their ethical consideration for others. We can view ethics progressing through time in a generalized way outward from the self.

What is behind this ongoing expansion of ethical consideration? Rising economic prosperity in Western cultures, as people became less anxious about their day-to-day survival, has helped enlarge our ethical domain. Science has also played a role in demonstrating that humans do not stand apart from nature but rather are part of it. Ecology, as it has developed over the past 75 years, has made clear that all organisms are interconnected, and what affects plants, animals, and ecosystems can in turn affect humans. Evolutionary biology has shown that humans are merely one species out of millions and have evolved subject to the same pressures as other organisms.

For many non-Western cultures, expansive ethical domains are nothing new. Many traditional cultures have long granted ethical standing to nonhuman entities. Aborigines, like the Mirrar, Innu, and Dene, who view their landscape as sacred and alive, are a case in point. However, it is worthwhile to examine Western ethical expansion because it underlies so many of modern secular society's beliefs and actions regarding the environment. We can simplify the continuum of attitudes toward the natural world by dividing it into three ethical perspectives: anthropocentrism, biocentrism, and ecocentrism.

Anthropocentrism   **Anthropocentrism** takes a human-centred view of our relationship with the environment. An anthropocentrist denies or ignores the notion that nonhuman entities can have rights, and measures the costs and benefits of actions solely according to their impact on people (**FIGURE 15.3**). To evaluate an action that affects the environment, an anthropocentrist might use such criteria as impacts on human health, economic costs and benefits, and aesthetic concerns.

For example, if a mine provides a net economic benefit while doing no harm to human health and having little aesthetic impact, the anthropocentrist would conclude it was a worthwhile venture, even if it might drive some native species extinct. If protecting the area would provide spiritual, economic, or other benefits to humans now or in the future, an anthropocentrist might favour its protection. In the anthropocentric perspective, anything not providing benefit to people is considered to be of negligible value.

Biocentrism   In contrast to anthropocentrism, **biocentrism** ascribes values to actions, entities, or properties on the basis of their effects on all living things or on the integrity of the biotic realm in general (see **FIGURE 15.3**). In this perspective, all life has ethical standing. A biocentrist evaluates actions in terms of their overall impact on living things, including—but not exclusively focusing on—human beings. In the case of a mine proposal, a biocentrist might oppose the mine if it posed a serious threat to the abundance and variety of living things in the area, even if it would create jobs, generate economic growth, and pose no threat to human health. Some biocentrists advocate equal consideration of all living things, whereas others advocate that some types of organisms should receive more than others.

FIGURE 15.3
An anthropocentrist extends ethical standing only to humans and judges actions in terms of their effects on humans. A biocentrist values and considers all living things, human and otherwise. An ecocentrist extends ethical consideration to living and nonliving components of the environment. The ecocentrist also takes a holistic view of the connections among these components, valuing the larger functional systems of which they are a part.

Ecocentrism   **Ecocentrism** judges actions in terms of their benefit or harm to the integrity of whole ecological systems, which consist of biotic and abiotic elements and the relationships among them (see **FIGURE 15.3**). An ecocentrist would value the well-being of entire species, communities, or ecosystems over the welfare of a given individual. Implicit in this view is that the preservation of larger systems generally protects their components, whereas selective protection of the components may not always safeguard the entire system. Ecocentrism is a *holistic* perspective. Not only does it encompass a wide variety of entities, but it also stresses preserving the connections that tie the entities together into functional systems.

Environmental ethics has ancient roots

Environmental ethics arose as an academic discipline in the early 1970s, but people have contemplated our relationship with nature for thousands of years. Ancient Aboriginal oral traditions and dreaming-track stories treat the environment as a source of sacred teachings, worthy of contemplation and protection. In the Jain Dharma, one of the oldest religious traditions in the world, compassion for all life—human and nonhuman— is a core belief. Jains are typically vegetarian or vegan and try to avoid foods obtained with unnecessary cruelty; for some, this even involves refusing to eat root vegetables (such as potatoes and onions) to avoid killing the plant from which they were obtained. In the Western tradition, the ancient Greek philosopher Plato expressed what he considered humans' moral obligation to the environment, writing, "The land is our ancestral home and we must cherish it even more than children cherish their mother."

Some ethicists and theologians have pointed to the religious traditions of Christianity, Judaism, and Islam as sources of anthropocentric hostility toward the environment. They point out biblical passages such as, "Be fruitful and multiply, and fill the earth and subdue it; and have dominion over the fish of the sea and over the birds of the air and over every living thing that moves upon the earth." Such wording has justified and encouraged separation from and animosity toward nature over the centuries, some scholars say. Others emphasize sacred texts that encourage benevolent human stewardship over nature. Consider the directive, "You shall not defile the land in which you live. . . ." Although people have held differing views of their ethical relationship with the environment for millennia, environmental impacts that became apparent during the Industrial Revolution intensified debate about our relationship with the environment.

The Industrial Revolution inspired environmental philosophers

As the Industrial Revolution spread from Great Britain throughout Europe and elsewhere, its technological advances and resultant population growth amplified human impacts on the environment. In this period of social and economic transformation, agricultural economies became industrialized, machines enhanced or replaced human and animal labour, and much of the rural population moved into cities. Consumption of natural resources accelerated, and pollution increased dramatically as coal combustion fuelled railroads, steamships, ironworks, and factories.

Many writers and philosophers of the time criticized industrialization. British critic John Ruskin (1819–1900) called cities "little more than laboratories for the distillation into heaven of venomous smokes and smells." He complained that people prized the material benefits that nature could provide, but no longer appreciated its spiritual and aesthetic benefits. A number of citizens' groups sprang up in nineteenth-century England that could be considered some of the first environmental organizations. These included the Commons Preservation Society, the Coal Smoke Abatement Society, and the Selborne League, dedicated to the protection of rare plants, birds, and landscapes.

During the 1840s, a philosophical movement called *transcendentalism* flourished, espoused by American philosophers Ralph Waldo Emerson and Henry David Thoreau and poet Walt Whitman. The transcendentalists viewed nature as a direct manifestation of the divine, emphasizing the soul's oneness with nature and God. They objected to what they saw as their fellow citizens' obsession with material things. Through their writings the transcendentalists promoted a holistic view of nature. They identified a need to experience wild nature and portrayed natural entities as symbols or messengers of a deeper truth. Thoreau viewed nature as divine, but he also observed the natural world closely, in the manner of a scientist; he was in many ways one of the first ecologists. His book *Walden*, in which he recorded his observations and thoughts while he lived at Walden Pond away from the bustle of urban Massachusetts, is a classic of philosophical and environmental literature.

Conservation and preservation arose at the start of the twentieth century

One admirer of Emerson and Thoreau was John Muir (1838–1914), a Scottish immigrant who eventually settled in California and made the Yosemite Valley his wilder-

FIGURE 15.4

A pioneering advocate of the preservation ethic, John Muir is remembered for his efforts to protect the Sierra Nevada from development and for his role in founding the Sierra Club. Muir (right) is shown with President Theodore Roosevelt in Yosemite National Park. After his 1903 wilderness camping trip with Muir, the president instructed his interior secretary to increase protected areas in the Sierra Nevada.

ness home. Although Muir chose to live in isolation in his beloved Sierra Nevada for long stretches of time, he nonetheless became politically active and won fame as a tireless advocate for the preservation of wilderness (**FIGURE 15.4**).

Muir was motivated by the rapid deforestation and environmental degradation he witnessed throughout North America and by his belief that the natural world should be treated with the same respect that cathedrals receive. Today he is associated with the **preservation ethic**, which holds that we should protect the natural environment in a pristine, unaltered state. Muir argued that nature deserved protection for its own inherent value (an ecocentrist argument), but he also maintained that nature played a large role in human happiness and fulfillment (an anthropocentrist argument). "Everybody needs beauty as well as bread," he wrote in his 1912 work *The Yosemite*, "places to play in and pray in, where nature may heal and give strength to body and soul alike."

Canadian James Bernard Harkin (1875–1955) also believed in preserving the beauty of nature. He was strongly influenced by the writings of Muir, his contemporary. Harkin was the first commissioner of Dominion Parks (which eventually became Parks Canada) and is credited with saving vast areas of Canadian wilderness from development (**FIGURE 15.5**). He believed in the spiritual, healing, and restorative power of nature. He was drawn to mountains, which, he said, "elevate the mind and purify the spirit." Harkin believed that setting aside land

(a) Kootenay National Park

(b) James Harkin

FIGURE 15.5
Kootenay National Park **(a)** was designated as a national park in 1920. It was one of 11 national parks designated during the tenure of James Harkin **(b)** as Canada's commissioner of Dominion Parks. Mount Harkin in the Mitchell Range is named in his honour.

as national parks was only the beginning of preservation; the real challenge would be to maintain them as wilderness. Resource extraction and even some vehicle use were limited in national parks during his service, and he came to be known as the "Father of National Parks" of Canada.[7]

Some of the factors that motivated Muir and Harkin also inspired American forester Gifford Pinchot (1865–1946), who opposed rapid deforestation and unregulated economic development of land. However, Pinchot took a more anthropocentric view of how and why nature should be valued. He is today the person most closely associated with the **conservation ethic**, which holds that humans should put natural resources to use but also that we have a responsibility to manage them wisely. Whereas preservation aims to preserve nature for its own sake, conservation promotes the prudent, efficient, and sustainable extraction and use of natural resources for the benefit of present and future generations. The conservation ethic uses a utilitarian standard, stating that in using resources, humans should attempt to provide the greatest good to the greatest number of people for the longest time.

Pinchot's counterpart in Canada was Clifford Sifton (1861–1929), a controversial politician and conservationist. As minister of the interior, Sifton aggressively lured immigrants to settle and farm in the West; he was deeply committed to the agricultural development of land as Canada's principal natural resource—not an obvious conservationist position. However, Sifton was also a "champion" of Canada's natural resources, and was particularly devoted to forest conservation and reforestation. He was the first chairman of the Commission for the Conservation of Natural Resources, which undertook detailed inventories of Canadian natural resources.[8]

Conservation and preservation are rooted in fundamentally different ethical approaches, which often meant that advocates were pitted against one another on policy issues of the day. Nonetheless, both branches represented reactions against the prevailing "frontier develop-ment ethic," which held that humans should be masters of nature, and which promoted economic development without regard to its negative consequences. Those who led the conservation and preservation movements in the nineteenth and early twentieth centuries left legacies that reverberate today in our ethical approaches to the environment.

The land ethic and deep ecology enlarged ethical boundaries

As a young forester and wildlife manager, Aldo Leopold (1887–1949) (FIGURE 15.6) began his career as a conservationist. At first, he embraced the government policy of shooting predators, such as wolves, to increase populations of deer and other game animals. At the same time, however, Leopold was following the development of ecological science. He eventually ceased to view certain species as "good" or "bad" and instead came to see that healthy ecological systems depend on the protection of all their interacting parts, including predators as well as prey. Drawing an analogy to mechanical maintenance, he wrote, "to keep every cog and wheel is the first precaution of intelligent tinkering."

Leopold argued that humans should view themselves and "the land" as members of the same community, and that people are obliged to treat the land in an ethical manner based on mutual respect. In his 1949 essay "The Land Ethic," he wrote:

All ethics so far evolved rest upon a single premise: that the individual is a member of a community of interdependent parts . . . The land ethic simply enlarges the boundaries of the community to include soils, waters, plants, and animals, or collectively: the land . . . A land ethic changes the role of Homo sapiens from conqueror of the land-community to plain member and citizen of it.[9]

FIGURE 15.6
Aldo Leopold, wildlife manager and pioneering environmental philosopher, articulated a new relationship between people and the environment. In his essay "The Land Ethic," he called on people to include the environment in their ethical framework.

Leopold intended that the land ethic would help guide decision making. "A thing is right," he wrote in his 1949 book *A Sand County Almanac*, "when it tends to preserve the integrity, stability, and beauty of the biotic community. It is wrong when it tends otherwise." Many today view Aldo Leopold as the most eloquent and important philosopher of environmental ethics.

One philosophical perspective that goes beyond even ecocentrism is **deep ecology**, which emerged in the 1970s. Proponents describe the movement as resting on principles of "self-realization" and biocentric equality. They define self-realization as the awareness that humans are inseparable from nature and that the air we breathe, the water we drink, and the foods we consume are both products of the environment and integral parts of us. Biocentric equality is the concept that all living beings have equal value and that because we are truly inseparable from our environment, we should protect all living things as we would protect ourselves.

Ecofeminists see parallels between the oppression of nature and of women

As deep ecology and mainstream environmentalism were extending people's ethical domains during the 1960s and 1970s, major social movements, such as the civil rights movement and the feminist movement, were gaining prominence. A number of feminist scholars saw parallels in human behaviour toward nature and men's behaviour toward women. The degradation of nature and the social oppression of women shared common roots, these scholars asserted.

Ecofeminism argues that the patriarchal (male-dominated) structure of society—which traditionally grants more power and prestige to men than to women—is a root cause of both social and environmental problems. Ecofeminists hold that a world view traditionally associated with women, which interprets the world in terms of interrelationships and cooperation, is more compatible with nature than a world view traditionally associated with men, which interprets the world in terms of hierarchies and competition. Ecofeminists maintain that a tendency to try to dominate and conquer has historically been exercised against both women and the natural environment.

One of the most interesting environmental movements of our time is Chipko Andolan, which had its philosophical grounding in the principles of Gandhian nonviolent resistance, grassroots social activism, and ecofeminism.[10] Chipko emerged in the early 1970s in the northern Uttarakhand region of India, as an effort to stop clear-cutting from decimating the vast forests of northern India. The movement came to a climax in 1973, when government workers turned up unannounced to cut trees but were met by a group of village women who refused to allow the work to proceed (**FIGURE 15.7A**). Leader Gaura Devi reportedly stated, "The forest is like our mother. You will have to shoot us before you can cut it down." The women stood watch over the forest, wrapping their arms around the trees. Eventually, after considerable negotiation, the government declared the region to be an environmentally "sensitive" area. Today, Chipko is an international icon of grassroots environmentalism.

roots

CHIPKO

The name **Chipko Andolan** ("Chipko Movement") comes from the Hindi root word *chipka*, "stick" or "cling" or "embrace" (related to *chipku*, "hanger-on"). *Andolan* is Hindi for a "movement" or "campaign." Its use by the women of northern Uttarakhand in their nonviolent resistance against logging may have been the origin of the term *tree-hugger*, commonly used (often condescendingly) in reference to environmentalists.

(a) Villagers placed their bodies between the trees and the contractor's axes.

(b) Wangari Maathai

FIGURE 15.7   In the early 1970s, grassroots resistance efforts by village women led to the establishment of the Chipko Movement, dedicated to preventing deforestation in northern India's Himalayan foothills **(a)**. The founder of Kenya's Green Belt Movement, Professor Wangari Maathai **(b)** was awarded the Nobel Peace Prize in 2004 for her work to empower women and fight deforestation; she died in 2011.

Another movement rooted in ecofeminism and the empowerment of the poor is the Green Belt Movement of Kenya. This organization, which began by paying impoverished village women to plant tree seedlings, was founded in 1977. The Nobel Peace Prize was awarded to Green Belt's founder, Wangari Maathai, in 2004 (**FIGURE 15.7B**).[11]

Environmental justice seeks equitable access to resources and protection from environmental degradation

Our society's domain of ethical concern has been expanding from rich to poor and from majority races and ethnic groups to minority ones. This ethical expansion involves applying a standard of fairness and equality and has given rise to the environmental justice movement. **Environmental justice** is based on the principle that all people—regardless of race, colour, national origin, or income—have the right to live and work in a clean, healthy environment; to receive protection from the risks and impacts of environmental degradation, and to

be compensated for having suffered such impacts; and to have equitable access to environmental resources of high quality.

The environmental justice movement is fuelled by the fact that the poor and minorities tend to be exposed to a greater share of pollution, hazards, and environmental degradation than are richer people and whites. This has been supported by scientific research (**FIGURE 15.8**). For example, studies have found the percentage of minorities in areas with toxic waste sites to be twice that in areas without toxic waste sites. Researchers in many parts of the world who study air pollution, lead poisoning, pesticide exposure, and workplace hazards have found similar patterns.

A protest in the early 1980s by African Americans in Warren County, North Carolina, against a toxic waste dump in their community is widely seen as the beginning of the movement in North America. The state had chosen to site the dump in the county with the highest percentage of blacks, prompting residents to suspect "environmental racism." Environmental justice grew in prominence as more people began fighting environmental hazards in their communities.

The early environmental justice movement—like the Chipko and Green Belt movements internationally but

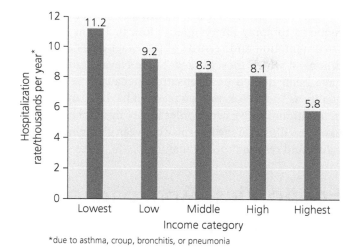

*due to asthma, croup, bronchitis, or pneumonia

FIGURE 15.8
Many studies have demonstrated links between exposure to pollution and socioeconomic status. This is demonstrated by a graph comparing incidences of hospitalization for respiratory illnesses—a common health impact of exposure to environmental pollutants—among children of different income levels in Toronto.

in contrast to early environmental movements in North America—was made up largely of low-income people and minorities. Today the movement has broadened to encompass worker health and safety; education and financial services for preparation for, response to, and recovery from natural disasters; and access to land, water, and other environmental resources worldwide.

There are two basic ways that environmental injustice is manifested. First, a community or group can be denied equitable access to environmental resources. This often occurs where poverty is common, or where land of high quality is scarce. For example, in many developing countries rich landowners control the best agricultural land, while poor subsistence farmers are left to scratch out a living on small patches of unsuitable land. In North America we may see this inequity expressed as expensive beachfront or mountain-view properties that are available only to the wealthiest few, or as limited access to an expensive diet rich in vitamins and nutrients.

Second, a community or group can be subjected to environmental injustice by having disproportionate risks or costs of pollution or degradation transferred to them, as in the example (above) of toxic waste dumps sited in communities of racial or ethnic minorities. In less economically developed parts of the world, the poor and other marginalized groups are directly dependent on the environment for survival and therefore suffer the harshest and most immediate impacts of environmental degradation. Cultural differences also can lead to disproportionate exposure of specific groups to the effects of environmental degradation. For example, the traditional diet of many

of Canada's Aboriginal people is heavily reliant on fish and marine mammals, which tend to have high concentrations of harmful pollutants, such as mercury.

Aboriginal groups struggling to maintain a traditional lifestyle have been linked with the environmental justice movement. Many such struggles originate not as environmental causes but as social justice causes. The rubbertappers or *seringueiros* of the Brazilian Amazon are representative of causes that originate at this intersection of environmental justice and social justice. The *seringueiros* and their leader, Chico Mendes (**FIGURE 15.9**), caught the world's attention when it became apparent that the battle to save their traditional economy—based on the sustainable extraction of latex and other forest resources—was intimately connected with efforts to stop deforestation of the Amazonian rainforest for ranching.

The *seringueiros* forged a partnership with indigenous Amazonians, who face many of the same challenges to their traditional lands, resources, and lifestyle. Chico Mendes thought of himself first as a social activist, fighting on behalf of his people and their way of life. Would the international environmental movement have embraced his cause if it had *not* been intimately connected with the rainforest? Sadly, Chico Mendes' iconic status and effectiveness as an activist on behalf of his people and their beloved forests and traditions were dramatically heightened by his assassination, in 1988, by Brazilian ranchers.

FIGURE 15.9
Chico Mendes, seen here shortly before his assassination in 1988, was a social activist on behalf of the traditional lifestyle of his people, but he caught the eye of the world because of his struggle to preserve the Amazon rainforest.

Critics have characterized the attempts of the predominantly white Australian government and uranium mining companies to open mines on traditional lands of the Mirrar as environmental injustice. In North America, as well, uranium mining has been a focus of environmental justice concerns. As discussed in the Central Case, Dene mineworkers from the Northwest Territories and Saskatchewan, as well as Navajo mineworkers from the United States, suffered delayed health effects that may have been caused by working in uranium mines with minimal safeguards.

Dene workers were hired as early as 1930 to haul radioactive uranium ore wrapped in cloth bags at Eldorado. The governments of Canada (then the world's largest supplier of uranium) and the United States (main purchaser of the ore) were aware of the health hazards of dealing with radioactive ores, as documented in government publications from the time.[12] However, these concerns were not communicated to Dene workers, many of whom did not speak English, and protective equipment was not provided. For decades, until the mine was shut down in the 1960s, Dene miners "slept on the ore, ate fish from water contaminated by radioactive tailings and breathed radioactive dust while on the barges, docks and portages," according to the *Calgary Herald*.[13]

The later deaths, from lung cancer, of many Port Radium miners led to the nickname "Village of Widows" for the settlement of Deline, and the Dene Nation called for an official response from the federal government. In 2005 the government of Canada issued the results of its study, which concluded that there was insufficient evidence to link the deaths of the miners with exposure to radiation during mining work at Port Radium. The report acknowledged that the mine had had an impact on soil and water quality in the immediate vicinity of Great Bear Lake and called for the proper decommissioning of the site, with provisions for continued environmental monitoring. Compensation for residents and the remaining miners was not addressed in the report.[14]

Although cases of lung cancer began to appear among uranium mineworkers in the early 1960s, scientific studies of radiation's effects on miners at the time specifically excluded Aboriginal mineworkers. The decision to include only white miners in those studies was attributed to the researchers' desire to study a "homogeneous population." A later generation would perceive this as negligence and discrimination.

In the United States, the *Radiation Exposure Compensation Act* of 1990 compensated Navajo miners who suffered health effects from unprotected work in the mines. Even the compensation process, though, has been controversial; as of 2006, approximately 80% of the $300 million allocated to compensate these miners and their families had been allocated to non-native miners. Many of the Navajo miners lacked the extensive documentation required to apply for compensation, including medical documentation and records of the exact dates and conditions in which they worked. Some Navajo miners also have been denied compensation because they fail to qualify as "nonsmokers" as a result of having participated in traditional native ceremonies involving smoke.[15] Cases like these illustrate the interplay between changing ethical values and resultant policy making.

Economics: Approaches and Environmental Implications

Economics, like ethics, addresses people's values, influences behaviour, and widely informs policy. People who oppose mining and other developments in wilderness areas or on traditional lands typically do so on the basis of ethical concerns and worries over environmental impacts. Few challenge such activities on economic grounds; even opponents generally recognize them as lucrative activities that generate jobs and income. On the other hand, support for mining and other development and resource extraction activities is primarily founded in economic reasoning.

Conflict between ethical and economic motivations is thus a recurrent theme in environmental issues. We often hear it said that environmental protection works in opposition to economic progress. Arguments are made that environmental protection costs too much money, interferes with progress, and leads to job loss. But is this necessarily the case? Growing numbers of economists assert that there need be no such trade-off—that, in fact, environmental protection can be *good* for the economy. The position one takes often depends on whether one thinks in the short term or the long term, and whether one holds to traditional economic schools of thought or to newer ones that view human economies as coupled to the natural environment.

Economics studies the allocation of scarce resources

Like ethics, economics examines factors that guide human behaviour. **Economics** is the study of how people decide to use scarce resources to provide goods and services in the face of demand for them. By this definition, environmental problems are economic problems that can intensify as population and resource consumption increase. For example, pollution may be viewed as depleting the scarce resources of clean air, water, or soil.

Several types of economies exist today

An **economy** is a social system that converts resources into **goods**, material commodities manufactured for and bought by individuals and businesses; and **services**, work done for others as a form of business. The oldest type of economy is the *subsistence economy*. People in subsistence economies—who still compose much of the human population—meet most or all of their daily needs directly from nature and do not purchase or trade for most of life's necessities.

A second type of economy is the *capitalist market economy*. In this system, buyers and sellers interact to determine which goods and services to produce, how much to produce, and how these should be produced and distributed. Capitalist economies are often contrasted with state socialist economies, or *centrally planned economies*, in which government determines in a top-down manner how to allocate resources.

A utopian pure market economy would operate without any government intervention. In reality, all capitalist market economies today, including that of Canada, are hybrid systems (often called *mixed economies*). In modern market economies, governments intervene for several reasons: (1) to eliminate unfair advantages held by monopoly buyers or sellers; (2) to provide social services, such as national defence, medical care, and education; (3) to provide "safety nets" (for older adults, the unemployed, those with chronic illnesses or disabilities, victims of natural disasters, and so on); (4) to manage commonly owned resources (the "commons"); and (5) to mitigate pollution and other types of environmental damage.

Environment and economy are intricately linked

All human economies exist within the larger environment and depend on it in important ways. Economies receive inputs from the environment, process them in complex ways that enable human society to function, and then discharge outputs of waste from this process into the environment. Economies are thus *open systems* integrated with the larger environmental system of which they are a part. Earth, in turn, is a *closed system*. This means that the material inputs Earth can provide to economies are ultimately finite and so is the waste-absorbing capacity of the planet.

Although the interactions between human economies and the nonhuman environment are readily apparent, traditional economic schools of thought have long overlooked the importance of these connections. Indeed, most conventional economists today still adhere to a world view that largely ignores the environment (**FIGURE 15.10A**), and this world view continues to drive most policy decisions. A conventional economic world view essentially holds that environmental resources (the inputs into the economy) are limitless and free and that wastes (outputs) can be endlessly exported and absorbed by the environment, at no cost. However, modern economists belonging to the fast-growing fields of environmental economics, ecological economics, and natural resource accounting explicitly accept that human economies are subsets of the environment and depend crucially on the environment (**FIGURE 15.10B**).

Economic activity uses resources from the environment. Natural resources are the substances and forces we need to survive: the Sun's energy, fresh water, trees that provide lumber, rocks that provide metals, and fossil fuels and other energy sources that power our machines. We can think of natural resources as "goods" produced by nature. Without Earth's natural resources, there would be no human economies and no human beings.

Environmental systems also function in a manner that naturally supports economies. Earth's ecological systems purify air and water, cycle nutrients, provide for the pollination of plants by animals, and serve as receptacles and recycling systems for the wastes generated by our economic activity. Such essential services, often called **ecosystem services** (**TABLE 15.1**), sustain the life that makes our economic activity possible. Some ecosystem services represent the very nuts-and-bolts of our survival; others enhance our quality of life.

Although the environment allows economic activity to occur by providing ecosystem goods and services, that economic activity can affect the environment in return. When we deplete natural resources or produce pollution, we degrade the ability of ecological systems to function. The *Millennium Ecosystem Assessment* concluded in 2005 that 15 of 24 ecosystem services surveyed globally were being degraded or used unsustainably. The degradation of ecosystem services can in turn negatively affect

FIGURE 15.10
Standard neoclassical economics focuses on processes of production and consumption between households and businesses **(a)**, viewing the environment only as a "factor of production" that helps enable the production of goods. Environmental and ecological economists view the human economy as existing within the natural environment **(b)**, receiving resources from it, discharging waste into it, and interacting with it through ecosystem services.

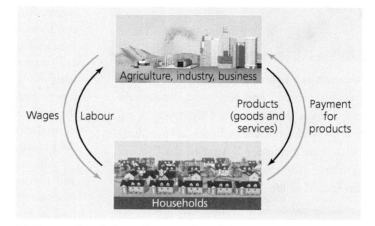

(a) Conventional view of economic activity

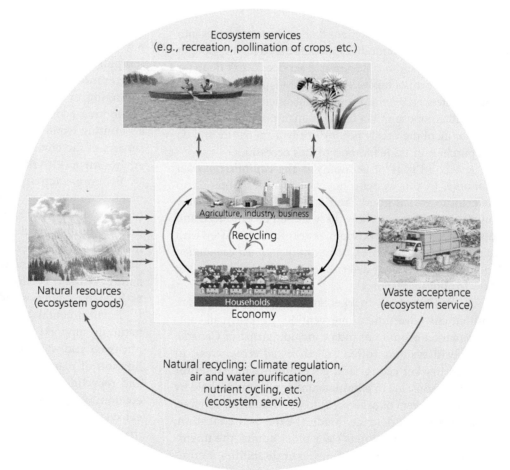

(b) Economic activity as viewed by environmental and ecological economists

economies. Ecological degradation harms poor people more than wealthy people, the Millennium Ecosystem Assessment found. As a result, restoring ecosystem services is a prime objective for alleviating poverty in much of the world.

These interrelationships have only recently become widely recognized. Let us briefly examine how economic thought has changed over the years, tracing the path that is now beginning to lead economies to become more compatible with natural systems.

Table 15.1   Ecosystem Services

Type of ecosystem service*	Example(s)
Regulation of atmospheric gases	Maintaining the ozone layer; balancing oxygen, carbon dioxide, and other gases
Regulation of climate	Controlling global temperature and precipitation through oceanic and atmospheric currents, greenhouse gases, cloud formation, and so on
Protection and buffering	Providing storm protection, flood control, and drought recovery, mainly through vegetation and shoreline structure
Regulation of water flow	Providing water for agriculture, industry, transportation
Storage of water	Providing water through watersheds, reservoirs, aquifers
Control of erosion	Preventing soil loss from wind or runoff; storing silt in lakes and wetlands
Formation of soil	Weathering rock; accumulating organic material
Cycling of nutrients	Cycling carbon, nitrogen, phosphorus, sulphur, and other nutrients through ecosystems
Waste treatment	Removing toxins, recovering nutrients, controlling pollution
Pollination of plants	Transporting floral gametes by wind or pollinating animals, enabling crops and wild plants to reproduce
Population control	Controlling prey with predators; controlling hosts with parasites; controlling herbivory on crops with predators and parasites
Provision of habitat	Providing ecological settings in which creatures can breed, feed, rest, migrate, winter
Provision of food	Producing fish, game, crops, nuts, and fruits that humans obtain by hunting, gathering, fishing, subsistence farming
Supply of raw materials	Producing lumber, fuel, metals, fodder
Genetic resources	Providing unique biological sources for medicine, materials science, genes for resistance to plant pathogens and crop pests, ornamental species (pets and horticultural plant varieties)
Recreational opportunities	Ecotourism, sport fishing, hiking, birding, kayaking, other outdoor recreation
Noncommercial services	Aesthetic, artistic, educational, spiritual, and/or scientific values of ecosystems

*Ecosystem "goods" are here included in ecosystem services.

Source: Adapted with permission from Costanza, R., et al. 1997. The value of the world's ecosystem services and natural capital. Nature 387:253–260.

Classical economics promoted the free market

Economics shares a common intellectual heritage with ethics, and practitioners of both have long been interested in the relationship between individual action and societal well-being. Some philosophers argued that individuals acting in their own self-interest would harm society (as in the tragedy of the commons). Others believed that such behaviour could benefit society, as long as the behaviour was constrained by the rule of law and private property rights and operated within fairly competitive markets.

The latter view was articulated by Scottish philosopher Adam Smith (1723–1790). Known today as the father of classical economics, Smith believed that when people are free to pursue their own economic self-interest in a competitive marketplace, the marketplace will behave as if guided by "an invisible hand" that ensures their actions

will benefit society as a whole. In his 1776 book *Inquiry into the Nature and Causes of the Wealth of Nations*, Smith wrote:

[Each individual] intends only his own security, only his own gain. And he is led in this by an invisible hand to promote an end which was no part of intention. By pursuing his own interests he frequently promotes that of society more effectually than when he really intends to.[16]

Smith's philosophy remains a pillar of free market thought today, and many credit it for the tremendous gains in material prosperity that industrialized nations have experienced in the past few centuries. Others argue that the policies spawned by free-market thought worsen inequalities between rich and poor and contribute to environmental degradation. Market capitalism, these critics assert, should be constrained and regulated by democratic government.

Neoclassical economics considers price, supply, and demand

Economists subsequently took more quantitative approaches to issues related to price, supply, and demand. Modern neoclassical economics examines the psychological factors underlying consumer choices, explaining market prices in terms of consumer preferences for units of particular commodities. In neoclassical economic theory, buyers desire the lowest possible price, whereas sellers desire the highest possible price. This conflict between buyers and sellers results in a compromise price being reached and the "right" quantity of commodities being bought and sold.

This is often phrased in terms of *supply*, the amount of a product offered for sale at a given price, and *demand*, the amount of a product people will buy at a given price if free to do so. Theoretically, when prices go up, demand drops and supply increases; when prices fall, demand rises and supply decreases. In theory, the market automatically moves toward an equilibrium point, a price at which supply equals demand (**FIGURE 15.11A**). Similar reasoning can be applied to environmental issues, such that economists can determine "optimal" levels of resource use or pollution control (**FIGURE 15.11B**).

Cost–benefit analysis is a useful tool

Neoclassical economists commonly use a method referred to as **cost–benefit analysis**. In this approach, estimated costs for a proposed action are totalled and compared with the sum of benefits anticipated to result from the action. If total benefits exceed costs, the action should be pursued; if costs exceed benefits, it should not. When choosing among multiple alternative actions, the one with the greatest excess of benefits over costs should be chosen.

This reasoning seems eminently logical; however, problems often arise in applying it to environmental situations because not all costs and benefits are easily quantified, or even easily identified. It may be simple to quantify wages paid to uranium miners or the market value of uranium extracted from a mine or even the cost of measures to minimize health risks for miners. But it is much more difficult to assess the cost of a landscape's being scarred by mine development or the cost of radioactive contamination of a stream or the costs in health and emotional well-being to the families of miners who die from mining-related cancers.

Because some costs and benefits cannot easily be assigned monetary values, cost–benefit analysis is often controversial. Moreover, because economic benefits

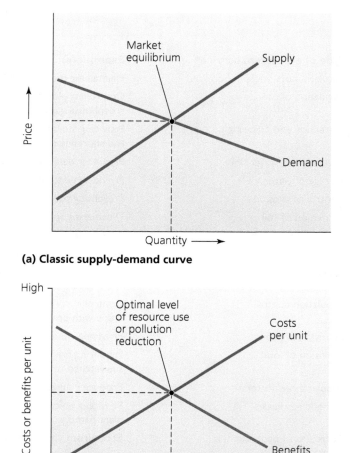

(a) Classic supply-demand curve

(b) Marginal benefit and cost curves

FIGURE 15.11
This basic supply-and-demand curve **(a)** illustrates the relationship among supply, demand, and market equilibrium, the "balance point" at which demand is equal to supply. We can use a similar graph **(b)** to determine an "optimal" level of resource use or pollution mitigation. In this graph, the cost per unit of resource use or pollution cleanup (blue line) rises as the resource use or pollution cleanup proceeds and it becomes expensive to extract or clean up the remaining amounts. Meanwhile, the benefits per unit of resource use or pollution cleanup (red line) decrease. The point where the lines intersect gives the optimal level.

usually are more easily quantified than environmental costs, economic benefits tend to be overrepresented in traditional cost–benefit analyses. As a result, environmental advocates often feel these analyses are biased in favour of economic development and against environmental protection.

A corollary to cost–benefit analysis has been the development of a variety of mechanisms for understanding, calculating, and defining the value, to society and to individuals, of environmental costs and benefits. In general, **valuation** refers to the attempt to quantify the value of a particular environmental good or service—even if it cannot easily be expressed in monetary terms. We will discuss how different valuation approaches can be used to more accurately represent the environment in cost–benefit analysis and asset accounting, below.

Aspects of neoclassical economics have profound implications for the environment

Today's capitalist market systems have generated unprecedented material wealth, employment, and other desirable outcomes, but they have also contributed to environmental problems. Four of the fundamental assumptions of neoclassical economics have implications for the environment:

1. Resources are infinite or substitutable.
2. Long-term effects should be discounted.
3. Costs and benefits are internal.
4. Growth is good.

Let us critically examine each of these assumptions in turn.

Are resources infinite or substitutable?

Neoclassical economic models generally treat the supply of workers and other resources as being either infinite or largely "substitutable and interchangeable." This implies that once we have depleted a resource—natural, human, or otherwise—we should be able to find a replacement for it. Human resources can substitute for financial resources, for instance, or manufactured resources can substitute for natural resources. Theory allows that the substituted resource may be less efficient or more costly, but some degree of substitutability is generally assumed. In other words, traditional economists have considered environmental goods and services to be so-called free gifts of nature—infinitely abundant and resilient, and ultimately substitutable by human technological ingenuity.

It is true that many resources can be replaced; societies have transitioned from manual labour to animal labour to steam-driven power to fossil fuel power and may yet transition to renewable power sources, like solar energy. However, Earth's material resources are ultimately limited. Nonrenewable resources, such as fossil fuels, can be depleted, and even renewable resources can be used up if we exploit them more quickly than they can be replenished. This has been experienced by many ancient civilizations, including the inhabitants of Rapa Nui, who harvested wood faster than their forests could regrow.

Should long-term effects be discounted?

Although few people would dispute that resources are *ultimately* limited, many assume that their depletion will take place so far in the future that there is no need for current generations to worry. For economists in the neoclassical tradition, an event far in the future counts much less than one in the present; in economic terminology, we say that these future effects are "discounted." In discounting, short-term costs and benefits are granted more importance than long-term costs and benefits. This encourages policy makers to play down long-term consequences of decisions we make today.

For example, a stock of uranium ore in the ground or living trees standing in the forest or fish in a stream represent potential commodities that would have monetary or **market values** if they were extracted or harvested and sold. In cost–benefit analysis, however, such commodities are typically discounted for future use to the extent that they appear to be of economic value only if they can be used up as quickly as possible. Some governments and businesses use a 10% annual discount rate for decisions on resource use. This means that the long-term value of a stand of ancient trees worth $500 000 for the timber it contains would drop by 10% each year; after 10 years of discounting, it would be worth only $174 339.22. By this logic, the more quickly the trees are cut down, the more they are worth.

A related problem is that accounting procedures at the national level typically do not assign an *asset value* to intact natural resources as they would, for example, for a physical asset, such as a factory or a system of roads. This means that an unexploited natural resource has *no discernible value* to the nation that possesses it, providing a powerful incentive for nations to exploit their natural resources to the greatest extent and as quickly as possible.

This was stated eloquently by Robert Repetto, one of the pioneers of **natural resource accounting**, which seeks mechanisms by which to incorporate the economic asset values of natural resources into national accounting systems. According to Repetto:

> *A country can cut down its forests, erode its soils, pollute its aquifers and hunt its wildlife and fisheries to extinction, but its measured income is not affected as its assets disappear . . . By failing to recognize the asset value of natural resources, the accounting framework that underlies the principal tools of economic analysis misrepresents the policy choices nations face.*[17]

To further complicate matters, national accounting systems also fail to incorporate certain categories of activities and expenses into the calculations. For example, an individual or a nation might spend money to prevent future environmental degradation, or to restore a degraded natural environment. This could include, for example, launching a program of pollution abatement, constructing windbreaks to prevent soil erosion, or installing heavy-walled containers in oil tankers to prevent spills. Such costs, which economists call *defensive expenditures*, are calculated only as current expenses; the future value of the resource these activities may be helping to preserve or restore is of no economic value to the system.

Are costs and benefits internal?   A third assumption of neoclassical economics is that all costs and benefits associated with a particular exchange of goods or services are borne by individuals engaging directly in the transaction. In other words, it is assumed that the costs and benefits of a transaction are "internal" to the transaction, experienced by the buyer and seller alone, and do not affect other members of society.

However, in many situations this is simply not the case. Pollution from a factory can harm people living nearby. In such cases, someone—often taxpayers not involved in producing the pollution—ends up paying the costs of alleviating it. Market prices do not take the social, environmental, or economic costs of this pollution into account. Costs or benefits of a transaction that involve people other than the buyer or seller are known as **externalities**. A positive externality is a benefit enjoyed by someone not involved in a transaction, and a negative externality, or *external cost*, is a cost borne by someone not involved in a transaction (**FIGURE 15.12**). Negative externalities often harm groups of people or society as a whole, while allowing certain individuals private gain.

External costs commonly include the following:

- Property damage
- Declines in desirable elements of the environment, such as poorer air quality, or fewer fish in a stream
- Aesthetic damage, such as that resulting from air pollution or clear-cutting
- Stress and anxiety experienced by people downstream or downwind from a pollution source
- Declining real estate values resulting from these problems

The Mirrar experienced external costs in the form of pollution from the Ranger mine. In March 2002, radioactive material from the Ranger mine contaminated a stream on Mirrar land with uranium concentrations 4000 times as high as allowed by law. According to an Aboriginal representative, this was the fourth such violation in less than three months. In 2004 the government temporarily shut down the mine and brought the owners to court for these violations.[18] For the Dene of Great Bear Lake the external costs of uranium mining have come in the form of lingering contamination of soil, water, and fish, as well

FIGURE 15.12
An Indonesian boy wading in a polluted river suffers external costs, costs that are not borne by the buyer or seller. External costs may include water pollution, aesthetic harm, human health problems, property damage, harm to aquatic life, aesthetic degradation, declining real estate values, and other impacts.

as health impacts on workers and, by extension, economic and psychological impacts on their families.

By ignoring external costs, economies create a false idea of the true and complete costs of particular choices, and unjustly subject people to the consequences of transactions in which they did not participate. External costs are one reason governments develop environmental legislation and regulations. Unfortunately, external costs are difficult to account for and eliminate. It is tough to assign a monetary value to illness, premature death, or degradation of an aesthetically or spiritually significant site.

Is growth good?   A fourth assumption of the neoclassical economic approach is that economic growth is required to keep employment high and maintain social order. The argument goes something like this: If the poor view the wealthy as the source of their suffering, they may revolt. Promoting economic growth can defuse this situation by creating opportunities for the poor to become wealthier themselves. By making the overall economic pie larger, everyone's slice becomes larger, even if some people still have much smaller slices than others.

The idea that economic growth is good has been encouraged over the centuries by the concept of material progress, espoused by Western cultures since the Enlightenment. Everywhere, every day in the modern industrialized world we see expressions of the view that "more and bigger" is always better. We hear constantly in business news of increases in an industry's output or percentage growth in a country's economy, with increases touted as good news and decreases, stability, or even a minor drop in the *rate* of growth presented as bad news. Economic growth has become the quantitative ruler by which progress is measured.

Is the growth paradigm good for us?

The rate of economic growth in recent decades is unprecedented in human history. As a result, the world economy is seven times the size it was half a century ago. All measures of economic activity—trade, rates of production, amount and value of goods manufactured—are higher than they have ever been and are still increasing. This growth has brought many people much greater material wealth (although gaps between rich and poor are immense, and growing).

To the extent that economic growth is a means to an end—a tool with which we can achieve greater human happiness—it can be a good thing. However, many observers today worry that growth has become an end in itself and is no longer necessarily the best tool with which to pursue happiness. Critics of the growth paradigm often note that runaway growth resembles the multiplication of cancer cells, which eventually overwhelm and destroy the organism in which they grow. These critics fear that runaway economic growth will likewise destroy the economic system on which we all depend. Resources for growth are ultimately limited, they argue, so nonstop growth is not sustainable and will fail as a long-term strategy.

Defenders of traditional economic approaches reply that critics have been saying for decades that limited resources would doom growth-oriented economies, yet most of these economies are still expanding dramatically. If resources are dwindling, why are we witnessing the most rapid growth of material wealth in human history?

One prime reason is technological innovation. In case after case, improved technology has enabled us to push back the limits on growth, effectively expanding the carrying capacity of the environment. More powerful technology for extracting minerals, fossil fuels, and groundwater has expanded the amounts of these natural resources available to us. Technological developments, such as automated farm machinery, fertilizers, and chemical pesticides, have allowed us to grow more food per unit area of land, boosting agricultural output. Faster, more powerful machines in our factories have enabled us to translate our enhanced resource extraction and agricultural production into faster rates of manufacturing.

Economists disagree on whether economic growth is sustainable

Can we conclude, then, that endless improvements in technology are possible and that we will never run into shortages of resources? At one end of the spectrum are those who believe that technology can solve everything—a philosophy that has greatly influenced economic policy in market economies over the past century.

At the other end of the spectrum, *ecological economists* argue that a couple of centuries is not a very long period of time and that history suggests that civilizations do not, in the long run, overcome their environmental limitations. Ecological economics, which has emerged as a discipline only in the past decade or two, applies the principles of ecology and systems science to the analysis of economic systems. Earth's natural systems generally operate in self-renewing cycles, not in a linear or progressive manner. Ecological economists advocate sustainability in economies and see natural systems as good models.

To evaluate an economy's sustainability, ecological economists take a long-term perspective and ask, "Could we continue this activity forever and be happy with the outcome?" Most ecological economists argue that the growth paradigm will eventually fail and that if nothing is done to rein in population growth and resource consumption, depleted natural systems could plunge our economies into ruin. Many advocate economies that do not grow and do not shrink but rather are stable. Such steady-state economies are intended to mirror natural ecological systems.

Environmental economists tend to agree that economies are unsustainable if population growth is not reduced and resource use is not made more efficient. However, they maintain that we can accomplish these changes and attain sustainability within our current economic systems. By retaining the principles of neoclassical economics but modifying them to address environmental challenges, environmental economists argue that we can keep our economies growing and that technology can continue to improve efficiency. Environmental economists were the first to develop ways to tackle the problems of external costs and discounting, and to weigh the true costs and benefits associated with resource use. They then went farther, proposing that sustainability requires far-reaching changes leading ultimately to a steady-state economy. The idea of a steady-state economy did not originate with the rise of ecological economics. Back in the nineteenth century, British economist John Stuart Mill (1806–1873) hypothesized that as resources became harder to find and extract, economic growth would slow and eventually stabilize. Economies would carry on in a state in which individuals and society subsist on steady flows of natural resources and on savings accrued during occasional productive but finite periods of growth.

Modern proponents of a steady-state global economy, such as the pioneering economist Herman Daly, believe we need to rethink our assumptions and fundamentally change the way we conduct economic transactions. They argue that quality of life can continue to rise under a steady-state economy and, in fact, may be more likely to do so. Technological advances will not cease just because growth stabilizes, they argue, and neither will behavioural changes (such as greater use of recycling) that enhance sustainability. Instead, wealth and human happiness can continue to rise after economic growth has levelled off.

Attaining sustainability will certainly require reforms and may well require fundamental shifts in thinking, values, and behaviour. How can these goals be attained in a world whose economic policies are still largely swayed by a cornucopian world view that barely takes the environment into account? While keeping in mind that ecological and environmental economic approaches are still actively being developed, we will now survey a few strategies for sustainability that have been offered so far.

We can measure economic progress differently

For decades, economists have assessed the economic robustness of a nation by calculating its gross domestic product (GDP), the total monetary value of final goods and services produced in a country each year (FIGURE 15.13). GDP is an extremely powerful indicator, used to make financial policy decisions by federal governments worldwide, with fundamental impacts on quality of life and well-being for billions of people.

However, there are problems with using this measure of economic activity to represent a nation's economic well-being. For one, GDP does not account for the nonmarket values of ecosystem goods and services, nor is GDP necessarily an expression of *desirable* economic activity. In fact, GDP can increase, even if the economic activities driving it hurt the environment or society.

For example, a large oil spill would increase GDP because oil spills require cleanups, which cost money and, as a result, increase the production of goods and services. Such activities generate income, and are therefore reflected by a positive change in GDP, but the negative health and ecological costs of disasters like these are typically *not* reflected in the GDP—unless they generate jobs or cash transactions, in which case they may show up as positive changes. A radiation leak at a uranium mine on Mirrar homelands would likely add to the Australian GDP because of the many monetary transactions required for cleanup and medical care. Similarly the $6.7 million in contracts offered by the government of Canada for the cleanup of abandoned uranium mine sites in the Northwest Territories will add to the GDP of Canada. Even Hurricane Katrina—which caused the deaths of almost 2000 people, the loss of tens of thousands

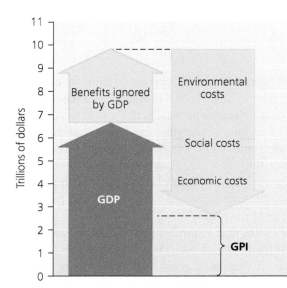

(a) Components of GDP vs. GPI

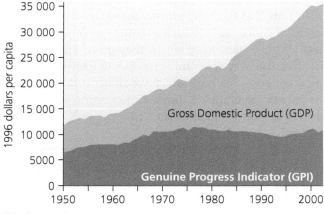

(b) Change in GDP vs. GPI

FIGURE 15.13

Gross domestic product (GDP; red arrow in **(a)**) sums together all economic activity, whether good or bad. As a result, many researchers today believe that GDP is lacking as an indicator of overall well-being. The genuine progress indicator (GPI) is one example of an alternative indicator of progress and well-being **(b)**. GPI adds to GDP benefits by accounting for the value of activities such as volunteering and parenting (upward-pointing gold arrow). The GPI also subtracts external environmental costs, such as pollution; social costs, such as divorce and crime; and economic costs, such as borrowing and the gap between rich and poor (downward-pointing gold arrow).
Source: Data from Venetoulis, J., and C. Cobb. (2004). The Genuine Progress Indicator, 1950–2002 (2004 Update). Redefining Progress.

of homes and jobs, and the contamination or permanent flooding of millions of square kilometres of coastal marshlands and forests in the United States—generated positive growth in GDP in the third quarter of 2005.

Some economists have attempted to develop economic indicators that differentiate between desirable and undesirable economic activity. Such indicators can function as more accurate guides to nations' welfare. One alternative to the GDP is the genuine progress indicator (GPI), introduced in 1995 by Redefining Progress, a nonprofit organization that develops economic and policy tools to promote accurate market prices and sustainability (see **FIGURE 15.13**). The GPI has not yet gained widespread acceptance, partly because it is tremendously data-intensive, but it has generated a great deal of discussion that has drawn attention to the weaknesses of the GDP.

To calculate GPI, economists begin with conventional economic activity and then add to it all *positive* contributions to the economy that do not have to be paid for with money, such as volunteer work and parenting. They then subtract the *negative* impacts, such as crime, pollution, gaps between rich and poor, and other detrimental social, environmental, and economic factors. The GPI thereby summarizes many more forms of economic activity than does GDP and differentiates between economic activity that increases societal well-being and economic activity that decreases it.

Thus, whereas GDP increases when fossil fuel use increases, GPI declines because of the adverse environmental and social impacts of such consumption, including air and water pollution, increased road congestion and traffic accidents, and global climate change. **FIGURE 15.14** compares changes in per capita GPI and GDP in Alberta from 1961 to 2003. The Pembina Institute in Alberta is a leader in the calculation and application of alternative indicators of economic and overall well-being. The province's GDP has increased greatly as a result of increased economic activity; however, GPI has declined over the same period.

GPI is not the only alternative to GDP. The *Index of Sustainable Economic Welfare (ISEW)* is based on income, wealth distribution, the value of volunteerism, and natural resource depletion. The *Net Economic Welfare (NEW) index* adjusts GDP by deducting the costs of environmental degradation. The United Nations uses a tool called the *Human Development Index*, calculated on the basis of a nation's standard of living, life expectancy, and education. Any of these indices, ecological economists maintain, should give a more accurate portrait of a nation's welfare than GDP, which policy makers currently use so widely.

We can give ecosystem goods and services monetary values

Economies receive from the environment vital resources and ecosystem services. However, any survey of environmental problems today—deforestation, biodiversity loss, pollution, collapsed fisheries, climate change, and so on—makes it immediately apparent that our society often mistreats the very systems that keep it alive and healthy. Furthermore, the values of environmental goods and services are routinely underrepresented in cost–benefit analysis, one of the most powerful tools of economic decision making. Why is this? From the economist's perspective, humans overexploit natural resources and systems because the market assigns them no quantitative monetary value or, at best, assigns values that underestimate their true worth.

Think for a minute about the nature of some of these services. The aesthetic and recreational pleasure we obtain from natural landscapes, whether wildernesses or city parks, is something of real value. Yet this value is hard to quantify and appears in no traditional measures of economic worth. Or consider Earth's water cycle, by which rain fills our reservoirs with drinking water, rivers give us hydropower and flush away our waste, and water evaporates, purifying itself of contaminants and readying itself to fall again as rain. This natural cycle is absolutely vital to our existence, yet because its value is not quantified, markets impose no financial penalties when we interfere with it.

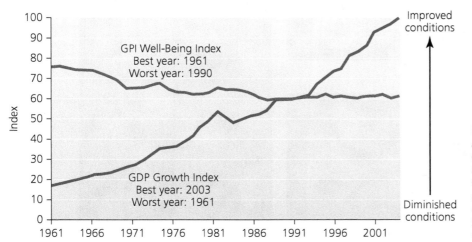

FIGURE 15.14
Although the GDP of Alberta has increased dramatically since 1961, the GPI actually shows a decline over the same period. GPI advocates suggest that this discrepancy means that we are spending more money than ever but that our lives are not that much better.
Source: Data from Pembina Institute, Alberta GPI Accounts, 1961–2003.

Ecosystem services are said to have nonmarket values, values not usually included in the price of a good or service (TABLE 15.2 and FIGURE 15.15). Because the market does not assign value to ecosystem services, debates, such as that over the Jabiluka mine, often involve comparing apples and oranges—in this case, the intangible cultural, ecological, and spiritual arguments of the Mirrar versus the hard numbers of mine proponents.

To partially resolve this dilemma, environmental and ecological economists have sought ways to assign values to ecosystem goods and services. One technique, *contingent valuation*, uses surveys to determine how much people are willing to pay to protect a resource or to restore it after damage has been done.

Such an exercise was conducted with a mining proposal in the Kakadu region in the early 1990s that preceded the Jabiluka proposal. The Kakadu Conservation Zone, a government-owned 50 km^2 plot of land surrounded by Kakadu National Park, was either to be developed for mining, or to be preserved and added to the park. To determine the degree of public support for environmental protection versus mining, a government commission sponsored a contingent valuation study to

Table 15.2 Values That Modern Market Economies Generally Do Not Address

Nonmarket value	Is the worth we ascribe to things that ...
Use value	We use directly
Option value	We do not use now but might use or find a use for at a later time
Aesthetic value	We appreciate for their beauty or emotional appeal
Cultural value	Sustain or help define our culture
Spiritual value	Are sacred to certain groups, or evoke spiritual, religious, or philosophical responses in us
Scientific value	May be significant as subjects of scientific research
Educational value	May teach us about ourselves and the world
Existence value	Are important or have value simply because they exist, even though we may never experience them directly (e.g., remote wilderness, or endangered species in a far-off place)

(a) Existence values

(b) Option values

FIGURE 15.15
Accounting for nonmarket values, such as those shown here, may help us to make better environmental and economic decisions.

(c) Aesthetic values

(d) Scientific values

(e) Educational values

(f) Cultural values

(g) Use values

determine how much Australian citizens valued keeping the Kakadu Conservation Zone preserved and undeveloped. Researchers interviewed 2034 citizens, asking them how much money they would be willing to pay to stop mine development.

The interviewers presented two scenarios: (1) a "major-impact" scenario based on predictions of environmentalists who held that mining would cause great harm, and (2) a "minor-impact" scenario based on predictions of mining executives who held that development would have few downsides. After presenting both scenarios in detail, complete with photographs, the interviewers asked the respondents how much their households would pay if each scenario, in turn, were to occur. Respondents on average said their households would pay $80 per year to prevent the minor-impact scenario and $143 per year to prevent the major-impact scenario. Multiplying these figures by the number of households in Australia (5.4 million at the time), the researchers found that preservation was "worth" $435 million annually to the Australian population under the minor-impact scenario, and $777 million under the major-impact scenario. Because both of these numbers significantly exceeded the $102 million in annual economic benefits expected from mine development, the researchers concluded that preserving the land in its undeveloped state was worth more than mining it.

Because contingent valuation relies on survey questions, critics complain that in such cases people will volunteer idealistic (inflated) values rather than realistic ones, knowing that they will not actually have to pay the price they name. In part because of such concerns, the Australian government commission decided not to use the Kakadu contingent valuation study's results. (The mine was stopped, ultimately, but mainly as a result of Aboriginal opposition.)

Whereas contingent valuation measures people's *expressed* preferences, other methods aim to measure people's *revealed* preferences—preferences as revealed by data on actual behaviour. For example, the amount of money, time, or effort people expend to travel to parks for recreation has been used to measure the value people place on parks. Economists have also analyzed housing prices, comparing homes with similar characteristics but different environmental settings to infer the dollar value of landscapes, views, greenspace, and peace and quiet. Another approach assigns environmental amenities value by measuring the cost required to restore natural systems that have been damaged or to mitigate harm from pollution.

In 1997 a research team led by Robert Costanza reviewed ecosystem valuation studies, with the goal of calculating the global economic value of all the services that ecosystems provide (**FIGURE 15.16**). The team identified more than 100 studies that estimated the worth of such ecosystem services as water purification, greenhouse gas regulation, plant pollination, and pollution cleanup. The studies used such methods as contingent valuation to estimate the values of such aspects of natural systems as biodiversity and aesthetics.

To estimate the worth of ecosystem services more accurately, the team reevaluated the data using alternative valuation techniques. One method was to calculate

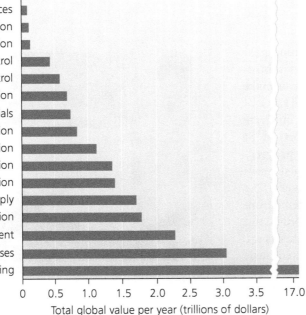

FIGURE 15.16
Costanza and colleagues estimated the total value of the world's ecosystem services at approximately $33 trillion. Shown are subtotals for each major class of ecosystem service. The $33 trillion figure does not include values from some ecosystems, such as deserts and tundra, for which adequate data were unavailable.
Source: Data from Costanza, R., et al. (2007). The value of the world's ecosystem services and natural capital. Nature 387:253–260.

the cost of replacing ecosystem services with technology. For example, marshes protect people from floods and filter out water pollutants. If a marsh were destroyed, the researchers would calculate the value of the services it had provided by measuring the cost of the levees and water-purification technology that would be needed to assume those tasks. The researchers then calculated the global monetary value of such wetlands by multiplying those totals by the global area occupied by the ecosystem. By calculating similar totals from other ecosystems, they arrived at a global value for ecosystem services.[19] The total figure was $33 trillion per year (1997 dollars)—greater than the combined gross domestic products of all nations in the world. A follow-up study in 2002 concluded that the economic benefits of preserving the world's remaining natural areas outweighed the benefits of exploiting them by a factor of 100 to 1. When markets do not reflect the full costs and benefits of actions, they are said to fail. Market failure occurs when markets do not take into account the environment's positive effects on economies (such as ecosystem services) or when they do not reflect the negative effects of economic activity on the environment or on people (external costs).

Traditionally, market failure has been countered by government intervention. Governments can dictate limits on corporate behaviour through laws and regulations. They can institute *green taxes,* which penalize environmentally harmful activities. Or they can design economic incentives that put market mechanisms to work to promote fairness, resource conservation, and economic sustainability.

Corporations are responding to sustainability concerns

As more consumers and investors express preferences for sustainable products and services, more industries, businesses, and corporations are finding that they can make money by "greening" their operations (**FIGURE 15.17**).

Some companies, such as the Body Shop, cultivate eco-conscious images; others donate a portion of their proceeds to environmental and other progressive nonprofit groups. Today, some newer businesses are trying to go even further than these pioneers. The outdoor apparel company Nau manufactures items from materials made of corn biomass and recycled bottles, and helps fund environmental nonprofits. Entrepreneurs are starting thousands of local sustainability-oriented businesses across the world.

In the past few years, corporate sustainability has gone mainstream, and some of the world's largest corporations have joined in, including McDonald's, Starbucks, IKEA, Dow, and British Petroleum. Nike collects millions of used sneakers each year and recycles the materials to create synthetic surfaces for basketball courts, tennis courts, and running tracks. Nike also uses more organic cotton and has developed less-toxic rubber and adhesives. In response to media attention and consumer concern, such corporations as Nike and the Gap are also working to improve labour conditions in their factories overseas.

Of course, corporations exist to make money for their shareholders, so they cannot be expected to pursue goals that are not profitable. Moreover, some corporate greening efforts are more rhetoric than reality, and corporate *greenwashing* may mislead some consumers into thinking that companies are acting more sustainably than they are. However, as consumer preferences turn increasingly to sustainable products and practices, many corporations are seeing the economic wisdom of moving toward a more sustainable model of operation.

Perhaps the most celebrated recent corporate greening is that of Walmart. Environmentalists have long criticized the world's largest retailer for its environmental and social impacts. In 2006 the company began a quest to sell organic and sustainable products, reduce packaging and use recycled materials, enhance fuel efficiency in its truck fleets, reduce energy use in its stores, cut carbon dioxide emissions, and preserve an equivalent area of natural land for every parcel of land developed. Many observers remain skeptical of Walmart's commitment, calling it superficial "greenwashing"; yet, if the company achieves only a fraction of its stated goals, the environmental benefits could be substantial because of the corporation's vast global reach.

FIGURE 15.17
Canada Post now boasts a fleet of "green" fuel-efficient hybrid and all-electric trucks.

CANADIAN ENVIRONMENTAL PERSPECTIVES

Matthew Coon Come

Matthew Coon Come is an advocate for the environmental, social, and political rights of Aboriginal people in Canada.

■ **Environmental** and **social activist**
■ Former **grand chief** of the Grand Council of the Cree
■ Former **national chief** of the Assembly of First Nations

Matthew Coon Come is a politician and activist of Cree descent. He was born in a bush tent on his father's trapline and was taken away at the age of six to attend La Tuque Indian Residential School almost 500 km from his home. He studied law at McGill University and as a young man was elected grand chief of the Grand Council of the Cree. He has since served in many leadership positions on behalf of Aboriginal communities in Canada and around the world. He is a past winner of the Equinox Environmental Award and the Condé Nast Environment Award, among others.[20]

Coon Come is an advocate for his people in a world where environmental rights and social justice collide with economic development. He led the Cree in the late 1980s and early 1990s in opposition to a massive hydroelectric development project, the Great Whale River Phase of Hydro-Québec's James Bay Project, which began in 1971. This phase of the project would have comprised more than 30 dams and 600 dikes, blocking nine major rivers,[21] affecting watersheds with an area the size of France, and creating reservoirs the size of Lake Erie.[22]

Coon Come gathered support from local, national, and international environmental, human rights, and tribal communities, creating a coalition that vocally and visibly opposed the project. As a result of the coalition's efforts, the state of New York cancelled major contracts to purchase electricity from Hydro-Québec,[23] putting the viability of the project in jeopardy. In 1994, the Supreme Court of Canada ruled that federal environmental assessments were required for all Hydro-Québec electricity exports. Shortly after that decision, the premier of Quebec announced the indefinite suspension of work on the Great Whale Project.[24]

For his role in this struggle, Matthew Coon Come was awarded the Goldman Environmental Prize, a prestigious international prize that honours grassroots environmental leaders around the world.

By 2002, though, many Cree had changed their position on the James Bay Project, citing the desperate need for economic development in the North. Cree leaders signed an agreement with the government of Québec that cleared the way for the project to proceed. The next phase, which passed its environmental assessment in 2006, will involve the diversion of about 50% of the water flow of the Rupert River, as well as the construction of two new power stations and four large dams, flooding for a new reservoir, new roads, and worker settlements.

After all these years, the project continues to polarize the Cree Nation. Its supporters argue that the participation of the Cree in this project is a crucial step toward modernization and economic and social stability. Opponents—including residents from the three communities nearest to the project, as well as current grand chief Matthew Mukash, who is pressing instead for the development of wind energy—are concerned that the negative environmental impacts will outweigh any economic benefits.

Meanwhile, Matthew Coon Come became the national chief of the Assembly of First Nations, a position he held until 2003. In 2008 he issued a statement in response to the apology by the government of Canada for the years of abuse suffered by Native children, including Coon Come, in church-run residential schools. The statement, while accepting the government's apology, detailed the damage done to him by the residential school. It said in part, "They told me that my culture, and my people's ways of life, would never sustain me. They lied. I am a son of a hunter, fisherman, and a trapper. My father taught me how to walk the land, and to love and respect the animals and all of creation. I have not lost my culture. Our way of life is thriving."[25]

"Business as usual will not ensure the protection of the land of our children, yet unborn."
—Matthew Coon Come

Thinking About Environmental Perspectives

Put yourself in the place of a Cree community leader like Matthew Coon Come. How would you handle a controversy like the Hydro-Québec James Bay Project? How would you weigh the importance of much-needed jobs and other economic development against the potential for negative environmental impacts like mercury contamination, loss of habitat, or variations in water flow? What do you think of Cree leaders who have changed their positions on this and other projects, first opposing and then supporting them—do you think they are indecisive, or fickle, or are they courageous and forward-thinking?

The bottom line is that corporate actions hinge on consumer behaviour. It is up to all of us as consumers to encourage trends in sustainability by rewarding corporations that truly promote sustainable solutions.

Conclusion

Corporate sustainability, alternative ways of measuring growth, and the valuation of ecosystem goods and services are a few of the recent developments that have brought economic approaches to bear on environmental protection and resource conservation. As economics becomes more environmentally friendly, it renews some of its historic ties to ethics.

Environmental ethics has expanded people's sphere of ethical consideration outward to encompass other societies and cultures, other creatures, and even nonliving entities that were formerly outside the realm of ethical concern. This ethical expansion involves the concept of *distributional equity*, or equal treatment for all, which is the aim of environmental justice. One type of distributional equity is equity among generations. Such concern by current generations for the welfare of future generations is the basis for the notion of sustainability.

Although we tend to think of sustainability as a "modern" idea, it is actually inherent to some of the most basic concepts of neoclassical economics. In his 1939 work *Value and Capital*, Sir John Hicks (1904–1989), one of the most influential economists of the twentieth century, defined income as "the maximum value [a person] can consume during a week, and still expect to be as well off at the end of the week as he was at the beginning." The implication is that *true* income is *sustainable* income—if your spending compromises your resource base and reduces your future ability to produce, then you are depleting your capital. As former World Bank economist Herman E. Daly explains,

> Why all the fuss about sustainability? Because, contrary to the theoretical definition of income, we are in fact consuming productive capacity and counting it as income in our national accounts. . . . Depletion of natural capital and consequent reduction of its life-sustaining services is the meaning of unsustainability.[26]

Is sustainability a pragmatic pursuit for us? The answer largely depends on whether we believe that economic well-being and environmental well-being are opposed to each other, or whether we accept that they can work in tandem. Equating economic well-being with economic growth, as most economists traditionally have, suggests that economic welfare entails a trade-off with environmental quality. However, if economic welfare can be enhanced in the absence of growth, we can envision economies and environmental quality benefiting from one another.

REVIEWING OBJECTIVES

You should now be able to:

Characterize the influences of culture and world view on the choices people make

- A person's culture strongly influences his or her world view. Such factors as religion and political ideology are especially influential.

Outline the nature, evolution, and expansion of environmental ethics in Western cultures

- Our society's domain of ethical concern has been expanding, such that we have granted ethical consideration to more and more entities.
- Anthropocentrism values humans above all else, whereas biocentrism values all life and ecocentrism values ecological systems.

- The preservation ethic (preserving natural systems intact) and the conservation ethic (promoting responsible long-term use of resources) have guided branches of the environmental movement during the past century.
- The environmental justice movement, seeking equal treatment for people of all races and income levels, is a recent outgrowth of environmental ethics.

Describe some basic precepts of economic theory and summarize their implications for the environment

- Classical economic theory proposes that individuals acting for their own economic good can benefit society as a whole. This view has provided a philosophical basis for free-market capitalism.

- Neoclassical economics focuses on consumer behaviour and supply and demand as forces that drive economic activity.
- Several assumptions of neoclassical economic theory contribute to environmental impact.

Compare the concepts of economic growth, economic health, and sustainability

- Conventional economic theory has promoted never-ending economic growth, with little regard to possible environmental impact.
- Economic growth is not necessarily required for overall economic well-being.
- In the long run, some economists believe that a steady-state economy will be necessary to achieve sustainability.

Explain the fundamentals of environmental economics, ecological economics, and natural resource accounting

- Environmental economists advocate reforming economic practices to promote sustainability. Key approaches are to identify external costs, assign value to nonmonetary items, find new approaches to measuring growth, and attempt to make market prices reflect real costs and benefits.
- Ecological economists support these efforts and others. Many support developing a steady-state economy.
- Consumer choice in the marketplace can help drive businesses and corporations to pursue sustainability goals.

TESTING YOUR COMPREHENSION

1. What does the study of ethics encompass? Describe the three classic ethical standards. What is environmental ethics?
2. Why in Western cultures have ethical considerations expanded to include non-human entities?
3. Describe the philosophical perspectives of anthropocentrism, biocentrism, and ecocentrism. How would you characterize the perspective of the Mirrar Clan?
4. Differentiate between the preservation ethic and the conservation ethic. Explain the contributions of John Muir, James Harkin, Gifford Pinchot, and Clifford Sifton in the history of environmental ethics.
5. Describe Aldo Leopold's "land ethic." How did Leopold define the "community" to which ethical standards should be applied?
6. Name four key contributions the environment makes to the economy.

7. For each of these basic tenets of neoclassical economics, explain the potential impacts on the environment and provide a hypothetical example:
   - Resources are infinite or substitutable.
   - Long-term effects should be discounted.
   - Costs and benefits are internal.
   - Growth is good.
8. Neoclassical economists have moved away from Adam Smith's original definition of *income* as "economic gains made with no negative impacts on the resource base." What are the environmental implications of straying from this definition of *income*?
9. Compare and contrast the views of neoclassical economists, environmental economists, and ecological economists.
10. What is contingent valuation, and what is one of its weaknesses? Describe an alternative method that addresses this weakness.

THINKING IT THROUGH

1. Do you feel that an introduction to environmental ethics and world views is an important part of a course in environmental science? Should ethics and world views be a component of other science courses? Explain your answers.

2. Describe your world view as it pertains to your relationship with the environment. How do you think your culture has influenced your world view? How do you think your personal experience has influenced it, including your gender and race? Do you feel that you fit into any particular category discussed in this chapter? Why or why not?

3. How would you analyze the case of the Mirrar Clan and the proposed Jabiluka uranium mine from each of the following perspectives? In your description, list two questions that a person of each perspective would likely ask when attempting to decide whether the mine should be developed. Be as specific as possible, and be sure to identify similarities and differences in approaches:
   - Preservationist
   - Conservationist
   - Deep ecologist
   - Environmental justice advocate
   - Indigenous land rights activist
   - Ecofeminist
   - Neoclassical economist
   - Ecological economist

4. Do you think we should attempt to quantify and assign market values to ecosystem services and other entities that have only nonmarket values? Why or why not? What is a steady-state economy? Do you think this model is a practical alternative to the growth paradigm? Why or why not?

5. A manufacturing facility on a river near your home provides jobs for 200 people in your community and pays $2 million in taxes to the local government each year. Sales taxes from purchases made by plant employees and their families contribute an additional $1 million to local government coffers. However, a recent peer-reviewed study in a well-respected scientific journal revealed that the plant has been discharging large amounts of waste into the river, causing a 25% increase in cancer rates, a 30% reduction in riverfront property values, and a 75% decrease in native fish populations.

   The plant owner says the facility can stay in business only because there are no regulations mandating expensive treatment of waste from the plant. If such regulations were imposed, he says he would close the plant, lay off its employees, and relocate to a more business-friendly community. How would you recommend resolving this situation? What further information would you want to know before making a recommendation? In arriving at your recommendation, how did you weigh the costs and benefits associated with each of the plant's impacts?

6. You are a researcher working for a large pharmaceutical company. You are doing botanical fieldwork, searching for a plant that may offer a new cure for cancer. Some of the indigenous people in the area have a deep understanding of the medicinal properties of local plants, and you would like to ask them some questions. Under what circumstances should you do this? What if you were to make a major discovery on the basis of something you learned from them, with potential earnings of billions of dollars for your company—would the people who passed along the crucial information have a legitimate claim to part of those earnings?

INTERPRETING GRAPHS AND DATA

Economists use various indicators of economic well-being. One that has been used for decades is the gross domestic product (GDP), the total monetary value of final goods and services produced each year. An alternative measure called the genuine progress indicator (GPI) is calculated as follows:

GPI = GDP + (Benefits Ignored by GDP) – (Environmental Costs) – (Social and Economic Costs)

Benefits include such things as the value of parenting and volunteer work. Environmental costs include the costs of water, air, and noise pollution; loss of wetlands; depletion of nonrenewable resources; and other environmental damage. Social and economic costs include investment, lending, and borrowing costs; costs of crime, family breakdown, under-employment, commuting, pollution abatement, and automobile accidents; and loss of leisure time.

1. Describe economic growth as measured by GDP for the province of Alberta from 1961 to 2003. Now describe economic growth as measured by GPI over the same time period. To what factors would you attribute the growing difference between these measures?

2. For GPI to grow, one or more things must happen: Either GDP must grow faster, benefits must grow faster, or social, economic, and environmental costs must shrink relative to the other terms. How would you explain the changes in GDP and GPI over the past few decades for the province of Alberta? How do the data in the graph support your answer?

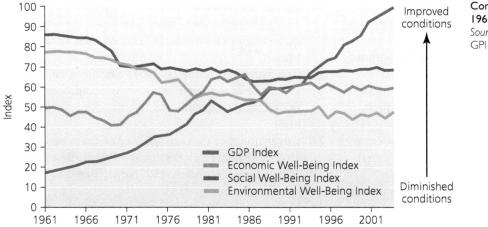

Components of GPI and GDP in Alberta, 1961–2003.
Source: Data from Pembina Institute, Alberta GPI Accounts, 1961–2003.

3. Even with regulations for air and water pollution control, hazardous waste disposal, solid waste management, forestry practices, and species protection, environmental costs continue to increase. Why do you suppose the trend is still in that direction?

4. Alberta in the 2000s is in the midst of a huge economic boom, related largely to the development of the Athabasca and other fossil fuel deposits. How do you think this ongoing resource development will affect Alberta's GDP and GPI for the province over the next few decades? Think about all of the factors—economic, environmental, and social—that will play a role, and whether the impacts will likely be positive or negative.

CHAPTER ENDNOTES

1. This piece is based on a summary of *Mining Denendeh: A Dene Nation Perspective on Community Health Impacts of Mining,* by Chris Paci (Lands and Environment Department, Dene Nation) and Noeline Villebrun, Dene National Chief, prepared for the 2004 Mining Ministers Conference, Coppermine, Nunavut.

2. Regarding the incident of contamination that led to the mine's closure in 2004, as reported by Friends of the Environment, Australia, www.foe.org.au/media-releases/2004-media-releases/mr_24_3_04.htm

3. *The Age,* July 27, 2007, as cited by World Information Service on Energy, www.wise-uranium.org/upjab. html

4. Based partly on information from *Living with the Land: A Manual for Documenting Cultural Landscapes,* NWT Cultural Places Program, Government of NWT, 2007.

5. Voisey's Bay Nickel Mine, Ltd., www.vbnc.com/iba. asp

6. Parts of this paragraph are based on information from *Mining Denendeh: A Dene Nation Perspective on Community Health Impacts of Mining,* by Chris

Paci (Lands and Environment Department, Dene Nation) and Noeline Villebrun, Dene National Chief, prepared for the 2004 Mining Ministers Conference, Coppermine, Nunavut.

7. Based on information from the Canadian Museum of Civilization, James Bernard Harkin, www. civilization.ca/hist/biography/biographi204e.html

8. Based on information from Canadian Museum of Civilization, Clifford Sifton, www.civilization.ca/hist/advertis/ads2-06e.html

9. Leopold, A. *A Sand County Almanac,* Oxford University Press, New York, 1949.

10. Rajiv Rawat (1996, May) *Women of Uttarakhand: On the Frontiers of the Environmental Struggle,* http://uttarakhand.prayaga.org/chipko.html

11. Green Belt Movement, http://eratos.utm.utoronto.ca/research.htm; and other sources.

12. Recall that radioactivity had only been discovered some 30 years earlier, in the late 1890s.

13. Andrew Nikiforuk (1998) "Echoes of the Atomic Age: Cancer kills fourteen aboriginal uranium workers," *Calgary Herald,* Saturday, March 14.

14. World Information Service on Energy, *Decommissioning of Port Radium*, www.wise-uranium.org/-uippra.html#MORE

15. Radiation Exposure Compensation Program www.usdoj.gov/civil/torts/const/reca/; and "Navajo President Joe Shirley, Jr., updates Navajo miners on progress toward getting fair RECA compensation," September 2006.

16. Smith, A., *An Inquiry into the Nature and Causes of the Wealth of Nations* ("The Wealth of Nations"), first published in 1776.

17. Repetto, Robert (1992) Accounting for environment assets, *Scientific American*, June.

18. Environment Centre Northern Territory (Australia), *Mining Archives*, www.ecnt.org/index.html

19. Costanza, R., et al. (1997) The value of the world's ecosystem services and natural capital. *Nature* 387: 253–260.

20. Matthew Coon Come, *Goldman Prize*, www.goldmanprize.org/node/93; and other sources.

21. Matthew Coon Come, *Goldman Prize* www.goldmanprize.org/node/93; and other sources.

22. Government of Canada (2007) *Key Economic Events: 1972–The James Bay Project*, www.canadianeconomy.gc.ca/English/economy/1972James_Bay_Project.html

23. Government of Canada (2007) *Key Economic Events: 1972–The James Bay Project*, www.canadianeconomy.gc.ca/English/economy/1972James_Bay_Project.html

24. Government of Canada (2007) *Key Economic Events: 1972–The James Bay Project*, www.canadianeconomy.gc.ca/English/economy/1972James_Bay_Project.html

25. Nation Talk (2008) *General Statement by Matthew Coon Come*, June 13, www.nationtalk.ca/modules/news/article.php?storyid=10522

26. Daly, Herman E. (2001) Sustainable development and OPEC. Paper invited for the conference OPEC and the Global Energy Balance: Towards a Sustainable Energy Future. Vienna, Austria.

MyEnvironmentPlace

Go to **www.myenvironmentplace.ca** where you will find quizzes, animations, your Pearson eText, and more.

Biogeography: Introduction to Space, Time, and Life

by Glen MacDonald

Reprinted from *Biogeography: Introduction to Space, Time, and Life* (2001)
by permission of John Wiley & Sons, Inc.

16 Humans as a Force in Evolution and Extinction

How the history of humans is itself a fascinating biogeographical story in which evolutionary forces, extinction, dispersal, and geography all played a role. The end result of this saga was the rise of modern humans to a global population size of six billion individuals and a geographic distribution that includes every continent, with forays to the depths of the ocean and the nearer reaches of outer space. What impact have the numerous and widespread members of the human species had on the rest of the biosphere? We could easily focus an entire textbook on this important question. In this chapter we will have to restrict our scope to looking at the role of humans in two key areas. First, we will examine how humans have influenced the evolutionary development of plant and animals species, particularly through domestication. The domestication of plants and animals and the development of agriculture are central to the growth of complex human societies, technological advancements, and increases in human population size that have occurred over the past 10,000 years. Second, we will consider the sobering evidence of how humans have become a major force in the extinction of plant and animal species around the world either directly by hunting or by causing landscape alterations and environmental change.

Humans as an Evolutionary Force

Humans can influence the evolutionary development of species in a number of different ways. Changes in the landscape caused by agricultural land clearance can lead to strong selective pressure for traits that allow wild species to live in open fields or utilize crop and pasture plants for food. The removal of predators by humans can cause the remaining species to evolve adaptations that decrease defenses against predation but increase foraging efficiency or reproductive rates. Hunting pressure by humans can cause compensatory evolutionary developments in prey species. For example, there is evidence that hunting by Neanderthals and early modern humans led to a decrease in the body size of the spur tortoise (*Testuda gracea*) in the Mediterranean region. Small body size may have been a beneficial adaptation because smaller individuals are less visible in the landscape and less attractive to hunters as they provide lower nutritional value than large prey.

In more recent times, the introduction of pesticides and pollutants into the environment has exerted selective pressure and led to evolutionary change in some organisms. One of the most widespread and economically significant examples of how human-introduced selective pressure has recently influenced the genotypic and phenotypic characteristics of other species comes from the evolutionary response of insects and mites to pesticides. When the use of insecticide chemicals such as pyrethroids became widespread in the 1950s there were very few instances of natural resistance by insects. By the late 1980s many populations of insect and mite species were almost completely resistant to the common pesticides. Over 400 species of insects were reported to have developed resistance to one or more classes of pesticides in this 30 year period. Individuals which possessed genes producing resistance to pesticides were selected for because they were able to survive and reproduce, while individuals without such genes were killed by the pesticides.

Animal and plant domestication

The most important examples of human impact on the evolution of other species come from the domestication of plants and animals. In addition, the process of domestication has been of critical importance to the geographic spread and population increase of humans over the past 10,000 years. Domesticated plants and animals are the basis of agriculture, and without agriculture the complex, technically innovative societies and large human populations that exist today could not have come into being.

Agriculture allowed people to become sedentary (living for a prolonged period in one place), establish permanent villages and towns, and develop stratified societies that included specialized and dedicated segments such as farmers, artisans, soldiers, religious leaders, educators, and governors. Because of the crucial importance of domestication and agriculture, some biogeographers, including the influential figure, Carl O. Sauer of Berkeley, have made the patterns and processes of plant and animal domestication, and resulting landscape change, a central focus of their work. Understanding the origins of domesticated plants and animals is of more than strictly academic interest. The ancestral species of crop plants may often still be found in areas where early domestication occurred and may provide important crop strains and genetic resources for breeding and agriculture today. It has been shown, for example, that careful use of native varieties of potatoes can aid in maintaining sustainable agricultural yields in Andean farming regions. Let's explore the fascinating and important area of biogeographical research into domestication and the development of agriculture.

Domestication refers to the process by which plant and animal species come to depend on humans for survival while in turn providing humans with practical or other benefits. Many domesticated species, such as corn (*Zea mays*) provide food. Others, such as garden roses (*Rosa* spp.) are used for nonpractical purposes such as providing color in gardens. During domestication, humans selectively breed plants or animals to propagate and enhance desired traits. These traits can include docility and trainability, increased meat, milk, or wool production in animals, or increased fruit size and production in plants. In many cases, the resulting domesticated species are markedly different in morphology and behavior from their wild progenitors. For example, the wild ancestor of domesticated corn is probably a small grass called teosinte (*Zea mexicana*, according to some authorities and *Zea mays mexicana* according to others). Some of the first archaeological evidence of corn domestication comes from ears and kernels preserved in caves in the Tehuacan Valley of Mexico. Through a process of natural mutation and then domestication that extended from about 7000 to 500 years ago, people in the highlands of southern Mexico produced increasingly large-eared and large-seeded domestic corn from this small-eared and small-seeded ancestor FIGURE 16.1. Domesticated corn provides several advantages over teosinte for humans. Domesticated corn has larger and more nutritious kernels and more kernels per ear. It has been estimated that a single kernel of modern corn contains as much nutrition as an entire ear of the earliest domesticated variety. In addition, the kernels of domesticated corn do not fall

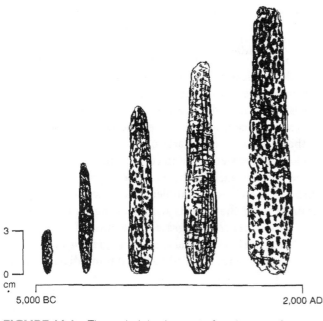

FIGURE 16.1   The gradual development of modern corn from teosinte.

off the ear easily. This makes it simple and efficient to harvest corn. However, the adherence of the kernels to the ears means that domesticated corn cannot disperse its own seeds. Corn seed dispersal must be done by humans. As a result, domesticated corn is entirely dependent on humans for its survival as a species. If humans did not plant and tend domesticated corn, it would go extinct almost immediately. Many domesticated plants and animals would not survive without human intervention. Although domestication and agriculture are tightly intertwined, the word "agriculture" has a different specific meaning than domestication. **Agriculture** is the cultivation of domesticated plants and animals for human use.

Charles Darwin was much interested in the selective pressures that humans apply to species during domestication. He saw that the domestication process was much like natural selection in nature, except that during domestication, human actions were the most important selection force. Darwin recognized that humans applied both conscious selection when they purposefully bred or removed certain individuals to achieve desired genotypically controlled traits and unconscious selection when maintenance or removal of certain genotypes was done inadvertently. We can consider both conscious and unconscious selection practiced by humans to be forms of **artificial selection** in contrast to natural selection where the selective pressures are generated by the natural physical and biological environment.

Homo sapiens sapiens are the only hominids conclusively shown to practice domestication and agriculture. Earlier hominids, and early *Homo sapiens sapiens*, were **hunters and gatherers** who relied on naturally occurring vegetation, fruits, nuts, carrion, and game for subsistence. Hunters and gatherers generally do not establish permanent settlements such as villages, They move their camps in response to the movement of game and changes in the season. Subsistence by hunting and gathering is still practiced by people in some extremely remote areas, such as portions of the Amazon Basin. Prior to the spread of European culture over the past 500 years, many people in areas of North America, South America, Africa, and Australasia lived by hunting and gathering.

The earliest domesticated species was probably the dog (*Canis familiaris*). The domestic dog appears to be a direct descendant of the wolf (*Canis lupus*). The modern dog, encompassing all of the different breeds we have today, was created by domestication by humans. We can speculate how domestication of the dog might have occurred. Wolves are relatively intelligent and social animals that hunt and live in packs. It is likely that humans and wolves competed for the same game and perhaps for protection in caves. Because of this close proximity, it is easy to imagine how wolf cubs could have been acquired and raised by humans. Wolf cubs that were particularly vicious would perhaps have been killed by their human captors. Other cubs that were not inclined to bond with the human group would have wandered away from the humans. Eventually, selection for traits such as loyalty and nonaggressive behavior toward humans would be dominant in the captive wolf population. After thousands of years, domestication has produced what many consider a new species, the domestic dog. Fossil evidence from *Homo sapiens sapiens* sites in Europe suggests that the domestication of the wolf and evolution of the modern dog were taking place in Eurasia and North America by 15,000 to 11,000 years ago. Interestingly, a molecular clock estimate based on the genetics of modern dog breeds and wolves suggests that the initial domestication of the wolf may have been started by *Homo sapiens neanderthalensis* over 100,000 years ago. Regardless of the initial date of dog domestication, all of the amazing breeds of dogs, from the tiny chihuahuas to huge Saint Bernards were developed through artificial selection and resulting evolutionary change caused by humans.

Some particularly good fossil evidence of the rate and timing of early animal domestication comes from the history of goats and sheep in southwestern Asia. The ancestors of the modern domestic goats and sheep lived in the Zagros Mountains of Iran and Iraq and were hunted by Neanderthals, and modern humans starting at least 40,000 years ago. Modern goats and sheep are smaller in size and have different horns and coats than their wild ancestors. The coats of wild sheep contain far less wool than is the case for domesticated sheep. The remains of sheep and goats found at hominid sites that are older than about 10,000 years ago show no evidence of domestication. In addition, it is clear that hunters were killing and eating female and male goats and sheep of all ages. After about 10,000 years ago, there is a shift toward a greater abundance of pre-adult male goat and sheep skeletons at hominid sites. It is possible that at this time humans realized that by taking pre-adult rams and sparing females and sexually mature rams for reproduction, the populations of sheep and goats would remain abundant for hunting. Many parts of the world have similar hunting laws today, allowing, for example, the hunting of male deer but not female ones. Shortly following the shift to selective hunting of young males, the development of domesticated sheep and goat species is evidenced by decreases in the size of goat and sheep skeletons and changes in horn morphology. It seems clear that shortly after 10,000 years ago people were keeping herds of these animals. By 9000 years ago, goat and sheep were being introduced and raised by people at sites that were outside the natural ranges of wild goats and sheep.

So, it is thought that human interaction with goats, sheep, and other domesticated herding animals first took the form of hunting, then selective hunting, and finally herding. In some locations, such as the Zagros Mountains, goat and sheep hunters may have begun the process of domestication by driving small wild herds into areas closer to human habitation or where the herds could be supported by water and vegetation but also be hunted easily. True domestication, caused by artificial selection and resulting genetic changes, could ensue only if natural wild populations were not allowed to breed with the herded ones. Natural populations may have been kept away from human herds either by fencing or eradication. It is likely that at first inadvertent actions by people kept the wild populations away from herded animals. Humans may have observed how some of the herded individuals had desirable traits, such as long coats, high milk production, or large amounts of meat, and selectively bred animals in the herds that had those traits. Evidence from archaeological sites in the Zagros Mountains and observations of recent and modern primitive herding peoples, such as reindeer herders in northern Eurasia, appear to support this model of early domestication.

Over the past 10,000 years, many animals have been domesticated in different parts of the world, and we often have reasonable archaeological information on the early period of domestication FIGURE 16.2. For example, pigs (*Sus scrofa*) and cattle were domesticated in southwest-

ern Asia at about the same time as sheep and goats. The horse (*Equus equus*) and bactrian camel (*Camelus bactrianus*) were domesticated in central Asia between 5000 and 3500 years ago. Water buffalo (*Bubalus bubalis*) were domesticated in India and adjacent southeastern Asia about 4500 years ago. Llama (*Lama guanicoe*) were domesticated in South America about 3500 years ago. In areas such as central Eurasia, portions of the Near East, northern Eurasia, and parts of Africa, human cultures developed that were organized around herding domesticated animals such as sheep, horses, cattle, camels, and reindeer. These people supplemented the meat and milk obtained from their herds with hunting and gathering. The human herders migrated and moved along with their herds during seasonal changes in grazing areas. This form of subsistence is called **pastoral nomadicism** and is still practiced in some areas of the world today.

Some of the earliest evidence for the domestication of plants comes from southwestern Asia and dates from about the same period as the domestication of goats and sheep. Indeed, a variety of important food plants, including wheat (*Triticum*), rye (*Secale cereale*), barley (*Hordeum vulgare*), lentils (*Lens culinaris*), chickpeas (*Cicer arietinum*), and peas (*Pisum sativum*) were all domesticated in the Near East about 11,000 to 9000 years ago. In southwestern Asia, the archaeological sites with evidence of early plant domestication occur along an inverted crescent that extends from the mouth of the Tigris and Euphrates rivers, north to eastern Turkey, and then south to the coastal regions of Lebanon and Israel FIGURE 16.2. This region of early plant domestication is called the **Fertile Crescent**. Today, many of the wild ancestors of domesticated plants such as wheat, barley, lentils, peas, and chickpeas are found in the vicinity of the Fertile Crescent. Many of the archaeological sites with evidence of early domestication and agriculture occur as low mounds, locally called tells. The tells are formed by the remains of human habitation. In most cases, these remains are dominated by the melted and broken mud bricks of structures such as houses and village walls. Many tells have been occupied and abandoned many times and have layers of artifacts dating from many different periods. In some instances, the earliest buildings and artifacts date from the very dawn of domestication. Studying the plant and animal remains from the tells shows how the process of domestication and development of agriculture went hand in hand with the development of permanent villages. The biblical city of Jericho FIGURE 16.2 is represented by such a tell that dates back to at least 10,000 years ago and provides important evidence for the early domestication of wheat. Some of the earliest evidence of domesticated plant cultivation and use comes from a site along the

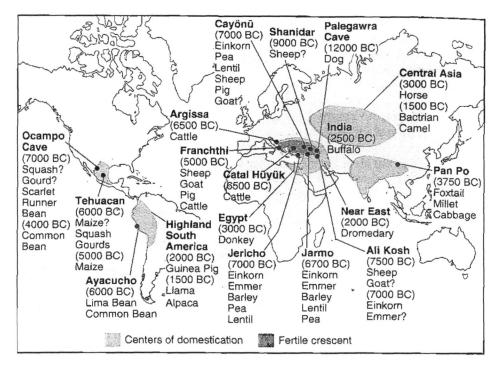

FIGURE 16.2
Areas and minimum ages for
domestication of selected animals and
plants around the world. Important
centers of domestication and agricultural
origins are indicated (after Simmons,
1989).

Euphrates River in Iraq called Tell Abu Hureyera. Finds from this site suggest that rye was used there as early as 10,900 years ago. Perhaps the best known settlement of this age is Catal Hüyük located in eastern Turkey FIGURE 16.2. By about 9500 years ago, this settlement supported some 10,000 inhabitants based on rudimentary agriculture combined with hunting and gathering.

We can speculate how hunting and gathering peoples living in the Fertile Crescent and other parts of the world initially domesticated plants. These people likely used the wild ancestors of domesticated plants as food sources for a very long period prior to domestication. Flint sickle blades from the Fertile Crescent date back at least 12,000 years ago and suggest the harvesting of the wild ancestors of wheat. Many of the wild progenitors of domesticated plants favor disturbed environments such as burned areas or areas with exposed mineral soils. These plants may have seeded into land near camp sites that were disturbed by human activity. Humans would have been able to observe the ecology of these plants at close quarters. They could have observed on what types of soils the food plants grew best and which varieties of food plants provided the most seeds or fruit. The domestication of plants likely began as selective cultivation of wild food plants, perhaps by transporting seeds to new camp sites or changing local environmental conditions to suit favored plants. Hunting and gathering people who lived in more recent times have been shown to practice such cultivation. For example, Australian aborigines were known to have replanted small wild yams after harvesting the larger ones. They also used burning and flooding to alter environmental conditions to benefit the growth of certain edible plants. Early human cultivators would also have noticed that some individuals of the same species produced larger seeds and fruits or more abundant seeds and fruits. They may have selectively planted seeds from those.

As in the case of animals, restricting the flow of wild genes into the plant population that is being domesticated is very important. However, it is much more difficult to restrict the flow of pollen than it is to control contact between cultivated and wild animals. Pollen is transported by the wind or insects and can easily move from wild to domesticated plants growing near each other. Interestingly, many of the ancestors of important early domesticated plants, such as wheat, typically self-pollinate more frequently than they are fertilized by other individuals. Therefore, it is less likely that pollen from a nonfavored wild stock of plants would introduce genes into plant populations that humans were cultivating.

Seeds from archaeological sites in the Fertile Crescent show that between 11,000 and about 8000 years ago, cultivation of wild plants led to domesticated varieties of grains such as wheat and barley that had larger seeds, more nutritious seeds, larger seed production, and in many cases, seeds that more strongly adhered to the plant. An important example of such evolutionary change due to domestication is provided by the early history of wheat. Because of its nutritious seeds, high yield, and wide environmental tolerance, wheat is the most important domesticated grain in the world today. About 20% of the calories consumed by the entire human population of the world are derived from wheat. Archaeological evidence and data from the modern genetics of domesticated and wild wheat provide information on the history of this important crop plant. A number of wild species of the wheat genus are found in southwestern Asia today. One of the earliest cultivated species was probably wild einkorn wheat *(Triticum boeoticum)*, which through artificial selection gave rise to domesticated einkorn *(T. monococcum)*. Domesticated einkorn has larger seeds that are more strongly attached to the rachis (central stem) of the plant compared to wild einkorn. A similar history is apparent for domesticated emmer wheat *(T. dicoccum)*, which arose from the wild species *T. dicoccoides.* Some taxonomists now combine both einkorn species together as *T. monococcum* and put both emmer species together as varieties of a species called *T. turgidum.* Archaeological evidence indicates that both wild einkorn and wild emmer wheat were being cultivated in the Fertile Crescent by almost 10,000 years ago. In addition to cultivation within the natural distributions of these species, wheat had also been introduced and cultivated in areas outside its native range on the higher floodplains of the Euphrates River. Modern bread wheat (*T. aestivum*) appears to be a hybrid produced by cross-fertilization between emmer wheat and a wild wheat species (*T. tauschii*). In addition to being a hybrid, modern bread wheat is also a polyploid, having a chromosomal count of 42 compared to 28 for emmer wheat, which is itself probably a polypolid progeny of einkorn that has a chromosome count of 14. Polyploid plants often have larger seeds than normal diploid varieties. Aside from having larger seeds, bread wheat also has seeds that lack the plumed bracts that cover the seeds of other wheat. The naked seeds of bread wheat are much easier to process for food. Archaeological evidence shows that bread wheat was being cultivated in the Fertile Crescent by about 8000 years ago. Events such as the mutation that caused polyploidy in the wheats and cross-fertilization between emmer and *T. tauschii* were fortuitous accidents that improved the food value of wheat. Through selecting these hybrids and polyploids for cultivation, humans capitalized on these chance genetic events. As is the case with corn, should humans cease to cultivate it, bread wheat would not be able to disperse adequate numbers of seeds for the species to survive.

Although many important domestic species come from southwestern Asia, people around the world domesticated plants FIGURE 16.2. As we have already seen, corn domestication occurred in Central America and spread

to South America. Lima beans, common beans, potato, and squash also come from Central and South American areas. Sorghum, finger millet, and some yams *(Dioscorea)* come from Africa. Domesticated Asian rice *(Oryza sativa)* is from India and perhaps adjacent portions of eastern Asia. Foxtail millett *(Setaria italica)* and cabbage *(Brassica oleracea)* come from China.

Questions of the origin and spread of agriculture

Two questions regarding domestication have long fascinated biogeographers and archaeologists. First, why did hunting and gathering people turn to agriculture, and second, what was the geographic pattern of agricultural origin and spread? Surprisingly, the impetus for people to abandon a hunting and gathering lifestyle and take up agriculture is not that clear. Experiments have shown that in the natural environment of southwestern Asia a hunter-gatherer can obtain up to 50 kilocalories of food energy for every 1 kilocalorie of energy expended on work. In contrast, because of energy needed for field preparation, sowing seeds, and protecting crops, low-technology subsistence farming nets only about 17 kilocalories of energy for every 1 kilocalorie expended by the farmer. From a per capita energy perspective, there seems no reason to shift from hunting and gathering to subsistence agriculture. In addition, it has also been shown that subsistence farming leaves less free time for recreation and other activities than does hunting and gathering in relatively resource-rich environments. Finally, of the fruits and seeds available to hunter-gatherers, grains such as wheat are not the most nutritious, flavorful, or easiest to process. From the individual's viewpoint, hunting and gathering is a relatively attractive mode of life compared to subsistence agriculture. Two factors may help explain how and why hunters and gatherers turned to agriculture. The first is the external pressure caused by environmental change, and the second is the intrinsic dynamics of human populations, particularly in the face of pressure from growth.

The premise that changes in human culture are driven mainly by changes in environment is often referred to as **environmental determinism.** In addition, environmental determinists believe that differences in present cultures can largely be explained by geographic differences in environment. Such theories were particularly popular with geographers, anthropologists, and biologists in the nineteenth and early twentieth centuries. In the mid-twentieth century, some of the most divisive debates within academic geography erupted over the validity of environmental determinism. In the early twentieth century, the archaeologist V. G. Childe advanced the

Oasis Theory to explain how environmental change led to the domestication of plants and animals and the development of agriculture in southwestern Asia and adjacent Africa. Childe supposed that the climate of southwestern Asia and northern Africa had been cool and wet during Pleistocene glaciations. He proposed that during the last glacial maximum, about 20,000 years ago, the climate of the region was moist, vegetation was lush, and game plentiful. As the global climate warmed at the close of the Pleistocene, southwestern Asia and northern Africa became warmer and drier. Under these conditions, productive vegetation, game animals, and humans all became restricted to sites near water, such as river valleys, lake shores, and oases. By being forced into such close contact, humans were able to observe the ecology of plants and animals that they relied upon. Eventually, this led to the selection of species and individuals for cultivation. As attractive as Childe's original hypothesis sounds, it has a fatal flaw. Since the 1960s, fossil pollen records have been recovered from the sediments of a number of lakes in southwestern Asia. Similar records have been obtained from dried up lakes in Egypt. These records show that the climate of the last glacial maximum was actually quite dry. Vegetation in southwestern Asia and adjacent Africa was sparser and more desertlike during the late Pleistocene than it was 11,000 to 8000 years ago when initial domestication and the development of agriculture occurred. This is exactly opposite to what Childe had envisioned when he constructed the Oasis Theory. Childe's hypothesis was discredited.

The possibility that climatic change may have prompted plant and animal domestication and the development of agriculture in southwestern Asia is now being reexamined. Evidence from a number of different sources suggests that the general pattern of warming and increasing moisture during the Pleistocene-Holocene transition was interrupted by a rapid and pronounced episode of cooler and drier conditions around 12,000 years ago. This episode correlates with the Younger Dryas cooling event. The Younger Dryas event was centered on the North Atlantic region but affected the climate of much of the world. The Younger Dryas was likely caused by the rapid drainage of glacial meltwater from North America into the North Atlantic Ocean. It has been suggested that decreases in plant and game resources during this period of rapid climatic change may have caused extreme stress to hunters and gatherers. The movement toward domestication and the development of agriculture may have been a response to the rapid decline in natural resources.

When we consider the world at large, two important facts argue against environmental determinism as the sole or universal factor that led to the domestication of plants and animals and subsequent development of agri-

culture First, the domestication of plants and animals occurred at different times in different parts of the world. It is often difficult to find any convincing evidence for significant environmental changes during initial domestication in these other regions. For example, the domestication of corn in Central America did not begin until about 8000 years ago, and there is no evidence of major environmental changes coincident with this process. Second, domestication and the shift to agriculture was not an instantaneous event. Evidence from Tell Abu Hureyra and other sites in the Fertile Crescent shows that it took several hundred years for the inhabitants to shift from dependence on wild plants, including wild einkorn wheat, and wild animals such as gazelle (*Gazella subgutturosa*) to goats, sheep, and domesticated grains. During the next two to three thousand years, additional plants were domesticated in the region. In Mexico and Central America, it took perhaps 5000 years from the early start of the domestication of corn until agricultural crops contributed as much as hunting or gathering to the food used by humans. It appears that once domestication and the development of agriculture is set in motion, there is a cultural dynamic that propels it, regardless of environmental change.

The isolated hunter and gatherer in an environment rich with food plants and game has little obvious inducement to develop and adopt an agricultural lifestyle. Agriculture does, however, provide several advantages when considered in the context of an increasing population of humans that are not isolated from other humans. First, although the effort required to obtain energy via subsistence farming is greater, a cultivated landscape provides much more energy per unit of land than does the harvesting of wild plants. More people can thereby be supported on a smaller area of land. Second, agricultural systems that permit the storage of grains or the keeping of herds allow people to use these reserves if environmental factors, such as drought or a particularly cold year, decrease the yields of crops. Hunters and gatherers can only move on and try their luck elsewhere, or in extreme cases perish, during periods of difficult climatic conditions. Third, in most environments, hunting and gathering requires mobility of populations. They must be able to move to follow game or take advantage of seasonal changes in plant availability. It is difficult to make large movements with the very young, the aged, and the infirm. In addition, as human populations increased, such movements would bring different bands of people into contact and conflict over hunting and gathering grounds. It would be advantageous for a band to remain near and defend a particularly good fishing or hunting site, even if this meant that natural plant resources were less than optimal. In view of these considerations, it has been suggested that one crucial factor in prompting the development of agriculture was the growth and geographic expansion of *Homosapiens sapiens* populations during the Holocene. Domesticated plants and animals allowed for a sedentary life, where the danger of conflict during foraging trips would be reduced and population size for defending resources in a small area would be maximized. With permanent habitation and larger populations, the stratified societies that developed would increase in power to defend and eventually subject other groups. Permanent settlements of large populations also meant that people were now tied to agriculture in order to sustain society. A dynamic feedback was set in place that continued to drive domestication and the intensification of agricultural production.

The geography of initial plant and animal domestication and the spread of agriculture have long been a topic of intense interest to biogeographers. In the first half of the twentieth century, a number of researchers speculated that domestication and agriculture developed in the Fertile Crescent and then spread from there throughout the world. Alternatively, the geographer Carl O. Sauer proposed that domestication and agriculture first developed in southeastern Asia and then spread from there. To support such claims, some scientists have pointed to the antiquity of agriculture in the Fertile Crescent relative to other parts of the world. Evidence for a southeastern Asian origin came from the fact that the bottle gourd *(Langenaria siceraria)* was an early domesticate in both Mexico and Thailand. The problem with such theories that envision one, and only one, center of the origination of domestication and agriculture is that there is no convincing archaeological or historical evidence to support the movement of people, crops, or technologies from the Fertile Crescent or Asia over great distances in the early Holocene. The initiation of corn domestication in Mexico or potato domestication in South America began about 8000 years ago and appears to be local innovations that took advantage of existing plants. Similarly, the domestication of finger millet in Africa or rice in Asia also appears to have been local innovations. There is no reason to suspect that people in many parts of the world were not all capable of independently domesticating plants and animals and developing agriculture.

Despite the universal ability of humans to domesticate plants and animals and to develop agriculture, both archaeological and genetic evidence from crop plants shows that certain areas of the world were **centers of domestication** for the early development of agriculture. Other areas either developed agriculture after contact with people and crops from one of these centers, or they never developed it at all. Notable centers of initial plant domestication and agricultural development include

southwestern Asia, a broad band of central Africa, India, and eastern Asia, Central America, and South America FIGURE 16.2. People in areas such as northern Europe, North America, and Australia practiced agriculture only after it was introduced from elsewhere.

The geographic diffusion of agriculture from centers of domestication has long been of interest to biogeographers and anthropologists. The geographic diffusion of domesticated plants and animals in Europe and pre-Columbian North America has been studied with particular intensity. Crops such as wheat and barley moved from the core of the Fertile Crescent to adjacent areas of southwestern Asia within a few hundred years. By 8000 years ago, these crops and agricultural practices had spread to Greece. Between 7000 and 6000 years ago, grains originating in the Fertile Crescent were grown across the European continent from northern France to close to the Russian border. By 5000 years ago, the growing of grain had spread to the climatic limits of such crops in Scandinavia and Britain. In North America, the cultivation of corn spread from central America to the southwestern United States about 3000 years ago and reached its northeastern climatic limits of corn cultivation in southern Ontario about 700 years ago. The diffusion of domesticated plants and animals, as well as agricultural practices, in Europe, North America, and other parts of the world was likely facilitated by many factors, including the movement of people and the transfer of materials and ideas from one group of people to another.

The cultivation of wheat and other grains formed the foundation for the rise of cities and civilizations in the Fertile Crescent. The diffusion of these crops across Europe was followed by the diffusion of technical practices such as pottery making and metal smelting. In the Americas, the cultivation of corn, along with beans and squash, satisfied a similar function serving as the foundation for the Mesoamerican civilizations such as the Maya and Aztecs, and the Inca in South America. (**Mesoamerica** is an archaeological term that refers to southern Mexico and northern central America.) The pre-Columbian Pueblo builders, or Anasazi people, of the southwestern United States built considerable towns and village complexes such as those found at Mesa Verde Colorado, Wupatki National Monument in Arizona, and Chaco Canyon, New Mexico, on the basis of the same three crops. Not only were these crops introduced from Mesoamerica, but the presence of ceremonial ball courts in pre-Columbian sites throughout the Southwest and Mesoamerica shows that other aspects of culture and technology also diffused along with agriculture.

The spread of both nomadic pastoralism, based on domesticated animals, and agriculture, based on crops and animals, occurred in many other regions of the world.

In some cases, climate, soils, and available crops led to complex stratified societies based on a variety of crops and animals. By 2000 years ago, such societies were present in Mesoamerica and South America, much of northern Africa, Europe, and southern Asia. In other regions, such as southwestern and eastern North America, simpler agricultural societies, based on a smaller number of domesticated species and often having only semipermanent villages, had also developed. Nomadic pastoralism was dominant in grassland and desert regions of Eurasia and Africa. European expansion, following the fifteenth century, would lead to further expansion of agriculture to areas such as Australia and central and western North America. It would also lead to the worldwide diffusion of crops such as wheat from the Near East, rice from Asia, and corn from the Americas. Today, for example, California is one of the largest producers of rice in the world, while China is a major producer of corn.

Domestication originated and took hold in some areas and not in others primarily because the availability of wild plants and animals that can be domesticated varies from geographic region to geographic region. The Fertile Crescent contained many wild plant and animal species such as the ancestors of wheat, barley, rye, lentils, chickpeas, sheep, goats, and pigs, which were ideal for domestication. Both grains, which are high in carbohydrates, and animals which could be domesticated and furnish meats high in proteins, were available. This abundance and variety of plants and animals that could be domesticated explains the rapid development of an agriculture-based society there. Southern Mexico and Central and South America also had a number of species suitable for domestication, such as corn and potatoes, but had fewer high-yield plants and no large animals aside from the lama and alpaca for domestication. These more limited resources may explain the slow rate of transition from hunting and gathering to a more or less completely agricultural society in Central and South America. Finally, areas such as North America, northwestern Europe, Australia, and many other regions simply did not possess plant and animal species that could be domesticated and form the basis for the transition to an agricultural society. In northwestern Europe, North America, or Australia, for example, there are no native species of plants that possess the combined properties of nutrition, crop yield, harvesting-processing ease, and range of growth conditions that have made wheat, Asian rice, and corn such important crops around the world. Although humans have shown a remarkable ability to shape the evolutionary development of many plants and animals, they have required the proper raw materials to accomplish this. Those raw materials are the plant and animal species that humans were able to domesticate because of

their morphology, physiology, or behavior. Perhaps, now, with the advent of biochemical techniques that allow the alteration of genetic codes and the splicing of new genes into organisms, we will shape species and fashion new ones that even more specifically suit our perceived needs. The wisdom of such manipulations of the evolutionary process remains highly controversial.

Humans as a Force of Extinction

The growth and geographic spread of *Homo sapiens sapiens* populations has been a remarkable episode in the biogeographical history of the earth. However, this growth and expansion has not been without significant cost. Perhaps the most regrettable byproduct of human success has been the global extinction of a great many plant and animal species. Unfortunately, the rate at which our species has caused other species to go extinct appears directly tied to human population size. As human population has exploded over the past few centuries, so has the number of plants and animals that we have lost forever to extinction. Niles Eldredge has compared the magnitude of these recent extinctions to five earlier mass extinctions represented in the geologic record. These are the Upper Ordovician, Upper Devonian, Permo-Triassic, Upper Triassic, and Cretaceous-Tertiary extinction events. He coined the term **sixth extinction** to refer to the episode of extinctions over the past 10,000 years or so that have been caused by humans. All of the five earlier mass extinctions were caused by catastrophic geologic events or strikes by extraterrestrial objects such as meteors. Although it is arguable that the number of extinctions over the past 10,000 years does not yet equal the massive loss of species during these earlier geologic periods, neither have these earlier extinctions been caused by the actions of one species—that species being *Homo sapiens sapiens*.

Human beings have caused the extinction of other species through both direct and indirect processes. In a number of cases, direct predation by humans has led to extinction. In other cases, the removal or reduction of prey species has created trophic cascades that have led to the extinction of predators. Humans have also introduced alien species into environments, and these have driven other species to extinction through predation or competition. Land clearance has caused species of plants and animals to go extinct due to loss of habitat. In many cases, extinctions have been due to combinations of factors, such as aggressive hunting coupled with the destruction of habitat due to land clearance.

Extinctions caused by modern humans can be divided into two general categories. The first category is a series of **prehistoric extinctions** caused by the initial geographic expansion of human beings from Africa and Eurasia. The second category is a series of **historic extinctions** caused by the combination of European colonization and socio-economic expansion, and the rapid global increase in human population. Let's look at both types of events.

Prehistoric extinctions

Prehistoric extinctions caused by the initial geographic expansion of modern humans can be regarded as being similar to the introduction of a nonselective (or eury-phagous) predator into a new environment. Much of the remarkable success of modern humans in terms of geo-graphic range and population size can be attributed to our relatively wide generalized niche. Humans are omnivores adapted to take advantage of a number of different prey species and plants. The increasingly sophisticated tools and social organization of prehistoric modern humans made them a very efficient predator. If a favored prey species goes extinct, humans can shift reliance to other animal prey and plants. Prey species that coevolve in the same geographic region as a nonselective predator will evolve adaptive strategies to persist in the face of this predation. However, when nonselective predators colonize or are artificially introduced to an environ-ment where prey species have not coevolved with them, the prey often are not adapted to escape or otherwise withstand predation by the new predator. The results can often be extinction of the prey species. Hominids lived and evolved in Africa and southern Eurasia for most of their history. Other animals in these regions evolved with hominids as predators. In the past 60,000 years, humans spread to regions where animals had evolved without the presence of hominid predators. We have little evidence of prehistoric humans causing significant widespread extinction of animals in Africa. We do have evidence for the role of modern humans in large prehistoric extinction events in areas such as North America, Australia, and the islands of the South Pacific where people have spread only in the last 60,000 years or less. Let's look at each of these examples in turn.

Fossil evidence from many sites shows that until the late Pleistocene, about 12,000 years ago, North America contained a richness of large mammal species that is remarkable by modern standards. Large mammals are those species in which the adults are greater than 44 kg in weight. The large mammal fauna is often referred to as the **megafauna**. Among other things, the megafauna contained species of mammoth (*Mammuthus primigenius, M. jeffersonii,* and *M. columbi*) and mastadon (*Mammut americanum*) related to elephants **FIGURE 16.3**, horses (*Equus* spp.), camels (*Camelops hesternus*), ground sloths (*Nothrotheriops shastensis*),

FIGURE 16.3   The skeleton of a Jefferson mammoth (*Mammuthus jeffersonii*) at the American Museum of Natural History in New York. This species of mammoth was approximately the same size as living elephants and was present in midwestern and eastern North America during the end of the Pleistocene. Mammoths were the largest mammals in North America at that time. By around 10,000 years, all species of mammoths in North America had become extinct. Hunting by humans was likely a major factor in the extinction of mammoths and other large mammals in North America.

sabertooth cats (*Smilodon fatalis*), and short-faced bear (*Arctodus simus*). The youngest radiocarbon dates on the remains of these extinct mammals suggest that all of the North American species of these large mammals, and many other species, disappeared around 10,000 to 4000 years ago **FIGURE 16.4**. In fact, of the 79 large mammal species that existed in North America at about 20,000 years ago, only 22 species were present when the Europeans first colonized the continent 500 years ago. This represents the extinction of roughly 70% of all large mammal species in North America. When the Europeans arrived, the largest mammals remaining in North America were species such as bison (*Bison bison*), muskox (*Ovibus moschatus*) in the far north, and bears. Interestingly, small mammals did not suffer the same high rate of extinction during the period of large mammal extinctions 10,000 to 14,000 years ago.

Two sets of hypotheses have been constructed to explain the megafaunal extinctions that occurred in North America at the close of the Pleistocene. The first hypothesis attributes the extinctions to climatic change. According to this hypothesis, large mammals could not cope with the rapid changes in climate and vegetation at the end of the last glacial maximum and beginning of the Holocene. This was because they were more sensitive to climatic and environmental conditions, had larger resource requirements, larger individual feeding ranges, smaller populations, and lower reproductive rates. The

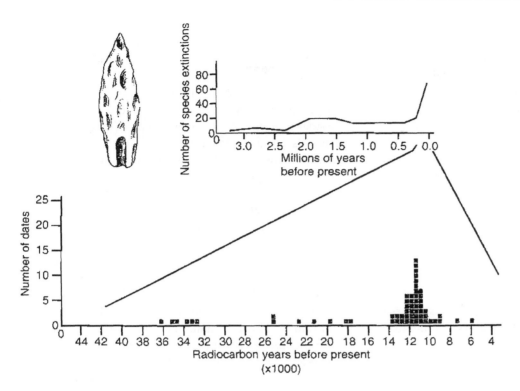

flaw in this argument is that these same genera, and indeed many of the same species, had survived earlier glacial to interglacial transitions in the Pleistocene. What was so different about the end of the last glacial episode that made it lethal to the North American large mammals?

The second hypothesis attributes the North American large mammal extinction directly to humans. This hypothesis has been particularly well developed and articulated by the American geoscientist Paul S. Martin of the University of Arizona. As we have reviewed earlier, there is compelling evidence that humans entered Alaska and the Yukon Territory from Siberia about 15,000 years ago and spread southward as the Laurentide ice sheet melted about 13,000 years ago. Martin theorizes that these newly arrived immigrants brought with them a hunting and gathering culture from Siberia that included acquisition of large game such as horse, bison, and mammoth. When these hunters first arrived in the interior of North America about 13,000 years ago, they would have found many different species of large mammals for hunting. These species would never have been preyed upon by human hunters and would not have developed physical or behavioral adaptations to human hunting pressure. Martin believes that the humans would have had great initial success in hunting and as a result experienced rapid population growth. Ease of hunting, coupled with increasing numbers of human hunters, would lead to local

extinction of large mammal prey species. Local extinction of this type by a predator is called **overkill**. This in turn would cause humans to move generally southward in search of new prey. The geographic expansion of humans southward in search of new prey explains the apparent rapid spread of humans from Canada to the southern tip of South America 12,000 years ago. Behind the southward-moving front of the large and geographically expanding population of human hunters would be a sparser population of humans who would likely hunt the remaining large mammals. Individuals of the large mammals that escaped the first arrival of humans would likely be hunted and potentially driven extinct by the humans behind the advancing front. The hypothesized expanding front of human hunters is sometimes called the *kill front*. The movement and actions of the human hunters under Martin's scenario are somewhat like a rapidly advancing army, and his hypothesis is referred to as the **Blitzkrieg Theory of Pleistocene Overkill**. (Blitzkrieg is the German word for lighting war.)

What evidence is there to substantiate the Blitzkrieg Theory in North America? The stone tools used by people in North America 12,000 years ago are very similar throughout the entire continent. They are characterized by the presence of large points with fluted bases. The fluting appears to have been used to fasten the points to spear shafts. These very distinctive artifacts are called **Clovis points** FIGURE 16.4 after the town near the archaeological site in New Mexico where the points were first discovered. The first Clovis points were found in 1929 by a teenager named Ridgely Whiteman who reported his find to the Smithsonian Institution. The people who used these points are often referred to as Paleoindians. The Clovis fluted points and other features of the Paleoindian tool kit are somewhat similar to prehistoric tools from 20,000-year-old archaeological sites in the region around Lake Baikal in Siberia. The Siberian peoples associated with these tools appear to have hunted mammoths and have been linked genetically with modern North American native peoples. This suggests the possible introduction of this hunting culture and technology from Siberia about 13,000 to 12,000 years ago, as Martin suggests. In North America there are at least 13 sites where Clovis points and tools are found in association with butchered mammoths. The site in New Mexico where the points were first discovered included the bones of butchered mammoths. All of these types of sites date from about 12,000 to 13,000 years ago, and many contain the remains of several mammoths. Clovis points are also found in association with the remains of other living and extinct large and small mammals. This evidence shows that at the time of the late Pleistocene extinctions, the Paleoindians in North America were generalist hunters and were capable of hunting very large mammals.

The evidence that humans played a role in the extinction of many large mammals in North America appears very strong, but it cannot be said that human hunting alone was responsible. It is likely that the North American biota was under stress during the late Pleistocene as climate warmed and vegetation changed. The foraging conditions and ranges for the large mammals were shifting geographically and in some cases contracting. The addition of humans, who were highly sophisticated and generalist predators, was more than the already environmentally stressed mammals could withstand. The removal of herbivores such as mammoths, mastodons, horses, and camels by hunting likely produced trophic cascades that led to the extinction of large predators such as sabertooth cats. Finally, it has recently been suggested that humans and their accompanying dogs may have inadvertently introduced diseases that contributed to the extinction of the American megafauna.

The magnitude of late Pleistocene mammal extinctions is no less severe in Australia than in North America. Indeed, the Australian extinctions were broader in scope. All marsupials weighing more than 100 kg disappeared between about 60,000 and 15,000 years ago. These included giant herbivorous and carnivorous kangaroos, representing a loss of 19 species. In addition, almost 60% of all marsupial species weighing between 10 and 100 kg suffered extinction during this period. Reptiles and birds also went extinct during this period. These include a

7-m-long carnivorous monitor lizard (*Megalania prisca*) and a flightless ostrich-sized bird (*Genvornis newtoni*). In all, at least 60 vertebrate animal species disappeared from Australia during this time.

What was the role of humans in the Australian late Pleistocene extinctions, and why was the event so much broader in terms of the size and type of extinct animals? There is good evidence that humans first arrived in Australia about 60,000 to 53,000 years ago. This time period corresponds with the last known ages for the large flightless bird *Genyornis newtoni* and a number of other marsupial species. Hunting by humans was likely a factor in these extinctions. Fossil pollen and charcoal in lake sediments also show evidence of increased fires and losses of forest and shrubland during the period 60,000 to about 20,000 years ago. Humans may have been responsible for setting frequent fires, which transformed the interior of the continent to more desertlike conditions. Thus, humans may have killed off species both by hunting and by creating fires that changed the vegetation. Detailed morphological and chemical analysis of the bones and eggs of extinct Australian vertebrates suggests that many were browsers who lived by eating the leaves of shrubs and trees. The replacement of forest and shrubland by desert would have destroyed their habitat. The loss of habitat explains why so many small as well as large animals went extinct during the late Pleistocene in Australia. Trophic cascades would have led to the extinction of large predators such as *Megalania prisca*. Natural climatic change likely played some role in the latter prehistoric faunal extinctions in Australia. During the last glacial maximum 20,000 years ago, Australia became very dry and experienced increased desertification.

In both North America and Australia, it might be argued that natural climatic change, in addition to human activity, may have contributed to prehistoric extinctions. In the case of the Pacific Islands, we have clear evidence of the power of prehistoric humans to cause widespread extinction in the absence of any other environmental changes. The eastward expansion of Polynesians between 2100 and 700 years brought humans to many uninhabited islands such as Hawaii and New Zealand. Although these remote islands did not possess mammal faunas aside from bats, they did have distinctive bird faunas (avifauna). New Zealand, for example, had 11 species of large flightless birds called moas. These birds ranged in size from 20 kg to a staggering 250 kg. Archaeological evidence shows that when humans first arrived on the islands of New Zealand about 700 years ago, they slaughtered and ate moas in huge numbers. It is estimated that all of the moa species were driven to extinction within about 100 years. Following the extinction of the moas, there is archaeological evidence that humans turned their focus to other prey, including now extinct species of penguin and petrels which nested along the coast. At least 77 species of birds went extinct in New Zealand following Polynesian colonization. Similar avifaunal extinctions are evident on other Pacific Islands that were formerly uninhabited by humans. Hawaii was discovered and occupied by humans about 1500 years ago. Fossil evidence from Hawaii shows that at least 35 species, and perhaps over 55 species, of birds went extinct following the arrival of the Polynesians. In some cases, these birds were hunted principally to supply feathers for ornamentation of clothing and jewelry. Flightless birds were particularly vulnerable to extinction. Hawaii had a number of flightless birds, including eight species of geese and an ibis species that went extinct following the arrival of the Polynesians.

Aside from direct hunting, several other factors contributed to the extinction of island biota. The Polynesians brought agriculture with them as they expanded across the Pacific. They transported and introduced domesticated animals, including dogs and pigs. In addition, they inadvertently introduced rats. All these mammals preyed upon bird, reptile, and invertebrate faunas and contributed to Pacific Island extinctions. The Polynesians also brought a number of crop species and edible plants, including coconut (*Cocos nucifera*), taro (*Colocasia esculenta*), yams (*Discorea*), Breadfruit (*Artocarpus communis*), sweet potato (*Ipomea batatas*) and other plants, together with many weedy species. In order to grow taro, the Polynesians cleared large areas of lowland vegetation. On wetter sites, the Polynesians practiced slash and burn agriculture. Finally, they cut down additional forest at low to mid-elevations for building materials and firewood. Following these clearances, much of the original island vegetation was replaced by plants introduced by the Polynesians. Today on the Hawaiian Islands almost all vegetation below 760 m in elevation is dominated by plants introduced by the Polynesians and later by the Europeans. It is estimated that about 130 species, or 10%, of Hawaii's native plants were driven to extinction. Undoubtedly, this landscape alteration significantly contributed to the extinction of birds and other animals such as snails and insects by destroying habitat.

The Polynesians dramatically changed the landscape on other islands. When the Europeans first arrived and settled in New Zealand between A.D. 1642 and 1800, they found the lowland landscape largely dominated by grasslands and extensive areas of bracken ferns (*Pteridium aquilinum*). Evidence from fossil soils, wood, and pollen shows that, prior to the arrival of the Polynesians, these areas had been dominated by forests of trees such as southern beech (*Nothofagus*). Charcoal found in soils shows that the forest clearance was caused by burning. Some of the forest was likely cleared to facilitate the cultivation of sweet potato.

However, there was also much clearing beyond the agricultural limits of this crop. Other areas were likely burned to ease the hunting of moas and to encourage the growth of bracken, which was used as food by the Polynesians. The clearance of forest on Easter Island was even more extreme. At its peak, the Polynesian population on Easter Island numbered about 7000 people. The people there had a very advanced culture and social structure. Polynesians cleared forest for agriculture and firewood, as well as to build and transport the island's famed monumental stone heads. Fossil pollen evidence shows that the present treeless vegetation of the island was strictly the result of land clearance by humans. Again, the destruction of habitat must had severe consequences for native plant and animals species. In the case of Easter Island, the destruction of the forest also led to the collapse of Polynesian society on the island and a regression in culture to very primitive conditions. The first Europeans to visit the island in the eighteenth century found only a small number of islanders living in primitive twig huts and caves. The surviving Easter Islanders had no memory of their earlier culture and how the great stone heads were carved or transported.

Although we have focused on North America, Australia, and the Pacific Islands, the geographic expansion of *Homo sapiens sapiens* is associated with increased extinction rates in many other parts of the world. Such areas include northern Eurasia, islands in the Mediterranean Sea, and the island of Madagascar off Africa. Humans arrived in Madagascar about 2000 years ago. All animals with a body mass larger than 12 kg were driven to extinction shortly thereafter. It would be wrong to think that the Native Americans, Australians, or Polynesian islanders are in any way worse than other groups of humans in terms of their intentional impact on the prehistoric environment. The aim of these and other peoples was not to produce massive extinctions of other species; it was simply to survive.

Historic extinctions

The last 500 years have witnessed a wave of extinctions for plants and animals that is greater in magnitude and geographic scope than any of the prehistoric extinction events FIGURE 16.5. In the case of mammals, at least 88 species have gone extinct since A.D. 1500. About 52% of the mammal species lost were rodents. Over 3% belonged to our own order, the primates. A careful analysis of historical records shows that at least 51 mammal species have disappeared in the time period from 1750 to the present. The others went extinct sometime between 1500 and 1750. Over 73% of those extinctions have occurred on islands, mostly in the Caribbean FIGURE 16.5. The Caribbean losses include a species of monkey (*Xenothrix mcgregori*) that once lived on Jamaica. Over

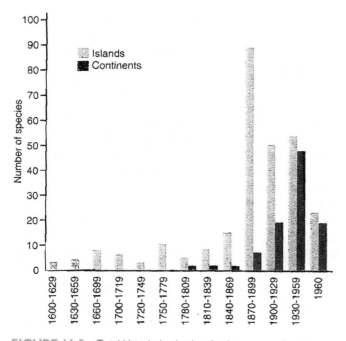

FIGURE 16.5 Total historical animal extinctions on continents and islands from A.D. 1600 to 1960 to the 1990s (after World Conservation Monitoring Center, 1992).

73% of all continental mammals that went extinct during the historic period were from Australia. The historic mammal extinctions in Australia range from small marsupials to species as large as kangaroos, and they rival the number of species lost during the prehistoric-late Pleistocene extinctions. In contrast, North America has experienced one known mammal species extinction since 1500. That extinct species is the rabbit *Sylvilagus insonus*, which was last reported from Mexico in 1991. One famous subspecies of mammal that has gone extinct in North America is the California grizzly bear, which was a variety of the grizzly bear *(Ursus arctos)*. Hunting by Spanish, Mexican, and American settlers was the primary cause of this demise of this distinctive variety of grizzly. The last California grizzly died in the San Francisco Zoo in the early twentieth century.

For birds, the rate of extinction over the past 500 years has been even more severe than for mammals. It is estimated that humans have caused a 1000-fold increase in bird extinctions. One estimate suggests that about 219 species have gone extinct in the historic period; of those, about 40% were island species.

Freshwater fish have also suffered greatly increased rates of extinction in the historic period. Over the past 100 years, at least 172 species of freshwater fish have gone extinct. Most of the extinct species were those that lived in lakes, rather than streams and rivers, or spring pools. A large proportion of those species have been cichlid fish from Lake Victoria in Africa. Lake fish often cannot escape from overfishing or environmental changes caused by humans.

Historic extinctions have also been high for many other groups of organisms. Over the past 500 years, at least 242 species of mollusks have been lost, and 194 species of insects have disappeared. Of the flowering plants, at least 713 species are known to have gone extinct. Again, a high proportion of these extinctions have occurred on islands. It is distressing to note that the number of extinctions is directly proportional to human population growth. Unfortunately, the known historic extinctions represent only minimum estimates of the actual number of species lost. Undoubtedly, hundreds of species went extinct before they were known to scientists. This is particularly true for insects, mollusks, and smaller plants. We will likely never know what most of these lost organisms were like. What we can be certain of is that thousands of species of plants and animals have gone extinct concomitant with the human population's unparalleled growth over the past 500 years.

The extinctions of plants and animals observed over the past 500 years have many causes, including habitat alteration, hunting and fishing, pollution, and introduced alien species of predators, competitors, and pathogens. Habitat alteration is perhaps one of the most important forces driving historic extinctions. As human populations have grown, they have altered terrestrial landscapes for agriculture, urban development, and resource extraction such as mining and logging. Such alterations of the landscape destroy the habitat of terrestrial organisms. Human alteration of the environment also impacts heavily on freshwater and coastal ecosystems. In the case of extinct fish, about 70% of the species lost over the past 100 years were victims to habitat alterations such as the damming of rivers, changes in lake water levels, additional sedimentation due to human land use, changes in river channels and lake bottoms, and disruption of aquatic vegetation.

We also have good historical evidence that aggressive hunting by Europeans played a central role in the extinctions of a number of animals such as the great auk *(Pinguinus impennis)* and Steller's seacow *(Hydrodarmalis gigas)*. The great auk was a flightless seabird of the North Atlantic that was very much like the penguins of the southern hemisphere. It lived in great numbers on rocky coastlines from Scotland to Newfoundland, Canada. During the 1800s, European sealers, fishermen, and sailors began to intensively hunt the great auk for food and to provide fish bait. Hunters were able to herd the birds straight from the shore to their deaths in the holds of ships. In addition, egg collectors in Europe paid high prices for great auk eggs; the taking of eggs for collectors may have been a major factor in the final demise of the birds. By 1844 the great auk had gone extinct. Steller's seacow, which was similar to manatees found in Florida, was first discovered in the Bering Sea in 1741 by George W. Steller, the naturalist on a Russian expedition led by Vitus Bering. The seacow became a prime prey for Russian sealers, and by 1768 it was driven into extinction. In addition to hunting animals for food, sport, and collecting, Europeans hunted predatory animals to protect their domesticated livestock. A large predatory marsupial called the Tasmanian Tiger *(Thalacinus cynocephalus)* was a direct victim of European eradication efforts. European colonists, perceiving the Tasmanian Tiger to be a major threat to sheep herds, launched a vigorous hunting campaign against the animals and by the 1930s it had disappeared.

Pollution has been an especially important factor in the extinction of many fish and other aquatic species. Many rivers and lakes have received large amounts of pollution either through the direct dumping of sewage and waste or through inadvertent spills and the runoff of polluted waters from urban and agricultural areas. Pollution has caused or played a major role in the historic extinction of three species of chub *(Evarra)* from the Mexico City region. It has also been blamed for the extinction of the fish species such as *Chondrostoma scodrensis* in Lake Scadar, Montenegro, and *Brycon acuminatus* and *Leptolebias marmoratus* in Brazil.

As European exploration led to frequent travel and trade between continents and islands, alien species of plants and animals were introduced either by accident or design. We discussed how the accidental introduction of mosquitoes carrying avian malaria led to the extinction of many bird species in Hawaii. Organisms that are purposely introduced to new areas can have similar disastrous results. It is often not possible to foresee the extinctions that may result from such introductions. The French introduced the African land snail *(Achatina fulica)* to the islands of French Polynesia as a source of food. However, the African snails quickly became serious pests to native vegetation and crops. To remedy this situation, the predatory snail *Euglandia rosea* was introduced to the islands to combat the African land snail. Unfortunately, this nonselective predator began to prey upon native island snails. Predation by *Euglandia rosea* caused the extinction of many native Pacific Island snail species.

In many cases, historic extinctions result from a combination of factors, as is illustrated by the dodo bird *(Raphus cucullatus)*. The dodo was first discovered on Muritius Island by European sailors in 1507. The flightless birds were easy prey, and so the island became a stop for providing meat for sailing ships. Europeans also cleared the native forests, which likely deprived the dodos of food. In addition, cats, rats, and pigs introduced by the Europeans probably preyed upon the dodo nestlings and eggs. By 1681 the dodo was extinct. During the same period, a similar fate befell the dodo's nearest relatives, *Raphus solitaires* and *Pezophaps solitaria*, flightless birds that lived on nearby islands in the Indian Ocean. This extinction event represents the loss of the entire Raphidae family to which the three species belonged. In more recent times, we have even clearer historical evidence of how a number of interacting factors produced the extinction of freshwater cichlids in Lake Victoria and the continental extinction of the North American passenger pigeon. Let's look at both of these examples.

It is unknown precisely how many species of cichlid fish *(Haplochromis)* have gone extinct in Lake Victoria in recent decades, but some estimates place the number at over 100. Many of these species were very specialized in terms of feeding and occurred in low population numbers in small areas of the lake. They were thus particularly prone to extinction. The widespread extinction of cichlids corresponds with a number of human-induced changes in Lake Victoria. During the twentieth century, the Nile perch *(Lates niloticus)* was introduced to the lake to develop a fishery that would support people living around the lake. The perch are predators that feed on the cichlids. After the introduction of perch, the cichlids also experienced increased fishing pressure. Cichlids were caught for use as bait or were inadvertently caught in perch nets. Cichlids were also killed as a byproduct of the application of fish poison to catch perch. By the late 1980s, an introduced aquatic plant, water hyacinth *(Eichhornia crassipes)*, had spread throughout the lake and covered many shallows with dense floating foliage. The plant cover destroyed the cichlid habitat by causing decreased sunlight penetration and decreased water oxygen concentrations. Finally, land clearance for agriculture and increased human population density around the lake have led to increased inputs of pesticides, fertilizer, and sediment, all of which have contributed to fish mortality and the loss of cichlid species. Some of the changes caused by humans to Lake Victoria were instituted with the best intentions of aiding local peoples, but the end result has been a catastrophic disruption of the ecosystem and the extinction of many species.

In many cases, the animals that have gone extinct in historic times have been species that had small population sizes and were highly endemic. We saw how such species are generally more prone to extinction. The small population sizes, highly endemic distributions, and often limited dispersal capability of island species made them particularly susceptible to extinction due to human hunting, introduced predator and competitor species, and landscape change. Historic extinctions, however, have certainly not been restricted to species with small population sizes or endemic distributions. Passenger pigeons *(Ectopistes migratorius)* were beautiful birds that resembled morning doves and turtle doves. When the Europeans first arrived in North America, the most abundant bird in the continent was the passenger pigeon. It is estimated that five billion passenger pigeons inhabited the eastern half of North America. That is almost equal to the total number of all birds that inhabit the continent today! The passenger pigeons were strong fliers, and the geographic range of the birds extended from the Gulf of Mexico to southern Canada. They traveled in great flocks that numbered in the millions, and it is said that their passing would darken the sky. During the mid-1800s two factors began to seriously impact on the passenger pigeon. First, land clearance for agriculture intensified and expanded westward from the Atlantic Coast states to the edges of the Great Plains. This destroyed the forest habitat of the pigeons. The pigeons relied on oaks, chestnuts, and beech as principal sources of food. The birds also required trees to nest. The cutting of a favored nesting tree could destroy over 100 nests. Second, the pigeons were hunted in great numbers. Random shots into the sky would bring down several birds when flocks were passing. It is estimated that one day of hunting using shotguns could yield up to 25,000 birds. The birds were also caught in nets when resting and got stuck in sticky

lime spread out on the ground. Millions were killed each year. The expansion of the railroad in the 1850s led to increased hunting as the birds could be easily transported to markets. Some of these birds were eaten by humans, and others were used to feed pigs. Many birds were ground up and used for fertilizer. Pigeons were also killed simply to keep them from eating newly planted crops. To get some perspective on this wide-scale slaughter, it is worth noting that in 1869 one Michigan county sent 7.5 million birds to markets in the east. During the 1870s and 1880s, a drastic decline was observed in the number of passenger pigeons. By 1880 the entire state of Michigan only shipped about 500,000 birds eastward. Even though commercial hunting eventually ceased, the decline could not be halted. By the 1890s, the passenger pigeon had disappeared from most of its native range. On September 1, 1914, the last living passenger pigeon died in captivity at the Cincinnati Zoo. The most abundant bird on the North American continent was driven to annihilation in a little over a century. A monument to the passenger pigeon was subsequently erected in a park in Wisconsin. The words on the monument are a sad but fitting epitaph for far too many species of plants and animals: "This species became extinct through the avarice and thoughtlessness of man."

KEY WORDS AND TERMS

Agriculture
Artificial selection
Blitzkrieg Theory of Pleistocene Overkill
Centers of domestication
Clovis points
Domestication
Environmental determinism
Fertile Crescent
Historic extinctions

Hunters and gatherers
Megafauna
Mesoamerica
Oasis Theory
Overkill
Pastoral nomadicism
Prehistoric extinctions
Sixth extinction

REFERENCES AND FURTHER READING

Baker, H. G. (1970). *Plants and Civilization*, 2nd edition. Wadsworth Publishing Co., Belmont, CA.

Balter, M. (1999). A long season puts Catalhoyuk in context. *Science* 286, 890–891.

Bell, M., and Walker, M. J. C. (1992). *Late Quaternary Environmental Change: Physical and Human Perspectives*. Wiley, New York.

Blumler, M. A. (1992). Independent inventionism and recent genetic evidence on plant domestication. *Economic Botany* 46, 93–111.

Blumler, M. A., and Byrne, R. (1991). The ecological genetics of domestication and the origins of agriculture. *Current Anthropology* 32, 23–54.

Brown, J. H., and Lomolino, M. V. (1998). *Biogeography*, 2nd edition. Sinauer Associates, Sunderland, MA.

Cuddihy, L. W., and Stone, C. P. (1990). *Alteration of Native Hawaiian Vegetation*. University of Hawaii, Honolulu.

Diamond, J. M. (1984). Normal extinctions of isolated populations. In *Extinctions* (ed. M. N. Nitecki), pp. 191–246. University of Chicago Press, Chicago.

Diamond, J. M. (1992). The Third Chimpanzee: The *Evolution and Future of the Human Animal*. Harper Perennial, New York.

Diamond, J. M. (1997). *Guns, Germs and Steel: The Fates of Human Societies* W. W. Norton, New York.

Diamond, J. M. (2000). Archaeology: blitzkrieg against the moas. *Science* 287, 2170–2171.

Eldredge, N. (1999). Cretaceous meteor showers, the human "niche" and the sixth extinction. In *Extinctions in Near Time* (ed. R. D. E. MacPhee), pp. 1–15. Kluwer Academic/Plenum, New York.

Fearn, M. L., and Lui, K. B. (1995). Maize pollen of 3500 B. P. from southern Alabama. *American Antiquity* 60, 109–117.

Flannery, T. F. (1999). Paleontology: debating extinction. *Science* 283, 182–183.

Flannery, T. F., and Roberts, R. G. (1999). Late Quaternary extinctions in Australasia. In *Extinctions in Near Time Causes, Contexts and Consequences* (ed. R. D. E. MacPhee), pp. 239–269. Kluwer Academic/Plenum, New York.

Gamble, C. (1994). *Timewalkers: The Prehistory of Global Colonization*. Harvard University Press, Cambridge, MA.

Georghiou, G. P. (1986). The magnitude of the resistance problem in (Committee on Strategies for the Management of Pesticide Resistant Pet Populations eds.). *Pesticide Resistance: Strategies and Tactics for Management*. pp. 14–43. National Academy Press. Washington.

Goldschmidt, T. (1996). *Darwin's Dreampond*. MIT Press, Cambridge, MA.

Harrison, I. J., and Stiassny, M. L. J. (1999). The quiet crisis. In *Extinctions in Near Time* (ed. R. D. E. MacPhee). Kluwer Academic/Plenum, New York.

Haviland, W. A. (1989). *Anthropology*, 5th edition. Holt, Rinehart and Winston, New York.

Heiser, C. B., Jr. (1973). *Seed to Civilization: The Story of Man's Food*. W. H. Freeman, San Francisco.

Heywood, V. H. (1995). *Global Biodiversity, Assessment*. Cambridge University Press, Cambridge.

Holdaway, R. N., and Jacomb, C. (2000). Rapid extinction of the moas (Aves: Dinornithi-formes): model, test and implications. *Science* 287, 2250–2254.

Jeffries, M. J. (1997). *Biodiversity and Conservation*. Routledge, London.

Kennedy, L. M., and Horn, S. L. (1997). Prehistoric maize cultivation at the La Selva Biological Station, Costa Rica. *Biotropica* 29, 368–370.

Kirch, P. V. (1982). The impact of prehistoric Polynesians on the Hawaiian ecosystem. *Pacific Science* 36, 1–14.

Lamb, H. F., Damblon, F., and Maxted, R. W. (1991). Human impact on the vegetation of the Middle Atlas, Morocco, during the last 5000 years. *Journal of Biogeography* 18, 519–532.

Lev-Yadun, S., Gopher, A., and Abbo, S. (2000). The cradle of agriculture. *Science* 288, 1602–1603.

MacPhee, R. D. E. (1999). *Extinctions in Near Time*. Kluwer Academic/Plenum, New York.

MacPhee, R. D. E., and Flemming, C. (1999). *Requiem aeternam. In Extinctions in Near Time* (ed. R. D. E. MacPhee), pp. 333–371. Kluwer Academice/Plenum, New York.

Martin, P. S. (1984). Catastrophic extinctions and late Pleistocene blitzkrieg: two radiocarbon tests. In *Extinctions* (ed. M. H. Nitecki), pp. 153–189. University of Chicago Press, Chicago.

Martin, P. S., and Steadman, D. W. (1999). Prehistoric extinctions on islands and continents. In *Extinctions in Near Time* (ed. R. D. E. MacPhee), pp. 17–55. Kluwer Academic/Plenum, New York.

Meltzer, D. J., and Mead, J. I. (1982). The timing of late Pleistocene mammalian extinctions in North America. *Quaternary Research* 19, 130–135.

Miller, G. H., Magee, J. W., Johnson, B. J., Fogel, M. L., Spooner, N. A., McCulloch, M. T., and Ayliffe, L. K.

(1999). Pleistocene extinction of *Genyornis newtoni*: human impact on Australian megafauan. *Science* 283, 205–209.

Ponting, C. (1992). *A Green History of the World.* Penguin, Middlesex.

Quammen, D. (1996). *Song of the Dodo: Island Biogeography in an Age of Extinctions.* Touchstone, New York.

Roberts, N. (1999). *The Holocene.* Blackwell, Oxford.

Sauer, C. D. (1952). *Agricultural Origins and Dispersals.* MIT Press, Cambridge.

Schorger, A. W. (1955). *The Passenger Pigeon, Its Natural History and Extinction.* University of Wisconsin, Madison.

Simmons, I. G. (1989). *Changing the Face of the Earth.* Blackwell, Oxford.

Steadman, D. W. (1993). Biogeography of Tongan birds before and after human impact. *Proceedings of the National Academy of Science* 90, 818–822.

Steadman, D. W. (1995). Prehistoric extinctions of Pacific Island birds: biodiversity meets zooarchaeology. *Science* 267, 1123–1131.

Stein, P. L., and Rowe, B. M. (1974). *Physical Anthropology.* McGraw-Hill, New York.

Stone, C. P., and Scott, J. M. (1985). *Hawaii's Terrestrial Ecosystems: Preservation and Management.* University of Hawaii Press, Honolulu.

Tankersley, K. B. (1999). A matter of superior spearpoints. *Archaeology* 52, 60–63.

Vila, C., Savolainen, P., Maldonado, J. E., Amorim, I. R., Rice, J. E., Honeycutt, R. L., Crandall, K. A., Lundebergy, J., and Wayne, R. K. (1997). Multiple and ancient origins of the domestic dog. *Science* 276, 1687–1689.

Warner, R. E. (1968). The role of introduced diseases in the extinction of the endemic Hawaiian avifauna. *Condor* 70, 101–120.

Wayne, R. K., Leonard, J. A., and Cooper, A. (1999). Full of sound and fury: the recent history of ancient DNA. *Annual Review of Ecology and Systematics* 30, 457–477.

World Conservation Monitoring Center. (1992). *Global Biodiversity: Status of the Earth's Living Resources.* Chapman and Hall, London.

Wuethrich, B. (1999). Proto-Polynesians quickly settled Pacific. *Science* 286, 2054–2056.

Zeder, M. A., and Hesse, B. (2000). The initial domestication of goats (*Capra hircus*) in the Zagros Mountains. *Science* 287, 2254–2257.

Zimmerer, K. S. (1991). The regional biogeography of native potato cultivars in highland Peru. *Journal of Biogeography* 18, 165–178.

Zohary, D., and Hopf, M. (1994). *Domestication of Plants in the Old World,* 2nd edition. Clarendon Press, Oxford.